Kaplan Publishing are constantly finding new wa
difference to your studies and our exciting online
offer something different to students looking for

This book comes with free MyKaplan online resources so that you can study anytime, anywhere. **This free online resource is not sold separately and is included in the price of the book.**

Having purchased this book, you have access to the following online study materials:

CONTENT	ACCA (including FBT, FMA, FFA)		FIA (excluding FBT, FMA, FFA)	
	Text	Kit	Text	Kit
Electronic version of the book	✓	✓	✓	✓
Knowledge checks with instant answers	✓		✓	
Material updates	✓	✓	✓	✓
Latest official ACCA exam questions*		✓		
Timed questions with an online tutor debrief using video icon***		✓		
Consolidation Test including questions and answers	✓		✓	

* Excludes BT, MA, FA, FBT, FMA, FFA; for all other papers includes a selection of questions, as released by ACCA

*** Excludes BT, MA, FA, LW, FBT, FMA and FFA

How to access your online resources

Kaplan Financial students will already have a MyKaplan account and these extra resources will be available to you online. You do not need to register again, as this process was completed when you enrolled. If you are having problems accessing online materials, please ask your course administrator.

If you are not studying with Kaplan and did not purchase your book via a Kaplan website, to unlock your extra online resources please go to www.mykaplan.co.uk/addabook (even if you have set up an account and registered books previously). You will then need to enter the ISBN number (on the title page and back cover) and the unique pass key number contained in the scratch panel below to gain access. You will also be required to enter additional information during this process to set up or confirm your account details.

If you purchased through the Kaplan Publishing website you will automatically receive an e-mail invitation to MyKaplan. Please register your details using this email to gain access to your content. If you do not receive the e-mail or book content, please contact Kaplan Publishing.

Your Code and Information

This code can only be used once for the registration of one book online. This registration and your online content will expire when the final sittings for the examinations covered by this book have taken place. Please allow one hour from the time you submit your book details for us to process your request.

Please scratch the film to access your unique code.

Please be aware that this code is case-sensitive and you will need to include the dashes within the passcode, but not when entering the ISBN.

KAPLAN
PUBLISHING

ACCA

Strategic Professional – Options

Advanced Performance Management (APM)

EXAM KIT

KAPLAN
PUBLISHING

British Library Cataloguing-in-Publication Data

A catalogue record for this book is available from the British Library.

Published by:

Kaplan Publishing UK

Unit 2 The Business Centre

Molly Millar's Lane

Wokingham

Berkshire

RG41 2QZ

ISBN: 978-1-83996-153-3

Printed and bound in Great Britain.

Acknowledgements

These materials are reviewed by the ACCA examining team. The objective of the review is to ensure that the material properly covers the syllabus and study guide outcomes, used by the examining team in setting the exams, in the appropriate breadth and depth. The review does not ensure that every eventuality, combination or application of examinable topics is addressed by the ACCA Approved Content. Nor does the review comprise a detailed technical check of the content as the Approved Content Provider has its own quality assurance processes in place in this respect.

CONTENTS

Section

Versions of some questions in this Exam Kit may also be available on the ACCA Practice Platform on the ACCA website. They are a very useful reference, in particular to attempt using ACCA's exam software. However, you should be aware that ACCA will decide when those questions will be amended ***for syllabus changes*** or replaced, so they may differ slightly from the versions in this ***Exam Kit***.

Features in this edition

In addition to providing a wide ranging bank of real past exam questions, we have also included in this edition:

- Exam specific information and advice on exam technique.
- Our recommended approach to make your revision for this particular subject as effective as possible.

  This includes step by step guidance on how best to use our Kaplan material (Study Text, Pocket Notes and Exam Kit) at this stage in your studies.
- Enhanced tutorial answers packed with specific key answer tips and technical tutorial notes from our experienced tutors.
- Complementary online resources including full tutor debriefs and question assistance to point you in the right direction when you get stuck.

You will find a wealth of other resources to help you with your studies on the following sites:

www.mykaplan.co.uk

www.accaglobal.com

Quality and accuracy are of the utmost importance to us so if you spot an error in any of our products, please send an email to mykaplanreporting@kaplan.com with full details or follow the link to the feedback form in MyKaplan.

Our Quality Co-ordinator will work with our technical team to verify the error and take action to ensure it is corrected in future editions.

INDEX TO QUESTIONS AND ANSWERS

INTRODUCTION

Some past exam questions have been amended to reflect the current APM syllabus and exam format. These are indicated by an 'A' (for amended).

KEY TO THE INDEX TO QUESTIONS AND ANSWERS

ANSWER ENHANCEMENTS

We have added the following enhancements to the answers in this exam kit:

Key answer tips

Most answers include key answer tips to help your understanding of each question.

Tutorial note

Most answers include more tutorial notes to explain some of the technical points in more detail.

ONLINE ENHANCEMENTS

Answer debrief

For selected questions, we recommend that they are to be completed in full exam conditions (i.e. properly timed in a closed book environment).

In addition to the examining team's technical answer, enhanced with key answer tips and tutorial notes in this exam kit, online you can find an answer debrief by a top tutor that:

- works through the question in full
- explains key elements of the answer
- ensures that the easy marks are obtained as quickly as possible.

These questions are indicated with the 'video' icon in the index.

Answer debriefs will be available on MyKaplan at:

www.mykaplan.co.uk

SECTION A TYPE QUESTIONS

SECTION B TYPE QUESTIONS

A – STRATEGIC PLANNING AND CONTROL

B – PERFORMANCE MANAGEMENT INFORMATION SYSTEMS AND DEVELOPMENTS IN TECHNOLOGY

C – STRATEGIC PERFORMANCE MEASUREMENT

D – PERFORMANCE EVALUATION

ANALYSIS OF PAST EXAMS

The table below summarises the key topics that have been tested in the published questions from recent Advanced Performance Management examinations.

Note that the references are to the number of the question in this edition of the Exam Kit.

Study Text Chapter and Topic	Sept/Dec 21	Mar/Jun 21	Sept/Dec 20	March 20	Sept/Dec 19	Mar/Jun 19
Introduction to strategic management accounting						
Performance hierarchy, CSFs, KPIs	1(iv)	2(a)	Specimen 1(i)	4(ii)	5(iii)	6(a)
Benchmarking						
SWOT						
5 forces and PEST		2(b)				
BCG						
Risk and uncertainty					34 (b)(c)	
Environmental, social and governance factors						
Stakeholders	18(a)		60(b)		34(a)	
ESG factors	18(a)					
Role of management accountant						
IR						
EMA	18(b)					
Budgeting and control						
Methods						25(a)
ABB and ABM						25(a), 62
Variances						25(b)
Non-budgetary methods						
Business structure and performance management						
Organisational forms and complex structures			60(a)			
Services						
Value chain					5(iv)	
7S model			20(a)			
BPR	58(a)					
Information systems and developments in technology						
Management information						
MIS						
IT developments			20(b)	4(iii)		
Big data						

Performance reports for management						
Performance reports	1(i)(ii)	2(a)		4(i)	5(i)	
Presentation techniques						
Quantitative and qualitative data	1(i)(ii)				61(a)	
Human resource aspects of performance management						
Reward schemes	1(iv), 58(b)					
Management styles						
Financial performance measures in the private sector						
Objectives						
Assessing financial performance	1(iii)					
Short and long term performance						
Divisional performance appraisal and transfer pricing						
Divisional performance including ROI, RI and EVA				Specimen 3(b)	5(ii)	
VBM				Specimen 3(a)		
Transfer pricing						
Performance management in not-for-profit organisations						
Performance management in NFPOs			Specimen 1(ii)			
Benchmarking (league tables) and targets			Specimen 1(iii)			
Non-financial performance indicators						
NFPIs						
Balanced scorecard					61(b)	
Building Block model	58(b)					
Performance pyramid		59				
The role of quality in performance measurement						
Role of quality						
Costs of quality				Specimen 2(b)		6(c)
Quality practices				Specimen 2(a)		6(b)
Lean production						

EXAM SPECIFIC INFORMATION

THE EXAM

FORMAT OF THE EXAM

	Total marks	Technical marks	Professional skills marks
Section A: One compulsory question	50	40	10
Section B: Two compulsory questions	50 (25 per question)	40 (20 per question)	10 (5 per question)
Overall	**100**	**80**	**20**

Note that:

- The exam is a 3 hour 15 minutes computer based examination (CBE).
- Technical syllabus sections A, B and C (not D) are examinable in Section A.
- Section B will contain one question mainly from technical syllabus section D. The other question will be from any other technical syllabus section(s).
- There will be 10 professional marks (syllabus section E) available in Section A and 5 professional marks in each Section B question.
- Candidates will receive a present value table and annuity table.
- Questions will be based around a scenario. It is important to refer back to this scenario when answering the question.
- There will be a mixture of written requirements and computational requirements.
- Earlier knowledge from previous exams will be drawn on at times.
- Dates will be in the format 20XX, e.g. 20X5. This will make the dates for each exam session generic.

PASS MARK

The pass mark for all ACCA Qualification examinations is 50%.

DETAILED SYLLABUS, STUDY GUIDE AND SPECIMEN EXAM

The detailed syllabus and study guide written by the ACCA, along with the Specimen Exam can be found at:

www.accaglobal.com

EXAM TECHNIQUE

In addition to reading the tips contained here, we recommend that you review the resources available on the ACCA Global Website before sitting the CBE. Here you will find guidance documents, videos and a link to the CBE question practice platform.

Before the exam starts – You will be given 10 minutes to read the introductory page and the four pages of instructions. These will be the same for each APM exam and therefore it is important that you familiarise yourself with these (using the ACCA practice exams) during your revision. The exam time (3 hours and 15 minutes) will start automatically at the end of the 10 minutes or earlier if actioned by you.

Time allocation – The time allowed for this exam is 3 hours and 15 minutes/195 minutes.

Read each question carefully, reviewing the format and content of the requirements so that you understand what you need to do.

There are 80 technical marks and 20 professional skills marks. Importantly, professional skills marks should be achieved as you work through the technical marks.

If 15 minutes are spent reading the examination requirements (it may be sensible to allocate time to this), your time allocation should be 2.25 minutes per mark (180/80). This gives 90 minutes for section A and 45 minutes for each section B question.

If you do not allow a specific amount of time for reading and planning (a more straightforward approach but the risk is that you run out of time) your time allocation will be 2.4 minutes per mark (195/80). This gives 97 minutes for section A and 49 minutes for each section B question.

If you plan to spend more or less time on reading and planning, your time allocation per mark will be different.

Planning your answers – When the exam starts spend a few minutes skimming through each question to get a feel for what is included. Once you have done this carry out an initial review of Section A. This will include a number of **exhibits** breaking down the scenario into relevant sections and including the detailed requirement. It will also include a list of the summarised **requirements** and an option to complete your answer in a **word processing** document and/or a **spreadsheet** document.

You can move around and resize the windows that you open to lay the screen out in a format that suits you.

Now copy and paste the specifics of the requirement into your answer document, perhaps highlighting in bold the different parts of the requirement and the verb used. Once complete review the exhibits in detail, highlighting and making notes as you do so and copy and pasting any relevant information to your answer document. These steps will help with your planning and structure but will also enable you to minimise the number of windows you have open.

The procedure will be similar for Section B.

Completing your answers – Start by revisiting the relevant exhibits for each requirement. Written answers should be in the word processor and calculations and numerical work only in the spreadsheet. For calculations, use a logical and well laid out structure. Calculations should be labelled and referenced in to any relevant discussion. For discursive answers use bold headings and sub-headings and professional language. Ensure all aspects of the requirement are addressed in a sensible and balanced way. It is vital that you relate your answer to the specific circumstances given. In Section A you will usually be required to produce a report. Head up your answer as a report and use the requirements as a basis for your introduction.

If you get completely stuck with a question return to it later.

If you do not understand what a question is asking, state your assumptions. Even if you do not answer in precisely the way the examiner hoped, you should be given some credit, if your assumptions are reasonable.

Finally, leave enough time to read through the answers, ensuring they are clear and organised, and to make any necessary changes.

KAPLAN'S RECOMMENDED REVISION APPROACH

QUESTION PRACTICE IS THE KEY TO SUCCESS

Success in Strategic Professional examinations relies upon you acquiring a firm grasp of the required knowledge at the tuition phase. In order to be able to do the questions, knowledge is essential.

However, the difference between success and failure often hinges on your exam technique on the day and making the most of the revision phase of your studies.

The Kaplan Study Text is the starting point, designed to provide the underpinning knowledge to tackle all questions. However, in the revision phase, poring over text books is not the answer.

Kaplan online Knowledge Check tests help you consolidate your knowledge and understanding and are a useful tool to check whether you can remember key topic areas.

Kaplan Pocket Notes are designed to help you quickly revise a topic area, however you then need to practice questions. There is a need to progress to full exam standard questions as soon as possible, and to tie your exam technique and technical knowledge together.

The importance of question practice cannot be over-emphasised.

The recommended approach below is designed by expert tutors in the field, in conjunction with their knowledge of the examiner.

The approach taken for the Applied Knowledge and Applied Skills exams is to revise by topic area. However, with the Strategic Professional stage exams, a multi topic approach is required to answer the scenario based questions.

You need to practice as many questions as possible in the time you have left.

OUR AIM

Our aim is to get you to the stage where you can attempt exam standard questions confidently, to time, in a closed book environment, with no supplementary help (i.e. to simulate the real examination experience).

Practising your exam technique on real past examination questions, in timed conditions, is also vitally important for you to assess your progress and identify areas of weakness that may need more attention in the final run up to the examination.

In order to achieve this we recognise that initially you may feel the need to practice some questions with open book help and exceed the required time.

The approach below shows you which questions you should use to build up to coping with exam standard question practice, and references to the sources of information available should you need to revisit a topic area in more detail.

Remember that in the real examination, all you have to do is:

- attempt all questions required by the exam
- only spend the allotted time on each question, and
- get them at least 50% right!

Try and practice this approach on every question you attempt from now to the real exam.

EXAMINER COMMENTS

We have included the examiner's comments to the more recent examination questions in this kit for you to see the main pitfalls that students fall into with regard to technical content.

However, too many times in the general section of the report, the examiner comments that students had failed due to:

Exam technique

- Repeating learned facts only.
- Inadequate application of technical knowledge to scenario.
- Not answering the question.
- Lack of practice.

Technical weaknesses

- Inability to do fundamental calculations.
- Poor use of models.
- No focus on performance management and measurement.
- Not adding value to the organisation; e.g. by creating useful information from the data provided.
- Difference between key principles not understood.

Knowledge

- Lack of knowledge. The whole syllabus should be covered. Articles from Student Accountant (available on the ACCA website) may also be a source of topics for the exam.
- Weak underpinning knowledge from Performance Management (PM). All PM knowledge is assumed but the emphasis in APM is on the synthesis and evaluation of key topics and techniques.
- Students who have studied SBL should understand that in APM the models are used for performance management and measurement and are not strategy models.

For additional support with your studies please also refer to the ACCA Global website.

STRATEGIC PROFESSIONAL COMPUTER BASED EXAMINATIONS

We advise consulting the ACCA Global website for additional CBE revision resources. On the ACCA website there is a CBE demonstration. It is **ESSENTIAL** that you attempt this before your real CBE. You will become familiar with how to move around the CBE screens and the way that questions are formatted, increasing your confidence and speed in the actual exam.

Be sure you understand how to use the **software** before you start the exam. If in doubt, ask the assessment centre staff to explain it to you.

Questions are **displayed on the screen** and answers are entered using keyboard and mouse.

For additional support with your studies please also refer to the ACCA Global website.

THE KAPLAN APM EXAM REVISION PLAN

Stage 1: Assess areas of strengths and weaknesses

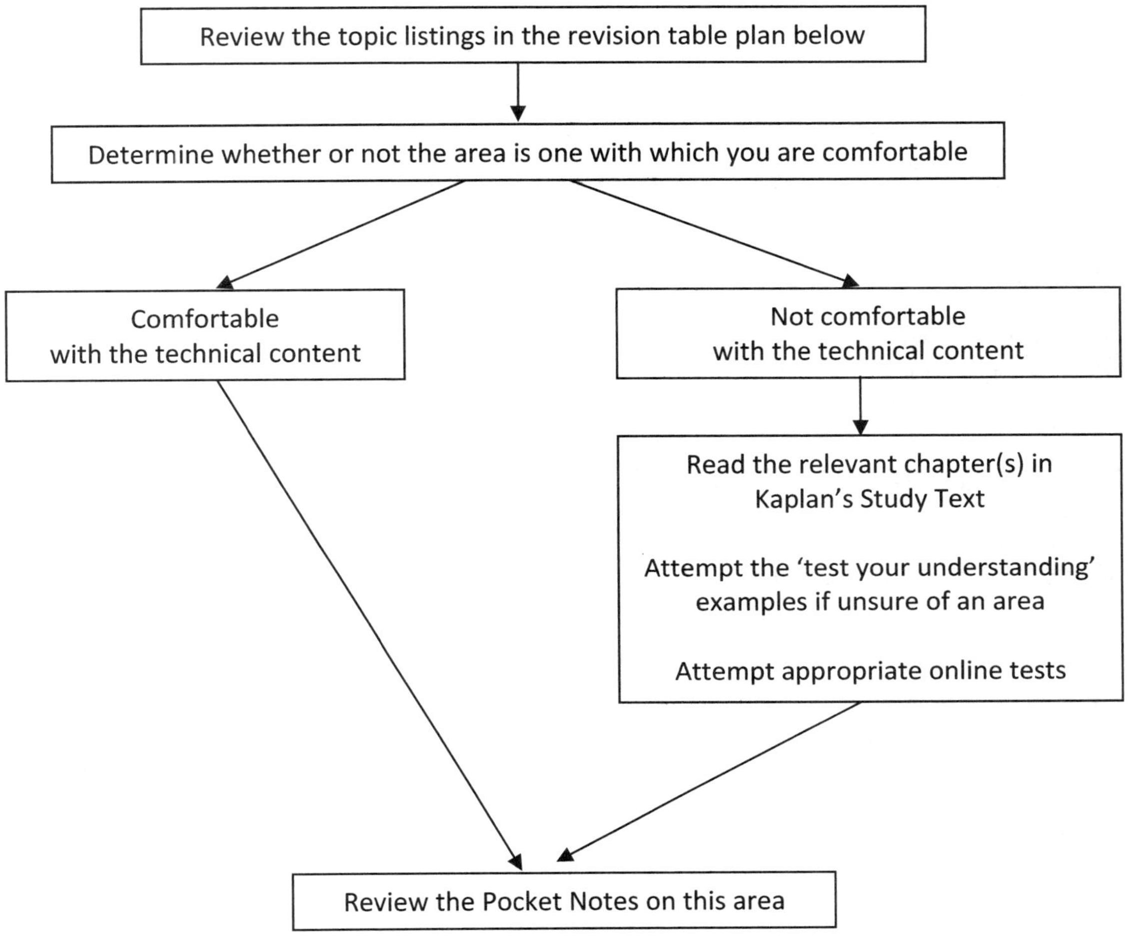

Stage 2: Practice questions

Ensure that you revise all syllabus areas as questions could be asked on anything.

Try to avoid referring to text books and notes and the model answer until you have completed your attempt.

Try to answer the question in the allotted time.

Review your attempt with the model answer and assess how much of the answer you achieved in the allocated exam time.

Fill in the self-assessment box below and decide on your best course of action.

Comfortable with question attempt

↓

Only revisit when comfortable with questions on all topic areas

Not comfortable with question attempts

↓

Focus on these areas by:

- Reworking test your understanding examples in Kaplan's Study Text
- Revisiting the technical content from Kaplan's Pocket Notes
- Working any remaining questions on that area in the Exam Kit

Note that:

The 'answer debrief' questions have an online debrief where a top tutor works through the question in full, explains key elements of the answer and how to gain marks.

Stage 3: Final pre-exam revision

We recommend that you **attempt at least one three hour and 15 minute mock examination** containing a set of previously unseen exam standard questions.

It is important that you get a feel for the breadth of coverage of a real exam without advanced knowledge of the topic areas covered – just as you will expect to see on the real exam day.

Ideally this mock should be sat in timed, closed book, real exam conditions and could be a mock examination offered by your tuition provider.

KAPLAN'S DETAILED REVISION PLAN

Topic	*Study Text Chapter*	*Pocket Notes Chapter*	*Questions to attempt*	*Tutor guidance*	*Date attempted*	*Self-assessment*
Introduction to strategic management accounting						
– Planning and control at different levels, mission, strategy, objectives, CSFs and KPIs	1	1	1(iv), 3(ii), 4(ii), 5(iii), 6(i), 9(ii), 10(ii), 11(i)(ii), 12(ii), 15(v), 17(i)(iii)(iv), 33(a)(b), 56(a), 69(a), Specimen Q1(i)	A core area that is commonly examined. It is important to complete a range of questions here. Mission may not be tested in isolation but, for example, you may need to evaluate the link between the mission, strategy, objectives, CSFs and KPIs or consider the impact of a change in the mission statement on the KPIs.		
– Benchmarking	1	1	7(c), 14(iii), 28, 43(b)	Students should be able to apply and evaluate the methods of benchmarking performance		
– SWOT	1	1	Not commonly examined but do review this in the context of how it may assist in the performance management process.			
– PEST and Porter's 5 forces	1	1	2(b), 17(ii), 19(a), 32(a), 35(a)	The focus for APM is how these models are useful for performance management rather than can you do the PEST or 5 forces analysis.		
– BCG	1	1	30, 53(c)	The classification from this model will be used to determine performance management issues and performance measures which are required depending on where in the matrix the division/product etc. falls.		
– Risk and uncertainty	1	1	19(c), 34, 35, 36(a)	The focus will be on the impact of risk and uncertainty on strategic planning and decision making, including the impact of stakeholders' risk appetites. Calculations will not be required but you may be asked to evaluate the different decision methods and the link to risk appetites.		

Topic	*Study Text Chapter*	*Pocket Notes Chapter*	*Questions to attempt*	*Tutor guidance*	*Date attempted*	*Self-assessment*
Environmental, social and governance factors						
– Stakeholders	2	2	14(ii), 34(a), 60(b)	Stakeholder influence on performance measurement and management (for example, using Mendelow) may be tested in terms of a plan, decision or strategy that is being considered.		
– Environmental, social and governance factors	2	2	18(a)	It is important to understand that the careful consideration of ESG factors can help (rather than hinder) an organisation in achieving its stated objectives and that these factors may impact strategy formulation.		
– The role of the management accountant in sustainability	2	2	New to the syllabus. No past exam questions as yet.	The focus will be on the evaluation of the role of the management accountant in the collection of data, measurement and reporting of these factors.		
– Integrated reporting	2	2	10(ii), 39	The emphasis will be on the role of the management accountant.		
– Environmental management accounting	2	2	18(b), 24(b)(c), 29, 31	It is important to be able to discuss, evaluate and apply (using the techniques available) EMA.		

Topic	*Study Text Chapter*	*Pocket Notes Chapter*	*Questions to attempt*	*Tutor guidance*	*Date attempted*	*Self-assessment*
Budgeting and control						
– Methods of budgeting	3	3	23, 26(b)(c)	Do not overlook this area. Knowledge of the different budgeting models (incremental, ZBB, rolling, fixed and flexible) can help you to score relatively easy marks in the exam. In addition, make sure that you can do the basic calculations for budgets.		
– Variances	3	3	26(a)	Some calculations may be examined but the emphasis will be on how these relate to issues in planning and control.		
– Activity-based budgeting and management	3	3	24(a), 25, 62, 65, 67	You need to be able to discuss and evaluate the application of activity-based management.		
– Non-budgetary methods for organisational control	3	3	New to the syllabus. No past exam questions as yet.	It is important to understand the reasons for the increased use of non-budgetary methods, such as beyond budgeting		

Topic	***Study Text Chapter***	***Pocket Notes Chapter***	***Questions to attempt***	***Tutor guidance***	***Date attempted***	***Self-assessment***
Business structure and performance management						
– Organisational forms and complex structures	4	4	36(b), 37(b), 60(a), 66(b), 70	Different business structures will have different information needs and implications for performance management. The organisations in the exam are often more complex in nature – these complex structures will present their own problems.		
– Services	4	4	No specific questions to review. A straightforward area but be ready to distinguish the needs of service and manufacturing organisations.			
– Value chain	4	4	5(iv), 9(iii)	It is important to understand that a focus on an organisation's activities (and the linkages between them) can help to improve performance.		
– McKinsey's 7S model	4	4	20(a)	The role of the 7S model in business integration should be understood.		
– BPR	4	4	21, 22(a), 27(a)(b), 58(a)	It is important to understand what BPR is and to consider its impact on systems development and performance improvement.		

Topic	*Study Text Chapter*	*Pocket Notes Chapter*	*Questions to attempt*	*Tutor guidance*	*Date attempted*	*Self-assessment*
Information systems and developments in technology						
– Management information	5	5	5(iii), 16(v), 32(b)(c), 37(a), 66(c)	The qualities of good information, the different sources of information and the types of information may be examined.		
– Management accounting information systems	5	5	13(v), 33(c), 38, 40(a)	The different types, design considerations and the importance of integration are all examinable. To remain competitive, an organisation must continually refine these systems.		
– IT developments	5	5	3(iv), 4(iii), 16(iv), 20(b), 37(a), 40(c), 41, 54(b), 66(a)	A number of different developments may be examined here; the emphasis will be on the opportunities and risks they present.		
– Big data	5	5	9(iv)	Think about the impact of big data and big data analytics on performance measurement and management and the role of the management accountant, including a consideration of ethical issues and the methods of data analysis and data analytics.		
Performance reports for management						
– Performance reports	6	6	1(i)(ii), 2(a), 4(i), 5(i), 7(a), 9(i), 10(i), 11(iii), 12(i), 15(i), 40(b), 42(a), 49(d)	A commonly examined area. Complete a number of questions to understand how it can be examined in a variety of contexts. It is important to be able to evaluate a performance report in the context of the organisation's mission and objectives.		
– Presentation techniques	6	6	Touched upon is some questions.	Consideration of techniques such as data visualisation.		
– Quantitative and qualitative data	6	6	1(i)(ii), 7(b), 48(c)	Be ready to discuss the difficulties associated with these types of data/information		

Topic	*Study Text Chapter*	*Pocket Notes Chapter*	*Questions to attempt*	*Tutor guidance*	*Date attempted*	*Self-assessment*
Human resource aspects of performance management						
– Reward schemes	7	7	11(v), 22(b), 27(c), 30(d), 51(c), 58(b), 71(b), 72(c)	The purpose of and different methods of rewards schemes could be examined and an understanding of the beneficial and adverse consequences of linking reward to performance measurement is required.		
– Hopwood's management styles	7	7	8(iii), 42(b), 44(c), 53(c)	Management style needs to be considered when designing a performance measurement system.		
Financial performance measures in the private sector						
– The objectives of profit seeking organisations	8	8	Touched upon in some questions.	The primary objective of financial performance in a profit-seeking organisation is to maximise shareholder wealth.		
– Assessing financial performance	8	8	1(iii), 13(iii), 43(a)	You must be able to calculate and evaluate the core ratios and comment on what they mean. You need to be ready to assess financial performance in the context of the scenario given rather than simply calculating every single measure that you know.		
– Short-term and long-term financial performance	8	8	Touched upon in some questions.	There are a number of credible reasons for using short-term financial measures to assess performance but the sole use of these can be to the detriment of long-term success.		

Topic	*Study Text Chapter*	*Pocket Notes Chapter*	*Questions to attempt*	*Tutor guidance*	*Date attempted*	*Self-assessment*
Divisional performance appraisal and transfer pricing						
– Divisional performance	9	9	3(i), 5(ii), 10(iii)(iv), 12(iii)(iv), 15(ii)(iii), 16(i), 46, 51(a), 53(a)(b), 57(b)(d), 64(c)	A commonly examined area. Be ready to discuss the problems of divisional structures, the types of responsibility centre and to calculate and evaluate RI, ROI and EVA.		
– Value-based management	9	9	15(iv), 57(a)(c), 64(a)(b), Specimen Q3	You need to be able to evaluate and apply the value-based management approaches to performance management.		
– Transfer pricing	9	9	16(ii)(iii), 52, 56(b)(c)	The transfer price negotiated between the divisions, or imposed by head office, can have a profound, but perhaps arbitrary, effect on the reported performance and subsequent decisions made.		
Performance management in not-for-profit organisations						
– Performance management in NFPOs	10	10	44(b), 48(b), 55(a), Specimen Q1(i)(ii)	Think about the problems and diversity of objectives and the different approaches to performance measurement in NFPOs, including an assessment of value for money.		
– Benchmarking (league tables) and targets	10	10	47, 55(b), Specimen Q1(iii)	A very topical issue. Be prepared to evaluate the use of benchmarking (league tables) and targets in the public sector.		

Topic	*Study Text Chapter*	*Pocket Notes Chapter*	*Questions to attempt*	*Tutor guidance*	*Date attempted*	*Self-assessment*
Non-financial performance indicators (NFPIs)						
– NFPIs	11	11	8(ii), 44(a), 48(a), 61(a)	You need to be able to talk about the reasons why, in addition to FPIs, NFPIs are useful for performance measurement and some of the areas where NFPIs play a key role.		
– Balanced scorecard	11	11	8(i), 13(i)(ii), 61(b), 72(a)(b), 73	Several tools are available for measuring financial and non-financial performance. A core area – practise a number of questions so that you understand how these models can be applied and evaluated in a range of contexts.		
– Fitzgerald and Moon's Building Block model	11	11	11(iv), 68			
– Performance pyramid	11	11	14(i), 59, 63(a)(b), 69(b)(c), 71(a)			
The role of quality in performance measurement						
– The role of quality in performance management including the costs of quality	12	12	10(iv), 13(iv), 49(a), Specimen Q2(b)	Ensure that you understand the importance of quality and the different quality-related costs.		
– Quality practices	12	12	3(iii), 6(ii)(iii), 10(iii), 14(iv), 16(v), 45, 49(b)(c), 50, 54(a), 63(c), Specimen Q2(a)	There are a number of quality practices. It is a good idea to complete a range of questions on these.		
– Lean production	12	12	38	Understand the link between quality and lean production and be able to apply the 5 Ss.		

MATHEMATICAL TABLES

PRESENT VALUE TABLE

Present value of 1 i.e. $(1+r)^{-n}$ where r = discount rate, n = number of periods until payment

Periods (n)	1%	2%	3%	4%	5%	6%	7%	8%	9%	10%	
1	0.990	0.980	0.971	0.962	0.952	0.943	0.935	0.926	0.917	0.909	1
2	0.980	0.961	0.943	0.925	0.907	0.890	0.873	0.857	0.842	0.826	2
3	0.971	0.942	0.915	0.889	0.864	0.840	0.816	0.794	0.772	0.751	3
4	0.961	0.924	0.888	0.855	0.823	0.792	0.763	0.735	0.708	0.683	4
5	0.951	0.906	0.863	0.822	0.784	0.747	0.713	0.681	0.650	0.621	5
6	0.942	0.888	0.837	0.790	0.746	0.705	0.666	0.630	0.596	0.564	6
7	0.933	0.871	0.813	0.760	0.711	0.665	0.623	0.583	0.547	0.513	7
8	0.923	0.853	0.789	0.731	0.677	0.627	0.582	0.540	0.502	0.467	8
9	0.914	0.837	0.766	0.703	0.645	0.592	0.544	0.500	0.460	0.424	9
10	0.905	0.820	0.744	0.676	0.614	0.558	0.508	0.463	0.422	0.386	10
11	0.896	0.804	0.722	0.650	0.585	0.527	0.475	0.429	0.388	0.350	11
12	0.887	0.788	0.701	0.625	0.557	0.497	0.444	0.397	0.356	0.319	12
13	0.879	0.773	0.681	0.601	0.530	0.469	0.415	0.368	0.326	0.290	13
14	0.870	0.758	0.661	0.577	0.505	0.442	0.388	0.340	0.299	0.263	14
15	0.861	0.743	0.642	0.555	0.481	0.417	0.362	0.315	0.275	0.239	15

(n)	11%	12%	13%	14%	15%	16%	17%	18%	19%	20%	
1	0.901	0.893	0.885	0.877	0.870	0.862	0.855	0.847	0.840	0.833	1
2	0.812	0.797	0.783	0.769	0.756	0.743	0.731	0.718	0.706	0.694	2
3	0.731	0.712	0.693	0.675	0.658	0.641	0.624	0.609	0.593	0.579	3
4	0.659	0.636	0.613	0.592	0.572	0.552	0.534	0.516	0.499	0.482	4
5	0.593	0.567	0.543	0.519	0.497	0.476	0.456	0.437	0.419	0.402	5
6	0.535	0.507	0.480	0.456	0.432	0.410	0.390	0.370	0.352	0.335	6
7	0.482	0.452	0.425	0.400	0.376	0.354	0.333	0.314	0.296	0.279	7
8	0.434	0.404	0.376	0.351	0.327	0.305	0.285	0.266	0.249	0.233	8
9	0.391	0.361	0.333	0.308	0.284	0.263	0.243	0.225	0.209	0.194	9
10	0.352	0.322	0.295	0.270	0.247	0.227	0.208	0.191	0.176	0.162	10
11	0.317	0.287	0.261	0.237	0.215	0.195	0.178	0.162	0.148	0.135	11
12	0.286	0.257	0.231	0.208	0.187	0.168	0.152	0.137	0.124	0.112	12
13	0.258	0.229	0.204	0.182	0.163	0.145	0.130	0.116	0.104	0.093	13
14	0.232	0.205	0.181	0.160	0.141	0.125	0.111	0.099	0.088	0.078	14
15	0.209	0.183	0.160	0.140	0.123	0.108	0.095	0.084	0.074	0.065	15

ANNUITY TABLE

Present value of an annuity of 1 i.e. $\frac{1-(1+r)^{-n}}{r}$ where r = discount rate, n = number of periods

Periods (n)	1%	2%	3%	4%	5%	6%	7%	8%	9%	10%	
1	0.990	0.980	0.971	0.962	0.952	0.943	0.935	0.926	0.917	0.909	1
2	1.970	1.942	1.913	1.886	1.859	1.833	1.808	1.783	1.759	1.736	2
3	2.941	2.884	2.829	2.775	2.723	2.673	2.624	2.577	2.531	2.487	3
4	3.902	3.808	3.717	3.630	3.546	3.465	3.387	3.312	3.240	3.170	4
5	4.853	4.713	4.580	4.452	4.329	4.212	4.100	3.993	3.890	3.791	5
6	5.795	5.601	5.417	5.242	5.076	4.917	4.767	4.623	4.486	4.355	6
7	6.728	6.472	6.230	6.002	5.786	5.582	5.389	5.206	5.033	4.868	7
8	7.652	7.325	7.020	6.733	6.463	6.210	5.971	5.747	5.535	5.335	8
9	8.566	8.162	7.786	7.435	7.108	6.802	6.515	6.247	5.995	5.759	9
10	9.471	8.983	8.530	8.111	7.722	7.360	7.024	6.710	6.418	6.145	10
11	10.37	9.787	9.253	8.760	8.306	7.887	7.499	7.139	6.805	6.495	11
12	11.26	10.58	9.954	9.385	8.863	8.384	7.943	7.536	7.161	6.814	12
13	12.13	11.35	10.63	9.986	9.394	8.853	8.358	7.904	7.487	7.103	13
14	13.00	12.11	11.30	10.56	9.899	9.295	8.745	8.244	7.786	7.367	14
15	13.87	12.85	11.94	11.12	10.38	9.712	9.108	8.559	8.061	7.606	15

(n)	11%	12%	13%	14%	15%	16%	17%	18%	19%	20%	
1	0.901	0.893	0.885	0.877	0.870	0.862	0.855	0.847	0.840	0.833	1
2	1.713	1.690	1.668	1.647	1.626	1.605	1.585	1.566	1.547	1.528	2
3	2.444	2.402	2.361	2.322	2.283	2.246	2.210	2.174	2.140	2.106	3
4	3.102	3.037	2.974	2.914	2.855	2.798	2.743	2.690	2.639	2.589	4
5	3.696	3.605	3.517	3.433	3.352	3.274	3.199	3.127	3.058	2.991	5
6	4.231	4.111	3.998	3.889	3.784	3.685	3.589	3.498	3.410	3.326	6
7	4.712	4.564	4.423	4.288	4.160	4.039	3.922	3.812	3.706	3.605	7
8	5.146	4.968	4.799	4.639	4.487	4.344	4.207	4.078	3.954	3.837	8
9	5.537	5.328	5.132	4.946	4.772	4.607	4.451	4.303	4.163	4.031	9
10	5.889	5.650	5.426	5.216	5.019	4.833	4.659	4.494	4.339	4.192	10
11	6.207	5.938	5.687	5.453	5.234	5.029	4.836	4.656	4.486	4.327	11
12	6.492	6.194	5.918	5.660	5.421	5.197	4.988	4.793	4.611	4.439	12
13	6.750	6.424	6.122	5.842	5.583	5.342	5.118	4.910	4.715	4.533	13
14	6.982	6.628	6.302	6.002	5.724	5.468	5.229	5.008	4.802	4.611	14
15	7.191	6.811	6.462	6.142	5.847	5.575	5.324	5.092	4.876	4.675	15

Section 1

PRACTICE QUESTIONS – SECTION A

Note: From September 2022, the 50 marks in Section A will comprise 40 technical marks and 10 professional skills marks. An updated Section A question for the specimen exam has been provided by the ACCA and is included at the back of the Exam Kit and some of the other Section A questions in the Exam Kit have been amended to reflect this approach.

In addition, in all questions the requirement will now be fully embedded within an exhibit (i.e a section of information) in the scenario and the requirements are simply a list of the areas which, for example, the CEO is requesting work on. Some of the Section A questions in the Exam Kit have been amended to reflect this approach.

The questions that have been amended to include 10 professional skills marks and the fully embedded requirements are indicated as such next to the question title in both the question and the answers. In addition, the 'Index of questions and answers' in the Exam Kit prelims shows the questions that have been amended in this way.

Section A of the APM exam will only examine technical syllabus sections A, B and C. Some of the questions below (those prior to September 2018) include requirements from other syllabus sections, i.e. B and D. These have been included since they serve as good revision of real past exam questions or exam standard questions and will also serve as good revision for Section B questions in the exam.

1 FREUCHIE (SEPT/DEC 21) (AMENDED)

Exhibit 1 – Company information

Freuchie Retail (Freuchie) is a family-owned business which sells a range of clothes from a chain of shops across Beeland. Freuchie's mission is 'to deliver returns to shareholders above the average for the retail sector by providing a superior customer experience from the appearance of the stores to the attractive range of clothes which are sold with enthusiasm'.

The board feel that performance has been poor compared to other similar retailers in the past five years. As a result, a new chief executive officer (CEO) was appointed a year ago and has spent this time conducting a fundamental review of the business. The review has identified a number of areas for improvement including those associated with performance reporting and management.

Exhibit 2 – Performance reporting: quantitative

The CEO is concerned that performance towards this mission and its subsidiary objectives are not being usefully discussed at board meetings. He believes that the fault lies in the board's performance report for annual strategic review. Therefore, he wants you to do an assessment of the current performance report in two parts in light of his concern (see Appendix 1 for the most recent example). The first part of the assessment should consider the quantitative elements of the report and can include some discussion of improved indicators and also, more generally, should take into account what is best practice for reporting performance.

Exhibit 3 – Performance reporting: narrative

The second part of the performance reporting assessment should be a review and rewrite of the current narrative commentary on the report. The CEO believes the current commentary is especially weak and wants a critical assessment of it, followed by an improved example based upon what you consider to be the crucial aspects of Freuchie's performance. He stated that the improved example commentary should consist of no more than four points in order to focus attention on the key areas. You should include figures to illustrate the points you have included using the data given where it is available but some can be left blank to be filled in later if the underlying data is not available.

Exhibit 4 – Operational gearing and cost structure

The CEO was at a business networking meeting recently where one speaker, a highly regarded management consultant, made a number of comments about fixed and variable costs, operational gearing and the importance of these to the operation of a store. The CEO did not understand the presentation, complaining that there was too much jargon. He wants to understand what operational gearing is and how it relates to fixed and variable costs. Therefore, he wants a calculation of operational gearing for Freuchie using current data (Appendices 1 and 2) and an assessment of the implications of the result for Freuchie's management.

Exhibit 5 – What gets measured, gets done

At the same business networking meeting, another CEO mentioned that she found the quote 'What gets measured, gets done' a useful starting point for thinking about the management implications of new performance indicators. She then used another list of jargon phrases that Freuchie's CEO did not follow. As a result, the CEO wants an assessment of the problems that the quote identifies and also, how phrases such as 'tunnel vision and sub-optimisation' might link to the quote. He wants illustrations from Freuchie's business.

Required:

It is now 1 September 20X5.

Write a report to the chief executive officer (CEO) of Freuchie to respond to his instructions for work on the following areas:

(i) Current performance reporting: quantitative (17 marks)

(ii) Current performance reporting: narrative (10 marks)

(iii) The calculation of operational gearing and its implications (8 marks)

(iv) The quote 'What gets measured, gets done' (5 marks)

Professional marks will be awarded for the demonstration of skill in communication, analysis and evaluation, scepticism and commercial acumen in your answer. **(10 marks)**

(Total: 50 marks)

Exhibit 6 – Appendix 1

Freuchie Retail: Strategic Performance Report

Year to 30 June 20X5

	Budget	**Actual**	**Actual**	**Costs and profit as a % of revenue**	**Change of previous year**
	20X5	**20X5**	**20X4**		
	$m	**$m**	**$m**		
Revenue	641	638.1	577.7		10.50%
Cost of sales	380.5	378.9	342.1		
Gross profit	**260.5**	**259.2**	**235.6**	40.60%	10.00%
Staff costs	136.2	135.8	123.1	21.30%	10.30%
Other operating costs					
Rent and property costs	71	71	63.4		
Marketing	34	34	34	5.30%	0.00%
Head office costs	11.9	11.7	11.9		
Total	**116.9**	**116.7**	**109.3**	18.30%	6.80%
Operating profit	**7.4**	**6.7**	**3.2**	1.00%	109.40%
Finance costs	4.9	4.9	4.8		
Group profit before tax	**2.5**	**1.8**	**–1.6**	0.30%	
Tax	0.5	0.4	–0.3		
Group profit after tax	**2**	**1.4**	**–1.3**	0.20%	
Other data:					
Number of employees		5,103	4,607		10.80%
Dividend per share ($)		0.51	0.51		0.00%
Inventory obsolescence/ loss write-downs ($m)		13.1	12.7		3.10%
Number of stores		42	38		10.50%

Commentary:

- Overall performance is satisfactory as the business has maintained its dividend.
- Revenue is up by 10.50% on the previous period.
- Gross margin has held at about 41%.
- Inventory write-downs were in line with the increased stock held at stores.

Exhibit 7 – Appendix 2

Freuchie – additional data

Cost of sales includes:

Year to 30 June	**Budget 20X5**	**Actual 20X5**	**Actual 20X4**
	$m	**$m**	**$m**
Insurance	18.2	18.2	16.2
Utilities	12	11.9	10.8
Depreciation	17	17	15.3
Total	**47.2**	**47.1**	**42.3**

Staff costs:

The employees are all paid an annual salary as a fixed sum stated in their contract, except for a bonus pool of 1% of revenue which is divided up between the sales staff who exceed their target revenue.

2 FIAG (MAR/JUN 21) (AMENDED)

Exhibit 1 – Company information

Fiag Bicycles (Fiag) is a large national bicycle manufacturer in the well-developed country of Beeland. It was a family-owned business until three years ago when it raised new funds from a venture capitalist (VC) to develop new models of bicycle. Of the eight models in its current range, two have been significantly redesigned and one totally new model has been launched in 20X4. This new model (the Zoam) has been developed over five years and is Fiag's most radical development to date, as it is lightweight and has an electrical battery which can assist less physically fit riders to cycle up hills.

The VC invested $30m in 20X2 and insisted that Fiag produce a mission statement as a clear indication of the company's objective. The objective of Fiag is 'to give the shareholders sustainable growth in returns by developing and manufacturing the best quality bicycles and so bring the joy of cycling to a broad customer base in Beeland'.

Exhibit 2 – Performance reporting

The VC has a non-executive director on the board of Fiag. She has criticised the executive directors over the most recent performance report that was presented to the board meeting in order to review the annual performance to 30 June 20X5 (Appendix 1). Firstly, she was very unhappy about what she felt were attempts to manipulate the picture presented in the report.

Secondly, she repeated criticism that she had given in earlier board meetings that the report does not address the company's objectives. She then demanded that the executive directors take action on these points immediately and asked that the board meeting be reconvened once this is done.

The chief executive officer (CEO) wants you, as a performance expert in the company, to give him advice on these matters. He is committed eventually to a redesign of the performance reporting at Fiag but needs to understand the non-executive director's concerns more clearly before this begins. He is happy that there are no arithmetic errors in the presentation of the performance report but wants a critical review from you:

1 addressing the question of manipulation in the impression given by the report

2 assessing whether the current report addresses the company's objectives and briefly, any other issues in its presentation

Exhibit 3 – External business environment

The CEO has recognised that the company operates in an increasingly volatile external business environment. Therefore, he has employed a consultant to perform a PEST analysis and he has given you the relevant extracts of their report (Appendix 2). He stated that he does not want you to re-perform the consultant's analysis of the external environment. Instead, he wants you to focus on the implications of the PEST factors identified on Fiag's business and then on providing a justified recommendation of suitable performance indicators to measure the impact of each of those factors.

Required:

It is now 1 September 20X5.

Write a report to the chief executive officer (CEO) to respond to his instructions for work on the following areas:

(a) **the performance reporting at Fiag focused on**

(i) **the question of manipulation in the board report** **(12 marks)**

(ii) **whether the report addresses the company's objectives and the report's presentation** **(14 marks)**

(b) **the consultant's report on the external business environment** **(14 marks)**

Professional marks will be awarded for the demonstration of skill in communication, analysis and evaluation, scepticism and commercial acumen in your answer. **(10 marks)**

(Total: 50 marks)

Exhibit 4 – Appendix 1

Performance Report

Year to 30 June	**20X5**	**20X4**	**Improvement year on year**	**Industry average**
	$m	**$m**	**%**	**%**
Revenue	273	289	–6	
Cost of sales	131	137		
Gross profit	142	152	–7	
Administrative expenses	50	52		
Distribution expenses	28	29		
Selling and marketing expenses	51	52		
Operating profit	13	19		
Operating margin	4.8%	6.6%		11%
Exceptional costs	0	12		
Net financing costs	0	0		
Profit before tax	13	7	86%	

Commentary:

- Revenue from new and redesigned bicycle models grew by 200% in 20X5
- PBT has improved by 86%
- Operating margin has fallen by a small 1.8%

Notes:

1 Administrative expenses includes the income from a two year government grant of \$5m p.a. (in 20X5 and 20X4) relating to Zoam.

2 Revenue includes revenue from the Zoam (new electrical bicycle) (\$25m in 20X5, \$5m in 20X4).

3 Exceptional costs are the costs of developing the new electrical bicycle.

Exhibit 5 – Appendix 2

External business environment at Fiag (August 20X5)

Extract of report by A Consultant

Political environment

- The government of Beeland has recently provided tax allowances to citizens who use a bicycle to commute to work.
- It has also supported cycling by building many new dedicated cycle-paths.

Economic environment

- Beeland has seen steady economic growth for the last 20 years and this wealth has spread through all parts of society.
- The introduction of significant import tariffs has surprised many businesses such as Fiag, who import raw materials or sub-components for final assembly.

Socio-cultural environment

- Having a healthy lifestyle has become an increasingly popular aspiration for the people of Beeland.
- The population of Beeland is ageing with increasing numbers of retired people.

Technological environment

- Cheap, new materials are enabling lighter bicycles to be built without compromising their strength.
- Battery technology has rapidly advanced so that it is feasible to fit lightweight electrical power units to bicycles.

3 IRON CHICKEN (DEC 15)

Exhibit 1 – Company information

Iron Chicken (IC) is a multinational business which manufactures commercial building control systems. Building control systems include heating and air-conditioning systems, lighting controls, power and water monitoring and security systems (e.g. keypad access, alarms and CCTV). IC's manufacturing takes place at a number of factory sites where some products have a long product life and are simple and mass-produced while other products are complex and have a short product life due to changing technologies.

IC's mission statement is 'to create value for shareholders through control products which improve productivity, save energy and increase comfort and safety'.

A new chief executive officer (CEO) has been appointed to address a decline in IC's share price in the last three years. This CEO has identified that the business has grown through acquisition and as a result she stated, 'senior management have focused on making corporate deals and not making control systems.' The CEO has declared that the business must focus on optimising its value generation rather than just getting larger through acquisitions. She has developed an improvement programme for IC.

You are a performance management expert within IC and the CEO has tasked you with aiding her on the following four aspects of her improvement programme:

Exhibit 2 – Economic value added (EVA™)

The CEO wants your views on the use of EVA™ as the key performance metric at IC. You have been supplied with the current EVA™ calculation (Appendix 1) but there is some doubt about whether the junior management accountant who has done this work was sufficiently trained in the method.

Therefore, the CEO requires you to evaluate its accuracy and the assumptions which form part of the calculation and advise her on your results, providing calculations as needed.

Exhibit 3 – CSFs and KPIs

The CEO believes that the poor performance of the company can be addressed by ensuring that the mission statement flows down into the performance management of the business. To that end, the following critical success factors (CSFs) and the associated current key performance indicators (KPIs) have been identified.

CSF	**Associated current KPI**
Greater staff productivity	Units produced per labour hour
Reduction of wastage in production	Power consumed per unit produced
Greater innovation of products	Number of new products launched

The CEO wants you to briefly explain a weakness of the current KPI associated with each CSF and then provide a justified alternative KPI.

Exhibit 4 – Improvement projects

In order to improve performance, the CEO plans to implement initiatives associated with 'lean' manufacturing. Specifically, there are three projects which have been suggested and the CEO needs your advice on these:

1 Move to just-in-time manufacturing

2 Use kaizen costing

3 Examine the costs of quality in achieving a 'zero defects' approach to manufacturing

The CEO has stated that she needs you to explain what the three improvement projects are, how they will help to meet the CSFs at IC also how they will impact on the existing three KPIs.

Exhibit 5 – New information system

The CEO is concerned about the implications of the improvement projects for IC's information systems as she feels that they are not currently suitable for the plan that she has. The current information systems of the company are based around the functional departments of the business such as manufacturing, marketing, finance and logistics. Each department has developed its own system although all feed into the finance system which is the main one used for strategic decision-making. In order that the department systems can all feed through to the current finance system, these current systems only handle quantitative data. The company is considering the implementation of a new information system. This new system will introduce networking technology in order to bring together all of the departmental systems into a new, single, corporate database. The CEO would like an assessment of the impact of this proposed, new information system on the three improvement projects.

It is now 1 September 20X5.

Required:

Write a report to the CEO of Iron Chicken to respond to her instructions for work on the following areas:

(i) use of economic value added (EVA™) as the key performance metric at IC (15 marks)

(ii) current key performance indicators (KPIs) (6 marks)

(iii) the three improvement projects (15 marks)

(iv) impact of the proposed new information system on the three improvement projects. (10 marks)

Professional marks will be awarded for the format, style and structure of the discussion of your answer. (4 marks)

(Total: 50 marks)

Exhibit 6 – Appendix 1 (spreadsheet)

Economic value added	**Year ended 30 June 20X5** $m	**Note**
Operating profit	551.4	
Add back		
Non-cash expenses	15.1	
Marketing capitalised	23.1	5
Less		
Tax	134.8	6
Loss tax relief on interest	24.5	7
Net operating profit after tax (NOPAT)	430.3	
Capital employed		
From the statement of financial position	2,401.0	9
Marketing spend capitalised	23.1	5
Adjusted capital employed	2,424.1	

WACC = (1/2 × 16%) + (1/2 × 6.8%) = 11.4%

EVA™ = NOPAT – (WACC × Capital employed) = 154

Assumptions and notes:

1	Debt/Equity	100.0%
2	Cost of equity	16.0%
3	Tax rate	30.0%
4	Cost of debt (pre-tax)	6.8%

5 There has been $23.1m of marketing spent each year for the last two years in order to build the brand of IC long term

6 Tax paid in the year was $130m while the tax charged per the accounts was $134.8m

7 Interest charged in the period was $81.6m

Lost tax relief on this interest was 30% × $81.6m

8 The only research and development spending identified in the last five years was $10m expensed during this year on a new product.

The product has not been launched yet.

9 Capital employed during the period (from the statement of financial position)

Opening	2,282.0
Change in period	119.0
Closing	2,401.0

4 ACHILTY (MAR 20) (AMENDED)

Answer debrief

Exhibit 1 – Company information

Achilty Retail (Achilty) is a stock exchange listed business which sells a range of clothes from a website to consumers in Beeland. Achilty started as a chain of clothing shops but has slowly transitioned into a website only business, and sold its last physical shop recently.

Achilty's mission is 'to deliver long-term returns to shareholders through a combination of sustainable growth in earnings per share and payment of cash dividends'. This mission will be achieved by the following subsidiary objectives:

- Improving product ranges;
- Increasing the number of customers and their individual spend;
- Focusing on customer service; and
- Improving profitability by efficient cost control in purchasing and inventory management.

The board feels that while performance has been good compared to other retailers in general, it is lagging behind the growth of the online retail clothing sector. It is felt that many of the systems and processes have yet to adjust to the new reality of web-only business. As a result, the chief executive officer (CEO) has been reviewing the business in order to identify areas for improvement. She has focused on current performance reporting and the more effective use of the data which Achilty collects.

Exhibit 2 – Current performance reporting

At a recent board meeting, there was a debate as to whether performance towards this mission and its subsidiary objectives are being usefully measured. The director raising the concern believed that any fault might lie in the board's performance report for annual strategic review, although the CEO is fairly happy with the report. Therefore, the CEO wants a full evaluation of the current performance report (see Appendix 1 for the most recent example) in light of this debate and also, more generally, in terms of the best practice for reporting performance. There is no need to suggest new indicators.

Exhibit 3 – Other proposed performance indicators

At this board meeting and as a result of the disagreement about performance reporting, a number of new performance indicators were discussed. The CEO wants an assessment of these indicators, including their calculation if that is possible from the information supplied, and also, whether and how they link to the mission and subsidiary objectives. The indicators and additional information are given in Appendix 2.

Exhibit 4 – Data warehouse

In order to catch up with the rest of the online retail sector, the CEO believes that the key step will be to effectively use the vast amount of customer data which the website collects. In a step forward in the use of information technology at Achilty, she plans to create a data warehouse and use its information to help to achieve the objectives of Achilty. The data warehouse will collect data from customer activities on the website and also, from social media. Given the $50m cost, she wants a brief description of what is meant by a data warehouse and an assessment of the opportunities and risks which such an expensive system would present.

Required:

It is now 1 September 20X5.

Write a report to the chief executive officer (CEO) of Achilty to respond to her instructions for work on the following areas:

(i) Current performance reporting. **(18 marks)**

(ii) Other proposed performance indicators. **(10 marks)**

(iii) The introduction of a new data warehouse. **(12 marks)**

Professional marks will be awarded for the demonstration of skill in communication, analysis and evaluation, scepticism and commercial acumen in your answer. **(10 marks)**

(Total: 50 marks)

Exhibit 5 – Appendix 1

Strategic performance report for Achilty for year ended 30 June 20X5

Financial performance by product area

	Women	**Men**	**Children**	**Sports**	**Total**	**Total**	**Change on previous year**
	20X5	**20X5**	**20X5**	**20X5**	**20X5**	**20X4**	
	$m	$m	$m	$m	$m	$m	
Revenue	85.1	53.2	42.5	31.9	212.7	192.6	10.40%
Gross profit	44.6	25.6	23.3	16.4	109.9	106.7	3.00%
Operating costs:							
Staff costs					45.3	44.1	2.70%
Marketing					17.8	17.8	0.00%
Other operating costs					27.6	25.6	7.80%
Operating profit					19.2	19.2	0.0%
Earnings per share (cents)					24.8	24.8	0.00%
Dividend paid per share (cents)					2.5	2.5	0.00%
Customer response							
Number of customer accounts (000s)					1,014	973	4.20%
Percentage of customer accounts with at least one purchase in the year					58%	61%	–4.90%
Average spend per customer purchase ($)					122.3	108.4	12.80%
Internal processes							
Deliveries within promised deadline					97%	97%	0.00%
Number of product lines sold					2,104	2,107	–0.10%

Commentary:

Overall performance is satisfactory as the business has maintained its earnings per share and dividend. Revenue is up by 10.4% on the previous year.

The number of customer accounts and average spend per purchase have increased in the year. Deliveries to customers continue to be made within promised deadlines to a significant extent.

Exhibit 6 – Appendix 2

Other proposed performance indicators:

1 Return on capital employed (ROCE)

2 Total shareholder return (TSR), which comes from share price change and dividend yield

3 Inventory days

4 Receivables days

Supplementary information for Achilty:

	20X5	20X4
	$m	$m
Assets and liabilities:		
Non-current assets	54	52
Current assets		
Inventory	8.7	7.9
Receivables	1.6	1.5
Cash	0	0
	10.3	**9.4**
Current liabilities	15.5	14
Non-current liabilities	21	22
Net assets	**27.8**	**25.4**
Equity	**27.8**	**25.4**

5 ARKAIG MANUFACTURING (SEPT/DEC 19)

Exhibit 1 – Company information

Arkaig Manufacturing (Arkaig) is a world-leading, listed manufacturer of production machinery for other industries. It has customers in the mining, cement and chemicals sectors and seeks to provide them with the equipment, software and service for their products.

The aim of Arkaig is 'to maximise shareholder wealth by providing world-class, tailored automation solutions, which use technology innovatively, show improved machine downtime and reduced energy consumption for our customers.' This is supported by an entrepreneurial culture among all employees who should 'treat the business as if they owned it'.

Exhibit 2 – Strategic internal performance reporting

There has been criticism of the business' current performance reporting by one of the directors at a recent board meeting. However, the chief executive officer (CEO) believes that the reporting system, which he put in place two years ago, is an excellent one.

In preparation for the next board meeting, the CEO needs an evaluation of the current report. As an example, a recent report used by the board for its strategic review is given in Appendix 1. The CEO stressed that it was the report and not the performance of the business which should be evaluated.

Exhibit 3 – Economic value added

Another criticism of the performance management of Arkaig was that it lacked an over-arching measure of performance. As a result, the CEO is considering the introduction of economic value added (EVA™) to replace return on capital employed (ROCE) as a principal performance measure. The CEO wants to present this idea at the next board meeting and so needs an illustrative calculation of EVA™ along with a brief explanation of its benefits as a replacement for ROCE. The data in Appendix 2 should be used for the calculation.

Exhibit 4 – Performance hierarchy

The earlier work requested focuses on the strategic level of the organisation and the CEO is keen to ensure that the other levels of the organisation (tactical and operational) do not get ignored in this discussion. However, before undertaking any specific work, he wants to make a presentation at the next board meeting. Therefore, he wants you to provide him with a brief description of the nature of the information required for performance measurement at these three different levels and explain how this information is influenced by the extent of planning and controlling activity at each of the levels of the performance hierarchy. He wants examples which would be relevant to Arkaig to illustrate these points in order that the presentation is made more concrete for the directors. He will then prepare the slides for the presentation himself.

Exhibit – Value chain

In order to analyse the operational aspects of Arkaig, the CEO has employed a consultant to produce a value chain analysis (Appendix 3). The value chain analysis has highlighted certain critical activities within Arkaig where there was concern about the performance management aspects. The CEO would like you to assess the performance management implications of the consultant's comments on the critical areas identified for Arkaig.

Required:

It is now 1 September 20X5.

Write a report to the chief executive officer (CEO) of Arkaig to respond to his instructions for work on the following areas:

(i) the performance reporting at Arkaig; (11 marks)

(ii) the introduction of economic value added (EVA™); (15 marks)

(iii) the information requested on the performance hierarchy; (10 marks)

(iv) the value chain analysis prepared by the consultant. (10 marks)

Professional marks will be awarded for the format, style and structure of the discussion of your answer. (4 marks)

(Total: 50 marks)

Exhibit 6 – Appendix 1

Arkaig: Strategic performance report

	Year ended 30 June 20X5					
	Mining	**Cement**	**Chemicals**	**Total**	**Previous year total**	**Industry average**
	20X5	**20X5**	**20X5**	**20X5**	**20X4**	
Orders ($m)	5,204	6,898	5,900	18,002	17,878	
Revenue ($m)	5,100	6,756	5,784	17,640	18,166	
Revenue growth (%)	0	–1.8	–6.5	–2.9		
Net profit ($m)	220	350	302	872	798	
Net profit margin (%)	4.3	5.2	5.2	4.9	4.4	4.6
ROCE (%)	16.1	17.3	17.4	16.8	15.7	15

Commentary:

1 The company has increased its return on capital employed on the previous year and exceeded the industry benchmark.

2 Revenue has fallen by 2.9% on the previous year but the order book has grown by 0.7%, indicating sustained sales levels going forward.

3 The net profit margin has increased to 4.9%, again exceeding the industry benchmark of 4.6%.

4 The company has continued to emphasise its entrepreneurial culture to its employees.

Exhibit 7 – Appendix 2 Economic value added

The following details have been gathered for the 20X5 EVA™ calculation:

1 The operating profit of Arkaig was $3,175m. This includes a depreciation charge of $1,780m.

2 Amortisation charges of $95m in the year have been incurred.

3 The corporation tax rate is 25%. Tax of $694m was paid in the year.

4 The company has spent $90m this year and each year for the previous 10 years on long-term brand building.

5 The economic depreciation for the year is estimated to be $1,907m.

6 This year and each year for the previous 10 years, economic depreciation has included a $10m write-down of the value of brand building.

7 Research and development expenditure of $705m was incurred in the period leading to an economic asset of $4,233m at the year end.

8 Interest paid in the period was $213m.

9 Capital employed during the period (from the statement of financial position):

	$m
Opening	19,404
Change in period	977
Closing	20,381

10 Costs of capital:

Equity	12.0%
Debt (pre-tax)	3.8%
Gearing:	45% debt/(equity + debt)

Exhibit 8 – Appendix 3 Value chain analysis

Primary activities:

– Inbound logistics (receiving, handling and storing inputs) – Warehouse and distribution operations are controlled by an old information system which feeds into operations management information.

– Operations – Not a critical area of concern at present.

– Outbound logistics (delivering the product to customers) – Warehouse and distribution operations are controlled by an old information system which is fed from operations management information.

– Marketing and sales – Not a critical area of concern at present.

– After-sales service – This is an important area of revenue generation for Arkaig. However, certain directors are worried about over-focusing on this activity.

Secondary activities:

– Procurement – Not a critical area of concern at present.

– Technology development – Not a critical area of concern at present.

– Human resource management – Arkaig aims to recruit, retain and motivate staff who can fit with its entrepreneurial culture.

– Firm infrastructure (planning, finance, quality control, legal matters) – Not a critical area of concern at present.

Note: The areas noted as not critical do not require comment.

6 FOLT MANUFACTURING (MAR/JUN 19) (AMENDED)

Exhibit 1 – Company information

Folt Manufacturing (Folt) is a company, which is majority owned by its management team. A number of years ago, it was bought out of a larger multinational business by the management team. The management were supported by a venture capital firm, who provided the remaining equity and now supply all the debt required by the business at market rates. The business manufactures and sells digital imaging devices for use in a variety of industrial situations. A key component in its products is the image processing software which is included. Folt has a small team of software developers who are beginning to gain a reputation for innovative solutions.

Folt has faced increasing pressure in its home market of Beeland from manufacturers in countries with lower cost bases. As a result, it has decided to invest in developing its image processing software rather than compete on the manufacturing of the hardware (the imaging devices). It will continue to sell the imaging devices but the manufacturing will be outsourced.

Folt's overall objective is unchanged and it is 'to provide an adequate return to its capital providers while growing the business into a world-class supplier in its areas of expertise'. The chief executive officer (CEO) has identified three factors which are critical success factors (CSFs) to achieving this objective. These are:

1 Keep capital providers satisfied

2 Build a world-class software development team; and

3 Ensure that quality of the imaging devices meets market standards.

The CEO has asked you to prepare a report to the board on several performance management matters for Folt.

Exhibit 2 – Performance measurement system

The CEO requires your assistance to create an appropriate performance measurement system for Folt. In the first part of the report, he would has asked you to recommend suitably justified key performance indicators (KPIs) for each CSF. The CEO has indicated that there should be a maximum of two KPIs per CSF in order to avoid information overload. He also wants an assessment of the use of this group of KPIs to measure the strategic performance of Folt.

Exhibit 3 – Outsourced manufacturing: Initial plans

The company has selected a suitable manufacturer for the outsourced work. Xela Manufacturing (Xela) is based in Ceeland, which is a much lower cost environment than Beeland. Folt is preparing to enter into detailed contract negotiations with Xela.

The manufacturing will be done under licence from Folt. This means that Folt supplies the product designs but retains the intellectual rights to them and Xela manufactures to agreed standards of quality. Xela then despatches the devices back to Folt who add the software, package the product and send it to their customers. The quality standards will be set by the service level agreements (SLAs) which will be agreed in the contract.

In preparation for these negotiations, the CEO needs advice on the following two critical areas (target costing and responsibility for quality areas) for the negotiation of the agreement.

Exhibit 4 – Target costing

The CEO realises that he needs to understand the cost structure of the products in order to have a firm basis for price negotiation with Xela. He has heard that target costing could be helpful. In the second part of the report, he has asked you to explain how target costing works and how it might be used in this situation. In order to clarify the explanation, he has gathered information (Appendix 1) on one product (Product 123) which requires a redesign before being relaunched into the market. Together with your discussion of target costing and its use, he also wants an example calculation of the target cost gap and an explanation of how the result of this would impact on negotiations with Xela.

Exhibit 5 – Responsibility for quality areas

The maintenance of existing quality is a critical concern for Folt, since it will focus on software as the key selling point but this will not be sufficient for market success if the hardware does not meet market standards. In the final part of the report, the CEO has asked you to explain the four quality cost areas and to evaluate, in terms of each of these areas, how responsibility should be divided between Folt and Xela under the outsourcing contract.

Required:

It is now 1 September 20X5.

Write a report to the CEO of Folt to respond to their instructions for work on the following areas:

(i) Key performance indicators (16 marks)

(ii) Target costing (12 marks)

(iii) Quality costs (12 marks)

Professional marks will be awarded for the demonstration of skill in communication, analysis and evaluation, scepticism and commercial acumen in your answer. **(10 marks)**

(Total: 50 marks)

Exhibit 6 – Appendix 1

Information on Product 123

The company aims for a profit margin of 20% on Product 123. Target price is $175 per unit, based on sales and marketing department research.

Cost details:

1 The remaining commercial life of the product is two years.

2 It is estimated that 250,000 units will be sold over the remaining life of the product.

3 Materials cost $37 per unit.

4 Each unit will take 0.5 hours of labour at an average cost of $25 per hour.

5 Each unit will use 1.1 hours of machine time at an average cost (including overheads) of $32 per hour.

6 Packaging and delivery will cost $8 per unit.

7 The design costs of the unit are expected to total $2m.

8 Inspections cost $100,000 per annum – the redesign will not affect this.

9 The rate of failed products, either spotted by customers or by the inspection team, is expected to remain at 2.5%.

10 Failed products will be reworked at an average cost of $20 per unit.

11 The software package supplied by Folt costs $40 per unit.

7 REZILLOS (DEC 18) (AMENDED)

Exhibit 1 – Company information

Rezillos Engineering (Rezillos) is a listed company, manufacturing pumps and valves for use in the chemical industries. These highly engineered components must be integrated into Rezillos' customers' own plant and equipment. The company has grown significantly via acquisition in the last 20 years to become a worldwide business.

The overall objective of the company is 'to deliver sustainable growth in value to the shareholders by working in partnership with customers to deliver innovative and value-for-money solutions utilising the skills of the highly-trained workforce.'

The chief executive officer (CEO) has recognised that the company has been so focused on making acquisitions that it has not improved other aspects of management. He has asked you to produce a report for the board of Rezillos to cover a number of areas.

Exhibit 2 – Performance reporting system

The CEO would like the report to include an evaluation of the performance reporting system used at the strategic board level by Rezillos. The current performance report used for the annual review at board meetings is given as an example (Appendix 1).

Exhibit 3 – Customer survey

At the most recent round of meetings with stock market analysts, the board has been criticised about a customer survey whose results were announced at these meetings. The criticisms centred on the method of calculation, sampling and the disclosures in the press release. The press release and some further internal details about the method and the results of the customer survey are given in Appendix 2.

The board of Rezillos is concerned by the impact of this on their reputation in the market and needs to understand whether the criticism is justified. The report should include an assessment of the analyst's criticisms of the customer survey results in Appendix 2.

Exhibit 4 – Benchmarking proposal

Rezillos has three divisions based in its three countries of operation (Beeland, Teeland and Veeland). In order to drive forward the integration of the divisions, the CEO has decided that they should be benchmarked against each other. He is aware that this is not the only method of benchmarking and so, initially, wants you in your report to provide an understanding of the different types of benchmarking and an evaluation of the usefulness of the proposed type of benchmarking for the divisions.

For the final part of your report, he has supplied data in Appendix 3 to allow you to complete the benchmarking exercise and comment on the metrics used and the results.

Required:

It is now 1 September 20X8.

Write a report to the board of Rezillos to respond to the CEO's instructions for work on the following areas:

(a) evaluation of the performance reporting system (10 marks)

(b) assessment of the criticisms of the customer survey results (8 marks)

(c) (i) the method of divisional benchmarking proposed; and (8 marks)

(ii) benchmarking the three divisions (14 marks)

Professional marks will be awarded for the demonstration of skill in communication, analysis and evaluation, scepticism and commercial acumen in your answer. **(10 marks)**

(Total: 50 marks)

Exhibit 5 – Appendix 1

Rezillos	**Year to 30 June**							
	Beeland	**Teeland**	**Veeland**	**Total**	**Total**	**Growth**	**Profit as a company**	**% of revenue Industry average**
	20X5	**20X5**	**20X5**	**20X5**	**20X4**			
	$m	**$m**	**$m**	**$m**	**$m**			
Revenue	738	2,030	923	3,691	3,504	5.34%		
Cost of sales	497	1,391	601	2,489	2,363			
Gross profit	241	639	322	1,202	1,141		32.6%	29.8%
Other operating costs								
Selling & distribution costs	89	208	101	398	380			
Administration costs (note 1)	74	171	83	328	321			
Total	163	379	184	726	701			
Operating profit	78	260	138	476	440	8.18%	12.9%	9.7%
Finance costs				88	88			
Group profit before tax				388	352		10.5%	
Tax				78	71			
Group profit after tax				310	281		8.4%	
Return on capital employed (ROCE)				8.64%				

Note

1 Administration costs contain an allocation of product development costs to each division.

Exhibit 6 – Appendix 2

Press release from Rezillos: Customer survey results

Rezillos has performed an extensive survey of its customer base and is proud to announce an average customer rating of 7.0 (out of 10). This bears positive comparison with a leading competitor of Rezillos who performed a survey last year scoring an average rating of 6.0.

The survey asked for a customer rating on a scale of 0 to 10, where 10 was exceptional, 5 was good and 0 was unacceptable.

End of press release

Extract from Rezillos internal document on calculation of customer rating

The survey was carried out by the staff at head office who sampled customers from all three divisions.

Raw data

Customer number	Rating	Account size ($m)	Division
1	10	1.5	Beeland
2	9	3.3	Beeland
3	9	2.1	Beeland
4	6	6.4	Beeland
5	6	152.0	Teeland
6	6	11.2	Beeland
7	6	10.5	Beeland
8	6	74.0	Veeland
9	5	21.0	Veeland

Other notes:

1 The company has 180 customers in total.

2 The customer number is an identification number for administrative purposes.

3 Each division has its own marketing and customer support function although product development is a head office function.

Exhibit 7 – Appendix 3 (all data is for 20X5 unless otherwise stated)

The benchmarking exercise is partly complete with the metrics requiring to be calculated identified by question marks.

	Beeland	Teeland	Veeland
Benchmarking metrics			
Growth of market	8.5%	3.2%	5.0%
Revenue growth	12.5%	3.2%	4.8%
Operating margin	10.6%	12.8%	15.0%
Inventory days	162	162	?
Order book growth	5.2%	5.3%	?
Number of face-to-face interactions with division's top 10 key customers	260	120	40
Percentage of revenue from new products introduced in the last three years	24.9%	29.0%	?
Reduction in incident rate	3.4%	0.0%	?
Utilisation of learning and development programme	1.20	1.26	?

Notes

1 The industry standard method of calculating incident rate is:

Incident rate = number of incidents per year × 200,000/number of employee labour hours paid

2 The company's employees work on average 40 hours per week for 50 weeks per year.

3 Utilisation of learning and development programme is measured by the number of training days per employee.

4 Key customers are designated by the divisional management.

5 A single inventory management system has been implemented across the whole company.

The following data has been collected to assist in the completion of the benchmarking exercise:

	Veeland
Revenue from new products introduced in the last three years ($m)	163
Cost of sales ($m)	601
Inventory ($m)	267
Number of incidents (20X5)	68
Number of incidents (20X4)	74
Number of employees (20X5)	6,600
Number of employees (20X4)	6,250
Order book ($m) (20X5)	932
Order book ($m) (20X4)	885
Number of training days	6,450

8 FEARTIES (SEPT 18) (AMENDED)

Exhibit 1 – Company background

Fearties Security (Fearties) is a business, owned and run by the Feartie family, which provides security personnel for other businesses (e.g. factory guards and security staff at large public events, for example, music concerts). The business has grown along with the market for outsourcing of security personnel roles and Fearties is one of the largest of such service providers in Beeland.

The Feartie family has always managed the business to increase profits without excessive risk-taking. Most of the family are financially dependent on the business through their pay and dividends. The founder of the business was an accountant and it has become a family tradition that the chief executive officer (CEO) would always have an accounting background. As a result, the performance reporting has always focused on financial results.

Exhibit 2 – Recent events

A new generation of the family has risen to power with a goal of increasing growth by expanding Fearties' operations into different countries, using its existing reputation for reliability. The newly appointed CEO has recognised that the choice of key performance indicators (KPIs) may not be suited to the current business environment, where the company is facing various issues:

- changing government regulation with most customer-facing Fearties staff now required to hold a certificate showing they are aware of the relevant laws and health and safety procedures regarding their duties. Indeed, this factor is a reason for the growth of outsourcing to Fearties
- difficulty in recruitment and retention as the pay for customer-facing staff is low by Beeland's standards (even though Fearties provides full training for them)
- legal difficulties arising from claims of Fearties staff being too aggressive in the pursuit of their duties.

The CEO has asked you to prepare a report to the board on several performance management matters for Fearties.

Exhibit 3 – KPIs and balanced scorecard

The CEO is considering the introduction of a balanced scorecard approach and wants an evaluation of whether the existing key performance indicators cover the financial perspective for the board. She has provided you with a draft copy of the most recent board report to illustrate current reporting (Appendix 1) and other financial information (Appendix 2). This draft has been prepared quickly by a junior accountant and the CEO believes that there is an error in the return on capital employed calculation which you should correct.

She then requires reasoned recommendations for two indicators within each of the remaining three perspectives (customer, internal business process and innovation and learning). These indicators should address the issues facing the business.

Exhibit 4 – Non-financial performance indicators

In the past, the board has resisted the introduction of customer surveys due to worries about the ability to measure performance using this method. The CEO is aware that many of the new indicators from the introduction of the balanced scorecard are likely to be non-financial. Therefore, she has asked that you evaluate for the board the problems associated with measuring and managing performance using non-financial performance indicators (NFPIs) at Fearties, using customer surveys as an illustration.

Exhibit 5 – Management style

Given these changes, there may have to be changes to the management style at Fearties. Therefore, the CEO also wants your assessment of the existing management style at Fearties and a justified recommendation for an appropriate approach. She has been taught about Hopwood's styles of using budget information (budget-constrained, profit-conscious, non-accounting) and so wants a brief definition of these prior to your assessment and recommendation.

Required:

It is now 1 September 20X5.

Write a report to the CEO of Fearties to respond to her instructions for work in the following areas:

(i) key performance indicators (KPIs) and the balanced scorecard **(22 marks)**

(ii) non-financial performance indicators **(8 marks)**

(iii) the management style at Fearties **(10 marks)**

Professional marks will be awarded for the demonstration of skill in communication, analysis and evaluation, scepticism and commercial acumen in your answer. **(10 marks)**

(Total: 50 marks)

Exhibit 6 – Appendix 1

Key performance indicators

	20X5	**20X4**
	$m	$m
Revenue	686	659
Operating profit	36	34
Cash flow from operating activities	64	64
Dividends paid	14	13
Return on capital employed	21.1%	20.4%

Exhibit 7 – Appendix 2

Other information:

Fearties Security

Year ended 30 June 20X5

Profit information

	20X5	20X4
	$m	$m
Revenue	686	659
Operating profit	36	34
Profit after tax	20	19
Assets and liabilities		
Non-current assets	54	51
Current assets	213	211
Current liabilities	151	148
Non-current liabilities	21	21
Net assets	95	93
Equity	95	93

Dividend history

	$m
20X5	14
20X4	13
20X3	13
20X2	13
20X1	11
20X0	10

9 CHIVEN STORES (MAR/JUN 18)

Exhibit 1 – Company background

Chiven Stores (Chiven) is a listed clothing retailer in Beeland. Its overall aim is 'to become the largest clothing retailer in Beeland and deliver exceptional value to its shareholders'. It has recently dropped down the clothing retailer rankings from fourth to fifth largest. Shareholders have expressed concern at the lack of dividend growth at a time when spending in the Beeland clothing market has been growing.

There has been a recent change of chief executive officer (CEO) and she has tasked you with preparing a report for the board to address the performance measurement and management issues which she views as important. Her plan is to achieve the overall aim of Chiven by 'maximising our opportunities from new technology and increasing our currently small web presence'. She would like the report to cover the following four areas.

Exhibit 2 – Performance reporting

The CEO has identified that the performance reporting at Chiven is not fit for the needs of the business. She wants a detailed evaluation of the existing set of measures and their presentation in the current performance report which is used by the board for its annual review of the business (Appendix 1).

She has stated that the report does not need a commentary as she and the finance director talk through the report in detail with the board.

Exhibit 3 – Performance measurement

The CEO would like you to use the data in Appendix 1 to recommend (with appropriate calculations and justifications) three new performance measures for Chiven that you believe address key issues for Chiven but are not currently included in the report.

Exhibit 4 – Value chain

In an additional effort to drive improvement and gain competitive advantage for Chiven, the board has decided to use the value chain as a business integration tool. The CEO has provided a copy of the value chain diagram which was discussed at the last board meeting (Appendix 2). She believes that further improvements in Chiven's performance can be achieved through simplification of the supply chain. The CEO believes that this has implications for the performance measurement and information systems at Chiven and wants your report to advise on appropriate performance measures and systems when using the value chain approach to simplify the supply chain.

Exhibit 5 – Big Data

Finally, the CEO has already identified one important reason for Chiven's poor performance and that is its failure to make use of 'Big Data' in relation to Chiven's web sales. She believes that the board does not understand the implications of the volume, velocity and variety of this data for the business and wants you to write a guide for them which includes a discussion of the development of Big Data and its potential impact on Chiven's information systems. She is aware that this is a new and rapidly developing area for most businesses, so she considers that the report should also include a discussion of the risks and challenges Big Data presents.

Required:

Write a report to the board of Chiven to respond to the CEO's instructions for work on the following areas:

(i) evaluation of the performance report (20 marks)

(ii) recommendation of new performance measures (8 marks)

(iii) advice on performance measurement and systems when using the value chain approach (7 marks)

(iv) Big Data development, impact on systems and risks/challenges (11 marks)

Professional marks will be awarded for the format, style and structure of the discussion of your answer. **(4 marks)**

(Total: 50 marks)

Exhibit 6 – Appendix 1

Chiven Stores

Annual performance report for year ended March 2018

Revenue ($m)		**Region**	**A**	**B**	**C**	**Total**	**2018 Total**	**2017 Total**
Clothing								
	Men's		178	356	178	712		
	Women's		297	593	297	1,187		
	Children's		119	237	119	475		
		Total	594	1,186	594		2,374	2,351
Other								
	Men's		19	39	19	77		
	Women's		32	65	32	129		
	Children's		13	26	13	52		
		Total	64	130	64		258	255
						Total	2,632	2,606

Operating profit margin (%)		**Region**	**A**	**B**	**C**		**2018 Total**	**2017 Total**
Clothing								
	Men's		15.5	15.7	15.2			
	Women's		16.2	16.3	15.9			
	Children's		18.1	18.3	18.0			
Other								
	Men's		15.5	15.8	15.2			
	Women's		16.2	16.4	15.8			
	Children's		18.1	18.2	17.8			
						Overall	16.5	16.5

	2018 Total	2017 Total
Number of stores	542	540
EPS ($)	0.56	0.56
Dividend per share ($)	0.28	0.28
EVA™ ($m)	21	24
Inventory turnover rate (days)	32	32
Average number of product lines bought per supplier	66	64
Floor space (square metres)	850,000	828,000
Market share (%)	9.8	10.1
Number of employees	40,500	39,400
Number of suppliers	161	161
ROCE (%)	8.3	8.5
Number of accidents in stores	256	255
Average queuing time for customers (seconds)	125	128
WACC (%)	5.8	5.7
Average time between customer entry and employee greeting (seconds)	248	232
Inventory obsolescence/loss write-downs ($m)	25	25

Appendix 2

Value chain diagram

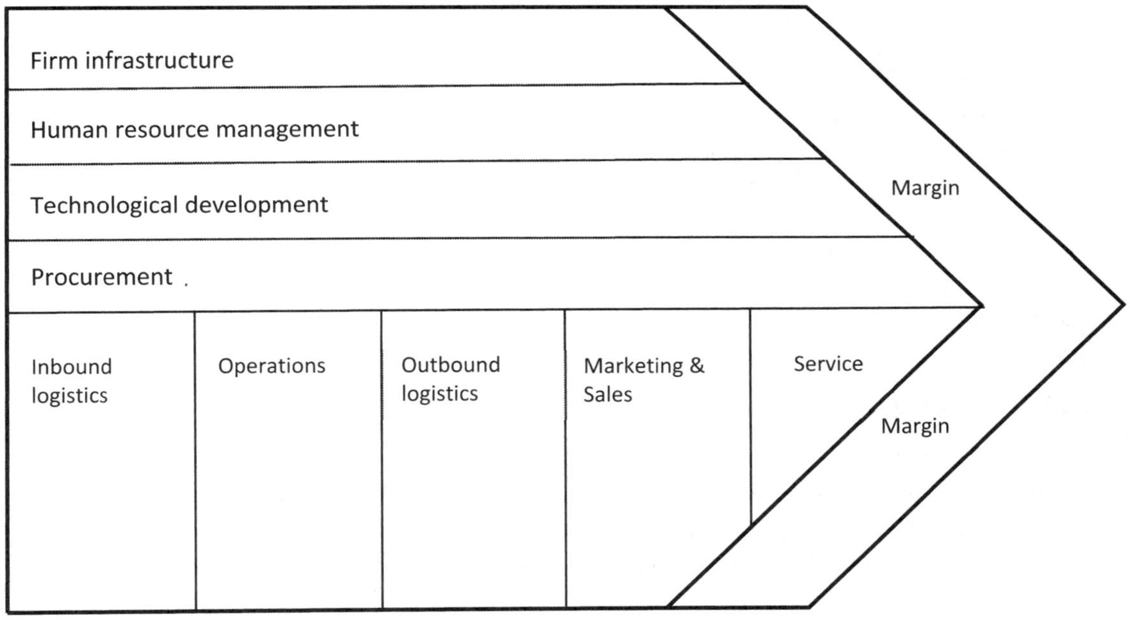

10 THYME (SEPT/DEC 17)

Exhibit – Company background, objective and strategy

Thyme Engine Products (Thyme) manufactures jet aircraft engines for the commercial aircraft market. This is a worldwide business although Thyme's production and development are all based in the country of Beeland. Thyme is a listed company and its stated overall objective is to be 'a world-class jet engine manufacturer trusted by our customers to deliver excellent products'. Its promise to its shareholders is that it will maximise their returns. The strategy to achieve this is to use world-class engineering to design engines and high quality production and customer service in order to drive profitable growth.

Exhibit 2 – Recent events

Thyme's share price has recently suffered as a result of the failure of a new engine design which led to large cash losses and a difficulty in obtaining new financing. There has also been a bribery scandal involving a senior manager and one of its key customers. As a result, a new chief executive officer (CEO) has been employed and she has begun a major review of systems at Thyme. You are a performance management expert within Thyme and the CEO has tasked you with aiding her with the following four aspects.

Exhibit 3 – Performance dashboard

The first area which the CEO wants to examine is the information given to the board for strategic decision-making in both the planning and controlling of the business. The government of Beeland has been encouraging information sharing between businesses and has recently sponsored awards for management accounting. The winner of the engineering sector has produced a sample dashboard template (with dummy figures) for an annual review and this is given in Appendix 1. The CEO realised that the winner had a very similar overall objective and strategies to Thyme and wants your report to include an evaluation of why the dashboard was award winning. She does not want a new dashboard for Thyme at this stage but there may be some useful, specific comments to make about the contents of the dashboard given Thyme's recent problems.

Exhibit 4 – Integrated reporting

The CEO has also recently been reading about integrated reporting and in the light of this review of the dashboard, the CEO has also asked you to explain broadly the role of the management accountant in providing information for integrated reporting and how integrated reporting might impact on the type of information prepared.

Exhibit 5 – Target costing and TQM approach

As high quality engineering products lie at the heart of Thyme's competitive advantage, there has been a total quality management (TQM) approach to the management of all resources and relationships throughout the business. Thyme currently has a project under consideration to develop a new simple jet engine which would compete in the crowded market for small corporate jets. In order to compete in this market, it is believed that a target costing approach to this new engine would be beneficial. The CEO wants you to calculate the target cost gap for the new engine using the data in Appendix 2. Next, she wants as assessment of how the use of target costing would fit within the existing TQM approach for this new engine.

Exhibit 6 – Costs of quality

The new engine project has further raised the profile of quality as a broad issue at Thyme and the CEO wants your advice on this issue. She has gathered data in Appendix 3 for this exercise on the quality costs in the current year. She would like you to use this information to categorise and calculate the costs of quality at Thyme. She is happy that she has identified that prevention costs are complete but is worried that some of the possible costs for the other three categories are missing and needs suggestions of cost areas to be examined to identify these missing items. Finally, she needs advice on the relative importance to Thyme of each of the four categories.

Required:

Write a report to the CEO of Thyme to respond to her instructions for work on the following areas:

(i) the award winning dashboard (15 marks)

(ii) the role of the management accountant in integrated reporting (6 marks)

(iii) calculation of the target cost and fit of this cost within the TQM approach (12 marks)

(iv) the costs of quality (13 marks)

Professional marks will be awarded for the format, style and structure of the discussion of your answer. **(4 marks)**

(Total: 50 marks)

Exhibit 7 – Appendix 1

Award winning performance dashboard

Report for the year to June 2017

	2015	**2016**	**2017**	**Budget variance 2017**	**Growth 2016 to 2017**	**Budget 2018**
Financial						
Revenue ($m)	10,652	11,213	11,500	234F	2.6%	11,776
Operating profit margin	16.2%	16.8%	17.2%	0.2 % points F	0.4 % points	17.2%
EVA™	746	774	815	48F	5.3%	803
Total shareholder return	6.5%	6.8%	11.1%	4.5 % points F	4.3 % points	7.5%
Design						
Class leading products in:						
fuel efficiency	3	3	3	0		3
noise levels	2	2	3	1F		3
chemical emissions	1	2	3	1F		3

Manufacturing					
Percentage of orders right first time	92.0%	92.4%	93.7%	0.7 % points F	93.0%
Delivery					
Deliveries on time	88.0%	89.9%	88.2%	0.2 % points F	88.0%
Market share (as % of market leader)	33.0%	35.2%	38.1%	1.1 % points F	39.0%

Commentary:

The revenue growth of the business remains strong above the average growth for the sector of 1.5%.

EVA™ is positive and growing indicating increased shareholder wealth.

Healthy and continuing growth in market share reflects an increased number of class-leading products and improvements in 'right on time' service to customers. There have been no major new business risks arising during the period while market volume growth continues as expected.

Exhibit 8 – Appendix 2

New jet engine

		$000/engine
Competitor price		2,500
Raw materials		200
Subcomponents bought in		600
Skilled labour		625
General labour		125
Production overheads		275
Planned profit margin	15%	

Notes:

1 Design and development has cost $100m and the engine is expected to sell approximately 1,200 units over its lifetime.

2 Sales and marketing costs are expected to be approximately 20% of the selling price.

3 The planned selling price is expected to match the competitor's price with the brand reputation of Thyme providing the competitive edge.

Appendix 3

Quality costs identified in current year

	$m
Repairs and replacements under customer warranties	223
Customer relationship management – complaint handling	56
Performance testing of final assembly	110
Performance testing of subcomponents from suppliers	28
Costs of re-inspection after repairs arising from final assembly testing	95
Training in quality control	11
Maintenance of inspection equipment	36

Notes:

1 The company spent $92m in the year buying higher quality raw materials to use in manufacture.

2 The company's revenue was $11,500m in the current year.

11 DARGEBOARD SERVICES (DS) (MAR/JUN 17)

Exhibit 1 – Company background

Dargeboard Services (DS), a listed company, provides facilities management (FM) services where it manages such activities as cleaning, security, catering and building services on behalf of its clients. Clients can outsource to DS a single activity or often outsource all of these aspects in a full service contract.

Exhibit 2 – Strategic performance reporting

The board have asked the chief executive officer (CEO) to review the effectiveness of Dargeboard's systems for performance measurement and management. She has turned to you to begin this process by considering the strategic performance dashboard of DS. She has supplied the most recent example in Appendix 1.

She wants a report to the board which will cover three aspects of strategic performance reporting at DS.

First, it should address whether the current set of KPIs measure the achievement of the mission by evaluating how each one links to all or part of the mission. She does not want suggestions of new indicators. The mission of DS is 'to give the shareholders maintainable, profitable growth by developing the best talent to provide world-class services with maximum efficiency.'

Second, taking each of the current indicators in turn she wants an assessment of the assumptions and definitions underlying the calculation of the indicators. There has been a suggestion made in the press that DS is producing a biased set of results aimed to mislead the markets. This would then artificially boost the share price and so boost the value of the senior management's share holdings.

Third, the report should evaluate the other presentational aspects of the DS dashboard against best practice.

Exhibit 3 – Current reward scheme

The idea of employee share ownership has always been at the heart of DS' remuneration schemes. Its aim is to support an entrepreneurial culture and is a key differentiator in the market for new employees. The current reward system grants shares based on the appraisal of the individual by the line manager against vague categories such as leadership and entrepreneurship. The results of this scheme have been that only about 5% of staff received their maximum possible bonus in previous years and half of them received no bonus at all. Increasingly, this has led to the staff ignoring the reward scheme and describing it as 'only for the bosses' favourite people'.

Exhibit 4 – Building block model

In response to this, the board have been discussing methods of analysing and improving the rewards system at DS. One non-executive director suggested using Fitzgerald and Moon's building block model. The CEO was asked to consider this as a project separate from the issues of performance measurement mentioned above. She will select suitable indicators from the dimensions but currently needs you to explain to the board what is meant by results and determinants in this context and how the dimensions link to standards and targets.

Exhibit 5 – Proposed reward schemes

Finally, she believes that there are two types of reward scheme which might suit DS and wants an evaluation of their relative strengths and weaknesses. The scheme details are given in Appendix 2.

Required:

Write a report to the board of DS responding to the CEO's instructions for work on the following areas:

(i) the link between the KPIs and mission (8 marks)

(ii) the assumptions and definitions used in the calculation of current KPIs (12 marks)

(iii) other presentational aspects of the dashboard (8 marks)

(iv) how the building block model works (6 marks)

(v) assessment of the proposed reward schemes (12 marks)

Professional marks will be awarded for the format, style and structure of the discussion of your answer. **(4 marks)**

(Total: 50 marks)

Exhibit 6 – Appendix 1

Dargeboard Services: Strategic performance dashboard

Year to 31 December 2016

	Cleaning	Security	Catering	Building services	Full service	Total	Total 2015
Operating profit margin	6.5%	6.4%	6.5%	4.9%	5.9%	5.9%	5.8%
Secured revenue	76%	85%	92%	88%	93%	88%	87%
Management retention	86%	74%	87%	82%	89%	85%	87%
Order book ($m)	1,160	875	357	1,553	3,359	7,304	6,807
Organic revenue growth	7.1%	4.3%	5.0%	8.1%	7.9%	7.2%	4.6%
ROCE						17.2%	16%

KPI definitions and notes

1 Cleaning, security, catering and building services headings are for single service contracts.

2 No commentary is provided as the CEO talks the board through the dashboard at each board meeting.

3 Secured revenue is long-term recurring revenue. This is the percentage of budgeted revenue which is already contracted. The budget is often not completed until well into the year as it is a complex process. In 2016, the original budget showed revenue of $1,565m with the final budget signed off at the end of Q1 showing $1,460m. The secured (contracted) revenue for the period was $1,285m. The accounts show a year end revenue of $1,542m.

4 Management retention is the percentage of managers who were still employed throughout the whole year. The figure only includes those employees on full-time contracts (about 65% of all managers).

5 Order book is the total cash value of future contracted revenue. DS has contracts which run up to 10 years into the future.

6 Operating profit margin. This excludes exceptional items such as the reorganisation of the catering business which cost $55m in 2016, where revenue was $245m.

7 Organic revenue growth is calculated by using the total revenue figure as reported in the accounts. It includes net acquisitions which brought in revenue of $48m in 2016.

8 Return on capital employed (ROCE). Capital employed is total assets less current liabilities from the statement of financial position.

Exhibit 7 – Appendix 2

The CEO is considering two schemes, one based on the current scheme and a new scheme.

Scheme 1 (based on the current scheme)

The reward system grants shares in DS based on the appraisal of the individual by the line manager against vague categories (leadership and entrepreneurship). The line managers have been informed that their bonus will in turn be partly dependent on how well they perform this appraisal. The expectation will be that as a result, 20% of staff will receive their maximum possible bonus and 20% will receive no bonus.

Scheme 2 (the new one)

Under scheme 2, employee targets are to be derived from the strategic indicators depending on the employee's area of responsibility. The senior management (with help from line management where appropriate) will cascade down the strategic indicators to the relevant operational or tactical level for that employee.

There will be five targets set by senior and line management in consultation and the employee will then get up to 50% on top of their basic salary as a bonus (10 percentage points for each of the targets achieved).

12 FLACK (MAR/JUN 16) (AMENDED)

Exhibit 1 – Company information and mission

Flack Supermarkets (Flack) is a multi-national listed business operating in several developing countries. The business is divided into two divisions: Metro, which runs smaller stores in the densely populated centres of cities and Hyper, which runs the large supermarkets situated on the edges of cities. Flack sells food, clothing and some other household goods.

Flack has a mission of being:

'...the first choice for customers by providing the right balance of quality and service at a competitive price. We will achieve this through acting in the long-term interests of our stakeholders: earning customer loyalty, utilising all our resources and serving our shareholders' interests.'

Exhibit 2 – Performance report

Competition between supermarkets is intense in all of Flack's markets and so there is a constant need to review and improve their management and operations.

A performance report is used at Flack's board level for their annual review. A copy of the most recent report is provided as an example in Appendix 1. The divisional boards have their own reports. The board have asked for an evaluation of the performance report of Flack, using the example provided in Appendix 1. As part of this evaluation you should include a review of the performance report in being fit for the purpose of achieving the company's mission. Also, there has been criticism of the board of Flack in the financial press that they are 'short-termist' and so the board wants your evaluation of the performance report to include comments on this.

Exhibit – Asset utilisation indicators

The board is considering introducing two new performance measures to address the objective of 'utilising all our resources'. These are revenue and operating profit per square metre. The board also wants an evaluation of these two measures explaining how they might address this aspect of the mission, what those ratios currently are and how they could be used to manage business performance. There is information in Appendix 1 to assist in this work.

Exhibit 4 – Divisional performance assessment

There have been disagreements between Flack's divisional management about capital allocation. The divisions have had capital made available to them. Both sets of divisional managers always seem to want more capital in order to open more stores but historically have been reluctant to invest in refurbishing existing stores. The board is unsure of capital spending priorities given that the press comments about Flack included criticism of the 'run-down' look of a number of their stores. The board wants your assessment of the effectiveness of the current divisional performance measure of divisional operating profit and the possibility of replacing this with residual income in the light of these problems. Note: No calculations of the current values are required.

Exhibit 5 – Use of expected return on capital employed (ROCE) in new store appraisal

As the company is opening many new stores, the board also wants an assessment of the use of expected ROCE as a tool for decision making, specifically deciding on new store openings. Illustrate this by calculating the expected ROCE for a new store using the data in Appendix 2 on one new store proposal. The focus of comments should be on the use of an expected value not on the use of return on capital employed, as this is widely used and understood in the retail industry.

Required:

It is now 1 September 20X5

Write a report to the board of Flack responding to their instructions for work on the following areas:

(i) Evaluation of the performance report of Flack. (16 marks)

(ii) Evaluation of the introduction of the two asset utilisation measures. (8 marks)

(iii) Assessment of the current divisional performance measure and the proposal to change this measure. (8 marks)

(iv) Calculation of the expected ROCE for the new store and assessment of the use of this tool. (8 marks)

Professional marks will be awarded for the demonstration of skill in communication, analysis and evaluation, scepticism and commercial acumen in your answer. **(10 marks)**

(Total: 50 marks)

Exhibit 6 – Appendix 1: Boards performance report
Flack Year to 31 March

	Metro	**Metro**	**Hyper**	**Hyper**	**Flack**	**Flack**	**Flack**	
	Budget	*Actual*	*Budget*	*Actual*	*Budget*	*Actual*	*Actual*	*Change*
	20X5	20X5	20X5	20X5	20X5	20X5	20X4	on PY
	$000	$000	$000	$000	$000	$000	$000	$000
Revenue								
Food	1,093,521	1,104,567	5,431,277	5,542,119	6,524,798	6,646,686	6,513,752	2.04%
Clothes	765,465	773,197	3,801,894	3,879,483	4,567,359	4,652,680	4,536,363	2.56%
Other goods	328,056	331,370	1,629,383	1,662,636	1,957,439	1,994,006	1,964,096	1.52%
Total	2,187,042	2,209,134	10,862,554	11,084,238	13,049,596	13,293,372	13,014,211	2.15%
Cost of sales	1,994,583	2,014,730	10,199,937	10,408,099	12,194,520	12,422,829	12,186,796	1.94%
Gross profit	192,459	194,404	662,617	676,139	855,076	870,543	827,415	5.21%
Gross margins		8.80%		6.10%		6.55%		
Other operating costs	34,993	35,346	173,801	177,348	208,794	212,694	208,227	
Operating profit	157,466	159,058	488,816	498,791	646,282	657,849	619,188	6.24%
Operating margins		7.20%		4.50%		4.95%		
Finance costs					76,993	79,760	75,482	
Group profit before tax					**569,289**	**578,089**	**543,706**	6.32%
Tax					142,322	144,522	135,926	
Group profit after tax					**426,967**	**433,567**	**407,780**	6.32%
Total shareholder return						3.10%	2.70%	
Return on capital employed	13.2%	13.3%	13.2%	13.5%	13.2%	13.4%	13.2%	
Number of stores		533		208				
Total square metres		161,227		841,967				

Exhibit 7 – Appendix 2: New store

The following data has been forecast by the marketing department for the new store based on Flack's existing experience. There are three possible scenarios:

Demand scenarios	Low	Medium	High
Revenue ($m)	12.5	13	13.5
Probability (%)	20	50	30
Forecast operating margin (%)	4.1	4.3	4.4

The new store is expected to cost $4.2m to buy, fit out and stock. The target ROCE for Flack has been set at 13%.

13 MONZA (SEPT/DEC 16)

Exhibit 1 – Company information

Monza Pharma (Monza) is a developer and manufacturer of medical drugs, based in Beeland but selling its products all over the world. As a listed company, the overall objective of the company is to maximise the return to shareholders and it has used return on capital employed (ROCE) as its performance measure for this objective. There has often been comment at board meetings that it is good to have one, easily-understood measure for consideration.

The company has three divisions:

- the drug development division develops new drug compounds, taking these through the regulatory systems of different countries until they are approved for sale
- the manufacturing division then makes these compounds
- the sales division then sells them.

The current performance measures are:

- Return on capital employed
- Average cost to develop a new drug
- Revenue growth

Exhibit – Implementation of a balanced scorecard approach

Monza's share price has underperformed compared to the market and the health sector in the last two years. The chief executive officer (CEO) has identified that its current performance measures are too narrow and is implementing a balanced scorecard (BSC) approach to address this problem.

The CEO engaged a well-known consulting firm who recommended the use of a BSC. The consultants began by agreeing with the board of Monza that the objective for the organisation's medium-term strategy was as follows:

- Create shareholder value by:
  - Innovating in drug development
  - Efficiency in drug manufacturing
  - Success in selling their products

The consulting firm has presented an interim report with the following proposed performance measures:

- Financial : ROCE
- Customer : Revenue growth
- Internal business process : Average cost to develop a new drug
- Learning and growth : Training days provided for employees each year

Exhibit 3 – Problems with using the balanced scorecard

The CEO and the lead consultant have had a disagreement about the quality and cost of this work and as a result the consultants have been dismissed. The CEO has commented that the proposed measures lack insight into the business and do not appear to tackle issues at strategic, tactical and operational levels.

The CEO has decided to take this work in-house and has asked you as the performance management expert in the finance department to assist him by writing a report to the board to cover a number of areas.

Following the disagreement with the consultants, the CEO is worried that the consultants may not have been clear about the problems of using the BSC in their rush to persuade Monza to use their services. So firstly, the CEO would like you to assess the problems of using a balanced scorecard at Monza.

Exhibit 4 – Choice of current and proposed performance measures

Second, he wants you to evaluate the choice of performance measures currently used by Monza and those proposed by the consulting firm.

Exhibit – ROCE calculation

There has been a debate at board level about how ROCE should be calculated. The marketing director stated that she was not sure what profit figure (of at least four which were available) should be used and why, especially given the large variation in result which this gives. She also wondered what the effect would be of using equity rather than all capital to calculate a return on investment. Thirdly, the CEO has asked you to evaluate the effect of choosing different profit and capital measurements on ROCE. Some basic data has been provided in Appendix 1 to assist you in this.

Exhibit 6 – Quality costs and total quality management within the manufacturing division

In addition to these concerns, the board is considering introducing a total quality management approach within Monza. Obviously, quality of output is critical in such a heavily regulated industry where the products can be a matter of life and death. There has been discussion about testing this idea within the manufacturing division. In the fourth part of your report, the CEO wants you to analyse the current quality costs in the manufacturing division to understand the costs associated with quality issues within that division. To aid your analysis, he has supplied some detailed information in Appendix 2. The board also requires you to briefly discuss how implementation of a total quality management (TQM) approach would fit within the manufacturing division.

Exhibit 7 – Lean information system in drug development division

Finally, the drug development divisional managers have been lobbying for a new information system which will assist their research chemists in identifying new drug compounds for testing. The new system will need to be capable of performing calculations and simulations which require high computational power and memory but will also need to have access to external data sources so that these scientists can keep up with developments in the field and identify new opportunities. The new system should fit within the existing lean management approach within that division. The CEO is worried about the cost of such a new system. In the final part of your report the CEO would like you to advise how the drug development division can aim to make the new information system 'lean'.

Required:

Write a report to the board of Monza responding to the CEO's instructions for work on the following areas:

(i) Assessment of the problems of using a balanced scorecard. (8 marks)

(ii) Evaluation of the current and proposed performance measures. (12 marks)

(iii) Evaluation of the effect of choosing different profit and capital measurements for ROCE and recommendation of a suitable approach. (11 marks)

(iv) Analysis of the current quality costs and a brief discussion of the effect of TQM implementation. (10 marks)

(v) Advice on making the new information system 'lean'. (5 marks)

Professional marks will be awarded for the format, style and structure of the discussion of your answer. **(4 marks)**

(Total: 50 marks)

Exhibit 8 – Appendix 1

Financial data for Monza for the most recent accounting period

	$m
Revenue	8,001
Costs	2,460
Gross profit	5,541
Other costs	3,248
Restructuring costs	482
Operating profit	1,811
Finance costs	266
Profit before tax	1,545
Tax	419
Profit after tax	1,126
Capital structure from the statement of financial position	
Shareholders' equity	1,161
Long-term debt	8,739

Note: Restructuring costs relate to a major project which completed during the period.

Exhibit 9 – Appendix 2

Cost information for the manufacturing division for the most recent accounting period

1 Batches rejected at factory valued at $17m which have a scrap value of $4m.

2 Training of factory staff which cost $8m.

3 Regulatory fines costing $5m (due to drug compounds being outside the specified range of mix of chemical ingredients).

4 Discounts given following customer complaints due to late delivery costing $22m.

5 Factory product testing department cost $12m.

6 Cost of raw materials was $1,008m.

14 BOLTZMAN (DEC 14) (AMENDED)

Exhibit 1 – Company information and initiatives

Boltzman Machines (Boltzman) is a listed, multinational engineering business. It has two divisions, one manufacturing aerospace parts and the other automotive parts. The company is known for innovation and it allows its managers much autonomy to run their own divisions and projects. There has been recent criticism at a shareholders' meeting of the executive management for not listening to shareholders' concerns and allowing this autonomy to run out of control. Therefore, the board at Boltzman have decided to create a framework which brings together all of the initiatives described below.

The initiatives which are running at present are:

1 An analysis of stakeholder influence at Boltzman leading to suitable strategic performance measures.

2 A benchmarking exercise of the performance measures from initiative 1 with Boltzman's main competitor, General Machines.

3 The introduction of quality initiatives bringing lean production methods to Boltzman.

The chief executive officer (CEO) has asked you to prepare a report to the board on several performance management matters for Boltzman.

Exhibit 2 – Performance pyramid

The CEO feels that the performance pyramid may be a suitable model for linking objectives and performance measures and has asked you to in the first part of the report to explain the four levels of the performance pyramid and discuss how the three initiatives relate to these levels.

The CEO also requires your input on each of these initiatives as they are all at various stages of progress.

Exhibit 3 – Stakeholder analysis

A stakeholder analysis has been completed by one of Boltzman's managers (in Appendix 1) but she has gone on holiday and has not written up a commentary of her results. Therefore, the CEO wants you to take the information in Appendix 1 and briefly justify appropriate management approaches to each of the stakeholders and, based on this analysis, evaluate the appropriateness of the performance measures suggested in Appendix 1. The CEO has asked that you do not, at this stage, suggest long lists of additional indicators.

Exhibit 4 – Benchmarking

The CEO wants you to use these suggested measures to benchmark the performance of Boltzman against General Machines. The CEO stated, 'Make sure that you calculate the measures given in Appendix 1 and briefly conclude on the relative performance of the two companies. However, restrict your calculations to the five measures and don't drown us with detail about individual business units.' A junior analyst has gathered data to use in the benchmarking exercise in Appendix 2. The CEO would also like you to evaluate the approach to benchmarking used.

Exhibit 5 – Just-in-time (JIT) manufacturing

The company has stated that one of its strategic aims is to be the highest quality supplier in the market place. In order to achieve this, the head of the aerospace division has already started a project to implement JIT manufacturing. An extract of his email proposing this change is given in Appendix 3. The CEO feels that there are some important elements hinted at but not developed in this email. In the final part of the report, the CEO wants you to explain the problems which will accompany a move towards JIT manufacturing at Boltzman.

Required:

It is now 1 September 20X5.

Write a report to the board of Boltzman responding to the CEO's instructions for work on the following areas:

(i) **The performance pyramid and how the three initiatives fit within it** **(8 marks)**

(ii) **The approach to stakeholders and the performance measures** **(13 marks)**

(iii) **Benchmarking performance and the approach to benchmarking used** **(14 marks)**

(iv) **Problems of a move towards JIT manufacturing** **(5 marks)**

Professional marks will be awarded for the demonstration of skill in communication, analysis and evaluation, scepticism and commercial acumen in your answer. **(10 marks)**

(Total: 50 marks)

Exhibit 6 – Appendix 1

Key stakeholders	**Level of interest**	**Level of power**
Shareholders	Low – institutions have delegated management to the board and are only interested in financial returns	High – ability to vote out existing management
Employees	Medium – in a high skill industry employees are interested in the new opportunities which the market can present	Low – although there is a group of key employees in product development whose skills must not be lost
Customers	Medium – some of the parts supplied by Boltzman are unique and specifically designed for the customer	High – as there are few major players in the aerospace and automotive businesses, the loss of a customer would have a significant impact on Boltzman
Suppliers	Medium – Boltzman is one of the large customers to many of the company's suppliers	Low – the suppliers are generally bulk component producers and there is significant competition for Boltzman's business

Suggested performance measures:

- Return on capital employed
- Economic value added
- Revenue growth
- Average pay per employee
- Net profit margin

Exhibit 7 – Appendix 2

The figures are drawn from the financial statements for the year to June 20X5.

	Boltzman	**General Machines**
	$m	$m
	20X5	*20X5*
Revenue	23,943	25,695
Cost of sales	18,078	20,605
Other costs	2,958	3,208
Operating profit	2,907	1,882
Financing costs	291	316
Tax	663	718
Net income	1,953	848

	Boltzman		**General Machines**	
	$m	$m	$m	$m
	20X4	**20X5**	**20X4**	**20X5**
Non-current assets	16,335	16,988	17,716	17,893
Current assets	10,618	11,043	11,515	11,630
	26,953	28,031	29,231	29,523
Equity	8,984	9,961	9,744	10,083
Non-current liabilities	9,801	9,739	10,629	10,405
Current liabilities	8,168	8,331	8,858	9,035
	26,953	28,031	29,231	29,523

		Boltzman 20X5	General Machines 20X5
Notes:			
No of employees		86,620	93,940
Staff costs	($m)	4,731	4,913
Revenue for 2013	($m)	22,506	25,438
Product development costs	($m)	2,684	2,630
No. of top 10 biggest potential customers where the business has top tier supplier status			
Aerospace		6	6
Automotive		7	8

A suitable cost of capital for both companies is 11%.

The tax rate is 28%.

Exhibit 8 – Appendix 3

Extract of Head of Aerospace's email on his quality initiative:

In order to improve the quality and profitability of our products, we intend to begin by introducing a lean approach to manufacturing.

The first step in our move to lean manufacturing will be the introduction of JIT manufacturing. Although this will be a difficult process, the financial rewards in reduced working capital required and a decluttering of the workplace should be significant. We will have to consider how this change impacts up and down our supply chain with customers and suppliers.

15 CANTOR (JUN 14)

Company information, mission and structure

Cantor Group (Cantor) is a listed company with two subsidiaries, both involved in food and drink retailing in the small country of Deeland. Its mission is 'to maximise shareholder value through supplying good value food and drink in appealing environments for our customers'.

Cantor Cafes (Cafes) is the original operating company for the group and is a chain of 115 cafes specialising in different coffee drinks but also serving some simple food dishes. Cafes has been running successfully for 15 years and has reached the limit of its expansion as the cafe market is now considered to be saturated with competition. Further growth will occur only as the opportunity to obtain profitable, new sites is presented, although such opportunities are not expected to be significant over the next few years.

Cantor Juicey (Juicey) was started by the Cantor Group two years ago. Now, it is made up of 15 juice bars which serve a variety of blended fruit juice drinks and health snacks. The products served by Juicey have benefited from an increased awareness in Deeland of the need to eat and drink healthily. Cantor Group expects to increase the rate of property acquisition in order to feed the rapid growth of this business, intending to open 25 outlets per year for the next four years.

Cantor Group organises its two subsidiaries in a similar way, as they are involved in similar areas of business. There is one exception to this, namely in the arrangements over the properties from which the subsidiaries operate. Cafes rent their properties on the open market on standard commercial terms with a five-year lease at a fixed rental payable quarterly in advance. Juicey, on the other hand, has made a single arrangement with a large commercial landlord for all of its properties. Juicey has agreed that the rent for its sites is a percentage of the revenue generated at each site. Juicey believes that it can continue its expansion by obtaining more sites from this landlord under the same terms.

The chief executive officer (CEO) requires assistance from you, a performance management expert and has asked you to produce a report for the board of Cantor to cover a number of areas.

Performance reporting

First, the board of Cantor is reviewing their performance reporting systems. You have been asked to evaluate the current performance report given in Appendix 1. This performance report contains information for both of the subsidiaries and the group and is used by all three boards. The CEO has advised you that the board does not require an evaluation of Cantor's performance.

Cost structures

Second, the CEO wants you to consider the cost structures at Cantor. Your report should assess the balance of fixed and variable elements of the key cost areas of staff and property in each of the two subsidiaries and the impact which this may have on performance management of these costs. Note: Detailed calculations are not required.

Value based management

At a recent shareholder meeting of Cantor, one of the large shareholders expressed concern that the group lacks focus and suggested the introduction of value-based management (VBM) using economic value added (EVA™) as the measure of value.

The CEO has asked you, in the next part of your report, to evaluate the EVA™ of Cantor Group, justifying any assumptions made. An example calculation of the EVA™ for the Group should be carried out using the current data (Appendices 1 and 2).

Next, the board needs you to explain how VBM could be implemented at Cantor and evaluate its potential impact on the group.

Change in mission statement

Finally, the board is considering amending the mission statement to include more information on the ethical values of the company. The area being considered for inclusion in the overall mission is on the treatment of employees as it is felt that they should share in the progress and profitability of Cantor since a happy working environment will help them to better serve the customers.

The proposed new mission statement would read:

'to maximise shareholder value and to provide a fair deal to our employees by supplying good value food and drink in appealing environments for our customers.'

The CEO has asked you to use the information in the appendices to provide justified recommendations for suitable performance measures to reflect the proposed change in the company's mission statement. You have obtained additional information from the management information system to assist with this task, given in Appendix 3.

Appendix 1

Cantor Group	Year to 31 March							
	Cafes	Cafes	Juicey	Juicey	Group	Group	Costs and profit as a % of revenue	
	Budget 2014	Actual 2014	Budget 2014	Actual 2014	Budget 2014	Actual 2014	Group	Industry average
	$	$	$	$	$	$		
Revenue								
Drink	47,437,500	46,521,000	5,130,000	5,398,000	52,567,500	51,919,000		
Food	15,812,500	15,913,000	570,000	582,000	16,382,500	16,495,000		
Total	**63,250,000**	**62,434,000**	**5,700,000**	**5,980,000**	**68,950,000**	**68,414,000**		
Cost of sales								
Drink	12,808,125	12,560,670	1,385,100	1,457,460	14,193,225	14,018,130		
Food	3,478,750	3,500,860	125,400	128,040	3,604,150	3,628,900		
Total	**16,286,875**	**16,061,530**	**1,510,500**	**1,585,500**	**17,797,375**	**17,647,030**	25.8%	
Gross profit	**46,963,125**	**46,372,470**	**4,189,500**	**4,394,500**	**51,152,625**	**50,766,970**	74.2%	72.8%
Staff costs	**16,128,750**	**15,920,670**	**1,453,500**	**1,524,900**	**20,082,250**	**21,345,000**	31.2%	30.9%
Other operating costs								
Rent	2,875,000	2,875,000	342,000	358,800	3,929,000	3,945,800		
Local property tax	920,000	920,000	60,000	60,000	980,000	980,000		
Insurance	276,000	282,000	18,000	18,400	294,000	300,400		
Utilities	874,000	861,000	61,500	62,900	935,500	923,900		
Marketing	6,957,500	6,888,000	627,000	750,000	7,584,500	7,638,000	11.2%	10.0%
Depreciation	4,427,500	4,427,500	353,400	353,400	4,780,900	4,780,900		
Total	**16,330,000**	**16,253,500**	**1,461,900**	**1,603,500**	**18,503,900**	**18,569,000**	27.1%	
Operating profit	**14,504,375**	**14,198,300**	**1,274,100**	**1,266,100**	**12,566,475**	**10,852,970**	15.9%	15.3%
Finance costs					798,000	801,000		
Group profit before tax					**11,768,475**	**10,051,970**	14.7%	
Tax					2,942,119	2,512,993		
Group profit after tax					**8,826,356**	**7,538,977**	11.0%	

Appendix 2

Additionally, you have discovered the following data about the group for the financial year:

1. Debt/Equity 30.0%
2. Cost of equity 15.7%
3. Tax rate 25.0%
4. Group ROCE 19.0%
5. Group capital employed: $53,400,000 at period start and $58,500,000 at period end.
6. Pre-tax cost of debt 6.5%
7. There has been $2.1m of tax paid in the year.
8. It is estimated that half of the marketing spend of $7.638m is building the Cantor brand long term.
9. It is further estimated that there has been the same level of annual spending on long-term brand building in the years leading up to 2014.

Appendix 3

Additional management information

	Cafes	**Juicey**	**Group**
No of employees			
At year start	1,495	96	1,611
Leavers	146	15	161
Joiners	152	35	187
At year end	1,501	116	1,637

Note:

1 Group numbers include Cafes, Juicey and head office numbers.

Required:

Write a report to the board of Cantor responding to the CEO's instructions for work on the following areas:

(i) Evaluation of the current performance report. (15 marks)

(ii) Assessment of the cost structure of the two subsidiaries and the impact which this may have on performance management of these costs. (6 marks)

(iii) Evaluation of the EVA™, justifying any assumptions made. (9 marks)

(iv) Explaining how VBM could be implemented and evaluation of its potential impact. (10 marks)

(v) Justified recommendations for suitable performance measures to reflect the proposed change in the mission statement. (6 marks)

Professional marks will be awarded for the format, style and structure of the discussion of your answer. **(4 marks)**

(Total: 50 marks)

16 JHK COFFEE MACHINES CO (JUN 11)

Company information

JHK Coffee Machines Co (JHK) manufactures coffee makers for use in bars and cafes. It has been successful over the last five years and has built and maintained a loyal customer base by making a high quality machine backed by a three-year warranty. The warranty states that JHK will recover and repair any machine that breaks down in the warranty period at no cost. Additionally, JHK always maintains sufficient spare parts to be able to quote for a repair of any of its machines made within the previous 10 years. The company's mission is to maximise shareholder wealth.

Divisional structure and performance measures

JHK is structured into two divisions: manufacturing/sales (M/S) and service. The board are now considering ways to improve coordination of the activities of the divisions for the benefit of the company as a whole. They have asked you, a performance management expert, to assist with this.

Currently, the board use total shareholder return (TSR) as an overall corporate measure of performance and return on investment (ROI) as their main relative measure of performance between the two divisions. The board's main concern is that the divisional managers' performance is not being properly assessed by the divisional performance measure used. They now want to consider other measures of divisional performance. Residual income (RI) and economic value added (EVA™) have been suggested. First, they have asked you to evaluate the divisional performance at JHK and critically discuss the proposed measures of divisional performance. A colleague has collected the data which will allow calculation of ROI, RI and EVA™. This is shown in appendix 1.

Service division information

In addition to the divisional performance measures, the board want to consider the position of the service division. The standard costs within the service division are shown in appendix 2.

Currently, the service division does two types of work. There are repairs that are covered by JHK's warranty and there are repairs done outside warranty at the customer's request. The service division is paid by the customer for the out-of-warranty repairs while the repairs under warranty generate an annual fee of $10m, which is a recharge from the M/S division. The company sells 440,000 units per year and in the past, 9% of these have needed a repair within the three-year warranty. Parts are charged by the M/S division to the service division at cost and average $75 per repair. A repair takes two hours, on average, to complete.

The board want to ensure that they have an effective transfer pricing system in place and they have asked you to outline the criteria for designing a transfer pricing system at JHK.

Amendment to transfer pricing system

The board are considering amending this existing $10m internal recharge agreement between M/S and service. There has been some discussion of tailoring one of the two transfer-pricing approaches (these are market price or cost plus) to meet the company's objectives.

Although the service division has the capacity to cover all of the existing work available, it could outsource the warranty service work, as it is usually straightforward. It would retain the out-of-warranty service work as this is a higher margin business. It would then begin looking for other opportunities to earn revenue using its engineering experience. A local engineering firm has quoted a flat price of $200 per warranty service repair provided that they obtain a contract for all of the warranty repairs from JHK.

The board have asked you to evaluate the two methods discussed of calculating the transfer price between the service division and the M/S division. Appropriate calculations should be performed.

New information system

The board are also considering a change to the information systems at JHK. The existing systems are based in the individual functions (production, sales, service, finance and human resources). The board are considering the implementation of a new system based on an integrated, single database that would be accessible at any of the company's five sites. The company network would be upgraded to allow real-time input and update of the database. The database would support a detailed management information system and a high-level executive information system.

Next, the board would like you to evaluate the potential impact of the introduction of the new information systems at JHK on performance management. Finally, you have been asked to briefly describe the types of external information which the new system should seek to capture.

Required:

Write a report to the board of JHK responding to their request for assistance with the following:

(i) **Evaluation of divisional performance and critical discussion of the proposed measures.** **(15 marks)**

(ii) **Outlining the criteria for designing a transfer pricing system.** **(5 marks)**

(iii) **Evaluating the two methods of calculating the transfer price.** **(12 marks)**

(iv) **Evaluating the potential impact of the new information systems at on performance management.** **(10 marks)**

(v) **Briefly describing the types of external information which the new system should capture.** **(4 marks)**

Professional marks will be awarded for the format, style and structure of the discussion of your answer. **(4 marks)**

(Total: 50 marks)

Appendix 1

	Manufacturing/sales	Service
	$m	$m
Revenue	880	17.0
Operating costs	494	11.0
Operating profit	386	6.0
Apportioned head office costs	85	1.0
Profit before tax	301	5.0
Capital employed	1,294	38.0

The notional cost of capital used is	9% pa
The current cost of debt is	5.5%
The tax rate is	30%

Operating costs include:

	Manufacturing/sales	Service
	$m	$m
Depreciation	88	2.7
Other non-cash expenses	4	0.3

All operating costs are tax deductible.

Appendix 2

Standard costs within the service division

	$
Labour (per hour)	18
Variable divisional overhead (per hour)	12
Fixed divisional overhead (per hour)	25

Overheads are allocated by labour hours.

17 LOPTEN INDUSTRIES (DEC 13)

Company information, market and products

Lopten Industries is one of the largest, listed consumer durables manufacturers in the world, making washing machines, tumble dryers and dishwashers. It has recently expanded into Beeland which is a developing country where incomes have risen to the point where demand is increasing for Lopten's goods among the growing middle-class population.

Lopten believes in the economies of scale of large manufacturing sites with dispersed selling branches in the markets in which it operates. Therefore, it has entered the Beeland market by setting up a local sales force and supporting them with a national marketing campaign. The company is currently selling only two products in Beeland (both are types of washing machines):

- a basic product (called Cheerful) with functions which are comparable with the existing local competitors' output and
- a premium product (called Posh) which has functions and features similar to Lopten's products in other developed countries.

Both products are manufactured and imported from its regional manufacturing hub, which is in the neighbouring country of Kayland.

Competitive environment in Beeland

The competitive environment in Beeland is changing rapidly. The washing machine market used to be dominated by two large local manufacturers who make simple, cheap and reliable machines. There are two other major international manufacturers apart from Lopten. One of these has already opened a factory in Beeland and is producing machines similar to Cheerful to compete directly with the existing local producers. The government of Beeland has supported this new entrant with grants, as it is keen to encourage inward investment by foreign companies and the resulting expertise and employment which they provide. The other international competitor is now considering entering the Beeland market with more highly specified machines similar to Lopten's Posh brand.

Mission statement, critical success factors (CSFs) and key performance indicators (KPIs)

Lopten's stated mission is to be the 'most successful manufacturer of its type of products in the world'. The board has set the following critical CSFs for Lopten's Beeland operations:

1 to obtain a dominant market presence

2 to maximise profits within acceptable risk

3 to maintain the brand image of Lopten for above average quality products.

The board is considering using the following KPIs for each product: total profit, average sales price per unit, contribution per unit, market share, margin of safety, return on capital employed (ROCE), total quality costs and consumer awards won.

(**Note:** Margin of safety has been defined as [actual sales units – breakeven sales units]/actual sales units.)

Performance measurement system

The board has asked you, as a consultant, to assess its current performance measurement systems and want you to prepare a report covering a number of different areas.

First, the board would like you to calculate the KPIs suggested by them for the assessment of performance of the Beeland operations.

Second, you should use PEST analysis to identify issues in the company's external environment and then evaluate the effectiveness of the suggested KPIs in addressing these issues.

Third, you should take each CSF in turn and evaluate how the suggested KPIs fit into the CSFs given.

Fourth, you should assess the extent to which the suggested KPIs would be suitable for use in planning rather than controlling activities.

The data given in Appendix 1 on Beeland's operation's information for the most recent financial year has been collated for your use with these four tasks.

Marketing strategies

Finally, the board is considering two new marketing strategies going forward:

Plan A is to continue operations as at present allowing for 4% growth p.a. in volumes of both Cheerful and Posh.

Plan B is to dramatically reduce the marketing spend on Cheerful and to reallocate resources to focus the marketing on Posh. This is expected to lead to an anticipated growth in volume of 15% p.a. for Posh and flat sales for Cheerful.

The target operating profit for the Beeland operation in two years' time is set at $135m and the board.

For your final task, the board has asked you to evaluate whether the two proposed marketing strategies result in Beeland hitting its operating profit target in two years' time.

Appendix 1: Beeland operation's information for the most recent financial year

	Cheerful	**Posh**	**Total**
Variable costs	$ per unit	$ per unit	
Materials	90	120	
Labour	60	80	
Overheads	40	50	
Distribution costs	45	45	
Quality costs	20	30	
Fixed costs	$m	$m	$m
Administration costs	18	18	36
Distribution costs	16	16	32
Quality costs	6	6	12
Marketing costs	80	80	160
Other data	$m	$m	$m
Revenue	448	308	756
Capital employed	326	250	576
	Units	**Units**	**Units**
Total market size (millions)	9.33	1.33	10.66
Beeland operation's sales (millions)	1.12	0.44	1.56

Notes:

1 Cheerful has won one best buy award from the Beeland Consumer Association.

2 Posh has won four best buy awards from the Beeland Consumer Association.

3 The allocations of fixed costs are based on a recent activity-based costing exercise and are considered to be valid.

Required:

Write a report to the board of Lopten responding to their request for work on the following:

(i) Calculation of the suggested KPIs. (11 marks)

(ii) PEST analysis to identify issues and the effectiveness of the suggested KPIs in addressing these issues. (11 marks)

(iii) How the suggested KPIs fit to the CSFs given. (10 marks)

(iv) The extent to which the suggested KPIs would be suitable for use in planning rather than controlling. (5 marks)

(v) The two proposed marketing strategies. (9 marks)

Professional marks will be awarded for the format, style and structure of the discussion of your answer. **(4 marks)**

Note: All figures are real for the purpose of this scenario so that inflation can be ignored. Also, round to the nearest $million as appropriate.

(Total: 50 marks)

Section 2

PRACTICE QUESTIONS – SECTION B

Note: From September 2022, the 25 mark questions in Section B will comprise 20 technical marks and 5 professional skills marks. Two updated Section B questions for the Specimen exam have been provided by the ACCA and are included at the back of the Exam Kit. In addition, some of the Section B questions in the Exam Kit have been amended to reflect this approach.

In addition in all questions, the requirement will now be fully embedded within an exhibit (i.e a section of information) in the scenario and the requirements are simply a list of the areas which, for example, the CEO is requesting work on. Some of the Section B questions in the Exam Kit have been amended to reflect this approach.

The questions that have been amended to include 5 professional skills marks and the fully embedded requirements are indicated as such next to the question title in both the question and the answers. In addition, the 'Index of questions and answers' in the Exam Kit prelims shows the questions that have been amended in this way.

From September 2018, Section B of the APM exam will include one question mainly from syllabus section D and one question from any other technical syllabus section(s). In addition, there will be two compulsory 25 mark questions in Section B. Previously, candidates chose 2 from 3 questions worth 25 marks each. Any reference to question choice (for example, in the Examiner's comments) relates to exams set prior to September 2018.

A – STRATEGIC PLANNING AND CONTROL

18 SGOLTAIRE (SEPT/DEC 21) (AMENDED)

Answer debrief

Exhibit 1 – Company information

Sgoltaire is a large company listed on the Jayland stock exchange. Its main objective is to maximise the long-term wealth of its shareholders. The largest shareholder is a pension fund which only invests in companies which behave ethically towards their stakeholders and the environment. All companies listed in Jayland must produce an annual corporate sustainability report (CSR).

Sgoltaire manufactures a diverse range of chemicals, ranging from those for use in industrial processes to household detergents and cleaning products. Sgoltaire is a well-known and trusted brand in Jayland. Many of its household products command premium prices because they use ingredients and manufacturing processes which cause less harm to the environment than those of competitors.

Exhibit 2 – Kayland manufacturing plant

As part of a wider strategy, Sgoltaire plans to produce a new product, Chemical K, which will require the building of a new manufacturing plant. The company has always manufactured in Jayland, but in order to increase business performance, the board is considering whether to build the new plant overseas at a site identified in Kayland.

Due to high unemployment in Kayland, labour costs are lower there. Environmental regulations are also much less strict than in Jayland. Kayland is a hot, dry country where there is often insufficient water available to meet the needs of the population and their livestock.

Sgoltaire's largest shareholder, the pension fund, is aware that the company lacks experience in operating outside Jayland. Because of this, the shareholder is concerned that the board may pay insufficient attention to the impact of ethical issues on both strategy formulation and business performance, when taking the decision whether to manufacture in Kayland.

The board have asked for your advice on how ethical issues may affect the decision to manufacture in Kayland.

Exhibit 3 – Environmental impact of chemical K

The manufacture of Chemical K would consume large volumes of water taken from a nearby river. To comply with the limited environmental regulations in Kayland, some of this water would be used to dilute a toxic waste product, Waste Product A (WPA), which arises from the manufacturing process. The diluted WPA would then be discharged back into the nearby river. The discharge of WPA into rivers is not permitted in Sgoltaire's home country of Jayland because there is some scientific evidence that contact with WPA may cause serious long-term health problems to people, which may not become apparent for many years.

Production of Chemical K would cease after ten years and the plant must be decommissioned. The site would remain contaminated with harmful chemicals for many years after decommissioning, unless a separate cleaning operation is undertaken.

Exhibit 4 – Environmental management accounting

It has been suggested that Sgoltaire uses environmental management accounting (EMA) to improve business performance. EMA is the identification, collection and analysis of information related to the physical and financial impact of an organisation's activities on the environment. The board wants your advice on how EMA will help Sgoltaire in the following four areas:

1 Calculating costs

2 Investment appraisal

3 Setting performance measures and targets

4 Product pricing

In relation to investment appraisal, the board calculated that the net present value (NPV) of the proposal to manufacture Chemical K in Kayland is $240m, compared to $200m if the manufacturing was done in Jayland. It has since been identified that the costs of decommissioning the plant and cleaning the site were not included in these calculations, so the board has now begun the work of estimating the present values of the costs to decommission and clean the two possible sites (Appendix 1).

Required:

It is now 1 September 20X5.

Respond to the board of Sgoltaire's request for work on the following areas:

(a) The affect of ethical issues on the manufacturing decision. **(10 marks)**

(b) How EMA will help Sgoltaire. **(10 marks)**

Professional marks will be awarded for the demonstration of skill in analysis and evaluation, scepticism and commercial acumen in your answer. **(5 marks)**

(Total: 25 marks)

Exhibit 5 – Appendix 1

Present value of the costs of decommissioning the plant and cleaning the site

	$m	**$m**
	Jayland	**Kayland**
Decommissioning the plant[1]	20	30
Cleaning the site[2]	60	–
Total	80	30

1 The board has estimated that because of logistical difficulties due to Kayland being 8,000 km from Jayland, decommissioning costs, which do not include the costs of cleaning the site, would be 50% higher than in Jayland.

2 The board has not yet estimated the costs of cleaning the site in Kayland, though because of the same logistical difficulties which apply to decommissioning costs, costs of cleaning the site in Kayland will also be higher than in Jayland.

19 STOKENESS ENGINEERING (JUN 13) (AMENDED)

Exhibit 1 – Company information and mission

Stokeness Engineering's (Stokeness) mission is to provide world-leading, reduced-emission, fuel-efficient products for the motor industry in order to optimise shareholder returns.

Stokeness has existed for only five years and is owned by its management and venture capitalists (VCs). The management were all engineers who had been working on the basic research associated with new fuel technologies and saw the opportunity to commercialise their expertise. Stokeness is highly regarded in the industry for its advanced, efficient fuel cell designs. As a result, the VCs were eager to invest in Stokeness and have assisted by placing experienced managers into the business to aid the original engineering team.

Exhibit 2 – New product development

Stokeness is developing hydrogen fuel cells for use in powering large motor vehicles such as buses and trucks. They will replace standard petrol/diesel engines. The fuel cells have a clear advantage over these older technologies in having lower carbon dioxide (a greenhouse gas) emissions. The governments of many developed countries are keen to see cuts in such emissions and are supportive of a variety of possible technological solutions to this issue (such as fuel cells, electrical batteries and compressed natural gas).

Exhibit 3 – External business environment

It takes five to ten years to develop a viable product for sale in this motor market. There are a number of companies developing fuel cells but Stokeness is believed to have a two-year lead over them and to be only three years away from commercial launch.

Alternative power technologies like the hydrogen fuel cells would be fitted by the major international vehicle manufacturers into their vehicles for sale to their customers. The vehicle manufacturers will need to form a close partnership with any engine producer in order to make their technologies compatible and this has already begun to happen, with two of the major manufacturers signing deals with other engine makers recently.

A major problem which needs to be overcome with any of these new technologies is that there must be an infrastructure accessible to the end users for refuelling their vehicles (as the petrol station chains do for petrol engine vehicles at present).

Governments have indicated their desire to support the development of such technologies to address environmental issues and to try to establish new, high-value industries in their jurisdiction. They may do this through tax breaks and investment to support the development of the refuelling infrastructure.

Production of Stokeness' fuel cells uses a special membrane which requires rare and expensive elements. Also, it has partnered with two other engineering firms to subcontract the production of certain components in the fuel cell. Stokeness has had to share much of its fuel cell design with these firms in order to overcome certain engineering difficulties.

Also, there are a number of start-up companies developing the other technologies mentioned above, as well as large, existing diesel and petrol engine manufacturers who are constantly reducing the emissions from their existing engines.

The VCs have stressed the need to analyse competition and competitive advantage in order to understand how to make the business profitable in the long term.

The chief executive officer (CEO) of Stokeness has asked you, a performance management consultant, to assist with three tasks.

Firstly, she has asked you to use Porter's five forces model to assess the impact of the external business environment on the performance management of Stokeness and give a justified recommendation of one new performance measure for each of the five force areas at Stokeness.

Secondly, she has asked you to discuss how the problems of defining the market in measuring a market share apply for Stokeness.

Finally, she has asked you to assess the risk appetite of the venture capitalists and discuss how this might impact on performance measurement at Stokeness.

Required:

It is now 1 September 20X5.

Respond to the CEO's request for work on the following areas:

(a) the use of Porter's five forces model and performance measures for each force **(12 marks)**

(b) problems of defining the market in measuring a market share and **(4 marks)**

(c) the risk appetite of the venture capitalists **(4 marks)**

Professional marks will be awarded for the demonstration of skill in analysis and evaluation and commercial acumen in your answer. **(5 marks)**

(Total: 25 marks)

20 CLONYARD AND ELRIG (SEPT/DEC 20) (AMENDED)

Exhibit 1 – Company information

Clonyard is a private company which sells shoes to adults and children. Clonyard has several retail shops. The mission of Clonyard is 'to satisfy customers by providing footwear of excellent quality for the modern world.' Clonyard has built its reputation on providing footwear to those who have specialist needs in footwear, such as minor medical issues, and Clonyard's staff excel at spending time with customers to determine customers' correct requirements. Clonyard has achieved modest growth over the past five years.

Twelve months ago, Clonyard was the subject of a successful but hostile take-over bid by Elrig, a listed company. Elrig's mission is 'to return value consistently to our shareholders by growing our market share and by offering unrivalled value for money for our customers.'

Elrig's primary motivation for the takeover was to enhance its market share by acquiring a niche operator. In addition, Elrig's directors also believe that there is likely to be consolidation in the industry in the near future and the purchase of Clonyard by Elrig is a reaction to that belief. Having acquired Clonyard, Elrig is keen to retain the Clonyard brand and is also keen to ensure that all aspects of Clonyard's business operations are integrated into those of Elrig.

Exhibit 2 – Business alignment

Elrig has taken a decision at board level that a similar range of inventory is maintained throughout all Elrig and Clonyard shops. Managers of Clonyard's individual shops are unhappy with this as this is contrary to the individual specialisms which shop managers were encouraged to develop previously. As a result, several managers have left the business.

In order to help with the integration of Clonyard into Elrig's business, Elrig has ensured that each Clonyard shop will have at least one of Elrig's employees working there. Clonyard's staff have complained that the Elrig members of staff are more focused on ensuring a sale is made than spending the required time with customers. Clonyard staff have also expressed concern about the lack of technical product knowledge of Elrig's staff.

Elrig has retained most of Clonyard's directors. These directors have found it challenging to adjust to Elrig's focus on pursuing market share and recently said, 'It's as though they don't measure anything else. Every report we get is about market share and the message is always that we need more of it, as quickly as possible.'

The chief executive officer (CEO) of Elrig was recently told by a management consultant that Elrig should consider using the McKinsey 7S model to help with the integration of Clonyard into Elrig's operation. The management consultant indicated that she felt that Elrig should only focus on the four soft elements in this model for now.

The CEO would like you to evaluate whether Elrig is properly aligned with Clonyard using **only** the skills, staff and style components of the soft elements.

Exhibit 3 – Introduction of an ERPS

Elrig and Clonyard are currently utilising different computer systems. It is therefore difficult for staff at all levels of Elrig's operations to obtain access to Clonyard's performance data. The board of Elrig has complained that any information it receives on Clonyard's operations or performance is too late to enable the board to make decisions. The director of operations for the group, for example, has indicated that she does not see any reports on inventory levels at each Clonyard shop until at least three months into the financial year. She has also indicated that Clonyard shops appear to wait too long for goods to be delivered to them from their suppliers.

The group sales director indicated that the data he receives on Clonyard's monthly financial performance is at least three weeks late. This offers no opportunity to introduce discounted products at an appropriate time, which is a very common sales approach for Elrig.

Elrig's employees in general have expressed concern that Clonyard's computerised information systems are outdated and that Clonyard's employees do not use the computer system as much as they should. For example, it was reported that it is common practice for a Clonyard employee to place an order for inventory over the telephone and not enter the order onto the computer system until after the order has been delivered.

The board of Elrig has decided that it needs real time access to Elrig's overall business operations, including Clonyard, and is considering the purchase of an enterprise resource planning system (ERPS). Further, a director of Elrig has indicated: 'the use of a shared up-to-date information system such as an ERPS will ensure that the Clonyard operation is completely integrated within the Elrig one. The Clonyard employees will also be delighted with the brand new system.'

The CEO wants you to evaluate the introduction of an ERPS into Elrig's overall business, including Clonyard.

Required:

It is now 1 September 20X5.

Respond to the CEO of Elrig's request for work on the following areas:

(a) alignment between Elrig and Clonyard (10 marks)

(b) the introduction of an ERPS (10 marks)

Professional marks will be awarded for the demonstration of skills in analysis and evaluation, scepticism and commercial acumen in your answer. **(5 marks)**

(Total: 25 marks)

21 JOLT (SEPT 18) (AMENDED)

Exhibit 1 – Company information

Jolt manufactures high quality swimwear and cycling clothing in its only factory, which employs 1,000 manufacturing staff and 200 support staff. Its products are used by both amateur and professional sports players in its home country. Jolt is known for its high ethical standards towards its workers, suppliers and the environment, and has voluntarily published a corporate sustainability report for many years.

Jolt is organised into traditional functional departments such as procurement, finance and sales, most of which have their own unreliable spreadsheet-based systems for planning and reporting. As a result, Jolt often fails to produce accurate, timely and consistent data to monitor its own performance, which contributes to failures in achieving the performance targets set by its retail customers.

Jolt's market is seasonal and competitive. Retailers, who are Jolt's customers, for both swimwear and cycling clothing have two key demands: they want lower prices to pass on to consumers and they also require suppliers to meet performance targets relating to lead times and quality.

To help them comply with the retailers' demands, Jolt's competitors have closed down all of their own manufacturing facilities and outsourced all production to overseas suppliers, who have much larger factories and lower costs. To mitigate the cost of shipping goods over long distances, Jolt's competitors have invested in sophisticated software to consolidate orders so that each shipping container is completely full before despatch from their suppliers. Purchase invoice processing is also automated by the integration of information systems into the suppliers' bespoke systems.

Exhibit 2 – BPR proposal

In order to reduce costs, it has been proposed to outsource the manufacture of swimwear, which is 50% of Jolt's total output, to a supplier 17,000 km away. A comparison of the cost of manufacturing and the cost of outsourcing swimwear is given in Appendix 1.

The change to outsourced supply for swimwear will mean that staff from Jolt's functional departments will reorganise into multi-disciplinary teams, each serving major customer accounts. Each team will perform all aspects of account management from taking sales orders and procurement through to arranging shipping and after sales service. Team members dealing with customers will work in Jolt's home country, while those managing quality and supplier audits will work close to the manufacturing site. Teams will be given greater autonomy to set selling prices to reflect market conditions. Many support staff will work in unfamiliar roles, or be offered new jobs overseas after the reorganisation.

A consultant has advised Jolt that the outsourcing and reorganisation proposal has characteristics of re-engineered processes, and could be described as business process re-engineering (BPR). She advised that, as well as evaluating how BPR will improve its business performance in meeting its customers' demands and requirements, Jolt should take into account any development in information systems which may be required, as well as the ethical aspects of the proposed changes.

In response to the consultant's advice, the board have asked you to help them. The work the board requires is in two parts:

- First, the board would like an evaluation of how the BPR proposal could improve Jolt's performance in relation to its retail customers' two key demands, and
- Second, an assessment of the potential impact of Jolt's high ethical standards on the BPR proposal and consequently on business performance.

Required:

Respond to the board of Jolt's request for work on the BPR proposal (20 marks)

Note: there are 12 marks available for the first part of the work required on this area (refer to this as (a) in your answer) and there are 8 marks available for the second part of the work required on this area (refer to this as (b) in your answer).

Professional marks will be awarded for the demonstration of skill in analysis and evaluation, scepticism and commercial acumen in your answer. **(5 marks)**

(Total: 25 marks)

Exhibit 3 – Appendix 1

Comparison of the average cost of manufacturing and outsourcing swimwear production

	Manufacturing	**Outsourcing**
Average cost per unit	$	$[1]
Materials cost	1.85	–
Labour cost	2.20	–
Factory overhead	0.95	–
Purchase cost from supplier2	–	3.50
Total	5.00	3.50

Notes

1 Purchase cost of outsourced products is translated into $ from the supplier's home currency.

2 In addition to the purchase cost from the supplier, Jolt must pay for shipping costs at the rate of $5,000 for each large, standard sized shipping container, regardless of the number of units in it. Each container holds 10,000 units when fully loaded.

3 Due to changes in international trade tariffs expected in the near future, swimwear imports into Jolt's home country will be subject to 10% import duty on the cost of imports excluding shipping costs.

22 CUTHBERT (MAR/JUN 16)

Company information

Cuthbert is based in Ceeland and manufactures jackets for use in very cold environments by mountaineers and skiers. It also supplies the armed forces in several countries with variants of existing products, customised by the use of different coloured fabrics, labels and special fastenings for carrying equipment. Cuthbert incurs high costs on design and advertising in order to maintain the reputation of the brand.

Production process

Each jacket is made up of different shaped pieces of fabric called 'components'. These components are purchased by Cuthbert from an external supplier. The external supplier is responsible for ensuring the quality of the components and the number of purchased components found to be defective is negligible. The cost of the components forms 80% of the direct cost of each jacket, and the prices charged by Cuthbert's supplier for the components are the lowest in the industry. There are three stages to the production process of each jacket, which are each located in different parts of the factory:

Stage 1 – Sewing

The fabric components are sewn together by a machinist. Any manufacturing defects occurring after sewing has begun cannot be rectified, and finished garments found to be defective are heavily discounted, or in the case of bespoke variants, destroyed.

Stage 2 – Assembly

The garments are filled with insulating material and sewn together for the final time.

Stage 3 – Finishing

Labels, fastenings and zips are sewn to the finished garments. Though the process for attaching each of these is similar, machinists prefer to work only on labels, fastenings or zips to maximise the quantity which they can sew each hour.

Jackets are produced in batches of a particular style in a range of sizes. Throughout production, the components required for each batch of jackets are accompanied by a paper batch card which records the production processes which each batch has undergone. The batch cards are input into a production spreadsheet so that the stage of completion of each batch can be monitored and the position of each batch in the factory is recorded.

There are 60 machinists working in the sewing department, and 40 in each of the assembly and finishing departments. All the machinists are managed by 10 supervisors whose duties include updating the batch cards for work done and inputting this into a spreadsheet, as well as checking the quality of work done by machinists. The supervisors report to the factory manager, who has overall responsibility for the production process.

Reward system

Machinists are paid an hourly wage and a bonus according to how many items they sew each week, which usually comprises 60% of their total weekly wages.

Supervisors receive an hourly wage and a bonus according to how many items their team sews each week. The factory manager receives the same monthly salary regardless of production output. All employees are awarded a 5% annual bonus if Cuthbert achieves its budgeted net profit for the year.

Production process issues

Recently, a large emergency order of jackets for the Ceeland army was cancelled by the customer as it was not delivered on time due to the following quality problems and other issues in the production process:

- A supervisor had forgotten to input several batch cards and as a result batches of fabric components were lost in the factory and replacements had to be purchased.
- There were machinists available to sew buttons onto the jackets, but there was only one machinist available who had been trained to sew zips. This caused further delay to production of the batch.
- When the quality of the jackets was checked prior to despatch, many of them were found to be sewn incorrectly as the work had been rushed. By this time the agreed delivery date had already passed, and it was too late to produce a replacement batch.

Business process reengineering (BPR)

This was the latest in a series of problems in production at Cuthbert, and the directors have decided to use BPR in order to radically change the production process.

The proposal being considered as an application of BPR is the adoption of 'team working' in the factory, the three main elements of which are as follows:

1 Production lines would re-organise into teams, where **all** operations on a particular product type are performed in one place by a dedicated team of machinists.

2 Each team of machinists would be responsible for the quality of the finished jacket, and for the first time, machinists would be encouraged to bring about improvements in the production process. There would no longer be the need to employ supervisors and the existing supervisors would join the teams of machinists.

3 The number of batches in production would be automatically tracked by the use of radio frequency identification (RFID) tags attached to each jacket. This would eliminate the need for paper batch cards, which are currently input into a spreadsheet by the supervisors.

You have been asked as a performance management consultant to advise the board on whether business process reengineering could help Cuthbert overcome the problems in its production process.

Required:

(a) Advise how the proposed use of BPR would influence the operational performance of Cuthbert. (14 marks)

(b) Evaluate the effectiveness of the current reward systems at Cuthbert, and recommend and justify how these systems would need to change if the BPR project goes ahead. (11 marks)

(Total: 25 marks)

23 FRAMILTONE (SEPT/DEC 16) (AMENDED)

Exhibit 1 – Company information

Framiltone is a food manufacturer based in Ceeland, whose objective is to maximise shareholder wealth. Framiltone has two divisions: Dairy division and Luxury division. Framiltone began manufacturing dairy foods 20 years ago and Dairy division, representing 60% of total revenue, is still the larger of Framiltone's two divisions.

Exhibit 2 – Dairy division

This division manufactures cheeses and milk-based desserts. The market in Ceeland for these products is saturated, with little opportunity for growth. Dairy division has, however, agreed profitable fixed price agreements to supply all the major supermarket chains in Ceeland for the next three years. The division has also agreed long-term fixed volume and price contracts with suppliers of milk, which is by far the most significant raw material used by the division.

In contrast to Luxury division, Dairy division does not operate its own fleet of delivery vehicles, but instead subcontracts this to a third party distribution company. The terms of the contract provide that the distribution company can pass on some increases in fuel costs to Framiltone. These increases are capped at 0.5% annually and are agreed prior to the finalisation of each year's budget.

Production volumes have shown less than 0.5% growth over the last five years. Dairy division managers have invested in modern production plant and its production is known to be the most efficient and consistent in the industry.

Exhibit 3 – Luxury division

This division was set up two years ago to provide an opportunity for growth which is absent from the dairy foods sector. Luxury division produces high quality foods using unusual, rare and expensive ingredients, many of which are imported from neighbouring Veeland. The product range changes frequently according to consumer tastes and the availability and price of ingredients. All Luxury division's products are distributed using its own fleet of delivery vehicles.

Exhibit 4 – Incremental budgeting

Since the company began, Framiltone has used a traditional incremental budgeting process. Annual budgets for each division are set by the company's head office after some consultation with divisional managers, who currently have little experience of setting their own budgets. Performance of each division, and of divisional managers, is appraised against these budgets. For many years, Framiltone managed to achieve the budgets set, but last year managers at Luxury division complained that they were unable to achieve their budget due to factors beyond their control. A wet growing season in Veeland had reduced the harvest of key ingredients in Luxury's products, significantly increasing their cost. As a result, revenue and gross margins fell sharply and the division failed to achieve its operating profit target for the year.

Exhibit 5 – Rolling budgets

Framiltone has just appointed a new CEO at the end of Q1 of the current year. He has called you as a performance management expert for your advice.

'In my last job in the retail fashion industry, we used rolling budgets, where the annual budget was updated to reflect the results of every quarter's trading. That gives a more realistic target, providing a better basis on which to appraise divisional performance.'

You have obtained the current year budget (20X5) for Luxury division and the division's Q1 actual trading results (Appendix 1) and notes outlining expectations of divisional key costs and revenues for the rest of the year (Appendix 2).

You have been asked, firstly, to use the data in the appendices to recalculate the current year budget to the end of the current year and to briefly comment on the overall impact of this on the expected operating profit for the year.

Secondly, you should evaluate whether a move from traditional incremental budgeting to a system of rolling budgets would be appropriate for Dairy and Luxury divisions.

Required:

It is now 1 September 20X5.

Respond to the CEO's request for work on the following areas:

(a) the recalculation of the current year budget and comment on expected operating profit and (10 marks)

(b) a move from incremental to rolling budgets. (10 marks)

Professional marks will be awarded for the demonstration of skill in analysis and evaluation and commercial acumen in your answer. **(5 marks)**

(Total: 25 marks)

Exhibit 6 – Appendix 1

Luxury division current year budget (20X5)

C$000	**Q1**	**Q2**	**Q3**	**Q4**	**Total**	**Q1 Actual**
Revenue	10,000	12,000	11,000	7,000	40,000	10,400
Cost of sales	(6,100)	(7,120)	(6,460)	(4,720)	(24,400)	(6,240)
Gross profit	3,900	4,880	4,540	2,280	15,600	4,160
Distribution costs	(600)	(720)	(660)	(420)	(2,400)	(624)
Administration costs	(2,300)	(2,300)	(2,300)	(2,300)	(9,200)	(2,296)
Operating profit	1,000	1,860	1,580	(440)	4,000	1,240

Exhibit 7 – Appendix 2

Expected key costs and revenues for remainder of the current year

1 Sales volumes are expected to be 2% higher each quarter than forecast in the current budget.

2 Average selling price per unit is expected to increase by 1.5% from the beginning of Q3.

3 The exchange rate between the Ceeland Dollar (C$) and the Veeland Dollar (V$) is predicted to change at the beginning of Q2 to C$1.00 buys V$1.50. For several years up to the end of Q1, C$1.00 has been equivalent to V$1.40 and this exchange rate has been used when producing the current year budget. Food produced in the Luxury division is despatched immediately upon production and Framiltone holds minimal inventory. The cost of ingredients imported from Veeland represents 50% of the division's cost of sales and suppliers invoice goods in V$.

4 The rate of tax levied by the Ceeland government on the cost of fuel which Luxury uses to power its fleet of delivery vehicles is due to increase from 60%, which it has been for many years, to 63% at the beginning of quarter 3. 70% of the division's distribution costs are represented by the cost of fuel for delivery vehicles.

5 The CEO has initiated a programme of overhead cost reductions and savings of 2.5% from the budgeted administration costs are expected from the beginning of Q2. Q3 administration costs are expected to be a further 2.5% lower than in Q2, with a further 2.5% saving in Q4 over the Q3 costs.

24 ALFLONNSO (SEPT/DEC 16)

Company information

Alflonnso is a large producer of industrial chemicals, with divisions in 25 countries. The agrochemicals division produces a chemical pesticide, known internally as 'ALF', to control pests in a crop which is of worldwide significance, economically and for food production. Pesticides such as ALF only remain effective for a limited time, after which pests become resistant to them and a replacement product needs to be found. A scientific study has shown that the current variant, ALF6, is becoming ineffective in controlling pests and in some places, it has accumulated in the soil to levels which may significantly reduce crop yields in the future if it is continued to be used. The agrochemicals division is evaluating three new products to find one replacement for ALF6.

ALF7

ALF7 is produced by a small chemical modification to the existing product and requires little research and development (R&D) resources to develop it. As it is closely related to the current variant, it is only expected to remain effective, and in use, for three years. It is unclear whether ALF7 will accumulate in the soil in the same way as ALF6 does.

Red

Red is a new type of pesticide which will incur large amounts of R&D expenditure to develop a commercial version. In addition, the agrochemicals division will have to fund a long-term scientific study into the effect of Red on the environment at a cost of $4m for each of the 15 years that the product will be in use, and for five years afterwards.

Production of Red generates large amounts of toxic by-products which must be treated in the division's waste treatment facility. The production plant used to produce Red must also be decommissioned for cleaning, at an estimated cost of $45m, at the end of the life of the product.

Notes to the statement of profit or loss:

[1] – All figures exclude the contribution from the GFPO towards the R&D costs of the new product.

[2] – Waste treatment is an overhead cost incurred in the division's waste treatment facility. Currently, costs of waste treatment are apportioned to products according to expected revenue. The total annual cost of the waste treatment facility, which processes a total of 55m litres of waste each year, is $300m. Any waste treatment capacity not used by any of the three new products can be used to treat waste created during the manufacture of other products in the division. One litre of waste by-product is produced for every 12.5 litres of ALF7 produced, for every 2.5 litres of Red produced and for every 100 litres of Green.

[3] – R&D costs are incurred in the division's R&D facility. In accordance with the group's accounting policy, R&D expenditure is not currently apportioned to individual products. The annual cost of the R&D facility is $60m and has a total of 30,400 R&D hours available, of which 800 hours would be required to develop ALF7, 8,500 hours to develop Red, and 4,000 hours to develop Green.

Required:

(a) (i) **Explain how activity based costing may help the agrochemicals division in assessing the profitability of the three new products. (5 marks)**

(ii) **Using activity based costing, and excluding the value of the grant from the GFPO, calculate the total R&D costs and waste treatment costs of the three new products. (3 marks)**

(b) **Using your answers from part (a) (ii), calculate the average net profit per litre of each of the three alternative new products over their expected lifecycles and comment on the results. (9 marks)**

(c) **Advise how environmental management accounting (EMA) may help improve the performance of the agrochemicals division. (8 marks)**

(Total: 25 marks)

25 CORTINAS RETAIL CLOTHING (CRC) (MAR/JUN 19)

Company information

CRC started as a clothing retailer 20 years ago with one store. The business expanded steadily and had 10 stores after 18 years of trading. Since then, the rate of expansion has increased rapidly with an average of four stores opening per year.

CRC is planning to open its first large out of town store soon and is also considering the acquisition of a food retailing business. Both of these will be supplied with items using CRC's existing central warehouse.

Introduction of RFID system

At the beginning of the 20X5 accounting year, to cope with this rapid growth, CRC acquired a RFID (radio frequency identification device) system at its single central warehouse. This was to help manage inventory more effectively and speed up the processes for receiving items from suppliers and despatching them to stores. Items are still moved manually by staff in the CRC warehouse where there is little automation compared to competitors. There has been some resistance from staff to the RFID system, which they find difficult to use. CRC is currently trying to reduce the number of suppliers it has to help increase efficiency in the warehouse.

Budgeting system

The budget setting process has remained unchanged since CRC was formed. All managers prepare draft budgets using spreadsheets and submit them to the CRC board for approval. Managers use the previous year results as a starting point when drafting the budgets and increase the variable costs in line with any anticipated growth in volumes. For example, when preparing the budget for the year ending 30 June 20X6, the manager of the central warehouse used the actual costs of running the warehouse from the previous year and increased them all by the same percentage. This was to reflect an anticipated increase in volumes in 20X6 over 20X5. Managers are appraised on their performance against the approved budgets.

CRC has needed all its financial resources to fund its expansion and so it has only old and basic IT systems which are not enterprise resource planning systems, unified databases or networked systems.

It has been suggested to the CRC board that the current system of budgeting is no longer suitable and that the business should move to activity-based budgeting (ABB). The CEO has asked you to evaluate the potential introduction of ABB at CRC.

Central warehouse activity in July 20X5

The board has never seen an activity-based budget before and is unsure how it could be used to explain variances between actual and budgeted performance in the central warehouse. As an example, they would like to see how an activity-based budget for the year ending 30 June 20X6 could be used to explain variances from the actual results for the month of July 20X5.

The two key activities which drive costs in the central warehouse are receipts of items into the goods inwards section and despatches of items from the goods outwards section. A receipt into good inwards involves accepting a delivery of items from a supplier, tagging those items and putting them away in the warehouse. Receipts from suppliers contain variable numbers of individual items. Despatches of items from goods outwards are to CRC's own retail stores. Cost driver rates for these two activities will be used to set monthly cost budgets for the warehouse.

The board asked an analyst to prepare an activity-based budget for the central warehouse for the year ending 30 June 20X6. The analyst has collected relevant information on the costs for the year needed to prepare the activity-based budget and has begun the work (Appendix 1).

The total annual cost relating to goods inwards needs to be determined. This should be used to calculate the budgeted cost of each receipt into goods inwards, in order to explain the variance between the budgeted cost and the actual cost of receipts of goods inwards for the month of July 20X5. The analyst has already correctly included the costs of the warehouse manager's salary and the lease of the RFID system into the incomplete activity-based budget in Appendix 1. The board has asked you to complete the analyst's work.

To enable you to complete your calculations, you are told that in July 20X5 there were 650 receipts into goods inwards. These receipts contained 100,000 items, which is the same as the budgeted number of items for the month. The actual total cost of activities driven by receipts into goods inwards for the month was $18,000.

It is now 1 September 20X5.

Required:

(a) Evaluate whether CRC should move from its current budgeting system to ABB. **(13 marks)**

(b) Complete the analyst's work in Appendix 1 as required by the board and explain the variance between the budgeted cost and the actual cost for each receipt into goods inwards for July 20X5. **(12 marks)**

(Total: 25 marks)

Appendix 1

Analyst's incomplete activity-based budget for the central warehouse for YE 30 June 20X6.

	Total $	**Goods inwards** $	**Goods outwards** $	**Other** $
Warehouse manager's salary[1]	55,000	–	–	55,000
Lease of RFID system[2]	75,000	45,000	30,000	–
RFID tagging[3]				
Warehouse staff wages[4]				
Heating and lighting[5]				
Sub-total cost of activities driven by the receipt of goods inwards				

Analyst's notes

Relevant information on costs in the central warehouse for the year ending 30 June 20X6

1 The cost of the warehouse manager's salary relates to all sections of the warehouse and cannot be apportioned directly to goods inwards or goods outwards.

2 The cost for the RFID system is invoiced by a lease company. 60% of this cost is allocated to goods inwards and the remainder relates to goods outwards.

3 The cost of RFID tagging is the wages cost for specially trained staff, known as taggers. Their only job is to attach RFID tags to items when they are received, before the items are put away in the warehouse. All items received are RFID tagged and the costs of tagging are allocated entirely to the cost of goods inwards. Each tagger can attach 35,000 tags per month and is paid an annual salary of $24,000. The cost of each individual RFID tag is negligible.

4 There were 12 full-time warehouse staff throughout the year to 30 June 20X5 who were each paid an annual salary of $22,500. Two more staff will be recruited at the beginning of the new budget year. 50% of the warehouse staff work in goods inwards and 50% in goods outwards.

5 The cost of heating and lighting relates to all sections of the warehouse and cannot be apportioned directly to goods inwards or goods outwards. The actual heating and lighting cost for last year was $10,000 and the warehouse manager has proposed a budget of $10,500 for the coming year. The general cost of inflation though is expected to be zero.

6 The annual number of receipts into goods inwards expected is 9,000, containing a total of 1,200,000 items. These are expected to occur evenly over the year.

26 GODEL (JUN 14)

Company information

Godel Goodies (Godel) manufactures a variety of own-label sweets for the two largest supermarket chains in Seeland. The business makes several different flavours of the same basic product. The strategy of the business has been to be a cost leader in order to win the supermarkets' business. The sales of Godel vary up and down from quarter to quarter depending on the state of the general economy and competitive forces.

Most of the sweet manufacturers have been in business for decades and so the business is mature with little scope to be innovative in new product development. The supermarkets prefer to sign suppliers to long-term contracts and so it is difficult for new entrants to gain a foothold in this market. The management style at Godel is very much command-and-control which fits with the strategy and type of business. Indeed, most employees have been at Godel for many years and have expressed their liking for the straightforward nature of their work.

Variance analysis

The chief executive officer (CEO) of Godel has asked your firm of accountants to advise him as his finance director (FD) will be absent for several months due to a recently diagnosed illness. As the CEO is preparing for the next board meeting, he has obtained the operating statement and detailed variance analysis from one of the junior accountants (Appendix 1).

The CEO is happy with the operating statement but wants to understand the detailed operational and planning variances, given in Appendix 1, for the board meeting. He needs to know what action should be taken as a result of these specific variances.

Budgeting system

The FD had been looking at the budgeting process before she fell ill. The CEO has decided that you should help him by answering some questions on budgeting at Godel.

Currently, the budget at Godel is set at the start of the year and performance is measured against this. The company uses standard costs for each product and attributes overheads using absorption costing based on machine hours. No variations are allowed to the standard costs during the year.

The standard costs and all budget assumptions are based on adjusting previous year figures, along with discussions with the relevant operational manager before being set. However, these managers grumble that the budget process is very time-consuming and that the results are ultimately of limited value from their perspective. Some of them also complain that they must frequently explain that the variances are not their fault. The CEO wants to know your views on whether this way of budgeting is appropriate and whether the managers' complaints are justified. He is satisfied that there is no dysfunctional behaviour at Godel which may lead to budget slack or excessive spending and that all managers are working in the best interests of the company.

Zero-based budgeting

Finally, in the last few months, the FD had been reading business articles and books and had mentioned that there were a number of organisations which were adopting zero-based budgeting to reduce planning variances. The CEO is concerned that he does not understand what budgeting does for the business and this is why he wants you to explain what are the benefits and problems of budgeting at Godel before considering switching to an alternative approach.

Required:

(a) **Advise the CEO on the implications for performance management at Godel of analysing variances into the planning and operational elements as shown in Appendix 1.** **(6 marks)**

(b) **Evaluate the budgeting system at Godel.** **(11 marks)**

(c) **Evaluate the proposal to move to zero-based budgeting at Godel, giving a recommendation on whether to proceed.** **(8 marks)**

(Total: 25 marks)

Appendix 1

Note: You may assume that all figures in this appendix are correct.

Operating statement for Godel

Period: May 2014

				$	$	
Budgeted profit					214,200	
Budget fixed production costs					264,180	Favourable
Budgeted contribution					478,380	
Sales variances	volume			20,100		Adverse
	price			8,960		Adverse
					29,060	Adverse
Actual sales minus standard cost of sales					449,320	
		Favourable	**Adverse**			
		$	$			
Variable cost variance						
Material	price		4,200			
	usage	3,500				
Labour	rate	1,100				
	efficiency	24,480				
	idle time		5,600			
Variable overhead	expenditure		1,080			
	efficiency	3,060				
		32,140	10,880			
					21,260	Favourable
Actual contribution					470,580	
Budgeted fixed production overhead				271,728		
Expenditure variance				18,696		Adverse
Actual fixed production overhead					290,424	
Actual profit					180,156	

Detailed variances

Total variable cost variances		$	
	Planning	20,680	Favourable
	Operational	580	Favourable
Sales price variances			
Planning		15,600	Adverse
Operational		6,640	Favourable

27 BOOXE (JUN 14)

Company information

Booxe is a furniture manufacturing company based in the large, developed country of Teeland. Booxe is the largest furniture manufacturer in Teeland supplying many of the major retail chains with their own-brand furniture and also, making furniture under its own brand (Meson). In a highly competitive market such as Teeland, Booxe has chosen a strategy of cost leadership.

Traditional culture

Booxe has been in business for more than 70 years and there is a strong sense of tradition and appreciation of craft skills in the workforce. The average time which an employee has worked for the firm is 18 years. This has led to a bureaucratic culture; for example, the company's information systems are heavily paper based. In addition and in line with this traditional culture, the organisation is divided into a set of functional departments, such as production, warehousing, human resources and finance.

Business process re-engineering (BPR)

In order to drive down costs, the chief executive officer (CEO) decided to re-engineer the processes at Booxe. She decided that there should be a small pilot project to demonstrate the potential of BPR to benefit Booxe and she selected the goods receiving activity in the company's warehousing operations for this.

Financial impact of BPR

The CEO has asked you as a performance management expert to complete the post-implementation review of the pilot project by assessing what it has delivered in financial terms. The project identified that 10 of the warehouse staff spend about half of their time matching goods delivered documents to purchase orders and dealing with subsequent problems. It was noted that 25% of all such matches failed and the staff then had to identify the issue and liaise with the purchasing department in order to get the goods returned to the supplier and a suitable credit note issued. The project introduced a new information system to replace the existing paper-based system. The new system allowed purchase orders to be entered by the purchasing department and then checked online to the goods delivered as they arrived at the warehouse. This allowed warehouse staff to reject incorrect deliveries immediately.

The following are further details provided in relation to the project:

Notes relating to old system:

1 Average staff wage in warehouse $25,000 p.a.

2 Purchasing staff time in handling delivery queries 8.5 days per week

3 Average staff wage in purchasing is $32,000 p.a. for working a 5-day week

Notes relating to new system:

New IT system costs:

4	Hardware for warehouse and purchasing depts	220,000
5	Software total cost	275,000
6	On-going servicing cost (p.a.)	22,500
7	It is expected that the new system will last for eight years.	

Changes to culture and management information systems

The CEO now plans to apply BPR across Booxe and as well as completing the post-implementation review, she also needs to know how BPR will change the accounting information systems and the culture at Booxe. Booxe's current accounting system is a traditional one of overhead absorption based on labour hours with variances to budget used as control indicators.

She has heard that an activity-based approach using enterprise resource planning (ERP) systems is fairly common and wants to know how these ideas might link to BPR at Booxe.

Staff appraisal

The CEO is concerned that middle management unrest may be a problem at Booxe. For example, the warehouse manager was uncomfortable with the cultural change required in the BPR project and decided to take early retirement before the project began. As a result, a temporary manager was put in place to run the warehouse during the project.

The CEO has also begun to reconsider the human resources system at Booxe and she wants your advice on how the staff appraisal process can improve performance in the company. The existing system of manager appraisal is for the staff member to have an annual meeting with their line superior to review the previous year's work and discuss generally how to improve their efforts. Over the years, it has become common for these meetings to be informal and held over lunch at the company's expense. The CEO wants to understand the purpose of a staff appraisal system and how the process can improve the performance of the company. She also wants comments on the appropriate balance between control and staff development as this impacts on staff appraisal at Booxe.

Required:

(a) **Assess the financial impact of the pilot business process re-engineering (BPR) project in the warehousing operations.** **(6 marks)**

(b) **Assess the impact of BPR on the culture and management information systems at Booxe.** **(11 marks)**

(c) **Advise on the appraisal process at Booxe as instructed by the CEO.** **(8 marks)**

(Total: 25 marks)

28 GANYMEDE UNIVERSITY (JUN 12)

Background information

Ganymede University (GU) is one of the three largest universities in Teeland, which has eight universities in total. All of the universities are in the public sector. GU obtains the vast majority of its revenue through government contracts for academic research and payments per head for teaching students. The economy of Teeland has been in recession in the last year and this has caused the government to cut funding for all the universities in the country.

Benchmarking

In order to try to improve efficiency, the chancellor of the university, who leads its executive board, has asked the head administrator to undertake an exercise to benchmark GU's administration departments against the other two large universities in the country, AU and BU. The government education ministry has supported this initiative and has required all three universities to cooperate by supplying information.

The following information has been collected regarding administrative costs for the most recent academic year:

		GU	AU	BU
		$000	$000	$000
Research:				
contract management		14,430	14,574	14,719
laboratory management		41,810	42,897	42,646
Teaching facilities management		26,993	27,263	26,723
Student support services		2,002	2,022	2,132
Teachers' support services		4,005	4,100	4,441
Accounting		1,614	1,571	1,611
Human resources		1,236	1,203	1,559
IT management		6,471	6,187	6,013
General services		17,049	16,095	18,644
Total		115,610	115,912	118,488
Drivers:				
Student numbers		28,394	22,783	29,061
Staff numbers		7,920	7,709	8,157
Research contract value	$m	185	167	152

The key drivers of costs and revenues have been assumed to be research contract values supported, student numbers and total staff numbers. The head administrator wants you to complete the benchmarking and make some preliminary comment on your results.

Required:

(a) Assess the progress of the benchmarking exercise to date, explaining the actions that have been undertaken and those that are still required. (10 marks)

(b) Evaluate, as far as possible, Ganymede University's benchmarked position. (15 marks)

(Total: 25 marks)

29 MAXWELL (DEC 14)

Company Information

Maxwell Electricity Generation (Maxwell) is an electricity-generating firm producing power for industry and the general public in the country of Deeland. In the past, the company has been dominated by the need to make suitable returns on capital for its shareholders.

All power stations work in broadly the same way by taking in fuel (coal, gas or nuclear) and producing electricity and waste products.

Power stations

Maxwell has the following mix of power stations:

Power station type		Details for each type of station: Maximum generating power (MW)	Operating cost of electricity ($/MWh)	Capital cost ($m)	Totals for Maxwell: Number of stations	Total capital invested ($m)	Total CO_2 emissions (million tonnes)
Coal	(small)	300	25	1,320	4	5,280	3.15
	(large)	600	25	2,640	4	10,560	12.61
Gas	(small)	300	50	300	8	2,400	3.15
	(large)	900	50	900	2	1,800	7.10
Nuclear		1,200	20	6,000	2	12,000	0.50
						32,040	26.51

Notes:

1 Maximum generating power is the output of the station measured in megawatts (MW) at 100% operating capacity. The electricity produced by a station is measured in megawatt hours (MWh).

2 It is assumed that the same load factor applies across all the different types of station, i.e. they are working at the same percentage of capacity throughout the year.

3 Operating cost of electricity is the cost before the cost of financing the capital invested in a station.

4 The CO_2 (carbon dioxide) emissions are estimated based on industry standard figures for similar stations.

5 Capital costs and CO_2 emission figures are current best estimates.

The business has two alternative plans (plans 1a and 1b) to maintain current generating capacity while plan 2 will grow the business.

Plan 1a

Build a new nuclear power station (the same as the existing nuclear type) to replace one of the 300 MW coal stations, one of the 600 MW coal stations and, also, one of the 300 MW gas stations. The stations being replaced are all reaching the end of their useful lives.

Plan 1b

Replace the gas and coal stations mentioned in plan 1a with equivalent gas and coal stations, thus maintaining the current generating mix.

Plan 2

In order to grow the business, a new nuclear station is being considered in combination with one of plan 1a or 1b. This new nuclear station would be the same as the existing stations.

Maxwell is trying to raise finance for either plan 1a or plan 1b and, in addition to one of these plans, plan 2. A nuclear plant takes about five years to build (assuming no regulatory difficulties or problems over the design choice). It has a working life of 40 years and costs about $1bn at current prices to decommission although this estimate is uncertain as each site is unique in the decommissioning difficulties which it presents.

Deeland government – environmental concern

The government of Deeland has joined the international community in pledging to have greater concern for the environment. Initially, it has stated that there is a national goal to reduce carbon dioxide emissions by 20% in the next five years. The government is aware that electricity demand is estimated to rise by around 10% over the next five years; nevertheless, it is strongly encouraging businesses to help achieve this reduction in CO_2 emissions. There is a proposal to raise a carbon tax on CO_2 emissions in order to encourage reductions. The government is also concerned that there are other pollutants emitted by power stations but has decided to focus efforts on CO_2 initially, as it is a key cause of climate change.

Maxwell environmental goal

In order to join the wider community in achieving these aims and as one of the major electricity generators in Deeland, Maxwell has stated its own environmental goal as:

'to help reach national targets for reduction in CO_2 emissions while maintaining our ability to contribute to the electricity needs of the people of Deeland.'

Environmental costs and lifecycle costing

The finance director is interested in broadening environmental reporting within the company and has asked you as his performance measurement expert to explain some of the limitations of traditional accounting systems in dealing with environmental costs and to look at introducing environmental lifecycle costing.

Required:

(a) **Using Maxwell's stated environmental goal, assess the proposed investment plans 1a and 2.** **(10 marks)**

(b) **Explain, giving examples, how traditional accounting systems are unable to deal adequately with environmental costs.** **(8 marks)**

(c) **Discuss the lifecycle costing issues associated with Plan 2.** **(7 marks)**

(Total: 25 marks)

30 ENT ENTERTAINMENT CO (JUN 11)

Company information

ENT Entertainment Co (ENT) is a large, diversified entertainment business based in Teeland. The company's objective is the maximisation of shareholder wealth for its family owners. It has four divisions:

1 Restaurants

2 Cafes

3 Bars

4 Dance clubs

Boston Consulting Group (BCG) analysis

Recently, ENT's board have identified that there are problems in managing such a diversified company. They have employed consultants who have recommended that they should perform a BCG analysis to understand whether they have the right mix of businesses. The chief executive officer (CEO) has questioned whether using this analysis is helpful in managing the group's performance. A business analyst has prepared information on each division in the table below.

Revenue ($m)	**Actual 2010**	**Actual 2011**	**Forecast 2012**	**Forecast 2013**
Restaurants				
ENT	54	56	59	62
Market sector	10,752	10,860	10,968	10,968
Cafes				
ENT	31	34	41	47
Market sector	3,072	3,348	3,717	4,051
Bars				
ENT	349	342	336	336
Market sector	9,984	9,784	9,491	9,206
Dance clubs				
ENT	197	209	219	241
Market sector	1,792	1,900	2,013	2,195

In Teeland, the economy is generally growing at about 2% per annum. The restaurant, cafe and bar sectors are all highly fragmented with many small operators. Consequently, a market share of more than 3.0% is considered large as that is comparable to the share of the largest operators in each sector. There are fewer small late night dance club operators and the market leader currently holds a 15.0% market share. There have not been many new developments within the divisions except for a new wine bar format launched by the bars division which has surprised the board by its success.

Divisional performance measurement and remuneration package

Each of the division's performance is measured by economic value-added (EVA™). The divisional managers have a remuneration package that is made up in two equal parts by a salary set according to industry norms and a bonus element which is based on achieving the cost budget numbers set by the company board. The chairman of the board has been examining the consistency of the overall objective of the business, the divisional performance measure and the remuneration packages at divisional level. He has expressed the worry that these are not properly aligned and that this might lead to dysfunctional behaviour by the divisional management.

Required:

(a) Perform an analysis of ENT's business in terms of relative market share and market growth. (6 marks)

(b) Using your answer to (a) and the resulting BCG analysis, evaluate the company's performance. (5 marks)

(c) Critically evaluate this BCG analysis as a performance management system at ENT. (8 marks)

(d) Evaluate the divisional managers' remuneration package in light of the divisional performance system and your BCG analysis. (6 marks)

(Total: 25 marks)

31 PLX REFINERY CO (PILOT 10)

Company information

PLX Refinery Co (PLX) is a large oil refinery business in Kayland. Kayland is a developing country with a large and growing oil exploration and production business which supplies PLX with crude oil. Currently, the refinery has the capacity to process 200,000 barrels of crude oil per day and makes profits of $146m per year. It employs about 2,000 staff and contractors. The staff are paid $60,000 each per year on average (about twice the national average in Kayland). PLX has had a fairly good compliance record in Kayland with only two major fines being levied in the last eight years for safety breaches and river pollution ($1 m each).

Environmental accounting

The government of Kayland has been focussed on delivering rapid economic growth over the last 15 years. However, there are increasing signs that the environment is paying a large price for this growth with public health suffering. There is now a growing environmental pressure group, Green Kayland (GK), which is organising protests against the companies that they see as being the major polluters.

Kayland's government wishes to react to the concerns of the public and the pressure groups. It has requested that companies involved in heavy industry contribute to a general improvement in the treatment of the environment in Kayland.

As a major participant in the oil industry with ties to the nationalised oil exploration company (Kayex), PLX believes it will be strategically important to be at the forefront of the environmental developments. It is working with other companies in the oil industry to improve environmental reporting since there is a belief that this will lead to improved public perception and economic efficiency of the industry. PLX has had a fairly good compliance record in Kayland with only two major fines being levied in the last eight years for safety breaches and river pollution ($1m each).

Management accounting techniques

The existing information systems within PLX focus on financial performance. They support financial reporting obligations and allow monitoring of key performance metrics such as earnings per share and operating margins. Recent publications on environmental accounting have suggested there are a number of techniques (such as activity-based costing (ABC), a lifecycle view and flow cost accounting) that may be relevant in implementing improvements to these systems.

Capital expenditure programme

PLX is considering a major capital expenditure programme to enhance capacity, safety and efficiency at the refinery. This will involve demolishing certain older sections of the refinery and building on newly acquired land adjacent to the site. Overall, the refinery will increase its land area by 20%.

Part of the refinery extension will also manufacture a new plastic, Kayplas. Kayplas is expected to have a limited market life of five years when it will be replaced by Kayplas2. The refinery accounting team have forecast the following data associated with this product and calculated PLX's traditional performance measure of product profit for the new product:

All figures are $m's

	2012	**2013**	**2014**	**2015**	**2016**
Revenue generated	25.0	27.5	30.1	33.2	33.6
Costs					
Production costs	13.8	15.1	16.6	18.3	18.5
Marketing costs	5.0	4.0	3.0	3.0	2.0
Development costs	5.6	3.0	0.0	0.0	0.0
Product profit	0.6	5.4	10.5	11.9	13.1

Subsequently, the following environmental costs have been identified from PLX's general overheads as associated with Kayplas production.

	2012	**2013**	**2014**	**2015**	**2016**
Waste filtration	1.2	1.4	1.5	1.9	2.1
Carbon dioxide exhaust extraction	0.8	0.9	0.9	1.2	1.5

Additionally, other costs associated with closing down and recycling the equipment in Kayplas production are estimated at $18m in 2016.

The board

The board wishes to consider how it can contribute to the oil industry's performance in environmental accounting, how it can implement the changes that this might require and how these changes can benefit the company.

Required:

Write to the board of PLX to:

(a) **Discuss and illustrate four different cost categories that would aid transparency in environmental reporting both internally and externally at PLX. (8 marks)**

(b) **Explain and evaluate how the three management accounting techniques mentioned can assist in managing the environmental and strategic performance of PLX. (9 marks)**

(c) **Evaluate the costing approach used for Kayplas's performance compared to a lifecycle costing approach, performing appropriate calculations. (8 marks)**

(Total: 25 marks)

32 FGH TELECOM (FGH) (DEC 10)

Company information

FGH Telecom (FGH) is one of the largest providers of mobile and fixed line telecommunications in Ostland. The company has recently been reviewing its corporate objectives in the light of its changed business environment. The major new addition to the strategic objectives is under the heading: 'Building a more environmentally friendly business for the future'. It has been recognised that the company needs to make a contribution to ensuring sustainable development in Ostland and reducing its environmental footprint. Consequently, it adopted a goal that, by 2017, it would have reduced its environmental impact by 60% (compared to year 2001).

Business environment

The reasons for the board's concern are that the telecommunications sector is competitive and the economic environment is increasingly harsh with the markets for debt and equities being particularly poor. On environmental issues, the government and public are calling for change from the business community. It appears that increased regulation and legislation will appear to encourage business towards better performance. The board have recognised that there are threats and opportunities from these trends. It wants to ensure that it is monitoring these factors and so it has asked for an analysis of the business environment with suggestions for performance measurement.

Business travel and reduction initiatives

Additionally, the company has a large number of employees working across its network. Therefore, there are large demands for business travel. FGH runs a large fleet of commercial vehicles in order to service its network along with a company car scheme for its managers. The manager in charge of the company's travel budget is reviewing data on carbon dioxide emissions to assess FGH's recent performance.

Recent initiatives within the company to reduce emissions have included:

(a) the introduction in 2010 of a homeworking scheme for employees in order to reduce the amount of commuting to and from their offices and

(b) a drive to increase the use of teleconferencing facilities by employees.

Data on FGH Telecom: Carbon Dioxide emissions (measured in millions of kgs)

	2001 (base year)	**2009**	**2010**
Commercial Fleet Diesel	105.4	77.7	70.1
Commercial Fleet Petrol	11.6	0.4	0.0
Company Car Diesel	15.1	14.5	12.0
Company Car Petrol	10.3	3.8	2.2
Other road travel (Diesel)	0.5	1.6	1.1
Other road travel (Petrol)	3.1	0.5	0.3
Rail travel	9.2	9.6	3.4
Air Travel (short haul)	5.0	4.4	3.1
Air Travel (long haul)	5.1	7.1	5.4
Hire Cars (Diesel)	0.6	1.8	2.9
Hire Cars (Petrol)	6.7	6.1	6.1
Total	172.6	127.5	106.6

Required:

(a) **Perform an analysis of FGH's business environment to identify factors which will affect its environmental strategy. For each of these factors, suggest performance indicators which will allow FGH to monitor its progress. (9 marks)**

(b) **Evaluate the data given on carbon dioxide emissions using suitable indicators. Identify trends from within the data and comment on whether the company's behaviour is consistent with meeting its targets. (12 marks)**

(c) **Suggest further data that the company could collect in order to improve its analysis and explain how this data could be used to measure the effectiveness of the reduction initiatives mentioned. (4 marks)**

(Total: 25 marks)

33 FILM PRODUCTIONS CO (FP) (DEC 10)

Company information

Film Productions Co (FP) is a small international company producing films for cinema release and also for sale on DVD or to television companies. FP deals with all areas of the production from casting, directing and managing the artists to negotiating distribution deals with cinema chains and TV channels. The industry is driven by the tastes of its films' audience, which when accurately predicted can lead to high levels of profitability on a successful film.

The company's stated mission is to 'produce fantastic films that have mass appeal'. The company makes around $200 million of sales each year equally split between a share of cinema takings, DVD sales and TV rights. FP has released 32 films in the past five years. Each film costs an average of $18 million and takes 12 months to produce from initial commissioning through to the final version. Production control is important in order to hit certain key holiday periods for releasing films at the cinema or on DVD.

The company's films have been moderately successful in winning industry awards although FP has never won any major award. Its aims have been primarily commercial with artistic considerations secondary.

The CEO is planning a report to the board of Film Productions and has asked you to help by drafting certain sections of this report.

Objectives, critical success factors (CSFs) and performance indicators

The company uses a top-down approach to strategy development with objectives leading to CSFs which must then be measured using performance indicators. Currently, the company has identified a number of critical success factors. The two most important of these are viewed as:

(i) improve audience satisfaction

(ii) strengthen profitability in operations

At the request of the board, the chief executive officer (CEO) has been reviewing this system in particular the role of CSFs. Generally, the CEO is worried that the ones chosen so far fail to capture all the factors affecting the business and wants to understand all possible sources for CSFs and what it means to categorise them into monitoring and building factors.

Performance measurement systems

These CSFs will need to be measured and there must be systems in place to perform that role. The existing information system of the company is based on a fairly basic accounting package.

However, the CEO has been considering greater investment in these systems and making more use of the company's website in both driving forward the business' links to its audience and in collecting data on them.

Required:

(a) **Identify information that FP could use to set its CSFs and explain how it could be used giving two examples that would be appropriate to FP. (6 marks)**

(b) **For each of the two critical success factors given in the question, identify two performance indicators (PIs) that could support measurement of their achievement and explain why each PI is relevant to the CSF. (10 marks)**

(c) **Discuss the implications of your chosen PIs for the design and use of the company's website, its management information system and its executive information system. (9 marks)**

(Total: 25 marks)

34 DALDORN (SEPT/DEC 19) (AMENDED)

Exhibit 1 – Company information

Daldorn is a manufacturer of heavy steel items. It is funded by a venture capitalist organisation (VC). Following a period of poor performance, the VC has expressed concern that Daldorn's board members are focusing too much on their own interests, while neglecting to adequately measure and manage company performance in respect of other stakeholder groups.

The company has experienced severe cash flow difficulties due to financial losses made on the sale of several new products. These difficulties have been attributed to poor pricing decisions, which were the responsibility of the board and have resulted in many employees losing their jobs.

Exhibit 2 – Key stakeholder groups

The VC has identified three key stakeholder groups at Daldorn:

The board

The VC is concerned that due to the past losses made on several new products, the board has become too cautious in their attitude towards potential new projects and, in particular, to the pricing of new products. Given the importance of the board to the success of Daldorn, the VC has recently implemented a new bonus scheme. This is an attempt by the VC to revise the board's appetite for risk and encourage them to take more risks, for example, in deciding on the price of new products. Board members will now receive a very large annual performance-related bonus for Daldorn's achievement of challenging targets set on the financial performance measure of return on capital employed (ROCE).

Employees

The manufacturing process at Daldorn does not require employees to have a high level of skill and so most of the manufacturing employees are relatively low skilled. Other employees in other departments have roles which can require specific skills and qualifications. There is a high level of unemployment in the region where Daldorn is based.

Government and regulators

Daldorn operates in a strict regulatory environment. Daldorn has a good record of compliance, but recently its own scientists have discovered high concentrations of a toxic pollutant, which is a waste product from its own manufacturing processes, in the soil near to its factory.

The VC has asked for your advice on whether Daldorn's existing measures shown in Appendix 1 adequately measure the company's performance in managing the concerns of each of these three key stakeholder groups. You may justify the use of alternative measures, but the VC wants only one measure for each stakeholder group and is not concerned about the potential conflict between measures at this stage. As part of this work, the VC expects you to briefly comment on the power and interest of the three stakeholder groups.

Exhibit 3 – Pricing decision

Daldorn is about to launch a new product and needs to determine an appropriate price to charge. The variable cost of each product is uncertain and, hence, there are three possibilities for each demand level. The total contribution of the products at the three possible anticipated levels of demand are shown in Appendix 2.

You have been asked to evaluate which price the board would choose for the new product based on the board's revised attitude to risk and briefly comment on the drawbacks of the decision rule used.

Exhibit 4 – Investment projects

Two new mutually exclusive manufacturing projects, which are totally unconnected to Daldorn, have become available for the VC to invest in. The VC has undertaken many similar investments before and is an almost entirely risk neutral investor.

Two important exogenous (external) variables affecting the net present value (NPV) of the new projects, A and B, are the worldwide demand for steel products and the level of tariffs applied to the import of a key raw material. The probabilities of these two variables are independent. The VC has estimated the probabilities of there being low, medium or high levels of these two variables in Appendix 3, together with an estimate of the expected NPV for project A for each level of demand and tariff and an estimated of the overall expected NPV for project A. An analyst has already calculated that the overall expected value of project B is $1,347 million.

As a final requirement, you have been asked to advise the VC which of the two new investment projects it should undertake, including an evaluation of the appropriateness of the numerical technique used.

Required:

It is now 1 September 20X5.

Respond to the request for work on the following areas:

(a) **assessment of the performance measures in relation to the stakeholder groups as required by the venture capitalist organisation (VC)** **(9 marks)**

(b) **the price of the new product and the drawbacks of the decision rule used and** **(5 marks)**

(c) **the investment project to undertake and the appropriateness of the numerical technique used.** **(6 marks)**

Professional marks will be awarded for the demonstration of skill in analysis and evaluation, scepticism and commercial acumen in your answer. **(5 marks)**

(Total: 25 marks)

Exhibit 5 – Appendix 1

Stakeholder	**Measure**
Board	Return on capital employed
Employees	Training costs
Government/regulators	No measure specified

Exhibit 6 - Appendix 2

Demand, selling price and variable cost for the new product

Demand*	**Unit selling price**	**Unit variable cost**	**Unit contribution**	**Total contribution**
	$000	$000	$000	$000
1,200	75	37	38	45,600
1,200	75	40	35	42,000
1,200	75	50	25	30,000
950	95	37	58	55,100
950	95	40	55	52,250
950	95	50	45	42,750
500	140	37	103	51,500
500	140	40	100	50,000
500	140	50	90	45,000

* Total demand for the whole of the product's anticipated two-year life.

Exhibit 7 – Appendix 3

Project A – Expected NPV ($ million) for each possible demand level and tariff level combination

		Tariff level		
		High	**Medium**	**Low**
	Low	1,200	1,700	1,850
Demand level	Medium	1,000	1,500	1,600
	High	900	1,000	1,100

Project A – Joint probabilities for each possible demand level and tariff level combination

			Tariff level		
			High	**Medium**	**Low**
			0.20	0.50	0.30
	Low	0.20	0.04	0.10	0.06
Demand level	Medium	0.50	0.10	0.25	0.15
	High	0.30	0.06	0.15	0.09

Project A – Overall expected NPV calculation

		Tariff			
		High	**Med**	**Low**	**Total**
Demand	**Low**	48	170	111	329
		(1,200 × 0.04)	(1,700 × 0.10)	(1,850 × 0.06)	
	Med	100	375	240	715
		(1,000 × 0.10)	(1,500 × 0.25)	(1,600 × 0.15)	
	High	54	150	99	303
		(900 × 0.06)	(1,000 × 0.15)	(1,100 × 0.09)	
	Total	202	695	450	1,347

*Assuming the probabilities of the two variables are independent.

Notes

1 The standard deviation of the outcomes for project A has been correctly calculated to be 103 and the standard deviation of the outcomes for project B has been correctly calculated to be 106.

2 An analyst has already calculated that the overall expected value of project B is $1,347 million.

35 SWEET CICELY (SC) (SEPT/DEC 17) (AMENDED)

Exhibit 1 – Company background

Sweet Cicely (SC) manufactures sweets and confectionery and has delivered stable but modest increases to the shareholder wealth for many years. Following a change in ownership, the new shareholders are keen to increase the long-term performance of the business and are prepared to accept a high level of risk to achieve this.

SC is considering setting up a factory to manufacture chocolate bars. There are three options (1, 2 and 3) for the size and output capacity of the new chocolate factory. SC must choose a size most suited to the expected demand for its products.

Exhibit 2 – External factors

As well as the impact of the quality, branding and pricing of its products, demand for SC chocolate bars will be influenced by external factors such as consumer tastes for chocolate over other sweets, and even the suggested health benefits of certain types of chocolate.

A high-cost ingredient in chocolate bars is cocoa, a commodity traded on international markets. The market price of cocoa fluctuates with worldwide demand. Due to economic growth, chocolate consumption is rising in many countries, where it was once considered a luxury. In some countries, however, governments are considering introducing additional taxes on products containing sugar in order to reduce the consumption of chocolate and confectionery products. Being derived from an agricultural crop, the availability and price of cocoa is also influenced by climatic conditions, soil erosion, and disease. Conflicts and political instability in cocoa growing regions can also restrict its availability. Recent technological advances in the production of cocoa, such as the use of genetically modified crops, promise higher yields from cocoa plants in the near future.

The CEO has asked you to advise SC why decisions, such as what size of chocolate factory to build, must include consideration of risk and uncertainty, and evaluate the use of PEST analysis in managing the risk and uncertainty surrounding the project.

Exhibit 3 – Three options for new chocolate factory

SC will need to choose one of the three options for the new chocolate factory. One board member said: 'The board proposed expanding into cake manufacturing several years ago. With hindsight, our planning on that proposal was poor. We sold only slightly fewer cakes than expected, but hadn't realised how sensitive our operating profit would be to a small change in demand. The previous shareholders thought problems in the cake business would put their dividends at risk, so SC stopped manufacturing cakes, barely a year after it started. The board does not want to repeat these mistakes. We want to minimise the opportunity cost of making the wrong decision about the size of the new chocolate factory.'

Appendix 1 shows the net present values for the three options discounted at SC's current cost of capital and also includes a regret table showing the maximum regret for each option. The CEO has asked you to use the data in Appendix 1 to explain which of the three options for the new chocolate factory would be preferred by the board and the new shareholders according to their respective risk appetites.

Appendix 2 shows the expected operating profit generated by the three options in the first year of the project, according to the market price of cocoa, and assuming an annual demand of 70 million chocolate bars. It also shows the overall expected value for each option. Finally, the CEO has asked you to use the data in Appendix 2 to recommend which of the three options for the new chocolate factory a risk neutral investor would choose, and explain any problems with the approach used to make the choice.

Required:

It is now 1 September 20X5.

Respond to the CEO of Sweet Cicely's request for work on the following areas:

(a) consideration of risk and uncertainty and the use of PEST **(12 marks)**

(b) option for the new factory preferred by the board and the new shareholders **(5 marks)**

(c) option for the new factory preferred by a risk neutral investor and the problems of the approach used **(5 marks)**

Professional marks will be awarded for the demonstration of skill in analysis and evaluation, scepticism and commercial acumen in your answer. **(5 marks)**

(Total: 25 marks)

Exhibit 4 – Appendix 1

Net present values for the three options discounted at SC's current cost of capital ($m)

	Option 1	Option 2	Option 3
Annual demand for chocolate bars			
50 million	4.0	(8.0)	(32.0)
60 million	6.0	16.0	(24.0)
70 million	6.0	16.0	17.0

Regret table

	Option 1	Option 2	Option 3
50 million	0	(12.0)	(36.0)
60 million	(10.0)	0	(40.0)
70 million	(11.0)	(1.0)	0.0
Maximum regret	**(11.0)**	**(12.0)**	**(40.0)**

Exhibit 5 – Appendix 2: Expected value calculation

Expected operating profit generated by the three options in the first year of the project, assuming an annual demand of 70 million chocolate bars ($m)

Probability	Market price of cocoa ($ per ton)	Option 1	Option 2	Option 3
0.3	2,500	3.0	5.0	7.0
0.4	3,000	0.5	2.0	1.5
0.3	3,500	(2.0)	(1.0)	(2.0)

Expected values of each option

Option 1 – (0.3 × 3.0) + (0.4 × 0.5) + (0.3 × –2.0) = $0.5m

Option 2 – (0.3 × 5.0) + (0.4 × 2.0) + (0.3 × –1.0) = $2.0m

Option 3 – (0.3 × 7.0) + (0.4 × 1.5) + (0.5 × –2.0) = $2.1m

36 TURING (JUN 14) (AMENDED)

Exhibit 1 – Company information

Turing Aerodynamics (Turing) has formed a joint venture (JV) with Riemann Generators (Riemann) in order to design and manufacture high-performance wind turbines which generate electricity. The joint venture is called TandR with each party owning 50%. Turing will design and build the pylons, housing and turbine blades while Riemann will supply the generators to be fitted inside the housing.

Exhibit 2 – Turing

Turing is a medium sized firm known for its blade design skills. It is owned by three venture capital firms (VCs) (each holding 30% of the shares), with the remaining 10% being given to management to motivate them. The VCs each have a large portfolio of business investments and accept that some of these investments may fail provided that some of their investments show large gains. Management is an ambitious group who enjoys the business and technical challenges of introducing new products.

Exhibit 3 – Riemann

On the other hand, Riemann is a large, family-owned company working in the highly competitive electricity generator sector. The shareholders of Riemann see the business as mature and want it to offer a stable, long-term return on capital. However, recently, Riemann had to seek emergency refinancing (debt and equity) due to its thin profit margins and tough competition, both of which are forecast to continue. As a result, Riemann's shareholders and management are concerned for the survival of the business and see TandR as a way to generate some additional cash flow. Unlike at Turing, the management of Riemann does not own significant shareholdings in the company which has preferred to pay fixed salaries.

Exhibit 4 – New wind turbine design

TandR is run by a group of managers made up from each of the JV partners. They are currently faced with a decision about the design of the product. There are three design choices depending on the power which the wind turbines can generate (measured in megawatts [MW]):

Design type	**Description**
8 MW	a large 8 MW unit
3 MW	a 3 MW unit
1 MW	a basic 1 MW unit

The engineering for the 1 MW and 3 MW units is well understood and so design is much simpler than for the 8 MW unit which would be world leading if completed.

The demand for the different types of units will depend on government subsidies of the electricity price charged by the electricity generating companies who will buy the wind turbines and the planning regulations for building such large structures. It is believed that there will be orders for either 1,000 or 1,500 or 2,000 units but there is no clear picture yet of which demand level is more likely than the others. Appendix 1 shows the estimated costs and prices for the units together with a calculation of the expected profit for the three designs for each level of demand.

The JV managers have asked you to complete a number of tasks. Firstly, they would like you to assess the risk appetites of the two firms in the joint venture and provide a justified recommendation for each firm of an appropriate method of decision-making under uncertainty to assess the different types of wind turbines. In addition, they have asked you to evaluate the choice of turbine design types using your recommended methods. Secondly, the JV managers have asked you to discuss the problems encountered in managing performance in a joint venture such as TandR.

Required:

It is now 1 September 20X5.

Respond to the JV managers' request for work on the following areas:

(a) risk appetite, method of decision making and choice of turbine design and **(12 marks)**

(b) problems in managing joint venture performance. **(8 marks)**

Professional marks will be awarded for the demonstration of skill in analysis and evaluation and commercial acumen in your answer. **(5 marks)**

(Total: 25 marks)

Exhibit 5 – Appendix 1

The estimated costs and prices for the units are:

Type	**Variable cost per unit**	**Fixed costs**	**Price per unit**
	$m	$m	$m
8 MW	10.4	7,500.0	20.8
3 MW	4.8	820.0	9.6
1 MW	1.15	360.0	4.6

Demand	**1,000**	**1,500**	**2,000**
Variable cost			
8 MW	10,400	15,600	20,800
3 MW	4,800	7,200	9,600
1 MW	1,150	1,725	2,300
Total cost			
8 MW	17,900	23,100	28,300
3 MW	5,620	8,020	10,420
1 MW	1,510	2,085	2,660
Revenue			
8 MW	20,800	31,200	41,600
3 MW	9,600	14,400	19,200
1 MW	4,600	6,900	9,200
Profit			
8 MW	2,900	8,100	13,300
3 MW	3,980	6,380	8,780
1 MW	3,090	4,815	6,540

Notes:

1 The fixed costs cover the initial design, development and testing of the units.

2 The costs and prices are in real terms with the 8 MW unit likely to take two more years to develop than the others.

B – PERFORMANCE MANAGEMENT INFORMATION SYSTEMS AND DEVELOPMENTS IN TECHNOLOGY

37 LUVIJ (MAR/JUN 18) (AMENDED)

Exhibit 1 – Background information

Luvij manufactures high quality, luxury women's footwear. It sells its products on its own website and also to small independent retailers.

Exhibit 2 – Data collection and use

In order to monitor performance and aid decision-making, Luvij collects sales data on all of its footwear ranges and feedback on its designs from customers and retailers. In addition, to ensure that prices remain competitive, Luvij has a team of staff to monitor the prices of similar products on competitors' websites and to identify design trends in the market, which change frequently, and from season to season. Generating new footwear designs consistent with changing market trends is a critical success factor for Luvij. The large volume of data collected is entered into a complex spreadsheet by one data entry clerk.

Luvij operates a functional structure with different departments for sales, production, purchasing and design. The spreadsheet is sent by email to the senior manager of each of these departments at the end of each quarter. The senior manager for the sales, production and buying departments are expected to generate the relevant sales, production and purchasing forecasts by analysing information contained in the spreadsheet. The senior manager of the design department uses the information to generate new footwear designs consistent with market trends.

One recently appointed board member at Luvij has commented, 'I believe that the external information on market trends and competitors' prices compiled in the quarterly spreadsheet is of limited usefulness as I have heard complaints from managers that they have difficulty understanding the large volume of data given to them, and that they often receive this too late. The company I worked for in my previous job used a unified corporate database to share information in real time across all parts of the business. A similar unified corporate database may be useful for Luvij'.

The CEO has asked you, a management consultant to explain the factors which might limit the usefulness of the external information currently used by Luvij, and evaluate how the use of a unified corporate database could help to overcome these limitations.

Exhibit 3 – Potential joint venture

Luvij has a strategic objective to become the market leader in the sale of high quality, children's footwear to small independent footwear retailers. It has already invested heavily in market research and developing innovative designs. To reduce the risks of not achieving this strategic objective, for example, by having insufficient capacity to produce a larger range of footwear styles, the board is considering entering into a joint venture with Shirville.

Shirville is a large manufacturer of exclusively children's footwear. Its advanced manufacturing machinery and production techniques mean that it can produce the high volumes required to supply supermarkets and chain stores* found on the main streets of most towns and cities. Shirville's objective for the joint venture is to utilise spare production capacity it has in a factory which it holds on a lease which expires in three years.

The recently appointed board member also commented, 'I am concerned about the potential problems of measuring and managing the performance of the joint venture with Shirville. The fact that the two businesses have different objectives is just one example of why these problems may occur, though there will also be other reasons.'

The CEO has asked you to advise on the potential problems with the measurement and management of the performance of the joint venture with Shirville.

*Chain stores are large retailers with multiple stores based in different locations.

Required:

It is now 1 September 20X5.

Respond to the CEO's request for work on the following areas:

(a) **the usefulness of the external information and use of a unified corporate database and** **(10 marks)**

(b) **the joint venture.** **(10 marks)**

Professional marks will be awarded for the demonstration of skill in analysis and evaluation, scepticism and commercial acumen in your answer. **(5 marks)**

(Total: 25 marks)

38 NELSON, JODY AND NIGEL (NJN) (MAR/JUN 17)

Background information

Nelson, Jody and Nigel (NJN) operates a warehouse and distribution centre, storing and distributing 5,000 product lines on behalf of its client, an overseas sports equipment manufacturer.

Existing processes and warehouse information system

NJN receives goods in shipping containers, which should include a packing list of the items they contain. Sometimes, packing lists are lost in transit and the manufacturer is asked for duplicates. Packing lists are manually input into NJN's warehouse information system (WIS) in batches, usually within 48 hours of the goods being received. Goods are first unpacked into a sorting area, and later moved to wherever there is available warehouse space once the packing list has been input. The WIS records the location within the warehouse where each item is located. The client's customers, who are retail stores, place orders by email, and do not currently have access to real-time inventory levels in NJN's warehouse.

Each morning picking lists are printed in the warehouse office. These lists show the quantities of items to be picked and the items' 12 digit product codes. Staff use these codes to retrieve items from the warehouse locations for despatch to retailers. In 8% of picking lists, at least one item is not in the location or does not have the quantity specified by the WIS. As a result, the item is not despatched, or the wrong item is picked. A small team investigates these discrepancies, using special reports which the warehouse manager extracts from the WIS. The team manually reconciles quantities of missing items in the warehouse to the sports equipment manufacturer's own records of the items which should be in inventory. If missing items cannot be found, the customer is informed via an email that they are unavailable.

The sports equipment manufacturer has a service level agreement with NJN, covering the accuracy of picking and the proportion of customers' orders successfully fulfilled. NJN's performance on these has deteriorated, especially when there is increased seasonal demand for certain products. At these times staff are under increased pressure to pick items quickly, and so picking accuracy deteriorates and absenteeism increases. There have also been accidents where goods have not been safely placed or safely picked from warehouse locations at busy times. These accidents have resulted in minor injuries to some employees.

The sports equipment manufacturer has threatened to end NJN's contract if performance does not improve. In response, NJN has recruited more staff to investigate discrepancies between items physically in warehouse locations, and those shown on the WIS at busy periods. It has also begun a series of cyclical inventory counts where every product line is counted every month to correct the quantities and locations shown on the WIS. NJN has rented an additional nearby warehouse in which to sort incoming items before they are put away.

Application of 'lean' principles

NJN has hired a management consultant who is an expert in 'lean' principles and the application of these to management information systems. She believes that the WIS is wasteful, not adding value to the business or to its customers, and has suggested that NJN would benefit from the application of lean principles to this system.

She has suggested three proposals:

- that NJN reorganise the warehouse by storing high volume items close to the despatch area,
- shut down the additional warehouse, and
- discontinue the cyclical inventory counts.

5Ss

To help with the adoption of lean principles in the warehouse reorganisation, the management consultant recommends NJN apply the '5Ss'* of lean principles, and she has suggested performance metrics which can be used to evaluate NJN's progress towards adopting these (Appendix 1).

*Structurise, Systemise, Sanitise, Standardise, Self-discipline.

Required:

(a) Assess whether NJN's existing warehouse information system (WIS) is effective in reducing waste and adding value to NJN's workflow. (10 marks)

(b) Advise whether the three proposals suggested by the management consultant will help to eliminate the different types of waste identified under lean principles. (6 marks)

(c) Evaluate whether the application of each of the 5Ss following the warehouse reorganisation at NJN is adequately measured by the performance metrics in Appendix 1. (9 marks)

(Total: 25 marks)

Appendix 1 – Performance measures for 5Ss relating to warehouse reorganisation

1 Warehouse manager's daily assessment of the tidiness of the warehouse on a scale of 1–10.

2 The proportion of inventory not stored in order of its alphabetical description with products with names beginning with 'A' nearest the despatch area and 'Z' furthest away.

3 The number of accidents caused by goods being incorrectly stored or picked.

39 INTEGRATED REPORTING

TRE is a listed high street retailer that sells a range of goods such as food, drink, clothing, electrical goods, CDs, DVS and garden equipment.

At a recent board meeting the topic of Integrated Reporting (IR) was raised with very mixed views in the discussion.

The Marketing Director argued that IR was simply a mixture of the sustainability report and the financial report into a single communication intended mainly for investors. As such it had very little new to offer and was just another compliance requirement.

The Finance Director replied that, in his view, IR would give a greater emphasis on the different types of 'capital' within the firm and would assist in more focussed performance management.

Required:

(a) **Briefly explain what is meant by an 'Integrated Report' and comment on the views of the Marketing Director. (5 marks)**

(b) **Identify and describe the SIX different types of 'capital' described within the IR Framework. (9 marks)**

(c) **Explain FOUR objectives of integrated reporting. (6 marks)**

(d) **Explain how an emphasis on the six types of capital above could result in more focussed performance management. (5 marks)**

(Total: 25 marks)

Tutorial note

This is not a past exam question but is a good test of your knowledge of Integrated Reporting. An exam question on this area would contain a lengthier scenario and this scenario would have to be used more in your answer discussion.

40 BLUEFIN SCHOOL (DEC 11) (AMENDED)

Exhibit 1 – Background information

Bluefin School (Bluefin) is a school for 12 to 17-year-old pupils. It currently has 1,000 pupils attending drawn from its local area. The school is run by an executive group comprising the head of school and two deputy head teachers. This group reports to a board of governors who are part-time and selected from the local community and parents. The school is wholly funded by the government.

The school's ethos is 'to promote learning, citizenship and self-confidence among the pupils. This is developed from a consensus, led by the board of governors and the head of school and informed by the views of the pupils' parents.'

Exhibit 2 – Information systems and information provision

The school information systems are highly decentralised. Each department keeps its own records on a stand-alone PC using basic word processing and spreadsheet packages. The school's administrative department has a small network in its own offices with compatible applications and also a database and financial recording and reporting package for use in schools (provided by the government).

The school is broken down into 11 academic departments such as mathematics, science and history. Each department head must prepare information for reporting to the board by inputting and processing the data. They obtain some help from an administrator who visits each department to spend a few hours per week helping in the recording and preparation of the departmental information. The department heads have different approaches to reporting their performance, with some using average marks in the annual exams for each class and some using pass rates of the annual exams. Some department heads present graphs of their data while most use tables of figures.

The information is passed from each department to the school administration office on a memory stick (USB flash drive). The school administration office prints out the information for each department and adds it to a financial report creating a governors' pack of usually about 13 pages for the annual review board meeting. The financial report is a detailed income and expenditure statement for the period under review (usually a two page print-out from the reporting package). An example of one of the 11 departments' report is given in Appendix 1. The board of governors meets every quarter and reviews the governors' pack once a year.

The board are concerned that there are a number of problems with the control and security of some of the data and that the information that they are receiving is not meeting their needs. They have asked you to complete a number of tasks to address these concerns. Firstly, with reference to the current situation at Bluefin School, you have been asked to discuss the controls and security procedures that are necessary for management information. Secondly, using the limited information available, you should evaluate the usefulness of the pack that is provided to the board of governors.

Exhibit 3 – Improvements to information systems

It has been suggested that the school should consider improving its information systems by installing a network across the school to link the departmental computers and the administration department. A single database would be created to store all the performance information. The computers would then be linked to the internet in order to facilitate data transfer to other schools in the region and to the government. As a final requirement, the board have asked you to evaluate the improvements suggested to the information systems at Bluefin.

Required:

It is now 1 September 20X5.

Respond to the board's request for work on the following areas:

(a) the controls and security procedures necessary for management information **(9 marks)**

(b) the usefulness of the pack provided to the board of governors and **(6 marks)**

(c) the improvements suggested to the information systems. **(5 marks)**

Professional marks will be awarded for the demonstration of skill in analysis and evaluation, scepticism and commercial acumen in your answer. **(5 marks)**

(Total: 25 marks)

Exhibit 4 – Appendix 1: Bluefin School: Mathematics department average marks for year 20X4/20X4

	Class	Current year	Previous year
		%	%
Year 1	A	63	59
	B	60	61
	C	51	55
	D	47	44
Year 2	A	61	70
	B	58	62
	C	49	47
	D	45	43
Year 3	A	67	67
	B	61	57
	C	50	50
	D	42	41
Year 4	A	62	58
	B	59	59
	C	50	54
	D	46	47
Year 5	A	57	58
	B	51	49
	C	47	48
Year 6		54	53

Notes:

Each year contains pupils of the same age.

Annual national exams are set in years 4, 5 and 6.

Each year group is divided into different classes in order to ensure that classes do not exceed 35 pupils. (Not all pupils take every subject each year.)

Average marks are for the annual examinations.

41 QUARK HEALTHCARE (DEC 13)

Background information

Quark Healthcare (Quark) runs a number of large hospitals which provide general medical care for the people of Veeland. Veeland is an advanced economy and healthcare is considered to be a high skill, high technology and high status industry. It is compulsory for the people of Veeland to purchase health insurance and then the insurance companies reimburse the healthcare providers for services delivered. The insurance companies audit the healthcare providers and grade them for value for money. As there are a number of hospital chains (such as Quark), the insurers will encourage their insured customers to use those which are most efficient. The ultimate sanction for a healthcare provider is for an insurance company to remove them from the list of acceptable providers.

Inventory systems and non-current asset register

Quark has large amounts of capital tied up in expensive medical equipment and a drug inventory. The existing systems for accounting for these items are traditional ones aimed at avoiding theft and obsolescence. Quark has an inventory system which requires regular (weekly) physical checks of the drugs in inventory in order to update it. It is important that the right drugs must be in easily accessible stores (located throughout the hospital) in order to act quickly in case of a medical emergency. Also, the accounting staff at Quark maintain a non-current asset register (NCAR) which logs the location of all major assets including medical equipment. The problem with the non-current asset register is that it is often out-of-date as doctors will take equipment in time of emergency and not properly log its new location. This often leads to equipment lying unused in one area of the hospital while being searched for in another area, to the detriment of patient care.

Radio frequency identification devices (RFID)

Quark has recently instituted a tagging project where RFID will be attached to the most valuable pieces of equipment used in treatment and also to batches of high-value drugs. The hospitals are fitted with WiFi networks which can pick up the RFID signal so that the RFID tags will be detectable throughout a hospital. The tags will identify the object which they are attached to by a unique identification number and will give its location. The identifier number will link to the inventory system which will identify the product, the quantity initially delivered in that batch and the date of delivery. The RFID information will be accessible through the computer terminals throughout the hospitals.

The chief financial officer (CFO) of Quark has asked you to advise him on the impact of this new system on performance management at Quark. He has suggested that you look at the costs and benefits which will be associated with producing the information from the RFID system, the impact of the nature of the information supplied, the changes to performance management reporting and how the new information could be used for improved control at the hospital.

Lean systems

The CFO is keen to be seen to be at the forefront of accounting and management developments and has been reading about cost control techniques. Recently, he has heard about 'lean' systems, so wants to know how the RFID system and its impact on the hospital fit with this concept.

Medical staff behaviour

Given the importance of the medical staff in running the hospital, the CFO also wants to know how their behaviour will be affected by the control information from the RFID system. There is a very strict social order among these staff (in increasing order of skills: nurses, general doctors and specialist doctors) which regularly causes friction when one group feels it is not given its due status. For example, recently, the general doctors agreed to a new method for nurses to record drugs administered to patients but this new system has not been fully implemented due to complaints by the nurses and specialist doctors who were not consulted on the change.

Required:

(a) **Assess the impact of the radio-frequency identification devices (RFID) system on the performance management at Quark as suggested by the CFO. (12 marks)**

(b) **Evaluate whether the overall management of the hospital can be considered to be 'leaner' as a result of the RFID information system. (7 marks)**

(c) **Evaluate how the medical staff's attitudes will influence the design and implementation of the RFID system and how it might be used to promote responsibility and accountability at the hospital. (6 marks)**

(Total: 25 marks)

42 ALBACORE (PILOT 10)

Company information

Albacore Chess Stores (Albacore) is a chain of twelve shops specialising in selling items associated with the game of chess: boards, pieces, clocks, software and books. Three years ago, the company was the subject of a venture capital buyout from a larger group. A new senior management team was put in place after the buyout. They have the aim of running the business in order to maximise profits.

Performance management

The Chief Financial Officer (CFO) along with the other members of senior management sets the annual budget and uses a standard costing approach with variance analysis in order to control individual shop performance. The head office handles all capital purchases and brand marketing. All inventory purchasing is done centrally and the shop opening times are set as standard across the company. As an illustration of senior management attitude, the CFO had set the budget for 2011 staff costs at $7 per hour for part-time staff and this was rigorously observed in the period.

Each shop is run by a manager who reports their financial results to the operational director at head office. The shop managers recruit and manage the staffing of their shop. They have some autonomy in setting prices locally and have been given authority to vary prices by up to 10% from a master list produced by the CFO. They also have a local marketing budget agreed each year by the shop's manager and the marketing director as part of the annual appraisal process.

Shop managers' performance appraisal and reward system

The shop managers have approached the Chairman of Albacore to complain about the way that they are managed and their remuneration. They feel that their efforts are unrecognised by senior management. One manager commented 'I have had a successful year in hard economic circumstances. I have run a number of promotions in the shop that have been well received by the customers. However, the budgets that are set are impossible to achieve and as a result I have not been paid any bonus although I feel that I have done everything in my power to bring in good profits.'

The shop managers at Albacore are paid a basic salary of $27,000 with bonuses of up to 30% of basic salary dependent on two factors: performance above budget and the operational director's assessment of the manager's performance. The budget for the next year is prepared by the CFO and presented by the operational director at the shop manager's annual appraisal.

Chairman's request

The Chairman has come to you to ask if you can consider the system of performance assessment for the shop managers and give an independent perspective on the reward systems at Albacore. She has heard of variance analysis but is unsure as what would be relevant in this situation. She has provided the following illustrative branch report from the previous year for one shop:

Albacore Chess Stores

Tunny Branch Year to Sept 2011

		Budget	**Actual**	**Variance**
		$	$	$
Sales		266,000	237,100	–28,900
Cost of sales		106,400	94,840	11,560
Gross profit		159,600	142,260	–17,340
Marketing		12,000	11,500	500
Staff costs	Manager	27,000	27,000	0
	Part-time staff	38,000	34,000	4,000
Property costs		26,600	26,600	0
Shop profit		56,000	43,160	–12,840

Notes:

Property costs includes heating, lighting and rental.

Positive variances are favourable.

End of report

Tunny Branch – shop manager's performance appraisal

The manager of this shop commented at the appraisal meeting that she felt that the assessment was unfair since her failure to make budget was due to general economic conditions. The industry as a whole saw a 12% fall in revenues during the period and the budget for the period was set to be the same as the previous period. She was not paid a bonus for the period.

Required:

(a) Evaluate the suitability of the existing branch report as a means of assessing the shop manager's performance and draft an improved branch report with justifications for changes. (13 marks)

(b) Analyse the performance management style and evaluate the performance appraisal system at Albacore. Suggest suitable improvements to its reward system for the shop managers. (12 marks)

(Total: 25 marks)

C – STRATEGIC PERFORMANCE MEASUREMENT

43 CHICORY (SEPT/DEC 17) (AMENDED)

Exhibit 1 – Company information

Chicory operates a chain of depots in Deeland, supplying and fitting tyres and other vehicle parts to lorries, buses and agricultural vehicles. Chicory's objective is to maximise shareholder wealth. Due to a slowdown in the Deeland economy, Chicory's recent performance has been weak. An unsuccessful acquisition has also caused cash flow problems and a write-off of goodwill of $24.7m in the year to 30 June 20X5.

The chief executive officer (CEO) of Chicory has given you some tasks.

Exhibit 2 – Benchmarking exercise

The board has commissioned a benchmarking exercise to help improve Chicory's performance. This exercise will involve comparison of a range of financial and other operational performance indicators against Fennel, a similar business in Veeland. Fennel has agreed to share some recently available performance data with Chicory as they operate in different countries. The reason Fennel was chosen as a benchmark is that as well as supplying and fitting tyres and parts to heavy vehicles, a large part of Fennel's business involves supplying electricity to charging points to recharge electric cars. Fennel installs and operates the charging points in public places, and users pay Fennel for the electricity they use. The board of Chicory intends to follow a similar business model as the use of electric cars is increasing in Deeland.

The Veeland economy is growing strongly. Electric car use there has increased rapidly in the last two years, encouraged by tax incentives for businesses, like Fennel, to install and operate charging points. The Veeland government has also underwritten loans taken out by businesses to finance this technology, which has enabled Fennel to borrow funds for the significant capital investment required. The cost of components used in the charging points is falling rapidly. Capitalisation of development costs related to this technology is permitted in Veeland, but not in Deeland. In 20X3, Fennel invested heavily in IT systems which significantly improved performance by increasing the availability of parts in its depots, and reducing inventories.

Exhibit 3 – ROCE and EBITDA

Chicory uses return on average capital employed (ROCE) as its main financial performance indicator, and this is to be benchmarked against Fennel. One board member suggested that, though it may have some disadvantages, EBITDA (earnings before interest, tax, depreciation and amortisation) could have advantages as a performance measure over the existing measure, and should also be included in the benchmarking exercise.

You have been given the most recently available financial data for both businesses in Appendix 1, with the data for Fennel being converted into $ from its home currency.

The CEO has asked you to evaluate the relative financial performance of Chicory against Fennel using the two financial performance measures of ROCE and EBITDA identified in the benchmarking exercise. They have also asked you to evaluate the use of each of these as performance measures in this situation.

Exhibit 4 – Benchmarking problems

Finally, the CEO has asked you to advise Chicory on the problems of using the benchmarking exercise with Fennel as a way to improve performance.

Required:

It is now 1 September 20X5.

Respond to the CEO's request for work on the following areas:

(a) The relative financial performance using ROCE and EBITDA and the use of these performance measures.

(i) ROCE (6 marks)

(ii) EBITDA (7 marks)

(b) Benchmarking problems (7 marks)

Professional marks will be awarded for the demonstration of skill in analysis and evaluation, scepticism and commercial acumen in your answer. **(5 marks)**

(Total: 25 marks)

Exhibit 5 – Appendix 1

Benchmark data ($m)

Extract from statement of financial position

	30 June 20X5	**31 December 20X3**
End of year	**Chicory**	**Fennel**[1]
Total assets	140.0	296.0
Current liabilities	(81.0)	(120.0)
Beginning of year[1]	**Chicory**	**Fennel**
Total assets	138.0	290.0
Current liabilities	(60.0)	(120.0)

Income statement

	30 June 20X5	**31 December 20X3**
	Chicory	**Fennel**
Revenue	175.1	350.0
Cost of sales	(130.1)	(299.0)
Gross profit	45.0	51.0
Administrative expenses	(11.0)	(25.0)
Write off of goodwill	(24.7)	
Operating profit[2]	9.3	26.0
Interest payable	(1.8)	(8.0)
Profit before tax	7.5	18.0
Tax	(3.0)	(1.0)
Net profit	4.5	17.0

Notes:

1 $6m of new capital was introduced into Fennel on 31 March 20X3. Normally, new net investment is spread evenly over the year.

2 Operating profit is after charging depreciation of non-current assets of $18m in Chicory, and $25m in Fennel.

44 TOSEMARY AND RHYME HOSPITAL (TRH) (SEPT/DEC 17) (AMENDED)

Exhibit 1 – Background information

Tosemary and Rhyme Hospital (TRH) is a small hospital for the treatment of patients with only minor injuries. Patients arriving at TRH with more serious injuries are referred to a larger hospital nearby. Those with minor injuries are admitted into TRH and wait to be seen by a doctor. After treatment, most patients leave the hospital and need not return. If their treatment has failed, however, they are re-admitted for additional treatment.

Patients do not have to pay for treatment at TRH, which is a not-for-profit, public sector hospital. It is funded entirely by the government from taxation and a fixed level of funding is received from the government each year. It is up to TRH to allocate its funding to different areas, such as doctors' salaries, medicines and all other costs required to run a hospital.

TRH have asked you, a management consultant, to carry out a number of tasks.

Exhibit 2 – Objectives

TRH's objectives are:

– to give prompt access to high quality medical treatment for patients

– to provide value for money for the taxpayer, as measured by the '3Es' framework of economy, efficiency and effectiveness

– to contribute to medical science by developing innovative ways to deliver treatment to patients.

Exhibit 3 – Non-financial performance indicators

It has been suggested to TRH that the hospital has inadequate performance measurement systems in place to assess whether it is achieving its objectives, and that insufficient attention is given to the importance of non-financial performance indicators.

You have been asked to explain why non-financial performance indicators are particularly important to measure the performance of not-for-profit organisations such as TRH.

Exhibit 4 – Value for money

You have met with some of the doctors to get their opinions. One senior doctor has told you, 'I think TRH always delivers value for money. We've always achieved our total financial budgets. Doctors here work much longer hours than colleagues in other hospitals, often without being paid for working overtime. There is not enough government funding to recruit more doctors. At busy times, we've started referring more patients arriving at TRH to the larger hospital nearby. This has helped reduce average waiting times. Patients arriving at TRH are now seen by a doctor within 3 hours 50 minutes rather than 4 hours as was previously the case. So, we're already doing all we can. I don't know how much time we spend developing innovative ways to deliver treatment to patients though, as most of the performance data we doctors receive relates to financial targets.'

Recent performance data for TRH and national average information has been provided in Appendix 1. This is indicative of the data which the doctors at TRH receive.

You have been asked to justify one performance measure for each of the components of the value for money framework used at TRH and, using that measure evaluate whether TRH is delivering value for money.

Exhibit 5 – Management style

Finally, you have been asked to evaluate the extent to which the management style at TRH can be said to be budget constrained and advise on the implications of this approach for managing TRH's performance.

Required:

It is now 1 September 20X5.

Respond to the request for work on the following areas:

(a) **The importance of non-financial performance indicators** **(4 marks)**

(b) **Value for money** **(8 marks)**

(c) **Budget constrained management style** **(8 marks)**

Professional marks will be awarded for the demonstration of skill in analysis and evaluation and commercial acumen in your answer. **(5 marks)**

(Total: 25 marks)

Exhibit 6 – Appendix 1: Data for the year ended 31 August 20X5

	TRH	**National average**[1]
Number of doctors	25	24
Total doctors' salaries including overtime	$3.75m	$4.20m
Total doctors' salaries budget including overtime	$3.75m	$3.20m
Number of patients treated	24,375	20,000
Average staff satisfaction rating[2]	9%	89%
Number of patients re-admitted	1,830	300

Notes

[1] National average for other public sector minor injuries hospitals.

[2] Staff satisfaction rating was obtained by conducting a survey of all 25 doctors. A survey score of 100% represents 'totally satisfied', and a score of 0% represents totally unsatisfied.

45 PITLANE (MAR/JUN 17)

Company and industry background

Pitlane Electronic Components (Pitlane) manufactures components for use in the electricity distribution network in Deeland. Demand from Pitlane's biggest customer, to replace identical but worn out components, has been constant for many years. Pitlane has recently renewed an exclusive long-term supply agreement with this customer, who has always agreed to buy the components for their total standard cost plus a fixed profit margin of 15%. Variances between standard and actual costs of the components are negligible. Pitlane runs several production lines in two factories located in different areas of Deeland. The factories' layout is poorly designed and the production process requires components to be transported around and between the factories.

The Deeland government wants to encourage renewable electricity generation. It is offering a three-year subsidy scheme, beginning in 2018, for consumers to have solar panels installed on the roofs of their homes. As an added incentive, businesses will be exempt from tax on profits made on the sale of solar panels and related components.

New electrical component – the 'Booster'

To take advantage of this scheme, Pitlane has built a prototype of a new electrical component, known as the 'Booster', which increases the output from domestic solar panels. The Booster will be sold to installers of solar panels and not directly to consumers. Pitlane's marketing department has estimated market data for the duration of the scheme based on a similar scheme in Veeland (Appendix 1). As a result of its products being unchanged for many years, Pitlane has little recent experience of developing new products and estimating costs and potential revenues from them. It is expected that many competitor products will be launched during the scheme, at the end of which demand is expected to fall greatly, and production of the Booster will discontinue.

The Booster's total fixed costs during the scheme are estimated to be $10m, including $2.8m upfront development costs to enable the Booster to communicate the amount of solar energy generated directly to consumers' smartphones via an app. The product development team at Pitlane believes this feature, and the use of highest quality packaging, will allow it to charge 10% more that the average price of its competitors. The marketing team, however, has questioned the overall value of these two features and whether customers would be prepared to pay extra for them, as most of the Deeland population do not yet own smartphones.

Pitlane has estimated the direct costs for the Booster (Appendix 2). The largest direct cost is for the four main sub-components. These are bought in bulk from six different suppliers in Deeland, though all are readily available from suppliers worldwide. The sub-components are fragile. During production of the Booster prototype, many sub-components were found to be damaged during the production process by workers incorrectly assembling them. This resulted in the completed prototype Boosters being scrapped after testing by the quality control department. The manufacturing director is concerned that the incorrect assembly of sub-components by workers may mean that it may not be profitable for Pitlane to start full scale production of Boosters. To counteract these quality problems, Pitlane will employ more highly skilled workers, who are paid around 30% more than most other workers in the business which is accounted for in the cost estimate given in Appendix 2. Pitlane staff have never been encouraged to suggest any ways to improve the manufacturing process.

Shareholders' financial performance objective

Pitlane's shareholders insist that for the Booster project to go ahead, it must meet the financial performance objective of achieving a 15% net profit margin, after all costs, for the duration of the scheme.

Pitlane's directors are concerned that the Booster project will not meet the shareholders' financial performance objective. They have asked you, as a consultant experienced in target costing, Kaizen costing and other Japanese business practices, for your advice.

Required:

(a) **Calculate the cost gap per unit in each of the three years of the Booster's life, taking into account all estimated costs.** **(6 marks)**

(b) **Advise on the extent to which target costing would help Pitlane to achieve the financial performance objective set by the shareholders.** **(12 marks)**

(c) **Advise Pitlane how Kaizen costing may be used to help the Booster project achieve the financial performance objective set by the shareholders.** **(7 marks)**

(Total: 25 marks)

Appendix 1 – Estimated market data for Booster

	2018	2019	2020
Total market size (units)	600,000	500,000	460,000
Average price of competitors products ($/unit)	180	170	160
Booster market share of total market	10%	15%	20%

Appendix 2 – Estimated unit direct cost of Booster

	$
Sub-components	94
Assembly labour	21
Packaging	10
Distribution	2
Internal transport and handling	7
Total	134

46 JENSON, LEWIS AND WEBB (JLW) (MAR/JUN 17)

Answer debrief

Company and divisional information

Jenson, Lewis and Webb (JLW) manufactures tubes of acrylic paint for sale to artists and craft shops in Kayland and Seeland. JLW has two divisions, Domestic division and Export division, both based in Kayland. All costs are incurred in Kayland Dollars ($KL). Domestic division is an investment centre and sells only to customers in Kayland. Export division is a profit centre and exports all its products to Seeland, where customers are invoiced in Seeland Pounds (£SL), at prices fixed at the start of the year. The objective of JLW is to maximise shareholder wealth.

At the beginning of the year ended 31 December 2016, the head office at JLW purchased new production machinery for Export division for $KL2.5m, which significantly increased the production efficiency of the division. Managers at Domestic division were considering purchasing a similar machine, but decided to delay the purchase until the beginning of the following financial year. On 30 June 2016 the $KL weakened by 15% against the £SL, after which the exchange rate between the two currencies has remained unchanged.

Current performance appraisal system for divisional managers

The managers of the two divisions are currently appraised on the performance of their own divisions, and are awarded a large bonus if the net profit margin of their division exceeds 8% for the year. Extracts from the management accounts for the year ended 31 December 2016 for both divisions are given in Appendix 1. On being told that she would not be receiving a bonus for the financial year, the manager of Export division has commented that she has had difficulty in understanding the bonus calculations for her division as it is not based on traceable profit, which would consider only items which relate directly to the division. She also does not believe it is appropriate that the net profit margin used to appraise her performance is the same as 'that which is used to evaluate the performance of Export division itself'. She has asked for a meeting with the directors to discuss this further.

JLW's directors intend to award divisional managers' bonuses on the basis of net profit margin achieved in 2016 as planned, but have asked you as a performance management consultant for your advice on the comments of the Export division manager in advance of their meeting with her.

Potential use of economic value added (EVA^{TM})

One director has also suggested that, in future, EVA^{TM} may be a good way to evaluate and compare the performance of the two divisions. You are asked for your advice on this too, but you have been specifically asked not to attempt a calculation of EVA^{TM}.

Required:

(a) Evaluate the comments of the Export division manager that the net profit margin used to appraise her own performance should be different from that used to appraise the performance of the Export division itself. (7 marks)

(b) Recommend, using appropriate calculations, whether the manager of the Export division should receive her bonus for the year. (8 marks)

(c) Advise whether the use of economic value added (EVA^{TM}) is an appropriate measure of performance of the two divisions. You are not required to perform and EVA^{TM} calculation. (10 marks)

(Total: 25 marks)

Appendix 1 – Extracts from management accounts for year ended 31 December 2016

$KL000	**Export division**	**Domestic division**
Revenue **(1)**	8,000	12,000
Cost of sales	(4,800)	(7,800)
	———	———
Gross profit	3,200	4,200
Depreciation	(395)	(45)
Allocated head office costs	(360)	(540)
Other overheads **(2)**	(1,900)	2,300
	———	———
Net profit	545	1,315
Net profit margin on revenue	6.8 %	11.0 %
Capital employed **(3)**	6,500	8,500

1 Revenue accrues evenly over the financial year.

2 Other overheads for Domestic division include the creation of a bad debt provision equivalent to $KL75,000 for a wholesale customer who had financial difficulties during the year, and $KL90,000 for advertising a new range of paints launched at the end of the year.

3 JLW is financed in equal proportions by debt and equity. The cost of equity is 8% and the after tax cost of debt is 5%.

47 ESSLAND POLICE FORCE (DEC 13)

Background information

You are a performance management expert brought in by the Chief Executive Officer (CEO) of the Department of the Interior for the country of Essland. The department is a branch of the Essland government which handles security, policing, immigration and border control. The CEO is a civil servant and he reports to the Minister for the Interior. The Minister for the Interior is an elected politician selected by the Prime Minister of Essland, who leads its government.

The newly-elected Minister for the Interior has instructed the CEO to implement his policy for improving the regional police forces' performance by copying the method used for schools.

League table usage

In a recent initiative by the School's Ministry, a league table for the hundreds of schools in Essland was created, showing the best and worst in terms of examination performance only, in order to motivate senior school managers to improve. The league table was used to create targets for assessing the schools' and their managers' performance. Additionally, parents in Essland have the right to choose which school their children attend and so often base their selection on league table performance. Therefore, the Minister has had a policy review body draw up a method of creating a league table for the police forces.

The CEO has requested your help to clarify his own thinking on this new policy for the four regional police forces in Essland (Cashire (C), Dashire (D), Eshire (E) and Fashire (F)). The CEO needs you to assess the use of the league table using the policy review body's suggested method and has collected the data and calculation of the league table given in Appendix 1 to assist you. He also wants to assess whether the table will help in meeting the Department's aim and goals for the police. The overall aim of the Department (and its police forces) is 'to provide a value-for-money service to ensure that the community can live in safety with confidence in their physical and legal security'.

The detailed goals of the Department are to:

- Tackle the underlying causes of crime and achieve long-term sustainable solutions
- Bring perpetrators to justice
- Provide protection and support for individuals and communities at risk of harm
- Respond to community needs by being accessible and engaging with their concerns.

The CEO warned you, 'I'm not interested in the performance of the forces. I'm interested in the method of assessment, so don't waste time with your ideas on how to improve actual policing.'

The CEO also wishes to understand the strengths and weaknesses of the use of a league table, its link to targets and the likely reaction of employees to this system of performance management, especially as there is a strong union representing the police. He is worried about the employees' attitude to the introduction of the system and its effects on their behaviour and their sense of accountability. He is also concerned about importing the use of a league table from the schools sector, as it might not be appropriate here.

Required:

(a) **Evaluate the method of calculating and measuring the Force Scores for use in the league table in achieving the Department of the Interior's aims and goals.** **(14 marks)**

(b) **Discuss the merits of league tables in performance management and address the CEO's concerns over their use in managing the performance of Essland's police forces.** **(11 marks)**

(Total: 25 marks)

Appendix 1

The appendix defines the policy review body's method for scoring each force, provides the basic data for each force and then calculates the current force score placing the forces into a league table:

Force score = Rank 1 × 0.25 + Rank 2 × 0.25 + Rank 3 × 0.25 + Rank 4 × 0.25

where each Rank is the ranking from 4 to 1 which each force gets for each of the following variables (4 is best, 1 is worst):

- Rank 1 is based on the number of crimes per 10,000 of population
- Rank 2 is based on the solution rate for crimes reported in the year
- Rank 3 is based on the user satisfaction score (based on a survey of the population)
- Rank 4 is based on the percentage of calls to police answered within 10 seconds

For example, a force which was top ranked in each of the Ranks would get a Force Score of 4 (= 4 × 0.25 + 4 × 0.25 + 4 × 0.25 + 4 × 0.25).

Data by region: For the calendar year 2012

	C	D	E	F
Population	1,250,000	900,000	1,700,000	1,500,000
Number of crimes reported in year	62,500	47,250	83,300	63,000
Number of crimes solved in year	31,250	22,680	45,815	33,390
User satisfaction score	71%	80%	73%	68%
Percentage of calls to police answered within 10 seconds	92%	93%	91%	94%
Number of police force employees	6,200	4,400	8,500	7,900
Cost of police force for year ($m)	404	298	572	510

Calculation of Force Score:

	C	D	E	F
Number of reported crimes per 10,000 of population	500	525	490	420
Rank 1	2	1	3	4
Solution rate for crimes reported in year	50%	48%	55%	53%
Rank 2	2	1	4	3
Rank 3 (user satisfaction)	2	4	3	1
Rank 4 (call handling)	2	3	1	4
Force score	2	2.25	2.75	3

The league table for 2012 is:

	Force	Score
1	F	3.00
2	E	2.75
3	D	2.25
4	C	2.00

Note: You should assume that the calculations in Appendix 1 are accurate.

48 BEESHIRE LOCAL AUTHORITY (BLA) (DEC 14)

Background information

Beeshire Local Authority (BLA) is a local government body which provides a range of services for the area of Beeshire within the country of Seeland. Beeshire is a wealthy area within the country with many tourist attractions.

Waste collection

One of BLA's tasks is to ensure that waste is collected from the homes and businesses in Beeshire. The goal for BLA's waste management department is 'to maintain Beeshire as a safe, clean and environmentally friendly place where people and businesses want to both stay in and return to.' The need for waste collection is linked to public health concerns, the desire to keep the streets clean and attractive and the desire to increase the amount of rubbish which is recycled.

BLA is funded through a single local tax and does not charge its residents or businesses separately for most of its services, including waste collection. There is no public or political appetite for outsourcing services such as waste management.

Waste collection is performed by the workforce using a fleet of vehicles. The waste is either taken to recycling plants or else to landfill sites for burying. BLA obtains revenues from all the recycled waste but this only just covers the cost of running the recycling facilities.

Recycling of waste

Against a background estimate that waste will increase by 1% p.a. in the future, the national government has ordered local authorities, such as BLA, to promote the recycling of waste and has set a target of 40% of all waste to be recycled by 2015. In order to discourage the creation of non-recyclable waste, the government has imposed a levy per tonne of waste buried in landfill sites and has stated that this levy will rise over the next five years in order to encourage continuing improvement in the amount of recycled waste.

Seeland recession

Currently, Seeland is in a long recession and so local authority revenues have fallen as tax revenues reflect the poor state of the economy. Along with other local authorities, BLA has tried to cut costs and so has focused on financial measures of performance. In a recent, private meeting, the chief executive of BLA was heard to say 'keep costs under control and we will worry about quality of service only when complaint levels build to an unacceptable level.' As one of the area's largest employers, cutting staff numbers has been very difficult for BLA due to the impact on the local economy and the reaction of the residents.

Performance indicators

The current performance indicators used at BLA are drawn from the existing information systems with national figures given for comparison. Those relating to waste collection for the year ending 31 March 2014 are:

			BLA	National total
Total cost	($m)		250	2,850
Volume of waste				
	landfilled	(tonnes)	1,250,000	13,750,000
	recycled	(tonnes)	950,000	9,500,000
	total	(tonnes)	2,200,000	23,250,000
No. of staff			3,500	39,900
Staff cost	($m)		110	1,190
No. of households			2,380,952	26,190,476
No. of complaints about waste uncollected			18,250	200,750

	BLA	National average
Frequency of waste collections (days)	14	12

Notes on BLA data:

1 Cost data and no. of households comes from BLA's financial systems.

2 Waste data comes from weighing lorries at the landfill sites and recycling facilities.

3 Staff data is collected from BLA's HR system.

4 Complaints data is based on numbers of letters and phone calls to the waste management department.

5 Frequency of collection data is obtained from the department's vehicle schedules.

Required:

(a) **Explain why non-financial indicators are particularly useful for public sector organisations, illustrating your answer with brief examples relevant to BLA.** **(6 marks)**

(b) **Explain how the value for money provision of waste services by BLA should be assessed by suggesting and calculating justified performance indicators using the information in the scenario.** **(12 marks)**

(c) **Discuss the difficulties of measuring qualitative factors of performance, suggesting appropriate solutions for BLA.** **(7 marks)**

(Total: 25 marks)

49 TENCH CARS (DEC 11)

Background information

Tench Cars (Tench) is large national car manufacturing business. It is based in Essland, a country that has recently turned from state communism to democratic capitalism. The car industry had been heavily supported and controlled by the bureaucracy of the old regime. The government had stipulated production and employment targets for the business but had ignored profit as a performance measure. Tench is now run by a new generation of capitalist business people intent on rejuvenating the company's fortunes.

The company has a strong position within Essland, which has a population of 200 million and forms the majority of Tench's market. However, the company has also traditionally achieved a good market share in six neighbouring countries due to historic links and shared culture between them and Essland. All of these markets are experiencing growing car ownership as political and market reforms lead to greater wealth in a large proportion of the population. Additionally, the new government in Essland is deregulating markets and opening the country to imports of foreign vehicles.

Quality management

Tench's management recognises that it needs to make fundamental changes to its production approach in order to combat increased competition from foreign manufacturers. Tench's cars are now being seen as ugly, pollutive and with poor safety features in comparison to the foreign competition. Management plans to address this by improving the quality of its cars through the use of quality management techniques. It plans to improve financial performance through the use of Kaizen costing and just-in-time purchasing and production. Tench's existing performance reporting system uses standard costing and budgetary variance analysis in order to monitor and control production activities.

The Chief Financial Officer (CFO) of Tench has commented that he is confused by the terminology associated with quality management and needs a clearer understanding of the different costs associated with quality management. The CFO also wants to know the impact of including quality costs and using the Kaizen costing approach on the traditional standard costing approach at Tench.

Required:

Write to the CFO to:

(a) Discuss the impact of collection and use of quality costs on the current costing systems at Tench. (6 marks)

(b) Discuss and evaluate the impact of the Kaizen costing approach on the costing systems and employee management at Tench. (8 marks)

(c) Briefly evaluate the effect of moving to just-in-time purchasing and production, noting the impact on performance measures at Tench. (6 marks)

(d) Briefly discuss any problems that the existing performance reporting system may cause for Tench. (5 marks)

(Total: 25 marks)

50 THEBE TELECOM (JUN 12)

Company information

Thebe Telecom is a large national telephone business in Fayland. Thebe provides telephone service to more than 11 million customers through its fixed line and mobile services. Thebe has three strategic business units: mobile; fixed line telephone (incorporating broadband); and corporate services (serving other businesses' telephone needs). It has become the largest mobile operator in Fayland through a series of acquisitions of competitors and operating licences.

Competitive position

Thebe's CEO has won many awards for being an innovative businessman who recognises the rapid changes in technology, regulation and competitor action that occur in the sector. Thebe's major competitor in Fayland is the original nationalised telephone company, FayTel, which was privatised 20 years ago but which retains many of the features of a monopoly supplier including a massive infrastructure. As a result, Thebe's CEO realised long ago that competition on the basis of price and volume would not work against such a large competitor and so he has focused on customer service as the key to growing the business.

Six Sigma

In order to improve the company's competitive position, the CEO decided that the company should consider a Six Sigma initiative to give an immediate step change improvement to the service quality at Thebe. The initiative involved a number of projects including one to improve the quality of customers' bills. FayTel was publicly criticised by the government's consumer advocate who pointed to occasional misallocations of call minutes to the wrong numbers and also, more frequently, the application of incorrect tariffs in calculating the costs of calls. Thebe's CEO is aware that all telephone businesses (including Thebe) have these problems but this is an area in which Thebe can gain a competitive advantage and has taken a special interest in this project by championing it himself.

The project is focused on improving the accuracy of customers' bills and the handling of complaints. Within the billing department, the company divided activities into normal money collection, credit control on overdue payments and managing complaints. Process diagrams were created for each of these areas and then data was sourced from customer feedback at the various points of interaction with Thebe employees (such as complaint handling) and internal measurables created. The project team was formed from line managers from all three strategic business units and the billing department.

Required:

(a) Explain how the general way in which Six Sigma is implemented helps improve the quality of performance illustrating your answer with reference to Thebe. (8 marks)

(b) Explain and illustrate how the DMAIC method for the implementation of Six Sigma could be applied at Thebe. (9 marks)

(c) Evaluate the appropriateness of introducing other quality practices at Thebe. (8 marks)

(Total: 25 marks)

51 LINCOLN & LINCOLN ADVERTISING (DEC 12)

Tutorial note

This is an older Section B question. It is a useful question to complete as part of your revision but it is worth noting that more recent Section B questions tend to be much more consice (usually 1-2 pages).

Background information

Lincoln & Lincoln Advertising (LLA) is an advertising agency based in Veeland, which is a large well-developed country considered to be one of the wealthiest in the world. LLA operates out of three regional offices (North, East and West) with its head office functions based in the East offices. The business offers a wide range of advertising services:

Strategic: Advising on an overall advertising campaign (mix of advertising channels and overall themes)

Buying: Advising and buying advertising space (on television, radio, websites and in newspapers and magazines); and

Creative: Designing and producing specific adverts for the customers' use.

The company is one of the three largest agencies in Veeland with many years of experience and many awards won. Competition in advertising is fierce, as advertising spending by businesses has suffered recently during a general economic downturn. Most new business is won in tender competitions between different advertising agencies.

Veeland is a large country with considerable diversity of markets, economic conditions and fashions across its regions. As a result, the regional offices have developed with a considerable amount of decision-making autonomy. This also reflects the temperament of the key creative employees of the firm who have a strong attachment to their campaign ideas and take great personal pride in their success. The individualism of the key employees also comes from the way that LLA has grown. The business has been built through acquisition of small, local businesses in each of the three regions. Each of these acquisitions has been consolidated into the appropriate regional office.

Financial position of regional offices

You have been recruited in to LLA in order to take up the newly created post of senior management accountant. Your recruitment caused some concern amongst the board but was championed by the chief executive officer (CEO) as 'necessary to stay ahead of the game'. The board have asked that you prove yourself and also give a fresh perspective on LLA by providing them with a report. Initially, you have been asked to provide an assessment of the current financial position of the three regional offices. The most recent management accounts are in Appendix 1. The basic assessment calculations have already been accurately completed by one of the junior staff and the results are in Appendix 2.

Performance measures

As part of the briefing for this exercise, you attended part of a recent board meeting where you were told that the board want your views on the choice of net income as the performance measure for each of the regional offices. They want you to suggest other measures and why they are appropriate for each office. The CEO has advised you that you may want to use different key measures for each office, rather than have a 'one-size fits all policy'. During the board's discussion, issues around controllability and responsibility accounting appear to be the main concerns of the board. The CEO also stated that the board would not be interested in a long list of which numbers have gone up and which have gone down. They will want to be given a coherent picture of what is going on at each of the regional offices.

Remuneration policy

Finally, the CEO said, 'Well, if you are not completely tired out at the end of this little project then I'd also like you to comment on our remuneration policy at the regional offices including ideas based on your assessment of performance measures.' Later, the CEO gave you a note (see Appendix 3) describing these policies at LLA.

Required:

(a) **Assess the recent performance of the three regional offices by interpreting the data given in Appendices 1 and 2. (10 marks)**

(b) **Evaluate the choice of net income as the performance measure for the regional offices and suggest other measures and why they are appropriate for each office. (8 marks)**

(c) **Using the information provided, evaluate LLA's remuneration policy suggesting changes as appropriate. (7 marks)**

(Total: 25 marks)

Appendix 1: LLA financial data

The figures are drawn from the regional offices' management accounts for year to September 2012.

	North	**East**	**West**
	$m	$m	$m
Revenue	151	523	467
Cost of sales	45	147	159
Staff costs	53	194	145
Other costs	27	86	67
Operating profit	26	96	96
Allocated head office costs	6	31	16
Net income	20	65	80
Net cash flow in year	24	86	46
Current assets	22	82	119
Current liabilities	10	35	31
Capital expenditure	3	10.2	23.8
Capital employed	39	121	112

Notes:

1 East office data is for the regional office only. It excludes any costs of the head office function based there other than the allocated costs listed.

2 Notional cost of capital at LLA is 9%.

3 Current assets contains only accounts receivable for each office.

Appendix 2: Basic calculations

[These can be assumed to be calculated correctly.]

		Change on year			**Margins**	
		Sep–12	**Sep–11**	**Sep–12**	**Sep–11**	**Sep–10**
Revenue						
	North	–1.9%	–1.3%			
	East	1.0%	1.0%			
	West	8.9%	8.1%			
Cost of sales						
	North			29.8%	29.9%	30.1%
	East			28.1%	29.0%	30.0%
	West			34.0%	31.9%	30.0%
Staff costs						
	North			35.1%	35.1%	35.3%
	East			37.1%	37.1%	37.0%
	West			31.0%	31.0%	31.0%
Operating profit						
	North	–7.1%	0.0%	17.2%	18.2%	17.9%
	East	7.9%	8.5%	18.4%	17.2%	16.0%
	West	5.5%	4.6%	20.6%	21.2%	21.9%
Net Income						
	North	–4.8%	–4.5%	13.2%	13.6%	14.1%
	East	12.1%	13.7%	12.4%	11.2%	9.9%
	West	6.7%	5.6%	17.1%	17.5%	17.9%

Notes:

1 Other costs and allocated head office costs are fixed.

2 Margins are calculated as a percentage of revenue.

		Sep-12	Sep-11	Sep-10
Current ratio				
	North	2.2	2.3	2.1
	East	2.3	2.3	2.4
	West	3.8	2.9	2.4
Receivable days				
	North	53	55	54
	East	57	58	59
	West	93	68	55
ROCE	based on operating profit	**Sep-12**	**Sep-11**	**Sep-10**
	North	67%	88%	117%
	East	79%	90%	103%
	West	86%	106%	140%
	based on net income			
	North	51%	66%	92%
	East	54%	59%	64%
	West	71%	87%	115%
Residual income				
($m's)	based on operating profit			
	North	22.5	25.1	25.8
	East	85.1	80.1	74.8
	West	85.9	83.3	81.4
	based on net income			
	North	16.5	18.1	19.8
	East	54.1	49.1	43.8
	West	69.9	67.3	65.4

Appendix 3: Note on remuneration from the CEO:

There are broadly five grades of staff at each regional office. The following is an outline of their remuneration packages. (The head office staff are treated separately and are not part of this exercise.)

Senior management

All staff at this level are paid a basic fixed salary, which reflects industry norms over the last few years, plus a bonus dependent on the net income of their office.

Creative staff

The 'creatives' are on individual packages which reflect the market rates in order to recruit them at the time that they were recruited. Some are fixed salary and some have a fixed element plus a bonus based on their office's revenues.

Buying staff

The buyers are paid a fixed salary plus a bonus based on the prices for advertising space that they negotiate compared to the budgeted cost of space. The budget is set by the finance team at head office based on previous years' experience and their forecast for supply and demand in the year in question.

Account management staff

Account management handles relationships with clients and also develops new clients. They are paid a fixed market-based salary.

Administration staff

These staff are paid the market rate for their jobs as a fixed salary based on hours worked.

(**Note:** The scenario in this question is longer than you would expect to see under the current style of the examining team and therefore additional time may be required to read and absorb the information. However, it is a very useful question for revision purposes.)

52 LANDUAL LAMPS (JUN 13)

Company information and structure

Landual Lamps (Landual) manufactures and delivers floor and table lamps for homes and offices in Beeland. The company sells through its website and uses commercial logistics firms to deliver their products. The markets for its products are highly competitive. The company has traditionally relied on the high quality of its designs to drive demand for its products.

The company is divided into two divisions (components and assembly), plus a head office that provides design, administrative and marketing support.

Manufacturing process

The manufacturing process involves:

1 the components division making the housing components and electrical components for the lamp. This is an intricate process as it depends on the specific design of the lamp and so serves as a significant source of competitive advantage for Landual

2 the assembly division assembling the various components into a finished lamp ready for shipment. This is a simple process.

Transfer pricing policy

The finance director (FD) of Landual is currently overloaded with work due to changes in financial accounting policies that are being considered at board level. As a result, she has been unable to look at certain management accounting aspects of the business and has asked you to do a review of the transfer pricing policy between the components and assembly divisions.

The current transfer pricing policy at Landual is as follows:

(a) market prices for electrical components are used as these are generic components for which there is a competitive external market; and

(b) prices for housing components based on total actual production costs to the components division are used as there is no external market for these components since they are specially designed for Landual's products.

Currently, the components division produces only for the assembly division in order to meet overall demand without the use of external suppliers for housing and electrical components. If the components division were to sell its electrical components externally, then additional costs of $269,000 would arise for transport, marketing and bad debts.

The FD is considering two separate changes within Landual: one to the transfer pricing policy and a second one to the divisional structure.

Change to transfer pricing policy

First, the transfer pricing policy for housing components would change to use variable cost to the components division. The FD wants to know the impact of the change in transfer pricing policy on the existing results of the two divisions and the company. (No change is proposed to the transfer price of the electrical components.)

Change to divisional structure

Second, as can be seen from the divisional performance report below, the two divisions are currently treated as profit centres. The FD is considering splitting the components division into two further separate divisions: an electrical components division and a housing components division. If the board agrees to this proposal, then the housing components division will be treated as a cost centre only, charging its total production cost to the assembly division. The electrical components and assembly divisions will remain as profit centres.

The FD needs to understand the impact of this proposed new divisional structure on divisional performance assessment and on the company as a whole. She has asked that, in order to keep the discussion on the new divisional structure simple, you use the existing transfer pricing policy to do illustrative calculations. She stated that she would reallocate head office costs to the two new components divisions in proportion to their cost of sales.

Financial and other information

You are provided with the following financial and other information for Landual Lamps.

Actual data for Landual Lamps for the year ended 31 March 2013

		Components division	**Assembly division**	**Landual Lamps**
		$000	$000	$000
Sales	Electrical	1,557		
	Housing	8,204		
	sub-total	9,761	15,794	15,794
Cost of sales				
	Electrical	804	1,557	
	Housing	6,902	8,204	
	sub-total	7,706	9,761	7,706
Fixed production costs				
	Electrical	370		
	Housing	1,302		
	sub-total	1,672	1,268	2,940
Allocated head office costs		461	2,046	2,507
Profit		(78)	2,719	2,641

Note:

1 The components division has had problems meeting budgets recently, with an adverse variance of $575,000 in the last year. This variance arises in relation to the cost of sales for housing component production.

Required:

(a) **Evaluate the current system of transfer pricing at Landual, using illustrative calculations as appropriate.** **(10 marks)**

(b) **Advise the finance director (FD) on the impact of changing the transfer pricing policy for housing components as suggested by the FD and comment on your results, using illustrative calculations as appropriate.** **(6 marks)**

(c) **Evaluate the impact of the change in proposed divisional structure on the profit in the divisions and the company as directed by the FD.** **(9 marks)**

(Total: 25 marks)

53 BEACH FOODS (JUN 15) (AMENDED)

Exhibit 1 – Business information and structure

Beach Foods (Beach) is a family-owned business which has grown strongly over its 100 year history. The objective of the business is to maximise the family's wealth through their shareholdings. Beach has three divisions. It manufactures a variety of foods in two of the divisions: Beach Baby Foods (Baby) and Beach Chocolate Foods (Chocolate). Each of these divisions knows its own market and sets prices accordingly. The third division (R&D) researches new products on the instructions of the other divisions and is considered to be vital to the survival and growth of Beach. The board of Beach has been considering the impact of using a divisional structure and has come to you as a performance management consultant to ask for your advice.

Exhibit 2 – Divisional performance measurement

There is disagreement at board level about the correct choice of divisional performance measure to be used in the two manufacturing divisions. Currently, the business uses EVA™ but two directors have been questioning its value, complaining that it is complicated to understand. These directors have been promoting the use of either residual income (RI) or return on investment (ROI) as alternatives. The board wants to use the same measure for each division. They have asked you to evaluate the use of EVA™ as a divisional performance measure for the manufacturing divisions at Beach. This evaluation should, in part, focus on the advantages and disadvantages of using EVA™ in Beach compared to the alternative method of RI or ROI.

Exhibit 3 – Use of RI and ROI

As well as qualitatively evaluating these different measures, the board needs an assessment of the impact of a change in performance measure on their perception of these divisions' performance. Therefore, as an example, they require you to use the data given in Appendix 1 to calculate the ROI and RI for Baby and assess the impact of the assumptions made when calculating these metrics on the evaluation of the performance of this division and its management.

Exhibit 4 – Divisional control and management style

The chief executive officer (CEO) of Beach has engaged a business analyst to perform a study of the portfolio of manufacturing businesses which make up Beach. This has been completed in Appendix 2. The CEO wants your comments (based on the categorisation given in Appendix 2) on how this work will impact on the performance management of the divisions. Specifically, the CEO has asked for your justified recommendations on how to control each division; that is, whether each division should be treated as a cost/profit/investment centre and also, the appropriate management style to use for handling staff in each division. The CEO commented to you 'I have heard of different approaches to the use of budget information in assessing performance: budget-constrained, profit-conscious and also a non-accounting style. I need to know how these approaches might apply to each division given your other comments.'

All of this work has been partly prompted by complaints from the divisional managers. The Chocolate divisional managers complain that they had to wait for a year to get approval to upgrade their main production line. This production line upgrade has reduced wastage and boosted Chocolate's profit margin by 10 percentage points. The Baby division has been very successful in using the ideas of the R&D division, although Baby's managers do complain about the recharging of R&D costs to their division. Head office managers are worried about Chocolate as it has seemed to be drifting recently with a lack of strategic direction. Chocolate's managers are considered to be good but possibly not sufficiently focused on what benefits Beach as a whole.

Required:

It is now 1 September 20X5.

Respond to the board's request for work on the following areas:

(a)	**the use of EVA™ as a divisional performance measure**	**(6 marks)**
(b)	**calculation of ROI and RI and impact of assumptions and**	**(6 marks)**
(c)	**division's control and management style**	**(8 marks)**

Professional marks will be awarded for the demonstration of skill in analysis and evaluation, scepticism and commercial acumen in your answer. **(5 marks)**

(Total: 25 marks)

Exhibit 5 – Appendix 1

Figures from Beach management accounts for year ended 31 March:

Baby division	**20X5**
	$m
Revenue	220
Costs	
Divisional operating costs	121
R&D costs recharged	11
Allocated head office management fees	28
Profit before tax	60
Capital employed	424

Notes:

1 Baby launched a new product with a large publicity campaign during the year.

2 The notional cost of capital for Baby is estimated by the chief financial officer at 11%. WACC for Beach is 7.5%.

3 ROI for similar entities is 20%.

4 EVA^{TM} for Baby is calculated as $35m.

Exhibit 6 – Appendix 2

Star		**Problem child**
Baby:		
Market growth	18%	
Relative market share	105%	
Cash cow		**Dog**
Chocolate:		
Market growth	3%	
Relative market share	120%	

Relative market share is the market share of the division compared to that of the market leader. If an organisation is a market leader, then its market share is compared to the next largest competitor.

Note: You may assume that the calculations and this categorisation are accurate.

54 POSIE FURNITURE (SEPT/DEC 15)

Company information

Posie is a large business which manufactures furniture. It is made up of two autonomous divisions in Deeland. The manufacturing division purchases raw materials from external suppliers, and performs all manufacturing and packaging operations. All sales are made through the retail division which has 95 retail stores in Deeland, as well as through Posie's own well-developed website. Posie has retail operations in eight other countries as well as in Deeland. These overseas businesses operate as independent subsidiaries within the Retail Division, each with their own IT and accounting functions.

The furniture is sold in boxes for customers to assemble themselves. About 10% of the products sold by Posie are purchased already packaged from other manufacturers. All deliveries are outsourced through a third party distribution company.

Posie's corporate objective is to maximise shareholder wealth by producing 'attractive, functional furniture at low prices'. This is how customers generally perceive the Posie brand. The CEO of Posie is concerned about increasing levels of returns made by customers and increasing numbers of consumers complaining on online forums about products purchased from Posie.

Six sigma

Concerned about the impact on the Posie brand and the cost-leadership strategy, the CEO has asked you as a performance management expert to help Posie implement the six sigma technique to reduce the number of products returned and in particular to define customers' requirements and measure Posie's existing performance. The production director has been appointed to sponsor the project and you will be supported by a small team of managers who have recently received training in six sigma. The board member responsible for manufacturing quality recently resigned because she thought it was unfair that the manufacturing division was being held responsible for the increased level of customer returns.

You have been given access to some information concerning the reasons why customers return goods to help you measure existing performance in this area (Appendix 1). This is an extract from the management reporting pack presented to the board at their monthly meetings. The returns data, however, are only compiled every six months due to the lengthy analysis required of data from Posie's overseas retail operations. It is included twice a year in the board report along with the KPIs for customer satisfaction. The last time this information was produced 93% of customers indicated they were satisfied with the quality of the manufacture of Posie's products.

The CEO has heard that six sigma requires 'large amounts of facts and data'. He suggested that the returns data contain insufficient detail and that as part of your project you may need to do more analysis, for example, on why customers are not satisfied with the manufacturing quality.

Information requirements

He also added, 'I'm not sure that our current IT systems are capable of generating the data we need to identify which responsibility centres within the manufacturing division are the root causes of the problem of customer returns. We are planning to change the designation of the overseas retail businesses from profit centres to revenue centres, but again we need to know first how this will affect the information requirements of the business and any potential problems with doing so.'

Appendix 1

Reasons given by customers for returning goods

Category	Reason for return of goods	% Responses
1	Difficult to assemble or pieces missing	48%
2	Goods arrived damaged	14%
3	Goods were not as described or were defective	25%
4	Goods were of poor quality or no longer wanted	11%
5	Arrived late	2%
Total		100%

Required:

(a) **Advise the board how the six sigma project at Posie to reduce returns from customers could be implemented using DMAIC methodology.** **(15 marks)**

(b) **Evaluate the impact on Posie's information requirements arising from:**

(i) **The need to identify and improve on the level of customer returns.** **(6 marks)**

(ii) **The proposed re-designation of the overseas subsidiaries from profit centres to revenue centres.** **(4 marks)**

(Total: 25 marks)

55 UNIVERSITIES IN TEELAND (MAR/JUN 16)

Background information

Universities in Teeland have three stated objectives:

1. To improve the overall standard of education of citizens in Teeland.
2. To engage in high quality academic research.
3. To provide well-qualified university graduates to meet the needs of the graduate jobs market in Teeland.

Funding

Each university is funded by a fixed sum of money from the Teeland government according to the number of students studying there. In addition, universities receive extra funds from the government and also from other organisations, such as large businesses and charities. These funds are used to support academic research.

Following the onset of an economic recession, the Teeland government has stated its intention to reduce spending on publicly funded services such as the universities. One senior politician, following his recent visit to neighbouring Veeland, was controversially quoted as saying:

Comparison to universities in Veeland

'The universities in Veeland offer much better value for money for the citizens there compared to our universities here in Teeland. There are 25 students for each member of academic staff in Veeland, whereas in Teeland, the average number is 16, and yet, the standard of education of citizens is much higher in Veeland. The Veeland government sets targets for many aspects of the services delivered by all the universities in Veeland. Furthermore, league tables of the performance of individual universities are published on the internet, and university leaders are given bonuses if their university falls within the top quarter of the league table. In Veeland, the system of performance measurement of the universities is considered so important that there is a special government department of 150 staff just to measure it.'

League tables and value for money

He went on to add, 'I want to see a similar system of league tables, targets and bonuses for university leaders being introduced here in Teeland. To appear near the top of the league tables, I think we should expect each university to increase the number of graduates entering graduate jobs by at least 5% each year. I would also like to see other steps taken to increase value for money, such as reducing the number of academic staff in each university and reducing the salary of newly recruited academic staff.'

You have been asked to advise the Teeland government on the measurement of value for money of the universities and the proposed introduction of league tables for comparing their performance. Appendix A contains details and existing performance data relating to four of the best known universities in Teeland.

Existing university information

Northcity University is famous for its high teaching standards and outstanding academic research in all subjects. As such, it attracts the most able students from all parts of the world to study there.

Southcity University is a large university in the capital city of Teeland and offers courses in a wide range of subjects, though most of the funding it receives for academic research is for science and technology in which it is particularly successful.

Eastcity University is a small university specialising in the teaching of arts and humanities subjects such as history and geography.

Westcity University currently offers less strict entry standards to students to attract students from more diverse backgrounds, who may not normally have the opportunity of a university education.

Appendix A

Existing university performance data

	North	**South**	**East**	**West**
Number of students	17,600	30,400	5,200	11,200
Number of academic staff	1,750	2,400	485	625
Entry requirements[1]	100	77	72	48
Total annual payroll cost of academic staff	$109m	$149m	$20m	$37m
Graduate jobs filled each year[2]	4,180	6,555	1,154	1,750
Funds received for academic research	$491m	$474m	$26m	$14m
TSOR survey rating[3]	84%	76%	73%	90%
Position in league table[4]	1	11	14	21

Key to performance data

[1] – Entry requirements represent students' average attainment in examinations prior to entering university. The entry requirement of the highest ranking university is scored as 100, with the score of all other universities being in proportion to that score.

[2] – The number of graduates each year who go on to further study or who begin jobs normally undertaken by university graduates. In Teeland, students attend university for an average of 3.2 years.

[3] – The TSOR (Teeland students overall satisfaction rating) survey is undertaken by the Teeland government to assess students' overall satisfaction with the standard of teaching, the social and support aspects of university life and their optimism for their own future job prospects.

[4] – The education department of the Teeland government has produced a provisional league table ranking the overall performance of each of the 45 universities in Teeland, with 1 being the highest ranking university. This has been compiled using a number of performance measures, weighted according to what the government believes are the most important of these measures.

Required:

(a) **Advise the Teeland government how it could assess the value for money of the universities in Teeland, using the performance data in Appendix A.** **(12 marks)**

(b) **Assess the potential benefits of league tables for improving the performance of universities in Teeland and discuss the problems of implementing the proposal to introduce league tables.** **(13 marks)**

(Total: 25 marks)

56 LAUDAN ADVERTISING AGENCY (LAA) (SEPT/DEC 16)

Company information

Laudan Advertising Agency (LAA) is based in Geeland and has three autonomous subsidiaries: A, B and C. All three subsidiaries are profit centres and LAA seeks to maximise the long-term wealth of its shareholders. A is based in Geeland, while both B and C are located in other parts of the world. LAA is a highly respected advertising agency, which in the last five years has created advertising campaigns for 25 of the world's top 100 most recognised brands.

Objectives

LAA's four key objectives published on its website are:

- To delight our clients by the quality of our work
- Provide excellent value for money to our clients
- Give our clients access to specialist and local knowledge
- Ensure our clients return to us time after time

Functions

There are three main functions within LAA:

1. Campaign management, which involves researching and understanding clients' requirements and budgets and designing a suitable advertising campaign for them.
2. Creative design, which is where the visual appearance of the advert and graphics are created.
3. Media buying, which negotiates prices with, and buys advertising time and space from, magazine and newspaper publishers, internet search engines and TV companies.

Each subsidiary has its own department for campaign management and for media buying. Only A, however, has a creative design department.

Critical success factor

The directors at LAA believe that without visually appealing design, any advertising campaign is unlikely to be successful and meet the expectations of the client. They identified the importance of being able to produce high quality creative design as a critical success factor for the business. Two years ago, they decided to concentrate all of LAA's creative design at a 'centre of design excellence' within A. The intention was to improve the quality of creative design within the business by giving staff access to the latest design technology, and by attracting the most talented designers to work there.

Key performance indicator

To encourage the three subsidiaries to use the internal creative design department within A, instead of external third party design agencies, the directors created a new additional key performance indicator on which to appraise the performance of all subsidiaries and of subsidiary managers:

- All subsidiaries, including A, must purchase at least 90% of creative design work internally from A.

Prior to the introduction of this performance indicator, 40% of creative design work in each of the three subsidiaries was purchased from external design agencies.

The directors of LAA have become concerned that the introduction of the new key performance indicator may be causing managers to operate in ways which are not helping to meet LAA's stated objectives. They have asked for comments from subsidiary managers (Appendix 1) about whether they have met the 90% target in the most recent period and if not, to explain why this is.

Appendix 1

Subsidiary managers' comments on achievement of KPI for 90% creative design work purchased internally

Subsidiary A

'A purchased 86% of design work from our internal design department in the period. It would have been almost 100%, but we won a large order for a new client who operates in a specialised industry of which we have no experience. As a result, we had to use the services of a specialised external design agency, which was much more expensive than using our in-house team.'

Subsidiary B

'B purchased 62% of design work internally in the period. Though the quality of the designs is very good, they were more appealing to consumers in Geeland than here in Veeland, where B operates. The internal design department did not seem to understand consumer preferences in Veeland, and many of their designs were rejected by a key client of ours. As a result, an important advertising campaign missed key deadlines, by which time the internal design department had insufficient capacity to finish the work and we had to use an external agency.

'As there is no formal transfer pricing policy in place at LAA, the basis of the transfer price charged by the internal design department is also unclear to us. It appears to be based on full cost of the design work, including apportioned overheads and an allowance for bad debts and marketing expenses, plus a very substantial mark up. We have spent a long time trying to negotiate this price with A, which is much more expensive than external designers. Furthermore, we are currently being investigated by the tax authorities here in Veeland who have indicated that the prices charged by A for design do seem well in excess of market rates.'

Subsidiary C

'C purchased 91% of design work from the internal design department in the period, as well as achieving all our other performance targets. A key client of ours ran a major advertising campaign during the period. We used the internal design department for the first time for this campaign, instead of the usual external agency that we have used in the past for work for this client. The client was very unhappy with the extra cost that this incurred, as the number of design hours and the hourly rate was much higher than for previous campaigns. The internal design department refused to reduce the price after long negotiations and we had to give a large discount to the client before they would settle our invoice. As a result, our gross profit margin for the period was significantly reduced.

'It would be much fairer if the transfer price charged by A was based on the market price of the services provided.

Required:

(a) Evaluate how the following help LAA to manage performance in order to achieve its stated objectives:

(i) identifying the critical success factor of producing high quality creative design, and

(ii) setting the key performance indicator for the requirement to purchase 90% of design work internally. (8 marks)

(b) Assess the need for a formal transfer pricing policy at LAA. (9 marks)

(c) Advise the directors whether LAA should use a market value transfer price as suggested by the manager of subsidiary C. (8 marks)

(Total: 25 marks)

57 LOL CO (DEC 10)

Company information

LOL Co is a chain of shops selling cards and gifts throughout its country. It has been listed on the stock exchange for 10 years and enjoys a fairly high profile in the retail sector of the national economy.

Value-based management (VBM)

You have been asked by the chief executive officer (CEO) to advise the company on VBM, as a different approach to performance management. The CEO has read about this method as a way of focusing on shareholder interests and in the current tough economic climate, she thinks that it may be a useful development for LOL.

The company has traditionally used earnings per share (EPS) growth and share price in order to assess performance. The changes being proposed are considered significant and the CEO wants to be briefed on the implications of the new analysis and also how to convince both the board and the major investors of the benefits.

Financial data for LOL

		2009	2010
		$m	$m
Profit before interest and tax		50.7	43.5
Interest paid		4.0	7.8
Profit after interest and tax		35.0	26.8
Average number of shares in issue (millions)		160	160
Capital employed at the end of the year was		(in $m)	
	2008	99.2	
	2009	104.1	
	2010	97.8	

LOL aims for a capital structure of 50:50 debt to equity.

Costs of capital were:	2009	2010
Equity	12.70%	15.30%
Debt (post-tax cost)	4.20%	3.90%

Corporation tax is at the rate of 25%.

Stock market information	**2009**	**2010**
Stock market all-share index	2,225.4	1,448.9
Retailing sector index	1,225.6	907.1
LOL (average share price) ($)	12.20	10.70

Required:

(a) **Explain to the CEO what value-based management involves and how it can be used to focus the company on shareholder interests. (4 marks)**

(b) **Perform an assessment of the financial performance of LOL using Economic Value Added (EVA™) and evaluate your results compared with those of earnings per share (EPS) growth and share price performance. You should state any assumptions made. (12 marks)**

(c) **Evaluate VBM measures against traditional profit based measures of performance. (4 marks)**

(d) **The CEO has also read how the use of net present values (NPV) can focus a company on increasing shareholder value. Discuss the relationship between EVA™ and NPV. (5 marks)**

(Total: 25 marks)

58 PATTACK (SEPT/DEC 21) (AMENDED)

Exhibit 1 – Company information

Pattack is a company in Geeland which specialises in the delivery of parcels. Pattack collects parcels from online retailers and delivers them to the end user. Pattack's overall aim is: 'to maximise shareholder value through having a strategic focus on costs, by being the best delivery company in Geeland, by being innovative in our approach, and by having an engaged and committed workforce.'

Despite enjoying several years of growth, Pattack's performance has suffered recently as there have been new entrants into the market place. Pattack's current functions are run along departmental lines:

Collections – the collection drivers who collect parcels from retailers;

Internal operations – the computer operators who enter the orders;

Delivery administration – the administrators who schedule the deliveries; and

Deliveries – the delivery drivers who deliver the parcels to the end user.

Exhibit 2 – Current delivery process

Currently, Pattack collects parcels from the retailer and brings those parcels back to its premises. Collection drivers are employed for this purpose.

When on Pattack's premises, the parcels are then logged on Pattack's computer system. All details of the delivery are recorded at this time. These details are: the name of the retailer, the name of the end user to whom the parcel has to be delivered and the expected delivery date and time. On-time delivery is a key metric in the parcel delivery industry.

Pattack's drivers' delivery schedules are prepared for them by delivery administration after the computer operators have entered the order details. These schedules are presented to the drivers in paper form and the schedules are organised based on the time each order is due to be delivered.

The drivers return their completed delivery schedules after the day's deliveries. Computer operators should record the date and time of the actual delivery at this point. However, the operators are often too busy logging the delivery details of outgoing parcels for the next day to undertake this task and, additionally, the delivery drivers do not always record the actual time when the delivery was made. A lack of accuracy of recorded delivery data has been the cause of complaints from the retailers Pattack delivers for.

The manager of the deliveries department does not have a vehicle tracking system and assumes that the delivery drivers are following the schedule they have been given in the morning.

Exhibit 3 – BPR proposal

The chief executive officer (CEO) of Pattack recently met with a management consultant who advised him that the entire current operation should be re-engineered. The management consultant suggested that Pattack invests in a barcoding system which would electronically barcode all parcels with all details of the delivery. This coding could be undertaken by the retailers, which would ensure this data was entered as soon as the order is allocated to Pattack. This data would be electronically communicated to Pattack, enabling deliveries to end users to be arranged at this time.

Drivers collecting parcels from the retailers would be the same drivers who deliver the parcels to the end user. These drivers would know the delivery schedule in advance of collecting the parcels. End user receipt would be acknowledged by issuing each driver with a digital handheld device which would require a signature from the end user and which would also automatically note the delivery time when the parcel was signed for. Additionally, each vehicle would be fitted with a vehicle tracking device which would ensure its exact location could be checked at any time.

Appendix 1 provides a flowchart of the old process and the re-engineered process.

The board have asked you to evaluate how the BPR proposal could improve Pattack's performance in relation to its overall aim.

The management consultant also suggested that Pattack's bonus system should relate to the new process and indicated that he felt the drivers should be awarded a bonus when overall retailer satisfaction exceeded 85%. The board have also asked you to evaluate the bonus scheme for delivery drivers identified by the management consultant.

Required:

It is now 1 September 20X5.

Respond to the board of Pattack's request for work on the following areas:

(a) The BPR proposal **(12 marks)**

(b) The bonus scheme **(8 marks)**

Professional marks will be awarded for the demonstration of skill in analysis and evaluation, scepticism and commercial acumen in your answer. **(5 marks)**

(Total: 25 marks)

Exhibit 4 – Appendix 1

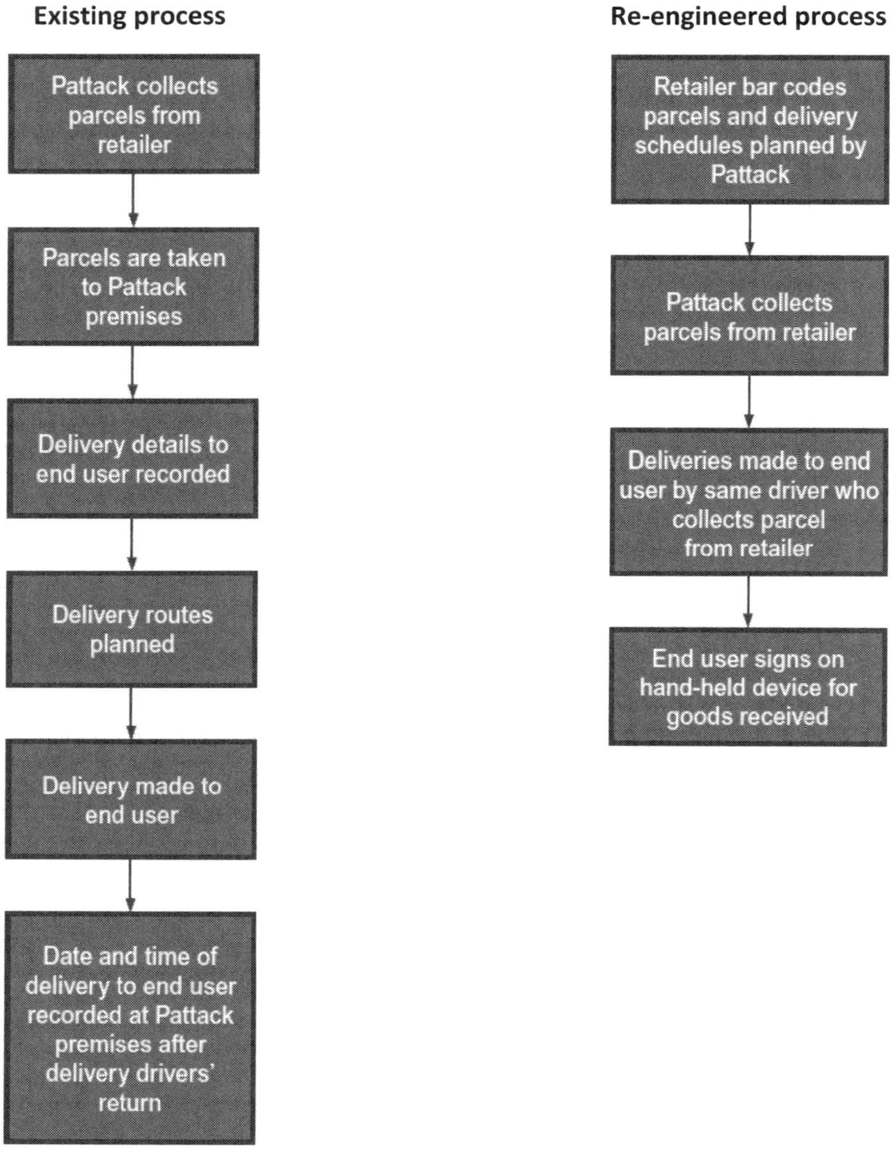

D – PERFORMANCE EVALUATION

59 HARRAY (MAR/JUN 21) (AMENDED)

Answer debrief

Exhibit 1 – Company information

Harray Keyboards (Harray) is a family-owned business which manufactures computer keyboards. It has contracts to supply three large desktop computer manufacturers. Harray won its contracts to supply these manufacturers under severe price competition as the manufacturers themselves have seen the price of their whole desktop package fall in the past 10 years. The contracts are for five years and have at least three years each left to run. At the end of the contract, the desktop manufacturers will retender for suppliers and Harray expects to be in a strong position as the existing supplier to win more work.

The chief executive officer (CEO) and leader of the Harray family is Graham Harray. He and the board believe that the success of the business has been built on an emphasis on strategic focus. He recently declared at a board meeting, 'Cost leadership wins business in our niche market and we should not over-stretch ourselves into non-core activities – we make cheap keyboards!'

Exhibit 2 – Performance pyramid

The CEO has indicated that he wants to use the performance pyramid to analyse the performance indicators used at Harray. He has asked you, as the company's performance management expert, to undertake two pieces of work on this area.

First, the CEO would like you to complete the analysis provided in Appendix 1. Appendix 1 contains the work done so far by a junior accountant on the pyramid headings and their associated indicators for Harray, with additional notes and information about Harray's performance. He would then like you to evaluate only the operational performance indicators at Harray.

Second, there are a number of non-financial indicators used in the performance pyramid and the CEO would like some advice on the reliability of these indicators compared to the financial ones which are usually presented in the board reports. He would like this part of the work to focus on the methods of measuring such indicators including the information sources, and the methods of processing and checking which is normally undertaken. He has told you to use the operational indicators from the first part of the work to illustrate your advice.

Required:

It is now 1 September 20X5.

Respond to the CEO of Harray's request for work on the following area:

the use of the performance pyramid **(20 marks)**

Note: there are 13 marks available for the first part of the work required on this area (refer to as (a) in your answer) and 7 marks available for the second part of the work required on this area (refer to as (b) in your answer).

Professional marks will be awarded for the demonstration of skill in analysis and evaluation, scepticism and commercial acumen in your answer. **(5 marks)**

(Total: 25 marks)

Exhibit 3 – Appendix 1

Harray's performance indicator information (for the year ended 30 June 20X5)

Pyramid heading	Indicator	Value
1 Vision	Cost leadership in keyboard manufacturing	
2 Financial	Profit in the financial year	$600,000
3 Market	Market share	12%
4 Customer satisfaction	Customer complaints	0.4% of keyboards
5 Flexibility	Time from order to delivery	28 (average)
6 Productivity	Operating profit margin	7.2%
7 Waste		
8 Quality		
9 Delivery		
10 Cycle time	Working capital cycle	37 days

Notes:

1 Vision does not have an indicator. There is a separate project being carried out within the finance department to deal with this.

2 The absolute profit figure is used.

3 Market share is measured by an external marketing expert.

4 Customer complaints are measured by customer returns.

5 Many orders require customisation of the production process. Customers see timely delivery as critical.

6 There are a number of other margins available for use in measuring productivity in specific areas of operations, but operating margin is used as the summary indicator of productivity.

7 There are 16 manufacturing production lines in the factory. These lines are active for nine hours a day for six days a week (52 weeks a year). A keyboard is produced from the production line every 2.2 minutes (including set-up time), while the machines are operating. Last year, the factory produced 1.05 million keyboards.

8 The number of keyboards rejected by quality inspectors in the factory was 15,750 in the year. Of these, 9,450 were able to be reworked at an average cost of $2 and the rest were scrapped. The standard cost of a keyboard is $8.

9 Harray uses an external logistics firm (Achall) to handle all deliveries. Harray calls Achall to collect an order and Achall's lorry fleet picks up orders from Harray's factory and delivers to the customer. There are service level agreements governing how long Achall has to deliver the goods to Harray's customers. Achall supplies Harray with data from its own systems on the number of packages delivered and how many were late. Below is the report for last year:

Deliveries made (in total in the period)	5,127
Deliveries made within agreed time after Harray's order received	4,717
Total time taken to deliver Harray's goods (i.e. the total, over all the orders, of the number of days each order spends in transit)	17,423

10 Working capital cycle is calculated as inventories days (22) + trade receivables days (42) – trade payables days (27).

60 ROAN UNIVERSITY AND SAUGH UNIVERSITY (SEPT/DEC 20) (AMENDED)

Exhibit 1 – Background

Roan University (Roan) is based in Teeland, which is a developed country. The government of Teeland has stated that it will cut part of the funding for the university and has made it clear that Roan must develop new replacement income streams. Roan will remain state owned.

Saugh University (Saugh) is based in Deeland, which has a developing economy and which is culturally different to Teeland. Saugh's funding is from the government of Deeland and this funding is secure for the foreseeable future. The government of Deeland has indicated that it wants the university to develop joint ventures and alliances with universities in developed countries.

Roan and Saugh have recently entered into a joint venture to set up a new university in Deeland. The new university is called RS University (RSU). Roan and Saugh each own 50% of the joint venture and a new purpose-built campus has been constructed. RSU will welcome students within three months.

Exhibit 2 – Details of the joint venture

Roan and Saugh have established a joint management board (MB) to manage the long-term and short-term operations of RSU. The MB's membership is 50% from each university, plus at least one government representative from Deeland. The MB meets at least three times per annum and the position of chairman on the MB rotates between Roan and Saugh on a meeting-by-meeting basis. The MB have asked you, as a performance management expert, to assist them with some tasks.

Roan has stated that its aim for the joint venture RSU is 'to internationally expand our provision and lead educational developments in the global arena by enhancing our revenue streams from innovative sources.' Saugh, however, has made it clear that it will view the success of RSU by the quality of the graduates who are produced and by the contribution these graduates make to society.

Saugh is keen that Roan sends as many home-based staff from Teeland to teach at RSU in Deeland as is possible but Roan would prefer to recruit local staff in Deeland to undertake its teaching obligations at RSU. Roan's teaching staff have voiced concerns about the extensive travel involved to teach at RSU and have also indicated that their work at Roan is likely to suffer if they teach at RSU. Specifically, they feel that they would not be able to effectively undertake their teaching duties, research activities or supervision of students at Roan. Negotiations are currently taking place between the teachers' trade union, which Roan's staff belong to, and management at Roan which could result in all Roan's teaching staff refusing to teach at RSU.

The management board would like you to discuss the problems that will be encountered when managing and measuring performance in the RSU joint venture.

Exhibit 3 – Stakeholder views

There has been some criticism of the joint venture within the local community in Teeland. A parent of one of the students studying at Roan has written, on behalf of a newly-formed public pressure group, to the local newspaper saying, 'All the attention at Roan is on this inappropriate joint venture. My son was told that he could not receive any help or guidance as the staff who could help him were all overseas helping with the development of RSU. His exam results were three weeks late as there was no one there to mark the exams. This is not acceptable. Roan should exist to educate Teeland students primarily. Everything else is secondary.' Membership of the public pressure group is growing.

Roan has undertaken an analysis of its stakeholders using Mendelow's matrix. Part of this work is supplied in Appendix 1, along with the justifications for the categorisation of the three stakeholder groups.

For each of the three stakeholder groups, the management board would like you to justify an appropriate performance measure which could be used by Roan.

Required:

It is now 1 September 20X5.

Respond to the RSU management board's request for work on the following areas:

(a) managing and measuring performance in the RSU joint venture (14 marks)

(b) performance measures for stakeholder groups (6 marks)

Professional marks will be awarded for the demonstration of skill in analysis and evaluation and commercial acumen in your answer. **(5 marks)**

(Total: 25 marks)

Exhibit 4 – Appendix 1

Stakeholder analysis

		Level of interest	
		Low	**High**
Level of power	**Low**	A	B
	High	C	D

Government of Teeland – the government would be keen to know of any financial problems or difficulties with the joint venture but, generally, it would belong in segment A so minimal effort should be expended.

Roan teachers' trade union – the teachers' trade union's power could be high if it has the backing to recommend to the management of Roan that Roan employees will not travel to or teach at RSU. If Roan can recruit local staff for RSU, the power and interest of the trade union will both be low as there will be little or no need for its involvement. If Roan cannot recruit local staff, then the power and interest of the trade union will both be high and it will fall into category D of being a key player.

Public pressure group in Teeland – the group has a very high level of interest in the joint venture and its power may be determined by its size. If it grows significantly, then its power may become high also. For the present, its power is likely to be low so the group will fall into category B – kept informed.

61 VEYATIE (SEPT/DEC 19) (AMENDED)

Exhibit 1 – Company information

Veyatie is a fashion clothing retailer which caters for both male and female customers of all adult age groups. Veyatie has 10 retail stores. The company's information systems are basic for a business of its size and focus solely on financial information.

Veyatie's strategic objectives are 'To maximise shareholder wealth by increasing the number of retail stores, making our customers completely satisfied, ensuring our stores are attractive and offering the widest range of fashion clothing in our market.'

The Veyatie board has seen little need for non-financial performance indicators (NFPIs) so far, preferring instead to focus attention on cost control and working capital management. As a result, all senior managers are appraised against targets for operating profit margin, inventory turnover and the current ratio.

Exhibit 2 – Customer satisfaction

Following a period of poor financial performance, Veyatie began collecting data on one aspect of non-financial performance, customer satisfaction, as the board had been advised that this is a key driver of financial performance.

The data collection began at the start of Quarter 3 20X3 and there is now data available for two complete years (Appendix 1). Veyatie has found it difficult to interpret this qualitative data and also the trends in this data. Some board members question its usefulness and propose reverting back to reporting just the financial indicators which they are used to.

Veyatie collects this data by asking customers to rate their satisfaction with their visit to the store as they are paying for their items. The scores range from 1 (completely dissatisfied) to 5 (completely satisfied). The mean score is the performance indicator reported to the board and the senior managers. Customers are encouraged to leave a score by having their names entered into a quarterly prize draw to win tickets to major football matches, concerts and amusement parks.

You are a performance management expert and have been asked by the board to assess the difficulties in using and interpreting the customer satisfaction data at Veyatie.

Exhibit 3 – Balanced scorecard

A consultant has suggested to the board that the introduction of a balanced scorecard approach may improve business performance, as Veyatie is unlikely to achieve all of its strategic objectives in the near future. The board has already heard what the benefits of the balanced scorecard are, but are sceptical about these.

The board has asked for your advice on the problems of implementing and using the balanced scorecard approach at Veyatie. One aspect of this advice should focus on the selection of suitable performance measures and the consultant has already chosen some performance measures which could be included in a balanced scorecard at Veyatie (Appendix 2). These have been provided to help you illustrate your advice on the problems of using the balanced scorecard.

Note: The board would welcome your advice on how to refine the performance measures as part of your advice on the problems of using and implementing the balanced scorecard, but does not want you to give a detailed evaluation of the advantages and disadvantages of each performance measure, or to suggest completely new measures.

Required:

It is now 1 September 20X5.

Respond to the board's request for work on the following areas:

(a) **customer satisfaction data and** **(8 marks)**

(b) **the problems of implementing and using the balanced scorecard.** **(12 marks)**

Professional marks will be awarded for the demonstration of skill in analysis and evaluation, scepticism and commercial acumen in your answer. **(5 marks)**

(Total: 25 marks)

Exhibit 4 – Appendix 1

Customer satisfaction data

Percentage of customers giving customer satisfaction scores* between 1 and 5

		20X3		**20X4**				**20X5**	
Narrative	**Score**	**Q3**	**Q4**	**Q1**	**Q2**	**Q3**	**Q4**	**Q1**	**Q2**
Completely satisfied	5	5%	5%	50%	5%	5%	0%	5%	45%
Very satisfied	4	10%	5%	0%	14%	15%	5%	20%	1%
Satisfied	3	70%	65%	0%	56%	50%	65%	45%	1%
Somewhat dissatisfied	2	10%	20%	0%	20%	25%	25%	25%	8%
Completely dissatisfied	1	5%	5%	50%	5%	5%	5%	5%	45%
Mean score		**3.00**	**2.85**	**3.00**	**2.94**	**2.90**	**2.70**	**2.95**	**2.93**

* Satisfaction scores were collected from a large number of customers when paying for their items.

Exhibit 5 – Appendix 2

Perspective	**Performance measure**
Financial	Operating profit margin
	Inventory turnover
	Current ratio
Customer	Customer satisfaction
	Market share
Internal business processes	Stock out percentage[1]
Learning and innovation	Total employee training days[2]

Notes:

1 Stock out percentage is the percentage of product lines which are unavailable for sale in each store at the beginning of each trading day.

2 The human resources department already records the total number of employee training days. Employee training covers the three main areas of health and safety training, training in handling customer complaints and training staff to understand the range of products available and how to display them attractively in the store.

62 VUNDERG (MAR/JUN 19)

Company information

Vunderg manufactures windows and related products. The overheads in the business are high and primarily relate to procurement, customer administration and product design. Procurement and customer administration overheads relate to all of Vunderg's product groups. Design overheads currently relate to only two product groups, glasshouses and conservatories. Vunderg's current costing system has been in use for a long time and absorbs overheads into product costs on a direct labour hours basis. The current costing system does not involve identifying the factors which drive the costs of the company's activities and allocating overheads to products based on their usage of those factors.

Current product range

Windows

For many years, Vunderg has manufactured UPVC window frames used for residential house building. Vunderg buys the glass from an external supplier, inserts it into a frame and sells the completed window units to a small number of large construction companies. These window units all have standard designs, specifications and sizes. This market is very competitive, and Vunderg must offer a complete range of windows for sale to the construction companies.

Glasshouses

Five years ago, Vunderg developed a range of small garden glasshouses, for non-commercial use, made of attractive and high quality materials. After initial quality problems due to the use of materials and manufacturing methods new to Vunderg, glasshouse production is now efficient, quality is high and the glasshouses now command premium prices. The glasshouses are sold nationwide through 40 retailers, who vary significantly in the size of orders they place and the level of customer support and trade discounts which they receive from Vunderg. As a result, the profitability of selling to different retailers, or types of retailer, varies significantly.

Conservatories

More recently, Vunderg began manufacturing conservatories* using the same materials as its glasshouse range. These conservatories are expensive and are made to measure for individual customers' houses. There are a wide range of finishes and options available to choose from. Conservatories which match garden glasshouses have become popular with customers who can afford them. Unlike Vunderg's other products, these are sold directly to individual home owners.

* Conservatories are structures made mainly of glass, which are attached to the side of residential houses. They form an additional room in a house and are popular in cool climates.

Future product development

Vunderg is looking to move into another new market soon, as the market for making windows for houses is now saturated. This new market will be the manufacture and design of large windows to be installed in the entrance halls of large, prestigious commercial buildings. These will be bespoke items, designed and manufactured to customers' own specifications.

Recent performance

The CEO is concerned by a recent fall in overall net profit margin despite modest revenue growth and good control of direct costs. In particular, he has said, 'The conservatories part of the business may not be as profitable as its positive contribution (Appendix 1) may suggest. For example, our procurement department spends a lot of time sourcing special materials and finishes requested by customers. Many conservatories have leaked in the rain so we have to rectify these faults and work on a new design to prevent this happening. As we have only basic information systems, it is unclear how much some of these activities are costing. Over 20% of our factory space is dedicated to manufacturing conservatories. We may be better off discontinuing these products.'

The CEO has some experience of activity based costing (ABC) in a previous role and believes that activity based management (ABM) could help to improve Vunderg's strategic performance. He is keen to know what the limitations are of using the ABM method for Vunderg's products and customer types and the problems with its implementation before he makes a decision to implement it.

It is now 1 September 20X5.

Required:

(a) **Advise the CEO how activity based management (ABM) could help improve the strategic performance of Vunderg. (13 marks)**

(b) **As required by the CEO, assess the limitations of using the ABM method for Vunderg's products and customer types and the problems with its implementation. (12 marks)**

(Total: 25 marks)

Appendix 1

Contribution by product type for the year ended 30 June 20X5

Product type	No. of units sold	Total contribution ($000)
Windows	175,000	9,800
Glasshouses	3,800	969
Conservatories	650	910

63 ZONES (DEC 18)

Company information

Zones is an overnight parcel delivery business. Since it was founded by the current CEO, it has grown rapidly due to a boom in online shopping. It now operates 1,000 delivery vehicles of various sizes. Recently, financial performance and market share have deteriorated. Zones has had no clear corporate vision, an excessive focus on financial objectives and inadequate systems to measure and manage performance of the underlying processes driving its financial performance.

Business model

Zones' collection and delivery service uses delivery vehicles to transport parcels to and from local depots and individual addresses. Vehicles may also pick up parcels from the addresses to which they deliver. Each time the vehicle calls to pick up or deliver parcels is known as a stop, and the time of day for each stop is booked in advance. At the end of each day, vehicles, along with any parcels not delivered, return to the depot. Regardless of who pays for the service, Zones regards anyone to whom it delivers, or from whom it picks up parcels, as a customer. In the long term, the requirements of both of these groups for a competitively priced, reliable and flexible service will be similar.

Performance improvement proposals

The CEO believes that reductions in customer satisfaction and flexibility, caused by a decline in operational performance, may have led to the recent deterioration in financial performance and market share. It has been suggested that Zones use the Lynch and Cross performance pyramid (Appendix 1) to reverse this deterioration, and three new measures for operational performance have been suggested in Appendix 2. The CEO has stated that Zones' corporate vision should be:

'To increase shareholder wealth by becoming the leading overnight parcel delivery business, providing quality, reliability and value for customers.'

It is also proposed to use the DMAIC (define, measure, analyse, improve and control) method to implement the six sigma methodology to improve the quality of delivery. Two measures have been defined in Appendix 3 which may help improve Zones' delivery performance.

Required:

(a) **Advise the CEO how the Lynch and Cross performance pyramid can help Zones achieve its corporate vision. (7 marks)**

(b) **Using the performance pyramid, evaluate the extent to which the suggested new measures in Appendix 2 can be used to measure and manage operational performance at Zones. (9 marks)**

(c) **Advise whether the two measures defined in Appendix 3 are suitable for use in the DMAIC method to implement the six sigma methodology in order to improve delivery performance. (9 marks)**

(Total: 25 marks)

Appendix 1

Lynch and Cross performance pyramid

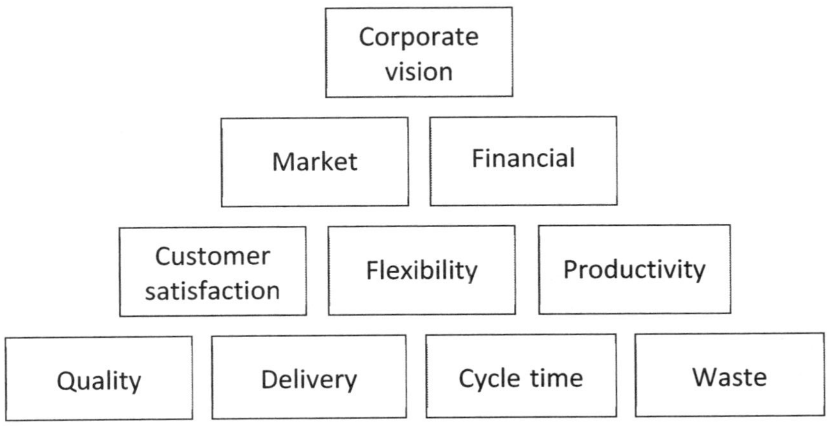

Appendix 2

Suggested new measures for operational performance

Measure	Description
Vehicle utilisation	Average utilisation of all vehicle capacity. This is measured by taking the average of vehicle load as a percentage of capacity when the vehicle leaves the depot at the beginning of each day and the vehicle load as a percentage of capacity when the vehicle returns to the depot at the end of each day. Capacity is measured either according to the internal volume or the length of the vehicle, depending on the type of vehicle being used.
Fuel consumption	Average litres of fuel per kilometre travelled for all vehicles.
On-time stops	Percentage of stops made within 30 minutes* of the booked time.

* Zones receives complaints from customers relating to deliveries not made on time. Of these, less than 0.0001% relate to deliveries made within 30 minutes of the booked time.

Appendix 3

Suggested new measures for improving quality of delivery using the DMAIC methodology

Measure	Description
On-time stops	Percentage of stops made within 10 minutes of the booked time.
Failed deliveries	Percentage of deliveries which cannot be made due to the customer being unavailable to take the delivery, or by parcels being incorrectly addressed. Currently, 5% of deliveries are failed and have to be returned to the depot.

64 BAZEELE (MAR/JUN 18)

Company background

Bazeele hires out plant and machinery to small firms working in the construction industry. Bazeele's senior managers, including the chief executive officer (CEO), have worked in the business since it was established 30 years ago, and they own the majority of the shares. During that time, Bazeele has acquired many smaller plant hire businesses. Of these business units, those which have underperformed after acquisition have either been sold on or restructured, for example, to increase their operating margins. Bazeele has recently diversified by hiring out large items of plant to large construction firms working on major infrastructure projects. These projects can last for up to 10 years. Strong growth in the general economy has increased the number of these large projects and has also led to a predicted large increase in bank interest rates.

Objectives

The shareholders' objective is for Bazeele to maintain its historic return on capital employed (ROCE). Managers at business units are given the objective of maintaining net profit margins of their own business units. Similarly, managers at individual branches of business units are given the same objective according to their own areas of responsibility.

Value-based management approach

Following two years of poor performance, it has been suggested to the CEO that Bazeele would benefit from adopting a value-based management (VBM) approach.

The CEO requires your advice and has said, 'The shareholders are unsure what VBM is, whether it will benefit Bazeele, and what changes the business would need to make if it were to adopt it. All managers in the business are already clear what their objectives are. For example, one business unit manager recently postponed some expensive staff training on improving customer satisfaction, which I believe was the correct decision. Our recent poor performance has meant we cannot afford this sort of expenditure, especially as we have no information on what levels of customer satisfaction actually are. Personally, I dislike change, but would not object to the adoption of VBM if it was thought to be beneficial for Bazeele.

Economic value added

The shareholders have heard that economic value added (EVA™) can be used to measure whether Bazeele has created or destroyed value for its shareholders, but this has not yet been calculated.'

Details of the company's recent performance are given in Appendix 1.

Required:

(a) **Evaluate whether a value-based management approach is appropriate for Bazeele.** **(7 marks)**

(b) **Explain to the CEO what changes Bazeele would need to make to its performance measurement and performance management systems if it were to adopt a value-based management approach.** **(7 marks)**

(c) **Using the information in Appendix 1, advise the CEO whether Bazeele has generated economic value for its shareholders.** **(11 marks)**

(Total: 25 marks)

Appendix 1 – Notes from Bazeele's management accounts for the most recent year end

1 Net profit after tax for the year: $10m

2 Capital employed at the start of the year: $250m

3 The interest charge for the year was $15m on a variable rate loan with an interest rate of 10%. Bazeele is funded 60% by debt and 40% by equity. The cost of equity is 12%. Bazeele pays tax at a rate of 20%.

4 The depreciation charge for non-current assets for the year was $6.0m; the economic depreciation of which was $14.0m. At the start of the period, the accumulated economic depreciation of non-current assets exceeded its accounting depreciation by $16.0m.

5 Brought forward at the start of the year was a provision of $4.8m which was made in respect of a debt owed by a customer who has since repaid it.

6 Within the current profit or loss account there is an expense for $0.6m for advertising in trade magazines. This led to several enquiries from new customers involved in large infrastructure projects, which has resulted in Bazeele signing at least two large contracts after the end of the accounting period.

65 DIBBLE (MAR/JUN 16)

Background information

Dibble is formed of two autonomous divisions, Timber and Steel, and manufactures components for use in the construction industry. Dibble has always absorbed production overheads to the cost of each product on the basis of machine hours.

Timber Division

Timber Division manufactures timber frames used to support the roofs of new houses. The timber, which is purchased pre-cut to the correct length, is assembled into the finished frame by a factory worker who fastens the components together. Timber Division manufactures six standard sizes of frame which is sufficient for use in most newly built houses.

Steel Division

Steel Division manufactures steel frames and roof supports for use in small commercial buildings such as shops and restaurants. There is a large range of products, and many customers also specify bespoke designs for short production runs or one-off building projects. Steel is cut and drilled using the division's own programmable computer aided manufacturing machinery (CAM), and is bolted together or welded by hand.

Steel Division's strategy is to produce novel bespoke products at a price comparable to the simpler and more conventional products offered by its competitors. For example, many of Steel Division's customers choose to have steel covered in one of a wide variety of coloured paints and other protective coatings at the end of the production process. This is performed off-site by a subcontractor, after which the product is returned to Steel Division for despatch to the customer. Customers are charged the subcontractor's cost plus a 10% mark up for choosing this option. The board of Steel Division has admitted that this pricing structure may be too simplistic, and that it is unsure of the overall profitability of sales of some groups of products or sectors of the market.

Recently, several customers have complained that incorrectly applied paint has flaked off the steel after only a few months' use. More seriously, a fast food restaurant has commenced litigation with Dibble after it had to close for a week while steel roof frames supplied by Steel Division were repainted. Following this, the production manager has proposed increasing the number of staff inspecting the quality of coating on the frames, and purchasing expensive imaging machinery to make inspection more efficient.

Activity based costing (ABC) and activity based management (ABM)

The chief executive officer (CEO) at Dibble has approached you as a performance management expert for your advice. 'At a conference recently', he told you, 'I watched a presentation by a CEO at a similar business to ours talking about the advantages and disadvantages of using ABC and how over several years the adoption of ABM had helped them to improve both strategic and operational performance.'

'I don't want you to do any detailed calculations at this stage, but I'd like to know more about ABC and ABM, and know whether they would be useful for Dibble', he said.

Management accounts

You are provided with extracts of the most recent management accounts for Timber and Steel Divisions:

Division ($000)	**Timber**	**Steel**
Revenue	25,815	20,605
Materials	12,000	10,100
Direct labour	4,500	850
Subcontract costs	75	650
Analysis of production overheads ($000)	**Timber**	**Steel**
Set up time for CAM machinery	–	575
Machining time	–	2,777
Storage of goods awaiting or returned from subcontractors	120	395
Transfer of goods to and from subcontractors	50	300
Inspection and testing	35	425
Total production overheads	205	4,472
Gross profit	9,035	4,533

Required:

(a) (i) Advise the CEO how activity based costing could be implemented. (4 marks)

(ii) Assess whether it may be more appropriate to use activity based costing in Timber and Steel Divisions than the costing basis currently used. (8 marks)

(b) Advise the CEO how activity based management could be used to improve business performance in Dibble. (13 marks)

(Total: 25 marks)

66 FORION ELECTRONICS (JUN 15)

Company information

Forion Electronics (Forion) manufactures a range of electronic goods. Its business has grown rapidly over the last ten years and is now complex and international. Forion manufactures over 100 different products, selling into 25 different countries. There is a supplier base of over 200 companies from which Forion sources.

Information requirements

As the business has become more complex, the board has found it difficult to pull together all the information that they require in order to make decisions.

The current information systems are developed in-house and are based in the functional departments (such as purchasing, manufacturing, warehousing and delivery, selling and marketing). The organisation uses the financial system as a means of bringing together information for an overview of corporate performance.

There have been a number of examples of problems encountered with information in Forion:

- there are inefficiencies arising from ordering the wrong amount of subcomponents
- there are often stock-outs or obsolescence of unsold goods in the warehouses, although the marketing department prepares good sales forecasts; and
- sometimes, there are insufficient delivery vehicles available to meet customer deadlines.

Enterprise resource planning system (ERPS)

The board of Forion believes the problems arise from poor information sharing within the company. They are considering the purchase of an ERPS to be the single information system for the whole organisation.

Strategic alliance

Also, Forion is planning to launch a smartphone. However, in order to make it competitive they need to have high-visibility, durable screens. As the cost of screen development is considerable, it has been decided to form a strategic alliance with a well-known screen manufacturer to provide this key component for the new smartphone. Bon Accord Screens (BAS) has been chosen as the strategic ally, as they have a strong reputation for their quality of manufacturing and new product development. BAS has been trying to break into the smartphone market for several years.

The alliance agreement has stipulated three critical areas of performance for BAS' supply to Forion:

1 quality of manufacturing, measured by fault rates of screens supplied being within agreed tolerances (so that they fit Forion's phone-bodies)

2 time of delivery, measured by the number of times a shipment is more than one day overdue; and

3 the ability to provide technical upgrades to the screens as the market demands.

The service level agreement (SLA) will be based on these three points and there will be financial penalties built into the agreement if BAS fails to meet these.

Required:

(a) Discuss the integration of information systems in an ERPS and how the ERPS may impact on performance management issues at Forion. (10 marks)

(b) Evaluate, from Forion's viewpoint, the usefulness of the three critical areas in the alliance agreement for measuring the performance of BAS. (8 marks)

(c) Evaluate the relative reliability of financial and non-financial data from internal and external sources in the context of the alliance between Forion and BAS. (7 marks)

(Total: 25 marks)

67 THE SPARE FOR SHIPS COMPANY (SFS) (JUN 10)

Company information

The Spare for Ships Company (SFS) has a specialist machining facility which serves the shipbuilding components market.

Current job-costing system

The current job-costing system has two categories of direct cost (direct materials and direct manufacturing labour) and a single indirect cost pool (manufacturing overhead which is allocated on the basis of direct labour hours). The indirect cost allocation rate of the existing job-costing system is $120 per direct manufacturing labour-hour.

Proposed activity-based approach to job-costing

Recently, the Visibility Consultancy Partnership (VCP) proposed the use of an activity-based approach to redefine the job-costing system of SFS. VCP made a recommendation to retain the two direct cost categories. However, VCP further recommended the replacement of the single indirect-cost pool with five indirect-cost pools.

Each of the five indirect-cost pools represents an activity area at the manufacturing premises of SFS. Each activity area has its own supervisor who is responsible for his/her operating budget.

Relevant data are as follows:

Activity area	**Cost driver used as allocation base**	**Cost allocation rate ($)**
Materials handling	Number of components	0.50
Lathe work	Number of cuts	0.70
Milling	Number of machine hours	24.00
Grinding	Number of components	1.50
Inspection	Number of units inspected	20.00

SFS has recently invested in 'state of the art' IT systems which have the capability to automatically collate all of the data necessary for budgeting in each of the five activity areas.

Illustrative cost per unit calculations

The management accountant of SFS calculated the manufacturing cost per unit of two representative jobs under the two costing systems as follows:

	Job order 973	**Job order 974**
	$	$
Current costing system	1,172.00	620.00
Activity-based costing system	1,612.00	588.89

Required:

(a) (i) **Compare the cost figures per unit for Job order 973 and Job order 974 calculated by the management accountant and explain the reasons for, and potential consequences of, the differences in the job cost estimates produced under the two costing systems. (8 marks)**

(ii) **Explain two potential problems that SFS might have experienced in the successful implementation of an activity-based costing system using its recently acquired 'state of the art' IT systems. (4 marks)**

(b) The application of Activity Based Management (ABM) requires that the management of SFS focus on each of the following:

(i) Operational ABM

(ii) Strategic ABM

(iii) The implicit value of an activity'.

Required:

Critically appraise the above statement and explain the risks attaching to the use of ABM. **(8 marks)**

(c) **Briefly discuss how ABM can assist other performance improvement strategies, such as Total Quality Management, Six Sigma and Business Process Reengineering.** **(5 marks)**

(Total: 25 marks)

68 APX ACCOUNTANCY (JUN 11)

Background information

APX Accountancy (APX) is an accountancy partnership with 12 branches covering each of the main cities of Emland. The business is well established, having organically grown over the last 40 years to become the second largest non-international practice in Emland. The accountancy market is mature and expands and contracts along with the general economic performance of Emland.

APX offers accountancy, audit, tax and business advisory services. The current business environment in Emland is dominated by a recession and the associated insolvency work is covered within the business advisory area of APX.

Strategic performance evaluation

At present, the practice collects the following information for strategic performance evaluation:

	Audit	**Tax**	**Business Advisory**	**Total**
Revenue ($m)				
APX	69.1	89.2	64.7	223.0
Accounting industry	557.0	573.0	462.0	1,592.0
Change in revenue on previous year				
APX	3.0%	8.0%	22.0%	10.0%
Accounting industry	2.5%	4.5%	16.0%	6.8%
Profit margin at APX	6.4%	7.8%	10.5%	8.1%
Customer service score (1 to 5 with 5 being excellent)				
APX	3.4	3.9	4.1	

The above figures are for the most recent financial year and illustrate the metrics used by APX. Equivalent monthly figures are produced for each of the monthly partner meetings which review practice performance.

Remuneration

The staff are remunerated based on their grade, with non-partners obtaining a bonus of up to 10% of basic salary based on their line managers' annual review. The partners receive a fixed salary with a share of profit which depends on their contractual responsibilities within the partnership.

Fitzgerald and Moon's building block model

The managing partner of APX is dissatisfied with the existing performance management system, as she is not convinced that it is helping to achieve the long-term goal of expanding and ultimately floating the business on the national stock exchange. Therefore, she has asked you to consider the impact of applying Fitzgerald and Moon's building block approach to performance management in the practice.

Required:

(a) **Briefly describe Fitzgerald and Moon's building block model. (4 marks)**

(b) **Evaluate the existing performance management system at APX by applying the building block model. (9 marks)**

(c) **Explain the main improvements the introduction of a building block approach to performance management could provide, and suggest specific improvements to the existing system of performance measures at APX in light of the introduction of the building block model. (12 marks)**

(Total: 25 marks)

69 COD ELECTRICAL MOTORS (DEC 11)

Background information

Cod Electrical Motors (Cod) manufactures electrical motors for some of the 24 different European domestic appliance manufacturers. Their motors are used in appliances such as washing machines and refrigerators. Cod has been in business for over 50 years and has obtained a reputation for producing reliable, low cost motors.

Mission statement

Cod has recently rewritten its mission statement, which now reads:

'Cod Electrical Motors is committed to providing competitively priced, high quality products, with service exceeding customer expectations. We will add value to our business relationships by investing in product development and highly trained personnel.'

Key performance indicators (KPIs)

The board have recognised that their existing KPIs do not capture the features of the corporate mission. They are worried that the staff see the mission statement as a public relations exercise rather than the communication of Cod's vision.

Monthly board papers

The monthly board papers contain a simple performance summary which is used as the key performance measurement system at that level.

Example of board papers for November 2011:

Cod Electrical Motors – key performance indicators for November 2011

	This month	YTD	Comparative
Profit ($m)	2.1	25.6	1.9
Free cash flow ($m)	3.4	17.6	1.6
Return on capital employed (%)	12.4	11.7	11.8

Notes:

(a) The year end is 31 December.

(b) The comparative figure is for the same month in the previous year.

(c) ROCE is an annualised figure.

(d) YTD means year to date.

Additional performance information

There are additional performance indicators not available to the board that line management use for a more detailed picture:

	Note	2011	2010
	1		
Activity			
No of orders		2,560	2,449
No of deliveries		1,588	1,660
Staff			
No of staff (FTE basis)	2	1,229	1,226
No of staff training days		2,286	1,762
No of vacant posts	3	11	17
Customers			
No of orders with a complaint	4		
late delivery		26	25
product quality		39	31
customer service		21	24
other		52	43
Preferential supplier status	5	14	12
Production			
New products			
begun in year to date		2	1
in development at month end		4	3
launched in year to date		1	1
Quality			
internal failure costs ($000)		3,480	2,766
external failure costs ($000)		872	693

Notes:

1 Figures are year to date with comparatives from the previous year quoted on the same basis.

2 FTE = Full-time equivalent staff numbers.

3 Post is considered vacant if unfilled for more than four months.

4 Complaints are logged and classified into the four categories given when received.

5 Number of customers where Cod holds preferred supplier status.

Required:

(a) Assess whether the current key performance indicators (KPIs) meet the expected features of a modern performance measurement system. (7 marks)

(b) Explain how the performance pyramid (Lynch and Cross) can help Cod's board to reach its goal of a coherent set of performance measures. (6 marks)

(c) Evaluate the current system using the performance pyramid and apply the performance pyramid to Cod in order to suggest additional KPIs and a set of operational performance measures for Cod. (12 marks)

(Total: 25 marks)

70 CALLISTO (JUN 12)

Background information

Callisto Retail (Callisto) is an on-line reseller of local craft products related to the historic culture of the country of Callistan. The business started ten years ago as a hobby of two brothers, Jeff and George. The brothers produced humorous, short video clips about Callistan which were posted on their website and became highly popular. They decided to use the website to try to sell Callistan merchandise and good initial sales made them believe that they had a viable business idea.

Callisto has gone from strength to strength and now boasts sales of $120m per annum, selling anything related to Callistan. Callisto is still very much the brothers' family business.

Virtual company structure

They have gathered around themselves a number of strategic partners into what Jeff describes as a virtual company. Callisto has the core functions of video clip production, finance and supplier relationship management. The rest of the functions of the organisation (warehousing, delivery and website development) are outsourced to strategic partners.

The brothers work from their family home in the rural North of Callistan while other Callisto employees work from their homes in the surrounding villages and towns. These employees are involved in video editing, system maintenance, handling customer complaints and communication with suppliers and outsourcers regarding inventory. The employees log in to Callisto's systems via the national internet infrastructure. The outsourced functions are handled by multinational companies of good reputation who are based around the world. The brothers have always been fascinated by information technology and so they depend on email and electronic data interchange to communicate with their product suppliers and outsourcing partners.

Customer complaints

Recently, there have been emails from regular customers of the Callisto website complaining about slow or non-delivery of orders that they have placed. George has commented that this represents a major threat to Callisto as the company operates on small profit margins, relying on volume to drive the business. He believes that sales growth will drive the profitability of the business due to its cost structure.

Warehouse and delivery contract with RLR Logistics

Jeff handles the management of outsourcing and has been reviewing the contracts that exist between Callisto and its strategic partner for warehousing and delivery, RLR Logistics. The current contract for warehousing and delivery is due for renewal in two months and currently, has the following service level agreements (SLAs):

1 RLR agree to receive and hold inventory from Callisto's product suppliers.

2 RLR agree to hold 14 days inventory of Callisto's products.

3 RLR agree to despatch from their warehouse any order passed from Callisto within three working days, inventory allowing.

4 RLR agree to deliver to customers anywhere in Callistan within two days of despatch.

Breaches in these SLAs incur financial penalties on a sliding scale depending on the number and severity of the problems. Each party to the contract collects their own data on performance and this has led to disagreements in the past over whether service levels have been achieved although no penalties have been triggered to date. The most common disagreement arises over inventory levels held by RLR with RLR claiming that it cannot be expected to deliver products that are late in arriving to inventory due to the product suppliers' production and delivery issues.

Required:

(a) Assess the difficulties of performance measurement and performance management in complex business structures such as Callisto, especially in respect of the performance of their employees and strategic partners. (17 marks)

(b) Evaluate appropriate measures that Callisto could use to assess the performance of its employees and strategic partners. Suggest suitable methods for collecting the data required to make this assessment. (8 marks)

(Total: 25 marks)

71 GRAVITON CLOTHING (DEC 13)

Background information

Graviton Clothing (Graviton) is a listed manufacturer of clothing with a strong reputation for producing desirable, fashionable products which can attract high selling prices. The company's objective is to maximise shareholder wealth. Graviton's products are sold through its own chain of stores. Graviton's markets demand designs which are in tune with current fashion trends which can alter every few weeks. Therefore, the business's stated aim is to focus production on these changing market trends by maintaining flexibility to adapt to that market demand through close control of all stages of the supply chain (design, manufacture and distribution).

Current performance measurement system

The chief executive officer (CEO) is unhappy with the current performance measurement system at Graviton. The system was created about five years ago by the finance director who has subsequently retired. The aim of the system was to provide the company with a list of measures which would cover performance at the strategic, tactical and operational levels of management. An example of the most recent performance report is given in Table 1.

Table 1: Graviton Performance Dashboard Report for the year to Sep 2013

	2013	**2012**	**2011**	**Change 2013/2012**
Financial				
Revenue ($m)	1,723	1,570	1,413	9.7%
Operating profit ($m)	320	314	308	1.9%
ROCE	15.8%	15.9%	15.9%	
Design				
Design awards won	3	2	3	50.0%
Manufacture				
Average time to market (days)	22.2	22.3	22.1	–0.4%
Distribution				
Deliveries on time	87.0%	86.8%	87.3%	0.2%

Commentary:

- The revenue growth of the business remains strong in a difficult market.
- Return on capital employed matches the industry average of about 16%.
- Time to market for new designs has been maintained at 22 days by paying overtime to designers in order to meet production schedules.

Review of performance measurement system

Recent press reports about Graviton have been mixed, with positive comments about the innovative new designs and much admiration over the growth of sales which the business has achieved. However, there has been some criticism from customers of the durability of Graviton's clothes and from institutional investors that the dividend growth is not strong.

The CEO believes that there are major gaps in the current list of key metrics used by Graviton. She wants an evaluation of the current system and suggestions for improvements. However, she has warned you that the board wants a reasoned argument for each measure to be included in the list in order to avoid overloading each level of management with too much data.

Recent problems appearing on internal audit reports

Although rapidly growing, Graviton has had some problems in the last few years which have appeared on recent internal audit reports. It was found that a senior manager at factory site 1 has been delaying invoicing for completed orders in order to ensure that profit targets are met in both the current and the next accounting period. At factory site 2, there has been excellent return on a low capital employed figure although there is a significant adverse variance in the equipment repairs account.

Three common problems

The board is dominated by long-serving executives who are sceptical of change, given Graviton's growth over the past three years. At a recent board meeting, they have shared the CEO's concern about data overload and also have pointed out a variety of problems with the use of performance measures. They presented the CEO with a list of three common problems (myopia, gaming, ossification) and argued that the current good performance of the business did not justify changing the performance measurement system. The CEO needs to know if these problems apply to Graviton and if they do, then what can be done to manage them.

Required:

(a) **Evaluate the current performance measurement system using the Performance Pyramid of Lynch and Cross. (15 marks)**

(b) **Assess whether the three problems listed by the board apply to Graviton and suggest appropriate performance management solutions to them. (10 marks)**

(Total: 25 marks)

72 VICTORIA-YEELAND LOGISTICS (JUN 15)

Background information

Victoria-Yeeland Logistics (Victoria) is a logistics support business, which operates a fleet of lorries to deliver packages of goods on behalf of its customers within the country of Yeeland. Victoria collects packages from its customers' manufacturing sites or from the customers' port of importation and delivers to the final user of the goods. The lorries are run and maintained from a set of depots spread throughout Yeeland.

The overall objective of Victoria is to maximise shareholder wealth. The delivery business in Yeeland is dominated by two international companies and one other domestic business and profit margins are extremely tight. The market is saturated by these large operators and a number of smaller operators. The cost base of Victoria is dominated by staff and fuel, with fuel prices being highly volatile in the last few years.

Balanced scorecard (BSC)

In order to improve performance measurement and management at Victoria, the chief financial officer (CFO) plans to use the BSC. However, she has been pulled away from this project in order to deal with an issue with refinancing the business' principal lending facility. The CFO has already identified some suitable metrics but needs you, as her assistant, to complete her work and address any potential questions which might arise when she makes her presentation on the BSC to the board. The CFO has completed the identification of metrics for three of the perspectives (Appendix 1) but has yet to complete the work on the metrics for the customer perspective. This should be done using the data given in Appendix 2.

Reward management system

Additionally, two issues have arisen in the reward management system at Victoria, one in relation to senior management and the other for operational managers. Currently, senior management gets a fixed salary supplemented by an annual bonus awarded by the board. Shareholders have been complaining that these bonuses are not suitable. The operational managers also get bonuses based on their performance as assessed by their management superiors. The operational managers are unhappy with the system. In order to address this, it has been suggested that they should be involved in bonus target setting as otherwise there is a sense of demotivation from such a system. The CFO wants an evaluation of this system of rewards in light of the introduction of the BSC and best practice.

Required:

(a) **Discuss how Victoria's success in the customer perspective may impact on the metrics given in the financial perspective.** **(5 marks)**

(b) **Recommend, with justification, and calculate a suitable performance metric for each customer perspective success factor. Comment on the problems of using customer complaints to measure whether packages are delivered safely and on time.** **(11 marks)**

(c) **Advise Victoria on the reward management issues outlined by the CFO.** **(9 marks)**

(Total: 25 marks)

Appendix 1

Financial perspective

(How do we appear to our shareholders?)

Return on capital employed

Profit margin

Revenue growth

Customer perspective

(How do we appear to our customers?)

Success factors:

Ability to meet customers' transport needs

Ability to deliver packages quickly

Ability to deliver packages on time

Ability to deliver packages safely

Internal process perspective

(What business processes must excel?)

Time taken to load and unload

Lorry capacity utilisation

Learning and growth perspective

(How do we sustain and improve our ability to grow?)

Leadership competence (qualitative judgement)

Training days per employee

Appendix 2

The process: A customer makes a transport request for a package to be collected and delivered to a given destination. The customer is supplied with a time window in which the delivery will occur. Packages are then loaded onto lorries and delivered according to a route specified by the depot's routing manager.

Total number of customer transport requests	610,000
Total number of packages transported	548,000
Total number of lorry journeys	73,000
Total package kilometres	65,760,000
Total package minutes	131,520,000
Number of delivery complaints from customers:	
from damaged packages	8,220
from late delivery (outside agreed time window)	21,920

Notes:

1 All figures are for the last financial year.

2 A package kilometre is defined as a kilometre travelled by one package.

3 A package minute is defined as a minute spent in transit by one package.

73 SOUP RAIL SERVICES (SEPT/DEC 15) (AMENDED)

Exhibit 1 – Company information

Soup operates passenger rail services in Deeland, a technologically advanced country, with high demand for fast reliable rail travel from business and leisure passengers. Many passengers choose train travel because they see it as less harmful to the environment than other forms of transport.

Soup's main objective is to maximise shareholder wealth. Since becoming licensed to operate routes in Regions A and B by the Deeland government five years ago, Soup has consistently delivered increased dividends and share prices for investors.

Exhibit 2 – Government warning

In its initial appraisal of the licensing opportunity, Soup expected to operate the routes for at least 15 years, however, their licence may not be renewed when it expires in three years' time. The government has warned Soup it 'is unhappy about high returns to shareholders while there are many reports of poor passenger service, overcrowded trains and unreliable services on certain routes and at busy times'.

Exhibit 3 – Operations, competition and government involvement

Soup owns its fleet of diesel powered trains. Each train in Region A has seven coaches with 70 passenger seats available per coach. In the less busy Region B, each train has six coaches each with 70 seats. As a condition of the licence, Soup runs a set number of services at both busy and quieter times in both regions. Soup has two larger rivals, both operating electric trains, which cause less harm to the environment than diesel powered trains. They run on the same routes in both regions.

The government regulates fares charged to passengers, which are the same per distance travelled for every operator in that region. The railway track, stations and other infrastructure are managed by the government which charges the operators a fee. There are several stations along the route which are only used by Soup trains and others where Soup trains do not stop at all.

Exhibit 4 – Current performance measures

Soup's trains are 25 years old, originally purchased cheaply from an operator whose licence was withdrawn by the government. Soup believes the low price it paid is a key competitive advantage enabling them to steadily increase their return on capital employed, the company's main performance measure, to a level well in excess of their rivals. The shareholders are pleased with the growth in passenger numbers over the last five years, which is the other performance measure Soup uses.

Exhibit 5 – Recent issues

Soup's ageing trains spend increasing time undergoing preventative maintenance, safety checks or repairs. A recent television documentary also showed apparently poor conditions on board, such as defective heating and washroom facilities and dirty, torn seating. Passengers complained in the programme of difficulties finding a seat, the unreliability of accessing wireless internet services and even that the menu in the on-board cafe had not changed for five years.

Soup's CEO responded that unreliable internet access arose from the rapid growth in passengers expecting to access the internet on trains. She said Soup had never received any formal complaints about the lack of choice in the on-board cafe, nor had she heard of a recent press report that Soup's trains were badly maintained, so causing harm to the environment.

Exhibit 6 – Development of balanced performance measures

The CEO has asked you, as chief management accountant, for your advice. 'In view of the government's warning, we must develop performance measures balancing the needs of passengers with the requirements of the shareholders', she has said. 'I don't want to know how to improve the actual performance of the business; that is the job of the operational managers, nor do I just want a list of suggested performance measures. Instead I need to know why these performance measures will help to improve the performance of Soup.'

She has tasked you to assist on three areas. Firstly, advise the CEO on how the use of the balanced scorecard could improve the performance management system of Soup. Secondly, using the performance data given in Appendix 1, evaluate the comments of the Deeland government that Soup's trains are overcrowded. Finally, assess the problems Soup may encounter in selecting and interpreting performance measures when applying the balanced scorecard to its performance management system.

Required:

It is now 1 September 20X5.

Respond to the CEO's request for work on the following areas:

(a) how the balanced scorecard could improve the performance management system **(9 marks)**

(b) the comments that Soup's trains are overcrowded and **(6 marks)**

(c) the problems in selecting and interpreting performance measures **(5 marks)**

Professional marks will be awarded for the demonstration of skill in analysis and evaluation and commercial acumen in your answer. **(5 marks)**

(Total: 25 marks)

Exhibit 7 – Appendix 1: Available data

The following data applies to Soup:

	Region A	**Region B**
Number of services per day:		
Peak times	4	4
Other times	6	8
Number of passengers per day:		
Peak times	2,500	1,400
Other times	2,450	1,850

Section 3

ANSWERS TO PRACTICE QUESTIONS – SECTION A

1 FREUCHIE (SEPT/DEC 21) (AMENDED)

Report

To: The board of Fruechie Retail (Frueuchie)

From: An Accountant

Date: Sept 20X5

Subject: Performance reporting and management issues at Freuchie

This report evaluates both the quantitative and narrative aspects of the current performance report used by the board for strategic review. Next, the meaning and calculation of operational gearing are discussed for Freuchie as are the implications of the results. Finally, the quote 'What gets measured, gets done' is discussed, along with certain other pieces of jargon with illustrations from the situation at Freuchie.

(i)

Key answer tips

The CEO is concerned that the performance report does not adequately measure the achievement of the mission and subsidiary objectives. Therefore, the answer should consider, in turn, the main aim of the business (deliver returns to shareholders above the average for the retail sector) and the supporting strategy of providing a superior customer experience (broken down into the three ways by which this will be achieved) and whether or not the current performance report adequately measures the achievement of each area, together with some discussion of improved indicators. It is vital to use this structure in order to show the examiner that you have addressed the specifics of the requirement.

The second part of the requirement asks for a more general assessment of the performance report in terms of best practice. There are a number of different and relevant points that could be made here and that would be awarded credit. Book knowledge can be used but this must be adapted and applied to the specifics of the scenario. Do take the time to read the suggested answer since this will give you some good ideas on how to use the scenario information in your answer.

Current performance reporting: quantitative

The current report has a number of strengths and weaknesses. These will be discussed according to whether the report:

- addresses the objectives of the business;
- contains appropriate information for decision-making; and
- is well-presented.

The mission of Freuchie can be broken down into a main aim with supporting strategies. The primary aim is to deliver returns to shareholders above the average for the retail sector. This is to be achieved by:

- providing a superior customer experience which in turn is done by:
  - the appearance of the stores;
  - the attractive range of clothes; and
  - selling with enthusiasm.

The report, as it stands, is designed from a traditional set of management accounts and is dominated by internally-generated, financial information. It is clearly not suitable to measure the achievement of the business' objectives.

1 The primary aim is not fully measured. The return to shareholders is partly measured by dividend payments but there is no measure of share value to allow for total shareholder return to be visible. It is not compared as required to the retail sector average and this reflects a lack of external information in the report.

2 The achievement of the supporting strategies is done through the customer experience although there is no measure of this in the report. Indirectly, revenue growth would provide an indicator. However, this indicator is currently unsatisfactory as it has not been adjusted for the increased number of stores, which increases sales without any change in the customer's experience of a store.

3 The superior customer experience should be measured through the three ways in which this is to be achieved:

   a Appearance of the stores is difficult to judge through financial indicators although possibly, spending on fixtures and fittings and cleaning may give some indication. (These are not provided in the current report.) An assessment by an external expert comparing Freuchie with competitors may be required to give an indication, although this is likely to suffer from its subjective nature.

   b The range of clothes is not measured in the report. This should include the number of product lines that achieve certain gross margin or revenue targets (so measuring their attractiveness). Alternatively, fashion awards won might indicate the attractiveness although the proliferation of industry awards mean that a comparison to competitors rather than the absolute figure would be needed.

   c Selling with enthusiasm is measured in the current report by revenue growth although, as already noted, this must be adjusted for the change in store numbers. The enthusiasm of the sales staff could be measured by the proportion who are paid a bonus for exceeding their target.

Other points to meet best practice in reporting:

1 At present, the report only reports on absolute sales and does not reflect the purchase of new stores. This distorts performance as it is unclear if the growth is organic or from these acquisitions. Revenue and operating profits per store or a categorisation of performance into existing and new stores would help to clarify this.

2 There is no mention in the current report of the capital that is being used by the business. As a result, it is not possible to give any comment on the return that investors are getting per $ invested. The use of return on capital employed would address this.

3 The current presentation of a detailed list of costs will tend to obscure important information and those headings that remain should relate to the main objectives. Therefore, it is recommended that all cost information not directly related to the achievement of objectives is removed from the report although there may be need from time to time to provide such information on an exception basis (such as if inventory losses became material in explaining performance).

4 The report provides both budget and actual figures but does not show variances. This presentation is useful for a detailed control of costs. However, it may be too detailed for consideration of strategic performance which should focus on performance against external measures such as competitor performance.

5 The report only shows the current year and previous year allowing a simple comparison. The board might want to consider if longer historic trends are of value, especially in a fashion business.

6 In terms of presentation, the initial table of data is clear and in a form that would be easily recognisable to those used to reading accounts. However, much of this information is not necessary in forming a view about the achievement of the mission, being too detailed or not directly relevant and so, the report overloads the board with internal information but lacks the necessary information on the external environment.

The section on other data in the report could be easily ignored as it appears to be a mere attachment to the main table of accounting data. It does get mentioned in the commentary (dividends). However, lacking structure or a necessary priority order, the importance of the points might be easily missed. For example, number of employees is placed first, while dividends paid is third in the list.

(ii)

Key answer tips

Start with a critical assessment of the narrative commentary. There are fewer marks available in (ii) than in part (i) and therefore the assessment can be relatively brief. Although there are one or two positive aspects of the current commentary (and these should be briefly highlighted in your answer), the focus should be on the shortcomings.

Demonstrate good 'communication' skills by adhering to the CEO's request to include no more than four points in the improved example commentary. It is easy to get carried away and write lots of 'good' suggestions but the CEO specifically wants to focus on the key areas, i.e. relevant commentary on the achievement of the main aim and supporting strategies.

Current performance reporting: narrative

The current commentary in the report does not justify its conclusion on whether the business is achieving its mission. The actual measure of the primary objective is insufficient, as already noted. It shows the dividend but not total return to shareholders and does not show a return on their capital. The subsidiary strategies are only indirectly mentioned through revenue growth, which relates to enthusiasm of selling. There is no statement on shop appearance, the range of clothes or attractiveness of the clothes. The gross margin should probably be stated to three significant figures which would show a slight fall year-on-year from 40.8% to 40.6%. The final comment on inventory write-downs appears unnecessary as it is neither key to the mission nor material in its impact or year-on-year change.

Suggested improved commentary:

- Overall performance is satisfactory as the business has maintained its dividend and improved its profits although these remain marginal at 0.2% of revenue.
- Revenue is up by 10.5% on the previous period which reflects the purchase of new stores. Revenue per store is static at $15.2m reflecting an unchanged customer experience in the stores.
- The clothing range had X% of lines achieving their gross margin targets.
- The enthusiasm of the sales force was illustrated by X% receiving a bonus for exceeding their target.

Tutorial note

There are many acceptable possibilities in the suggested commentary. For example, the first point here uses existing data but others might discuss percentage total shareholder return against the sector average.

(iii)

Key answer tips

Don't be surprised by this requirement. The examiner is willing to test any area of the syllabus and you cannot afford to overlook any area. There are a significant number of marks available here but it is a very manageable requirement so long as you know the definition and meaning of operational gearing. Most of the marks will be awarded for applying this knowledge to the scenario information.

Operational gearing and cost structures

Operational gearing measures the business risk relating to how fluctuations in sales volume might lead to falling profits as fixed costs are not covered. The higher the ratio the greater the risk. It can be defined as contribution/operating profit where contribution is revenue less variable costs. If the contribution is large but operating profit is low (as with Freuchie) then the fixed costs are only being marginally covered and a small loss of revenue could lead to losses (as happened in 20X4).It is difficult to measure precisely as most costs have both fixed and variable elements. The measure here has classified each cost into one or the other category based on their general expected behaviour.

Calculation:

	Budget 20X5	**Actual 20X5**	**Actual 20X4**
	$m	$m	$m
Revenue	641.0	638.1	577.7
Cost of sales	380.5	378.9	342.1
Adjusted for:			
Other fixed costs noted	47.2	47.1	42.3
Variable element of staff costs	6.4	6.4	5.8
Contribution	301.3	299.9	272.1
Operational gearing = Contribution/PBIT	40.7	44.8	85.0

In these calculations, other fixed costs noted include rent and property costs, marketing, head office costs, insurance, utilities and depreciation although all do change with the number of stores, they are not likely to change with changes in revenue per store. Staff costs seem to be mostly fixed but the variable bonus element has been calculated and adjusted for.

The results reflect the high fixed costs of Freuchie where, as can be seen by comparing this year and last year, a 10.5% change in revenue moved the business from overall loss to profit and more than doubled operating profit. Freuchie can be seen as a risky business with volatile results as a consequence.

Tutorial note

There are a number of possible acceptable definitions of operational gearing and these are given credit.

(iv)

Key answer tips

'What gets measured, gets done' is a hugely important phrase in APM and it is important that you can discuss its usefulness (or otherwise, as is the case here) in detail. The assessment can remain brief here due to the small number of marks. If you are unsure of the meaning of tunnel vision and sub-optimisation then do revise your book knowledge – there are a number of different phrases that need to be learned here.

'What gets measured, gets done'

The idea behind the quote, 'What gets measured, gets done', is that the staff will only react to the performance measures reported on. In other words, poor performance reporting can lead to inefficient management. If an area is not measured then there is a danger that it is not efficiently managed and equally, if an area is measured then there is the danger that it is over-managed. For example, the presence of inventory losses on the report might lead to a restriction in the clothing range in order to control this and so be to the detriment of the aim to have an attractive and wide range.

Tunnel vision is present within the quote as it refers to an undue attention on the aspects of performance which are measured and a consequent lack of resources being applied to unmeasured areas. The focus on revenue and dividend payment in the commentary may lead to a lack of attention to profit margins.

Sub-optimisation can be present within the quote as a criticism since if the areas measured are not optimally chosen then if performance is only driven by the measured factors, the outcome will not be the best possible for the business. As commented above, there is a lack of measure of capital employed at Freuchie and this might be driving the growth by acquisition of stores without addressing the individual profitability per store.

The quote may not be entirely applicable as management may still take action out of other motivations such as the results from training or personal motivation to demonstrate their own skills. However, the quote is intended to bring into focus the fact that many people will tend to focus effort on the explicit measures of their performance.

Examiner's comments

Requirement (i) of the question was generally quite well done. The examining team hoped this would be the case as the area of performance reporting is one which is examined regularly and normally through the case study 50-mark question in Section A. Where candidates could also have improved their responses was in being less generic and more specific. Answers that did not focus on Freuchie's aim and subsequent objectives tended not to score so well. The main area where candidates could have improved their responses in this question was in the area of best practice for performance reporting. The essence of this exam is analysis and justification. Points that read like a list of bullet points and are not appropriate as they are unsupported, unjustified, and ultimately not worthy of merit. To help illustrate what good practice in performance reporting actually is, each response really has to be justified.

Requirement (ii) was quite poorly done, in the main because candidates seemed to struggle with writing a commentary section. The first part of the question, which asked for a critical assessment of the current commentary, was generally quite well done though the majority of candidates did not recognise that the last comment on inventory was not aligned to any part of Freuchie's mission. Many candidates did not attempt to write their own version of the commentary at all, and it is hard to offer any feedback to those candidates. Many candidates answered this part by simply re-phrasing the comments which were already there to offer something by way of justification. In the second part of this question, candidates had to realise that they should stand back from the analysis that they had undertaken in the first part and ask themselves: "given the aim and subsequent strategies which Freuchie has, what should it be commenting on in the report?"

Requirement (iii) was very badly done and very few candidates would have emerged from this part of the question with a passing score. Indeed, many candidates did not respond at all to this part of the question which suggests that they lacked the basic knowledge to either discuss or calculate operational gearing. Some candidates spent a significant amount of time defining operational gearing. As it is assumed knowledge, this is not time well spent. Of those who did attempt the calculation part of the question, there seemed to be a fundamental misunderstanding as to which costs might be fixed and which might be variable. Candidates then seemed confused about how to actually undertake the calculation. Some candidates calculated a fixed cost to revenue ratio, others calculated ratios which contrasted one type of fixed cost (staff) against another (operating costs). Some candidates did calculate fixed costs/total costs and these responses were appropriately rewarded. However, better responses measured operating gearing by contribution/PBIT. Candidates tended to offer very little by way of analysis of Freuchie's situation.

The first part of requirement (iv), which asked candidates to assess the problems that 'what gets measured gets done' identifies, was reasonably done. It was clear that most, if not all, candidates had heard of the quote and seemed comfortable discussing some of the implications of it as requested. The only area where candidates could have improved their performance here was in the amount that was actually written. Many candidates wrote brief responses, of one paragraph that was 3 or 4 lines long in many cases. The main area where candidates could improve here, therefore, would be in developing their justifications and analysis further than the textbook problems which have been highlighted with the quote. Such development would have shown a more genuine understanding of the quote and would certainly have helped with the second part of the question, where candidates struggled a little more. Candidates also gave some generic responses here that did not relate to Freuchie.

ACCA marking scheme

		Marks
(i)	1 mark per point – must be based on scenario information Aim of performance report – 1 mark Breaking down mission – up to 3 marks, e.g. identify priority of objectives, pick out strategies, comment on connections Assessment of whether report meets mission – up to 11 marks, e.g. clear statement of inadequacy for mission, addressing each of the elements of the mission, information for relevant decision-making by board Other points – up to 5 marks, e.g. answering where growth is coming from (if not already discussed), lack of information on capital (for return on capital for shareholders) and liquidity (given poor profits), data overload, general presentation	
	Maximum	**17**
(ii)	1 mark per point – must be based on scenario information Comments on existing commentary – up to 5 marks, e.g. achieving its mission; whether the three subsidiary strategies are measured, relevance and accuracy of points made Proposed new commentary – 1 mark for observing requirement to have a max of four points and placing them in a sensible order and up to 4 marks for considering each point individually	
	Maximum	**10**
(iii)	Commentary of the general meaning of operational gearing – up to 3 marks Calculations, 1 mark for each of the following: Revenue – variable costs Variable – excludes other operating costs Variable – excludes insurance, utilities and depreciation Handling staff costs correctly Operational gearing Commentary on results – up to 2 marks	
	Maximum	**8**
(iv)	1 mark per point	
	Maximum	**5**

Professional marks
Communication:

- Report format and structure – use of headings/sub-headings and introduction
- Style, language and clarity – appropriate tone of report response, presentation of calculations, appropriate use of CBE tools, easy to follow and understand
- Effectiveness of communication – content of the report is relevant and tailored to the question scenario
- Adherence to the CEO's specific request to include no more than four points in the re-written narrative commentary.

Analysis and Evaluation

- Appropriate use of the data in appendix 1 to adequately assess the quantitative elements being reported on and to support discussion on improved indicators
- Appropriate use of data in both appendices to calculate the operational gearing and to support assessment of the implications of the result
- Balanced and reasoned assessment of current performance report
- Problems of quote 'What gets measured, gets done' and link of the two phrases to the quote clearly illustrated with examples

Scepticism • Recognition of the failings of the current performance report • Demonstration of the ability to challenge the usefulness of the quote 'What gets measured, gets done' **Commercial Acumen** • Effective use of examples drawn from the scenario information and other practical considerations related to the context to illustrate the points being made throughout the report. • Recommendation of improved indicators and example commentary and practical and plausible in the context of the company situation.	
Maximum	**10**
Total	**50**

2 FIAG (MAR/JUN 21) (AMENDED)

Report

To: CEO of Fiag

From: A. Accountant

Date: September 20X5

Subject: Performance reporting and other management issues at Fiag

Introduction

This report evaluates the current performance report used by the board of Fiag, firstly against the accusations that it misrepresents performance and then, secondly that it fails to measure Fiag's performance against its objectives. Finally, justified recommendations of performance indicators arising from an analysis of the external business environment are offered.

(a) (i)

Key answer tips

Performance reporting has been tested on a number of occasions in Section A of the exam. It is important that you have your book knowledge in place regarding what makes a good performance report. However, this knowledge must be applied to and adapted for the scenario given. 'Communication' is one of the Professional Skills. Part of effective communication is about ensuring the content of the report is relevant and tailored to the question scenario.

Do make sure that you address each of the three areas of this requirement. The first part of the requirement examines another Professional Skill, 'scepticism'. You need to challenge the performance report, considering if the information is truthful, correct and complete. Do not accuse people of wrongdoing. Rather challenge what has been presented in a courteous and professional manner. The other two areas of the requirement should be included under separate sub-headings and approached in a logical and clear way.

Manipulation of the board report

The non-executive director (NED)'s criticism of the current report seems to have good reason. The problems lie in omitting bad news by using classifications some of which appear to select only a positive view of performance and some that manipulate commonly used performance indicators.

Omitting the bad news

The report gives only one industry average (operating margin) but does not provide a revenue growth comparator. While cost and detailed profit information is often difficult to obtain, the revenue figures are clearly reported for most entities and so it should be straight-forward to see if Fiag's fall of 6% is representative of the market as a whole.

The report does not calculate many of the year on year changes. This may be because important headings such as gross profit show a deteriorating performance. It could be argued that many of these calculations are unnecessary (such as for the detailed cost headings). However, no such case can be made for not showing the percentage fall in operating profit.

The revenue performance fall may be worse than portrayed as the range without the electrical bicycle has seen revenue fall from $284m to $248m (13%). This category covers 91% of the current revenue earned by Fiag.

Misclassification of costs

Exceptional costs relate to the development of the new electrical bicycle which appears to be part of the main activities and a central part of the strategy of the business. These costs should be considered normal. Their placement after the operating profit line means that key performance indicators such as return on capital employed are not affected so over-stating performance.

Administrative expenses includes government grant income which probably should be stated separately as it is material, short term and will not match to the full five years of costs associated with developing the electrical bicycle.

Commentary

The commentary appears misleading. It gives a positive impression of revenue growth by only selecting the growth in revenue from new models rather than noting the underperformance of the range as a whole. It quotes the improved profit before tax figure while ignoring the widely used operating profit figure, thereby bypassing the reason for the rise in profit before tax which is the fall in exceptional costs resulting from the completion of development of the new electrical bicycle model.

The description that a fall in operating margin is small ignores a number of facts. The fall is not 1.8% but 1.8 percentage points which is 27% on 20X4. Also, no reference is made to the industry comparator of 11% against which Fiag's 4.8% looks poor.

Thus, the commentary fails to address the falling revenue, gross profit and operating profit and so, is not representing the performance of Fiag accurately.

(ii) Measuring the achievement of the objectives of Fiag

The critical measure of whether the report is fit for its purpose is that it shows whether the business is achieving its objectives. Fiag's overall objective is 'to give the shareholders sustainable growth in returns' and it intends to do this by:

- developing the best quality bicycles;
- manufacturing the best quality bicycles;
- bringing the joy of cycling to a broad customer base in Beeland.

Overall, the report is in the format of a profit and loss statement, so it contains a number of common financial measures, but these are only loosely connected to the stated mission. The following problems are noted about how the report measures the achievement of the objectives:

1 There is no direct measure of shareholder returns in the report, not even profit after tax which would allow an earnings calculation. There is no statement of the gains that shareholders would make in income (dividends paid) or capital terms. While it is not possible to give capital growth through share price rise as Fiag is unlisted, shareholder wealth changes could be measured through NPV or economic value added. Growth of the returns would require the change year on year of these indicators, and this is only partially recognised in the existing report where not all growths are provided.

2 The sustainability of the returns are unclear from the report. These require the determinants of future performance to be measured. This should be done by examining the success of the supporting strategies.

3 The first two supporting strategies of the overall objective relate to the qualities of Fiag's products. The report does not measure these individually. There is an indirect measure of customer attitude through the revenue growth figure but without competitor comparison or a market share it is not possible to draw a conclusion about any of the qualities of the products. These elements relating to the products are difficult to measure overall as they are likely to be dependent on each product line individually.

4 The objectives also make clear the need to separately measure development and manufacture.

   a There are no separate categories for all new products although there is a note on revenue from the Zoam. The number of development projects, their state of completion and then their market performance all require to be monitored.

   b There is little apart from the gross profit to indicate the efficiency of the manufacturing process.

5 The failures in points 3 and 4 reflect the choice to use only data from the financial systems in the report. The measurement of these aspects requires Fiag to move beyond its traditional information systems.

6 There is no measure of the customer base and so the broadening of the customer base cannot be commented upon. This final aspect would appear to be addressed by the Zoam which seems attractive to those who may previously have not been willing or able (elderly) to make the physical effort. This failure also reflects the lack of external competitor/market information in the report where the only external data given is the industry average operating margin.

Other aspects

From the perspective of a board report, it should provide information to allow the board to perform its tasks of planning for the future of Fiag and controlling its existing activities. For planning purposes, the lack of external information about customers and competitors makes some of the numbers difficult to interpret. For control purposes, there is previous year information given but not sufficient to establish a trend (which requires at least 3 years of information). Also, there is no indication of whether the business is meeting its budgets through the provision of variances.

In terms of presentation, the report is clear and in a traditional profit and loss format, would be easily understood by most readers. It uses terms that would be recognisable to those used to reading accounts. It is helpful that a narrative commentary is provided. However, problems with the quality of the narrative are noted above and often the commentary does not go beyond restating the figures in the table. It should provide the significant explanations for performance as measured by the key indicators which should be linked directly to the objectives of Fiag noted above.

(b) External business environment at Fiag

The political environment is characterised by government actions which appear aimed to increase the use of bicycles in Beeland. Tax allowances represent a financial incentive while the building of new cycle paths should make cycling safer and so increase participation. These factors are both beneficial to Fiag. Suitable indicators of the impact of these factors on Fiag would be the increased demand for their products (volumes purchased) and also the increased participation rates with total number of kilometres cycled or if this is not available then total market size for bicycles in Beeland. It is not unusual for retailers to ask if customers were buying under a government scheme and if Fiag did this it could measure how well it was exploiting this free sales promotion. The growth of these indicators should be compared with revenue growth at Fiag.

The broad economic environment is characterised by growth and the populace of Beeland has become wealthier. For Fiag, this should mean growing volumes and margins although the cost base (e.g. staff costs) will inflate too. Again, the size and growth of the overall market and Fiag relative performance against these will show if it is developing a competitive advantage. The introduction of tariffs will increase the costs and can be measured at Fiag by the negative impact on profit margins.

The socio-cultural factors include demographic trends and changes in customers' tastes. The increasing interest in health should again be a factor in driving the consumers' taste towards cycling and so, as above, indicators of the market size/growth and Fiag's relative performance are relevant. The ageing demographic factor should seem to increase the attractiveness of the electrical bicycle over other models and so the market/growth of this particular sector and Fiag's share along with the relative performance of electrical bicycles against the traditional models at Fiag should be monitored. Fiag seems at the forefront of this development and should be seeking to maintain that competitive advantage.

Technology impacts on Fiag in two ways. Firstly, the development of new models, such as the Zoam, where the lightweight aspect will further enhance the model's attractiveness especially to the elderly. In order to continue to monitor competitive advantage, the average weight of Fiag's models (especially the Zoam) should be compared to the average of its competitors. Secondly, new materials could improve further the contribution per unit as material costs are cut. The use of contribution or gross profit to measure this impact is plausible but may be indirect since this change may also influence the selling price. Therefore, a measure of direct material cost per unit would better capture the change.

Tutorial note

This is an excellent example of how PEST may be examined in APM. It is unlikely that you will have to carry out a full PEST analysis. Instead, you will need to evaluate how PEST can assist in the performance management process; so in this case considering the implications of the PEST for business performance and justifying performance indicators for each factor.

Examiner's comments

Part (a)(i) was poorly done with many candidates appearing to be asked such a question for the first time. For a requirement worth 12 marks, candidates' analysis was superficial and often very short. A successful approach was to consider the choices that the author of the report had made - what to include and what not to include and then to explain how this might give a wrong impression of performance. Candidates needed to identify misclassification of costs and in particular, explain the impact of those misclassifications on KPIs for the company, for example, exceptional costs' impact on ROCE. The commentary provided was also full of examples of 'telling only the good news' and failing to put the figures into a broader context. It was good to see that a large number of candidates noticed that the comments on revenue only mentioned the good performance of the new models while ignoring the overall drop in the company's revenue. Candidates must be able to demonstrate the ability to see the whole picture as well as the detail.

One detailed point worth noting again in an APM examiner's report is that candidates seem under the misapprehension that (audited) financial figures are more able to be manipulated than (unaudited) non-financial ones. This idea of financial figures being regularly manipulated appears time and time again in candidate answers to many different questions and the examining team are surprised at the failure by candidates at this stage of their qualification to understand the basic control systems of a company.

Part (a)(ii) required the candidates to assess whether the supplied performance report addressed the company's objectives and briefly comment on other presentation issues in that report. Although this is a frequently examined area for, candidate's performance was mixed. Candidates often showed an incomplete ability to break apart and prioritise a statement of the company's objectives. A feature of such answers was that the objective is merely 'cut and paste' into the report which offers no added value to the reader. Given that the analysis of the objectives is critical to achieving the purpose of a performance report, it is disappointing that this breakdown and prioritisation is not done. Many candidates' suggestions of possible issues in measuring the objectives were good but lack depth, by which we mean there is a failure to follow up their suggested solution with its implications. For example, it was correct to pick up on the need to measure sustainable growth in returns to shareholders, but many candidates did not say how that could be achieved, particularly in relation to the supporting strategies.

On the presentation aspects of the company's report, the lack of depth of answers offered was often illustrated by candidates who simply said that the report should contain 'both financial and non-financial indicators as well as information from external sources' without providing justification of this advice or company specific illustrations of what they meant. This justification is key to scoring marks so candidates should be articulating in their report why these additions would be useful for Fiag.

Part (b) was generally well done with candidates often getting close to maximum marks.

Most candidates followed the scenario instruction and related the consultant's analysis to Fiag's business. The KPIs suggested were then mostly linked to this analysis. Those that failed to show the link between their suggested indicator and the commercial point at issue limited the marks available to themselves. Weaker candidates showed a tendency to simply cut and paste the consultant's comments without adding any further comment - this added no value and so did not gain credit.

A good approach to this requirement would be:

– Heading, e.g. Political

– Advice on the implications for Fiag on the two factors identified by the consultant

– Suggested KPIs with justification as to how they link to implications of the factors

Then repeat for each PEST category.

ACCA marking scheme

			Marks
(a)	(i)	**Misrepresentation by report** 1 mark per point including: Omitted industry averages Omitted certain year on year changes Misclassification of costs; exceptional costs and grant income Commentary misleading Additional credit given where points are correctly supported by calculation	
		Maximum	**12**
	(ii)	**Measuring the achievement of the objectives of Fiag** Breakdown objectives of Fiag – up to 2 marks Show hierarchy and break into measurable parts Measurement of objectives within the report – up to 10 marks Other points – up to 4 marks	
		Maximum	**14**
(b)		**External business environment** For each Political, Economic, Socio-cultural, Technological: Discussion of the relevant issue in the PEST analysis – up to 2 marks Justification of suggested KPIs on the issue – up to 2 marks Points must be related to Fiag's business	
		Maximum	**14**

Professional marks	
Communication:	
• Report format and structure – use of headings/sub-headings and introduction	
• Style, language and clarity – appropriate tone of report response, presentation of calculations, appropriate use of CBE tools, easy to follow and understand	
• Adherence to the CEO's request to re-perform the PEST and to offer a justified performance indicator per PEST factor	
Analysis and Evaluation	
• Appropriate use of the data to provide relevant calculations to support discussion and draw a conclusion as to whether the report presents a manipulated picture	
• Appropriate use of the data to support discussion and draw a conclusion as to whether the report supports monitoring of Fiag's objectives	
Scepticism	
• Recognition that information relating to certain industry comparators can be difficult to obtain	
• Recognition that failures in measuring the supporting strategies are because of only using financial systems	
Commercial Acumen	
• Recognition that the NED's criticism seems to be merited with supporting evidence	
• Provision of suitable performance measures are practical and plausible in relation to the issues identified by the PEST analysis	
Maximum	**10**
Total	**50**

3 IRON CHICKEN (DEC 15)

Report

To: Board of Iron Chicken (IC)

From: A. Accountant

Date: December 20X5

Subject: Performance management issues at IC

Introduction

This report evaluates the accuracy and assumptions used in the calculation of EVA™. It then suggests new KPIs for the current CSFs at IC. Finally it considers the impact of three quality improvement projects on these CSFs and a proposed new information system.

(i) Economic value added (EVA™)

There are a number of errors in the existing calculation of (EVA™). These are described below and then the corrected EVA™ is calculated.

Non-cash expenses are correctly added back to profit as such costs are treated as unacceptable accounting adjustments on a cash-based view. Marketing activities for long-term benefit are correctly added back as they generate future value for the business and so the prior year expenditure is also added in to capital employed. Research and development (R&D) expenditure should be treated as for the long-term marketing spending (note that there was no R&D expenditure in the prior year). The tax cost in the calculation should be the amount paid adjusted for lost tax on interest and not the adjusted amount of tax charged in the accounts. The WACC is incorrectly calculated as it should be based on the post-tax cost of debt. The capital employed figure should be based on the year start figure.

Economic value added	Year ended 30 June 20X5
	$m
Operating profit	551.4
Add back	
Non-cash expenses	15.1
Marketing capitalised	23.1
Research and development	10.0
Less	
Tax	130.0
Lost tax relief on interest	24.5
NOPAT	445.1
Capital employed	
At 20X5 year start	2,282.0
Marketing spend capitalised from YE 30 June 20X4	23.1
Adjusted capital employed at 20X5 year start	2,305.1

WACC = (1/2 × 16%) + (1/2 × 6.8% x (1 – 30%)) = 10.38%

EVA™ = NOPAT – (WACC × Capital employed) = 206

The recalculated economic value added has increased from $154m to $206m which still indicates a positive position for the company as it adds to shareholder wealth.

In addition to the corrections above, the following assumptions in the calculation require comment:

1 There is an implicit assumption that accounting depreciation (included in operating profit) is equivalent to economic depreciation (which should be used for EVA™ calculations). This is questionable generally, although there is no information to allow a more accurate calculation. Also, there is additional marketing spending which will probably have a limited economic life in building the brand. No estimation of this life and the resulting additional economic depreciation has been attempted in the above calculation.

2 It has been assumed that no amortisation needs to be charged on the research and development costs since the product has not yet launched. This is in line with the accounting treatment of such items.

(ii) Key performance indicators for the critical success factors

Greater staff productivity

The current measure of units produced per labour hour does not reflect the skill and effort which goes into producing different units. The products of IC range from complex to simple and so revenue per employee would better reflect the different skill levels involved in production.

Reduction of wastage

The weakness of the existing measure is that it only looks at one cost area of production (power consumption). Stock obsolescence will measure the wastage due to technological change which is present in the complex products produced by IC.

Greater innovation of products

The number of patents filed will reflect greater innovation at IC. Patents will legally protect groups of products. This will represent a stronger measure of innovation than new products launched since the patent gives legal exclusivity.

Tutorial note

There are many possible acceptable answers to this question. For example:

Greater staff productivity

Actual staff hours as a percentage of standard hours for actual production as this would measure staff efficiency in producing a wide range of products.

Reduction of wastage

Input/output analysis of material which looks at the percentage of material purchased which goes into the final product.

Greater innovation of products

Percentage of income earned from products which did not exist last year. This will measure the ability of IC to develop successful products. (The existing measure would record unsuccessful products as innovation.)]

(iii) Lean manufacturing projects

The three projects link together as improvements to the quality of the manufacturing process at IC. There are common elements to these projects in the elimination of waste and empowerment of employees which will occur in the long term. In the short term, there may be increased costs due to these disruptive changes.

Just-in-time manufacturing (JIT)

JIT seeks to produce on a pull-basis to meet the customers' demands rather than to produce products for inventory, which then acts as a buffer between production levels and demand. The main impact of JIT is the reduction of inventory which is held. The main enablers for such a system are a need for close links to customers and suppliers in order to predict demand and to quickly supply that demand. In terms of IC's CSFs, this project will improve productivity as production lines must be made more flexible to meet changes in demand, although it should be noted that there could be a negative impact as constant changes in production lines will require more time to be spent setting up new production runs. It will also help to reduce wastage through losses in inventory as there will be less inventory. It also pushes some of the responsibility for improved quality of components (and reduced wastage) on to suppliers. However, it does not directly impact on product innovation.

The project will not necessarily immediately change any of the existing KPIs as it is about producing the right products at the right time not just more products for any given input and does not impact directly on new product launches.

Use kaizen costing

Kaizen costing aims to reduce current costs of production through continuous improvement. Each period, goals for lower costs are set and then performance monitored against these using variances. At the end of the period, a new lower cost goal is set for the next period. The process also often uses target costing to set the initial planned cost of a product thus incorporating the idea of only producing what the customer values. The purpose is to build into the control of the production process the idea of continuous improvement.

This project has the explicit aim of reducing waste and improving productivity and so is directly linked to the first two CSFs. As a result, it will have an impact on the KPIs which are related to productivity and resource consumption. The project will also require the empowerment of staff to make improvement decisions within their quality circles (teams) and so it may give scope for more innovative thinking. However, this thinking is not aimed at producing new products but at improving the production process, so new product innovation may only be affected indirectly.

Costs of quality and a 'zero defects' approach to manufacturing

Costs of quality can be broken down into four parts:

- prevention costs which occur before or during production and aim to prevent the production of defective products
- appraisal costs which occur after production and aim to check that products meet quality standards
- internal failure costs which occur when products are identified as defective before delivery to the customer and so are scrapped or reworked; and
- external failure costs which occur when defective products are delivered to the customer.

The 'zero defects' approach is also known as 'total quality management' (TQM). The TQM philosophy is that it is better to spend money on prevention, which involves challenging all aspects of the production process in order to improve and so avoid failure costs.

This project will affect the CSFs relating to improved productivity and waste by reducing defective products, provided that staff time is not adversely affected by aiming for perfection in production. In terms of the KPIs, it may lead to increased time in production but reduced wastage. It will not have a direct impact on power consumption. Again, this project is unlikely to affect the number of new products launched as it focuses on the production process not product development.

(iv) New information system

The move to a single database for the organisation will integrate the subsystems from different functions (such as production and sales). It will require existing systems to be networked and compatible or else be replaced. It will affect overall decision-making by improving the visibility of each function's operations to the others and to the strategic decision-makers. This shift is often achieved by using an enterprise resource planning system and a strategic enterprise management system.

The unified database will be critical in achieving the goal of JIT manufacturing as close links between production scheduling and demand forecasts will be required in order to match production runs with demand forecasts/orders. Also, the production schedules will need links to inventory levels in warehousing so that inventory is run down before new production is initiated. As closer communication with suppliers and customers will also be required, some change to existing information systems will be necessary in any case. It may be worthwhile to consider including electronic data interchange (EDI) in the specifications of the new system.

In using kaizen costing, cross-functional communication will be important. The design team will need to communicate with the production team so that the design is more easily streamlined for production. The financial systems will need to be frequently updated for information from the quality circles as improvements are made. This will affect the kaizen cost targets which need to be continually monitored and new targets set regularly. Quality circles often involve groups from across the business and so a common information system will facilitate communications amongst them.

The introduction of TQM will require clearer reporting of quality costs to assist in the on-going motivation of staff, which is often a problem in TQM. Informing the quality teams of the impact that increased prevention costs are having on lowering failure costs will be important in maintaining the push to zero defects. The quality improvements and changes to production processes will need to be communicated across IC's different sites which the new database can facilitate.

The nature of the data used in the current system is quantitative but with the new projects, there will be a need to communicate qualitative information, for example, relating to the nature of defects or the new production processes put in place. This will require a fundamental change to existing systems which again motivates the change to a new database.

ACCA marking scheme			
			Marks
(i)	Economic value added Calculation: 1 mark for each of: Research and development Tax paid Capital employed year start figure Non-cash expenses Marketing WACC Economic value added Conclusion Assumptions and corrections – up to 10 marks		
		Maximum	**15**
(ii)	KPIs for CSFs Up to 2 marks per CSF		
		Maximum	**6**
(iii)	Quality projects Definitions and descriptions up to 2 marks Analysis up to 6 marks per project		
		Maximum	**15**

(iv)	New unified database Definition and general points up to 3 marks Interaction with each project up to 3 marks each Other comments up to 3 marks		
		Maximum	10
	Professional presentation: up to 4 marks		
Total			50

4 ACHILTY (MAR 20) (AMENDED)

To: The CEO of Achilty Retail (Achilty)

From: An Accountant

Date: Sep 20X5

Subject: Performance reporting and management issues at Achilty

This report evaluates the current performance report used by the board for strategic review. Next, certain proposed performance indicators are evaluated by calculation and for their fitness in measuring the achievement of the company's objectives. Finally, the opportunities and risks associated with the introduction of a data warehouse system are assessed.

(i)

> **Key answer tips**
>
> The format of this sample answer is excellent. A heading and a short introduction is included before the first part of the requirement is fully addressed; looking at the mission and each supporting objective in turn. Points are concise and clear and there is no repetition.
>
> The answer then goes on to address the second part of the requirement; do ensure you cover both. Here some more generic points can be included. Credit will be given for sensible points but it is important to refer to the scenario.

Current performance reporting

The current report has a number of strengths and weaknesses. These will be discussed according to whether the report:

- addresses the objectives of the business
- contains appropriate information for decision-making; and
- is well-presented.

The mission of Achilty can be broken down into a main aim with supporting objectives. The primary aim is to deliver long-term returns to shareholders through a combination of sustainable growth in earnings per share and payment of cash dividends. This is to be achieved by:

- Improving product ranges
- Increasing the number of customers and their individual spend

- Focusing on customer service; and
- Improving profitability by efficient cost control in purchasing and inventory management.

The report does provide much information which is useful to assess the achievement of the company's objectives. However, it is not complete or always clear on all objectives.

1 Information on the primary objective is presented as the growth figures for EPS and dividends. However, the sustainability of these is not clear from the report. A percentage measure of the return on capital for shareholders may give them a simpler and clearer view of the overall performance (see later discussion on return on capital employed and total shareholder return). However, without forecast figures it is difficult to give a view of whether these are 'long term' returns.

2 The first subsidiary objective on improving product ranges can be inferred from revenue growth and other measures relating to the customer perspective such as number of active customer accounts and their average spend. However, these measures are not precise as they are also affected by service levels.

3 The second subsidiary objective is clearly measured under the customer response heading. However, rather than seeking to only increase the number of accounts, it would be more useful to measure the active accounts otherwise resources may be poured into account holders who never purchase.

4 The third subsidiary objective is indirectly measured through revenue growth and the measures noted in point 2. It is specifically addressed in meeting of delivery deadlines. However, there is no indicator for the website experience, for example, relating to its ease of use. As this is the primary contact point with customers, it should receive more attention.

5 The final objective is partially measured through gross margin for purchasing. There are no inventory control indicators offered, such as relating to obsolescence or write-offs.

Other points in meeting best practice in reporting

1 The report is usefully broken into different perspectives similar to the balanced scorecard (financial, customer and internal process). No mention is made of innovation and learning which is unusual for a company dependent on technology but it is not a strategic objective and so this seems reasonable.

2 At present, the financial part of the report breaks the sales into four areas and in light of the creation of teams at Achilty, it should be assessed whether the board requires team performance or this broader view of the performance by product types. Considering profitability in these areas, operating margins should be calculated for each product type if they are considered important enough to warrant separate disclosure.

3 Efficient cost control is measured through operating margins and it may not be possible to allocate other operating costs to specific areas to give margins for each area. However, there appears to be no use made of the detailed operating costs nor are they mentioned in the objectives and so these might all be taken under one summary heading 'other operating costs'. Also, if cost control is of major importance, then variances to budget may assist the board in monitoring and controlling them.

4 The mix of financial and non-financial indicators gives the board a good vantage point to judge customer satisfaction. However, the lack of any external benchmarks such as industry growth and margins might explain why other similar companies are outperforming Achilty.

The current commentary is succinct and in a sensible priority order given the order of Achilty's objectives. However, it does not address all of the objectives and the comments are sometimes vague.

The first point does address the primary objective but the claim that performance is satisfactory when the test is that growth occurs and, currently, performance is static seems questionable.

The second point measures the attractiveness of the product range through the sales growth and this appears a reasonable financial measure.

The third point is indirectly related to customer satisfaction which is notoriously difficult to measure. However, combined with the growing sales, the comment about average spend and growing number of customers appear to indicate satisfaction. However, a better measure might consider the number of active accounts rather than all accounts and, in fact, this number has fallen in the year from about 594,000 to 588,000 but this is covered by the large rise in average spend per purchase. Average spend per customer in the period is a better measure of customer satisfaction than average spend per purchase.

The final point on delivery times could also be considered part of the customer satisfaction measurement. This means that the final objective relating to efficiency is not commented upon.

(ii) Other proposed performance indicators

Calculations:

	20X5	**20X4**
ROCE (operating profit/(total assets – current liabilities))	39.3%	40.5%
Inventory days ((inventory/cost of sales) × 365)	31	34
Receivables days ((receivables/revenue) × 365)	2.7	2.8

Tutorial note

Use the spreadsheet in the exam to include a referenced table summarising the proposed performance indicators (PIs). Workings are not necessary but can be included underneath (if you would prefer that the marker can follow your workings in case you have made an error in arriving at the final figure(s)).

Return on capital employed is a measure used by businesses to identify the return provided to the capital providers overall. At Achilty, the primary objective relates specifically to shareholder returns and so return on equity may be a better alternative. The result requires comparison with other similar companies in order to be understood but appears to represent a strong return compared to likely costs of capital. However, this may not be a particularly useful measure for a company such as Achilty which depends heavily on intangible assets.

Total shareholder return (TSR) would fit very well with the primary objective as a good summary for the principal stakeholders. However, it is not possible to calculate TSR as no share price has been supplied in order to gauge the capital gain/loss nor the dividend yield, which are needed for TSR.

Inventory days measures the amount of stock carried and so relate to the final subsidiary objective of efficient inventory control since a lower inventory requires lower working capital to support it. It is likely that this measure varies widely during the year as clothing is a seasonal business.

Receivables days estimates the length of time it takes to collect revenue from sales. As Achilty is a website business, it will have no cash sales and the time it takes to receive funds will be dictated by the customers' credit card firms or banks. It is unlikely that Achilty can change this situation and so it may not be a relevant measure.

(iii) Data warehouse

The proposed new information system will collect data from customers' website visits and store it for data mining purposes in a data warehouse. The capital required will be significant at $50m and there will also be considerable annual running costs. However, the benefits could be significant although measuring them will be difficult as they depend on influencing customer behaviour and so are not simply cutting costs.

Data mining involves seeking relationships, for example, geographical preferences for products; links between price offers and volumes sold; products which are often bought together; seasonality of product purchases.

Opportunities

These relationships can then be used to create opportunities to address the objectives of Achilty:

- Improving product ranges by knowing customer preferences. A problem in most retail businesses is the large size of the product portfolio since more products (and potentially more suppliers) require more effort to manage. The new system may allow a Pareto-style analysis where the least profitable non-essential products are identified and can be cut from the product range
- Increasing the number of profitable customers and their individual spend by linking lower margin offers to high margin purchases and, also, identifying the most profitable customers
- Focusing on customer service by identifying the design factors in the website which generate most sales; and
- Improving profitability by efficient cost control in purchasing and inventory management by forecasting more accurately and quickly demand changes so that excess inventory is not purchased or held. Also, there will be cost savings by more efficient advertising. The data on each individual customer can be searched to profile customers and identify their individual preferences. Marketing can then be targeted to groups of customers using products which they commonly buy.

Risks

As can be seen from the $50m cost, systems which can handle the volumes of data being produced are expensive. In fact, this level of expenditure would almost double the existing non-current asset base of Achilty. Although costs in this area are falling, the volumes of data available are rising and, also, Achilty's competitors will be spending to achieve advantage in this area too. This project will require a large initial spend and then constant on-going spending to maintain a position in the competitive environment.

The storage of personal information (e.g. about customers, especially their payment details) is an active area of new laws and regulation. Breaking these rules can be punished in the legal sense and by loss of reputation. In particular, theft or loss of personal data can lead to civil legal action and bad publicity.

The data obtained from qualitative sources (such as social media) can be imprecise or inaccurate and lead to inaccurate conclusions. Some data collected may be incorrect. This is sometimes referred to as the veracity problem. Also, in large volumes of data, some data may become out-of-date quickly and so constant monitoring of the database will be required to avoid this.

Tutorial note

This is typical of how information systems may be examined, in that you may be asked to evaluate a proposed information system.

Examiner's comments

Part (i). This part, though a very commonly asked question at APM, was poorly done. Many answers discussed how to improve the performance of the business rather than the performance reporting of the business. The general incomprehension of the scenario extended to the point where numerous candidates gave advice to the company as if it was a manufacturer by discussing various ways in which production could be made more efficient. Future candidates need to consider the depth of answer required at the 'Advanced' level. At this level, candidates should realise that best practice is a generic term which needs to be applied in the scenario's context. Also, candidates need to appreciate the level of detail that they are expected to have in their grasp. For example, candidates are expected to know that dividends paid are not subject to accounting assumptions or that average spend per customer purchase is not the same as average spend per customer. The ability to consider the implications of the definition of a performance indicator is a critically important skill at this level.

Part (ii) was well done from the perspective of marks scored but given the basic nature of such a question, many markers felt candidates were failing to score the full potential of the question. As in previous diets, performance on the calculations was weak. However, the comments on the indicators were generally done well although, again, many candidates failed to pick up easy marks by simply not answering the question 'whether and how they link to the mission and objectives of the company' which was posed in the scenario.

Part (iii) was well done with candidates suggesting practical ways in which the new system could be used to improve the business and some of the risks associated with it. Some candidates cleverly used the 3 (or 4 or 5) V's of big data to discuss risks. The key to these better answers was that the candidates had thought about each point that they wanted to make and then explained how it was an opportunity or a risk.

ACCA marking scheme

		Marks
(i)	1 mark per point – must be based on scenario information Assessment of whether report meets mission – up to 8 marks e.g. Clear statement of inadequacy for mission, addressing each of the elements of the mission, information for relevant decision-making by board Other points – up to 5 marks e.g. Answering where growth is coming from (if not already discussed), lack of information on capital (for return on capital for shareholders), data overload, general presentation Commentary – up to 5 marks	
	Maximum	**18**
(ii)	Comments on each new indicator – up to 2 marks each • Return on capital employed • Total shareholder return, which comes from share price change and dividends received • Inventory days • Receivables days e.g. Calculation where possible (1 mark each), reason for not calculating TSR, link to a specific objective of Achilty	
	Maximum	**10**
(iv)	1 mark per point on the following: General description and definitions of data warehousing and mining – up to 2 marks Opportunities and risks – up to 11 marks	
	Maximum	**12**
	Professional marks **Communication:** • Report format and structure – use of headings/sub-headings and introduction • Style, language and clarity – appropriate tone of report response, presentation of calculations, appropriate use of CBE tools, easy to follow and understand • Effectiveness of communication – content of the report is relevant and tailored to the question scenario **Analysis and Evaluation** • Appropriate use of the data in appendix 1 to support discussion and draw conclusions on whether the report measures performance towards the mission and objectives and in light of best practice • Appropriate use of the data in appendix 2 to perform suitable calculations for proposed performance indicators and to support assessment of these new indicators • Balanced and reasoned assessment of the opportunities and risks of a new data warehouse **Scepticism** • Recognition of the need for changes to the performance report, highlighting its failure to adequately measure performance towards the mission and objectives • Recognition that new performance indicators only partly link to the mission and objectives of the company and the need for additional information for TSR calculation	

Commercial Acumen • Recognition that the criticism of the performance report by some board members seems to be merited with supporting evidence • Comprehensive assessment of the proposed performance indicators • Demonstration of an understanding of the risks and benefits of a new data warehouse in the context of an online clothing retailer	
Maximum	**10**
Total	**50**

5 ARKAIG MANUFACTURING (SEPT/DEC 19)

To: The CEO of Arkaig Manufacturing (Arkaig)

From: An Accountant

Date: September 20X5

Subject: Performance reporting and management issues at Arkaig

This report evaluates the current performance report used by the board for strategic review. Next, the use of economic value added (EVA™) at Arkaig is illustrated and its use compared to return on capital employed (ROCE). Then, the differences between performance measurement and management at the different levels of the management hierarchy are discussed with reference to Arkaig. Finally, the implications of a value chain analysis for performance management are assessed.

(i) Strategic performance reporting

The current report has a number of strengths and weaknesses. These will be discussed according to whether the report:

- addresses the overall aims of the business;
- contains appropriate information for decision-making; and
- is well-presented.

The primary aim of Arkaig is to maximise shareholder wealth by providing suitable products for its customers. These products should have a number of qualities: be world-class; tailored; use technology innovatively; show improved machine downtime; and reduce energy consumption for customers.

This should be supported by an entrepreneurial culture among the employees.

Overall, the report contains a number of common financial measures but they are only loosely connected to the stated mission. The following problems are noted about how the report measures the achievement of the mission:

1 There is no direct measure of shareholder wealth in the report. The overall measure of performance for shareholders is provided through the absolute profit after tax and ROCE. It usefully benchmarks the net profit margin and ROCE with industry averages. However, these measures are only indirectly linked to value. The suggestion to use EVA™ is, therefore, appropriate for Arkaig.

2 The supporting pillars of the mission are all qualities of the products produced by Arkaig. The report does not measure any of these individually. There is an indirect measure of customer attitude through the revenue growth figure but without competitor comparison or a market share, it is not possible to draw a conclusion about any of the qualities of the products. These elements relating to the products are difficult to measure overall as they are likely to be dependent on each product line individually. For each in turn:

(a) The 'world class' nature of the offering could be measured by market share or customer survey responses.

(b) The tailored nature of the products could be measured by the cost of individual design for each installation or customer survey responses.

(c) Technological innovation could be measured through comparison of features with the competition or alternatively, by number of industry awards won.

(d) Machine downtime and energy consumption requires specific testing of each product line.

3 There is no measure of the employee culture although there is a comment that it is being achieved but this lacks evidence.

The report shows the financial performance by sector as well as in total for the business and the provision of some industry averages is useful in benchmarking performance.

For planning purposes, the lack of external information about customers and competitors makes some of the numbers difficult to interpret. For example, there is no indication whether the fall in revenue is due to general economic conditions or specific faults with Arkaig.

For control purposes, there is previous year information given but not sufficient to establish a trend (which requires at least three years of information). There is no indication of whether the business is meeting its budgets through the provision of variances.

In terms of presentation, the report is clear and it avoids overloading the reader with data. It uses terms which would be easily recognisable to those used to reading accounts. It is helpful that a narrative commentary is provided. However, often the commentary does not go beyond restating the figures in the table. It should provide the significant explanations for each of the major changes commented upon. For example, by stating why the ROCE has exceeded the industry average.

The commentary is an appropriate place to handle the less quantitative aspects of performance such as innovation and employee culture but it does not offer anything substantive. For example, it would be helpful to state what mechanisms are in place to emphasise the entrepreneurial culture (such as percentage of employees who own shares and the total proportion of equity owned by staff).

Tutorial note

This is a common requirement in the exam and you should be well prepared to answer a similar requirement. However, do not assume that it will be examined in every sitting. In addition, if it does get examined then ensure that you tailor your points to the scenario given.

(ii) Economic value added (EVA™)

Workings:

	Year ended 30 June 20X5
	$m
Economic value added	
Operating profit	3,175
Add back:	
Amortisation	95
Marketing capitalised	90
Research and development capitalised	705
Depreciation	1,780
Less:	
Tax paid	694
Lost tax relief on interest	53
Economic depreciation	1,907
NOPAT	3,191
Capital employed	
At 20X5 year start	19,404
Research and development asset	3,528
Marketing spend capitalised	900
Marketing written-off	(100)
Adjusted capital employed	23,732

WACC = (55% × 12%) + (45% × 3.8% x (1 – 25%))
= 7.88%

EVA™ = NOPAT – (WACC × capital employed)
= 1,321

The business has created $1.32bn of value in the last year. The net operating profit after tax more than covers the cost of the capital used by the business.

The main benefit to EVA™ is its link to the overall corporate objective of maximising shareholder wealth. ROCE gives a much less direct link to shareholder wealth as it is less cash-like and more tied to the accounting assumptions around producing a profit figure.

The basic test of performance is simple since for EVA™ if it is positive, then the business is generating a return above that required by the providers of finance. ROCE requires a target level to be set usually based on benchmarking to the industry sector and the setting of this target return can be somewhat subjective.

EVA™ encourages investment for the future (for example, in advertising and development) by removing such costs from the performance period and treating them like capital expenditure. This will reduce the dysfunctional temptation for management to engage in some short-term decision-making, which can be a problem with the unadjusted capital employed figure from the financial statements which is used in ROCE. This is particularly relevant to Arkaig, where research and development is a significant activity.

EVA™ is consistent with net present value (NPV) as businesses with an increasing present value will increase EVA™. This will aid communication as NPV is a widely used appraisal measure for businesses.

Overall, however, the better link to shareholder wealth creation and the use of EVA™ in a value-based management framework may make this extra complexity worthwhile for a large entity such as Arkaig.

Tutorial note

It is important to be able to compare and contrast the use of EVA™ with the use of a more traditional measure of performance such as ROCE.

(iii) Performance hierarchy

According to Anthony, there are three tiers to decision-making in an organisation and each one has different needs which impact on the performance information which is required.

The strategic level is the one associated with the higher levels of management (such as the board). Strategic performance is measured over longer periods (3–10 years) since this depends on the achievement of the strategies which will enable the achievement of the overall mission of the business. The information will be externally focused requiring information on competitors and markets against which the company's performance can be benchmarked. This information will be used mainly for planning rather than controlling. At this level of the hierarchy, forecasts will be prepared and broad targets will be set for the lower levels of management and their performance measured against these targets. Therefore, information will often be heavily aggregated and qualitative in nature (such as customer attitudes). The board report evaluated above is an illustration of this type of information.

At the tactical level, the middle layer of management will be concerned with shorter term and more detailed objectives (possibly over a quarter or year) than the strategic level. The information will be collected on the deployment of the company's resources and activities on a functional department or business unit level. This information will be used to see that the strategic objectives are being supported by the company's activities. It will contain information to aid some short-term planning but will focus more on assisting this layer of management to control the operations of the business. Much of the information at this level will be internally generated and will be combined with the targets supplied by the strategic level in order to make decisions. For example, generally, the achievement of budget targets or more specifically, the sales and marketing department might be required to report quarterly on changes in the order book in order that the strategic level can forecast future revenue levels.

The operational level focuses on the day-to-day activities of the business ensuring that specific tasks set by the tactical level are achieved. Therefore, information at this level is detailed and task-specific. It will be prepared on a regular basis (often daily or weekly). It will be aimed to assist management at this level in controlling the business in order to achieve its short-term plans (weekly sales or monthly profit targets). There will be little external information needed at this level as there is very little planning activity being carried out.

(iv) Value chain

The value chain is a model of business integration showing the way that business activities are organised and linked. This model uses activities rather than traditional functional departments (such as finance) to describe the business, emphasising that it is activities which create value and incur costs. The activities are split into two groups: primary ones which the customer interacts with directly and can 'see' the value being created and secondary ones which support the primary activities. The business can then identify how value is created and so focus on improving this through its performance measurement system (for example, the board report).

Another important feature of the value chain is the idea of value creation through a chain linking activities to each other. Therefore, there must be a flow of information between the different activities and across departmental boundaries. In performance management terms, this will affect the information systems which will have to ensure good communication across functional boundaries and also, the job descriptions and reporting hierarchies, as these will have to reflect activities rather than being purely contained within functional areas.

This chain will not stop at the organisation's boundaries as can be seen at Arkaig, where the relationship with suppliers (inbound logistics and procurement) is identified as an area of concern.

A specific area of concern at Arkaig is inbound and outbound logistics where there is an old warehousing and distribution information system. For a business such as Arkaig which aims to use technology innovatively, this could lead to inefficiencies. A state-of-the-art system would be integrated with the production and sales systems and would allow better stock control with fewer errors in picking inventory and reduced obsolescence while improved distribution could lead to faster delivery to customers with reduced costs of transportation.

The concern regarding after-sales service may be due to an inconsistency in having an area which generates a significant amount of revenue but which relates in reality to the failure of reliability of the business' products. It would be important to identify that customers' attitude to product reliability is not affected and that they see this service as necessary (maybe by benchmarking failure rates/machine downtime against competitors).

Although the chain shows human resources as a secondary activity, it is recognised as important to achieving the entrepreneurial culture at Arkaig. This culture can be realised through the reward system where employees are rewarded by share ownership or a share option scheme. Its effect can be measured through improved profitability and increased innovation.

Tutorial note

Value chain analysis is not a commonly examined area but its inclusion here demonstrates that you can't afford to overlook any syllabus area.

Examiner's comments

Overall, this question was done fairly well, as it mainly covered frequently-examined, core topics in the syllabus.

Part (i) required an evaluation of the performance reporting system at the company. This is a particularly common topic for examination although candidates should not assume it will appear in every diet. As a result of this, candidates appear reasonably well-prepared and the question was reasonably well done.

In part (ii) the calculations of economic value added were generally fairly good with adjustments to NOPAT being generally better done than those on the capital employed part of the exercise. With weaker answers, there was often a lack of care, for example, tax paid was often added back to operating profit (although it is not present in its calculation) rather than being deducted in arriving at NOPAT (which candidates should recall stands for Net Operating Profit After Tax).

The second part of the question was more weakly done, which surprised the examining team as this is a common type of follow-up to the request for an economic value added calculation. The weakness reflected poor attention to detail as the question did not ask for the benefits and faults of economic value added but instead required a comparison of the benefits of economic value added compared to ROCE. Many answers solely discussed the benefits and problems of economic value added without the comparison and this meant that fewer marks could be awarded.

Part (iii) – generally, this question was reasonably well done. Those who used this requirement to structure their answer by dividing their answer by the levels and then discussing the nature of the information needed and then how this is affected by planning/controlling mix scored well. They used suitable examples relevant to the company to illustrate these points.

However, numerous candidates offered up a performance pyramid analysis of performance management at the company as an answer to this question. This did not directly address the question of the nature of the information for each level and tended only to score marks indirectly. Additionally, a notable minority could not correctly define the tactical and operational levels.

Part (iv) was the part of the question that was most weakly done by candidates. Only a few candidates could provide a brief general description of the purpose of the value chain analysis and so give context to the consultant's comments. However, candidates were able to discuss broadly the activities identified as critical but often; they did not clearly link to this to the company's circumstances. In particular, candidates did not address the after-sales service issue well. Few seemed to be able to imagine why the directors were concerned about this area. A significant minority of candidates chose to write about all the possible activities in the value chain despite being told only to address the critical areas identified.

ACCA marking scheme		
		Marks
(i)	1 mark per point – must be based on scenario information Breaking down mission, up to 2 marks e.g. identify priority of objectives, pick out strategies Assessment of whether report meets mission, up to 11 marks e.g. Clear statement of inadequacy for mission, addressing elements of the mission, information for relevant decision-making, illustrated by relevant examples Other points, up to 4 marks **up to** e.g. Lack of information in the commentary, data overload, general presentation	
	Maximum	**11**
(ii)	Calculations: 1 mark for each of the following Amortisation Marketing capitalised Research and development capitalised Accounting depreciation (for replacing with economic depreciation) Tax paid Lost tax relief on interest Capital employed (for opening figure) Research and development asset Marketing spend capitalised and w/off WACC EVA™ Comments on result. 1 mark Evaluation of EVA™ versus ROCE, 1 mark per point up to 5 marks	
	Maximum	**15**
(iii)	Each level of the hierarchy – up to 4 marks e.g. explanation of the nature of the information needed, impact of planning and controlling activity and illustrative examples	
	Maximum	**10**

(iv)	General points on value chain implications and use, up to 3 marks Specific points relating to the areas of concern, 1 mark per relevant point Inbound logistics Outbound logistics After-sales service Human resource management		
		Maximum	**10**
	Professional presentation:	**up to**	**4**
Total			**50**

6 FOLT MANUFACTURING (MAR/JUN 19) (AMENDED)

To: The CEO of Folt Manufacturing (Folt)

From: An Accountant

Date: 1 September 20X5

Subject: Performance measurement and outsourcing of manufacturing at Folt

This report recommends a set of key performance indicators (KPIs) for the identified critical success factors (CSFs) associated with the new strategy and evaluates these as a set of measures of the strategic performance of Folt. Further, in preparation for the negotiation of the outsourced manufacturing contract, advice is given on the use of target costing and the attribution of responsibility for areas of quality.

(i) Recommended KPIs for CSFs

The chief executive officer (CEO) has identified three critical success factors (CSFs) for the medium term. Performance towards these requires to be measured and so KPIs are recommended as follows:

1 Keep capital providers satisfied

There are two capital providers, the debt is all provided by the venture capitalist (VC) and the equity is provided by the management team and the VC combined with the management team taking the majority. A widely used and understood metric for performance would be return on capital employed (ROCE) which measures the returns to all capital providers as a group. It is defined as operating profit/capital employed. In order to properly understand performance, a target measure should be set for this, possibly by using an industry average as benchmark.

To break this down further would probably require return on equity and cost of debt measures and would, therefore, break the desire to keep the performance information brief. As there are only two capital providers and ROCE neatly summarises this, no other KPIs are suggested.

2 Build a world-class software development team

This is a difficult factor to measure with precision. Building a team could be measured by an increasing number of employees or number of projects undertaken. However, the important element in this CSF is the 'world-class' quality of the team. This could be measured by the input cost of the team, provided that they are recruited at competitive market rates, since higher wages would imply higher skills. Alternatively, it could be measured by the team's output in terms of commercial success (sales) or technical achievement (industry design awards).

Overall, therefore, being led by the output of the team, it is recommended that we use growth in number of projects undertaken and the number of industry design awards won as the KPIs for this CSF.

3 Ensure that quality of the imaging devices meets market standards

Again, this is a difficult factor to measure. Financial measures of quality are possible by looking at the effect on sales volume and profitability (both likely higher for higher quality). However, these are lagging indicators where quality effects can take some considerable time to trickle through to customer perceptions.

A more direct measure of the quality of current manufacturing would be through customer returns and product failure rates on factory testing. However, it can be difficult to obtain benchmarking information which will allow judgement of whether this is meeting market standards. Given that the company already does manufacture successfully, it should have historic data which, if products are selling at the required margins, would suggest that these data on failure rates and returns would be acceptable to the market. As the business is moving to outsourcing its manufacturing, it is the external failure rate data of the customer returns which will be more appropriate as Folt will retain the key contact with the customer.

Overall, it is recommended that gross profit (a measure of both volume and profitability) of products and value of customer returns be used as KPIs. Both of these will need to be benchmarked to historic values in order to judge the maintenance of standards.

Performance measurement system

The KPIs suggested are:

- ROCE
- growth in number of projects undertaken
- growth in number of industry design awards won
- gross profit and
- value of customer returns.

The question of whether this is a suitable set of metrics to measure strategic performance really asks, does this measure the achievement of Folt's overall objective 'to provide an adequate return to its capital providers while growing the business into a world-class supplier in its areas of expertise'.

This objective can be broken down into:

- to provide an adequate return to its capital providers – growing the business
- being a world-class supplier in its areas of expertise.

These KPIs do address the first part through ROCE and the second part partly, through building the software team. However, the overall growth of the business is not measured financially through sales or profits and its target of being world-class is not measured through the number of markets which it has entered and is considered a leader. The final two KPIs have a more supporting role to play for the overall objective and these could be replaced by others measuring the concepts of growth and world-class supplier in order to provide a strategic view for the board of whether the company's mission is being achieved.

Tutorial note

Credit is given for suitably justified metrics and then a consistent discussion of this in relation to the objectives of Folt.

(ii) Outsourced manufacturing: target costing

Working (per unit):

	$	$
Target price		175.0
Target profit		35.0
Target cost		140.0
Costs:		
Software	40.0	
Materials	37.0	
Machine costs	35.2	
Labour	12.5	
Packaging and delivery	8.0	
Design	8.0	
Inspections	0.8	
Reworking costs	0.5	
Total costs		142.0
Cost gap		2.0

[**Note:** It is assumed that it is the total design costs which are relevant to pricing the product although it would also be possible to consider the original design costs as sunk and so only include the redesign element.]

The target cost is calculated as the estimate of a competitive product price less the desired profit margin.

The illustrative calculation above shows that the current estimated cost is $2 per unit too high and so the product or the manufacturing process will need to be redesigned to cut these costs in order to meet the desired margin.

The costs will be split under the contract between the two parties. Therefore, Folt could press Xela to make cuts in its costs to meet the cost gap as the gap is not large (2.3% of the total costs for manufacturing [i.e. excluding software, design and packaging and delivery]) and it is stated that Ceeland is a lower cost environment than Beeland for manufacturing. However, it may be dangerous to Folt's strategy if these cuts adversely affect product quality.

(iii) Responsibility for quality areas within outsourced manufacturing

This discussion relates to the quality of the manufactured device and should exclude issues with the software, packaging and delivery which remain Folt's responsibility. Taking each of the four areas of quality costs in turn, the cost area is defined and the appropriate treatment under the contract discussed:

- **Prevention costs** are incurred to prevent the production of products which do not conform to specification (e.g. design of the product and manufacturing process). The product design costs will obviously lie with Folt and the costs for design of the manufacturing process will lie with Xela, although it would be sensible for Xela to replicate Folt's current process and indeed this may be required in order to maintain quality. However, Xela may want autonomy on this in order to make further gains from streamlining processes. There will need to be liaison between Folt and Xela to ensure that process designs are acceptable to both parties.

- **Appraisal costs** are costs to ensure that the products output by the manufacturer conform to standards. These costs will mostly lie with Xela as it will be the manufacturer. However, Folt will have to oversee this appraisal by checking on the quality data which Xela will supply under the contract.

- **Internal failure costs** arise when poor products are identified before despatch. These costs will remain the responsibility of the manufacturer (Xela) as they have control of the manufacturing facility and the appraisal operation there.

- **External failure costs** arise when poor products are identified after despatch to the customer. Where these costs relate to repair or replacement of faulty hardware products, they should lie with the manufacturer. It is worth noting in price negotiations that there are additional costs for Folt from these failures beyond immediate reworking costs, such as the impact on Folt's brand.

There may be reasonable argument from Xela that Folt should bear some of the non-conformance costs (internal and external failure) if the faults can be attributed to faulty product design work.

Obviously, all of these matters are subject to negotiation before the contract is finalised.

Tutorial note

In APM, limited credit will be given for simply defining the different quality costs. In this requirement, to secure a good mark you need to explain the costs in the context of the scenario and accurately divide responsibilities.

Examiner's comments

In part (i) candidates generally scored about half the marks available. Part of the problem candidates encountered here appeared to be in not fully comprehending, for the first CSF, that it was two particular groups of capital providers who had to be satisfied. It is also clear that many candidates felt that justifying the measure they had offered could be undertaken by providing a definition of that term. Clearly, such comments are not appropriate when a justification is being sought. Candidates also found it challenging to offer KPIs for CSFs that were essentially non-financial in nature.

Almost all candidates ignored the second part of the requirement of the question and the examination team cannot comprehend why. This is a topic which is examined almost every diet. One of the main learning outcomes of the APM examination – put simply, are the measures that they have come up with appropriate and fitting for the company to help it achieve its overall aims?

In part (ii) most candidates scored about 8 out of 12 for this question and some of the analysis with regard to the effect on negotiations was insightful with candidates discussing specific elements of cost and how they were likely to relate to the two companies.

Part (iii) - Most candidates passed this part of the question. However, there was a significant minority of candidates who did not understand what quality costs were and discussed costs in general. This is a fundamental lack of basic knowledge. Some candidates also struggled to divide responsibilities accurately and did not refer to the specifics of the scenario to explain their response. With regard to external failure costs, for example, most candidates assumed that it would be the company who subcontracted the production that would be wholly responsible for these costs. It is clear, however, that if such errors and costs related to errors made by the company that was subcontracted to manufacture the product, the replacement cost would lie with them, even if the reputational damage with regard to the end-customer lay with the company that subcontracted the manufacture.

ACCA marking scheme		
		Marks
(i)	Recommended KPIs – up to 4 marks for each CSF, must be justified in answer Assessment of KPIs to measure performance – 1 mark per point, up to 6 marks	
	Maximum	**16**
(ii)	Target costing calculation – 1 mark for each of the below: Target cost Design Inspections Reworking Other costs Cost gap Definition of target cost, 1 mark Conclusion, 1 mark Impact on contract negotiations – up to 4 marks	
	Maximum	**12**
(iii)	1 mark per point: For each of the four quality cost areas: Defining the cost area with illustration of how it applies to the scenario and giving a justified recommendation of its treatment under the contract	
	Maximum	**12**
Professional marks		
Communication:		
•	Report format and structure – use of headings/sub-headings and introduction	
•	Style, language and clarity – appropriate tone of report response, presentation of calculations, appropriate use of CBE tools, easy to follow and understand	
•	Adherence to the CEO's request to provide a maximum of two KPIs per CSF	
•	Reasoned justification of KPIs and assessment of their use to measure strategic performance	
•	Appropriate use of the data in appendix 1 to provide relevant calculations to support discussion of target costing and, more specifically how it would impact on contract negotiations	
•	Comprehensive evaluation of responsibility for each quality area	
Scepticism		
•	Recognition of the limitations of the recommended KPIs in measuring strategic performance	
•	Demonstration of the ability to probe into why it may be difficult to reduce a target cost gap and also to fully attribute responsibility for quality areas to either organisation	
Commercial Acumen		
•	Effective use of examples drawn from the scenario information and other practical considerations related to the context to illustrate points being made throughout the report	
•	Recommendation of KPIs are practical and plausible in the context of the company situation	
•	Demonstration of the use of target costing and how to attribute responsibility for quality areas in this outsourcing situation	
	Maximum	**10**
Total		**50**

7 REZILLOS (DEC 18) (AMENDED)

Key answer tips

Requirement (a) is a common requirement asking for the evaluation of a performance reporting system. This is more straightforward than many past exam questions on this area – an easy to review performance report is given in the appendix and there are plenty of potential comments that can be made.

Requirement (b) touches upon your knowledge of the difficulties of using qualitative information. However, it is more important to use the information within the scenario to apply this knowledge.

In requirement (c) may seem overwhelming for 22 marks but break the requirement down into the five different areas discussed.

To: The board of Rezillos Engineering (Rezillos)

From: An Accountant

Date: 1 September 20X5

Subject: Performance reporting and benchmarking at Rezillos

This report evaluates the current performance report used for the annual board review. Next, the customer rating survey method and reporting are examined. Finally, the method of benchmarking to be used for the divisions is evaluated and the divisional benchmarking exercise is completed and initial conclusions drawn.

(a) Performance report for annual board review

The current report has a number of strengths and weaknesses. These will be discussed according to whether the report:

- measures performance towards the overall aims of the company; and
- is well-presented.

The current mission of the group can be broken down into a number of parts:

- The overall objective of the company is to deliver sustainable growth in value to the shareholders.

This is to be done by:

- working in partnership with customers
- to deliver solutions which are
  - innovative; and
  - value-for-money
- utilising the skills of the highly-trained workforce.

Beginning with the overall objective of Rezillos, the report does not directly measure shareholder value and so does not report its growth which are the primary goals of the organisation. This could be done directly by economic value added (EVA™) or total return to shareholders. Also, the report is wholly historical and contains no information about the future prospects necessary to judge whether the growth in shareholder value is sustainable. The current report uses period profits and return on capital employed as its main measures of performance. These can suffer from being short term unlike economic value added.

Overall, the report does not give information about the performance of the strategies which are in place to deliver the overall objective. These will require non-financial measures and so do not appear in the report which is dominated by standard accounting information.

There is no measure in the report of how the company works with customers. The company does collect data on interaction with customers at a divisional level although measuring 'working in partnership' is a vague term which should be more accurately defined in order to be measured, possibly by measuring the number of joint product development projects undertaken.

An indirect measure of the customer value-for-money is being offered through the gross profit which, when compared to the industry average, gives a partial measure of value but without data on the price/quality mix compared to competitors, it is difficult to be conclusive about this. Revenue growth is given but should be compared to industry growth in order to give an impression of the attractiveness of our offering to the customer.

No measure of innovation is offered in the report either in terms of the number of new products or the revenue or profit generated from them. This appears to be an important fault as an engineering firm such as Rezillos will only be viable in the long term if it continues to innovate.

There is no information on the skills or training done with Rezillos' workforce and given the emphasis on innovation and the sector in which Rezillos operates, these appear to be important factors.

There are measures appropriate for these strategies available within the divisions (see the benchmarking exercise later). These could provide easy solutions to many of these gaps.

The report treats the divisions in the same way as the group, using profit and comparison to industry average margins and budgets as the main assessment tools. This may not be helpful as the divisions are in different markets and so may not be easily comparable. This problem could be solved by providing the targets set for each of the divisions for the major financial indicators.

It is unusual, given the preponderance of financial data in the report, that there is very little about the assets and liabilities of the company or its liquidity. This may be acceptable if the efficiency of capital use and the danger of insolvency are negligible but this appears unlikely as shareholder value is a key measure and the ROCE is narrow.

In terms of presentation, the data are clear and in a form which would be easily recognisable to those used to reading accounts. However, it is common to provide a narrative commentary with such a report in order to highlight the key features in the report such as major deviations from target or performance well outside industry norms.

(b) Customer survey ratings

In a recent analysts' meeting, Rezillos has been questioned about its disclosure that it has an average 7.0 customer rating. The average customer rating is correctly calculated as 7.0 from the sample data. However, there are a number of questions which could be raised over the method of calculation and sampling.

The first issue which might be raised is what does 'average' mean in this context. The method used for the calculation is the arithmetic mean but average can also be considered to be the mode (most common rating) or the median (the middle value of the sample, which here would be the 5th value). Both of these alternative methods of calculation would give the lower value of 6.0 for the rating.

The calculation method does not take into consideration the size of the account. The rating of the large accounts might be considered more important and so given some extra weighting in the calculation.

A larger area of concern would surround the sample selected for the calculation. There are a number of questions to be raised about this:

1 A confidence interval and level should be supplied for the rating. If the sample is a small one or the confidence level required is high, then the confidence interval might be shown to be unacceptably large.

2 The method of sampling is not disclosed. Ideally, it should be a random sample.

3 There are various ways in which the sample might be biased:

   (a) Only customers who are expected to give a favourable response may have been selected.

   (b) It could be that only the customers who chose to respond are included in which case the sample will often be populated with those at the extremes of opinion on Rezillos' service.

   (c) The majority of customers in the sample are from Beeland (six of nine) and only one from Teeland. This will not allow the rating to identify divisional performance, which, given each division has responsibility for customer support, may create a bias. In order to do this, random samples from each division should be taken separately.

   (d) There are only three customers sampled with an above average account size ($20.5m). It is common in such surveys to ensure that all of the major accounts are sampled.

Overall, the criticism appears justified and in future, Rezillos should consider disclosing more detail of the method of sampling and the sample size in order to build trust with the investing community.

(c) (i) **Methods of benchmarking**

There are broadly three methods of benchmarking relevant here. The proposed benchmarking exercise is an internal one comparing divisions within the same organisation.

The other methods are external (or competitor) benchmarking where comparison is drawn with competitors. This is valuable in identifying areas where the other companies demonstrate competitive advantage and also areas for improvement with a similar business. However, although this method can suggest areas where Rezillos can catch up with its major competitors, it will not identify how to gain advantage over these rivals.

At a practical level, the difficulty with this method is obtaining the information and even if a competitor can be persuaded to share information, it will often only give strategic improvements, not operational ones, as such detailed information is unlikely to be in the public domain.

A third method of benchmarking is functional benchmarking with a world-class company from another business sector. Rezillos could share detailed operational data without the worry of loss of confidential information directly to a competitor. The difficulty lies in translating lessons learned from one industry to another, so it is often done for generic activities such as logistics. Functional benchmarking against a company from outside Rezillos' industry sector could be challenging as it will require the use of information from another company which will likely use different systems to collect data.

The major advantage of internal benchmarking is the ability to obtain detailed operational information and so to share best practice amongst the divisions. This will show the different divisions the advantage of being part of a larger company and assist in integrating them.

This method of benchmarking suffers the drawback that it will often involve non-financial data whose production is often less robust than the financial systems involving subjective judgements. Also, it will not necessarily identify world-beating performance. Its internal focus may lead the company to ignore competitor performance. However, as a one-off exercise to harmonise and improve the divisions' performance, it seems to be suitable for Rezillos now.

(ii) **Divisional benchmarking exercise**

The benchmarking has been completed as follows:

	Beeland	**Teeland**	**Veeland**
Benchmarking metrics			
Growth of market	8.5%	3.2%	5.0%
Revenue growth	12.5%	3.2%	4.8%
Operating margin	10.6%	12.8%	15.0%
Inventory days	162	162	162
Order book growth	5.2%	5.3%	5.3%
Number of face-to-face interactions with division's top 10 customers	260	120	40
Percentage of revenue from new products introduced in the last three years	24.9%	29.0%	17.7%
Incident rate (20X5)	1.14	1.13	1.03
Incident rate (20X4)	1.18	1.13	1.18
Reduction in incident rate	3.4%	0.0%	12.7%
Utilisation of learning and development programme	**1.20**	**1.26**	**0.98**

The benchmarking metrics appropriately reflect many of the detailed strategies of the company:

- Order book growth reflects the sustainability of current levels of business;
- Number of face-to-face interactions with top 10 customers reflects working in partnership with customers;
- Innovative solutions is measured by percentage of revenue from new products introduced in the last three years; and
- Caring for employees and nurturing their skills is measured by reduction in incident rate and utilisation of learning and development programme.

The major missing piece is the change in shareholder value or profit generated by each division.

The initial three metrics identify the broad financial performance of each division:

- Beeland is operating in a high growth market and seems to be using lower prices and a sales drive (visiting top customers more regularly) in order to push growth above the market rate.
- Teeland operates in a more stable market but one where the take-up of new products is higher.
- Veeland is growing more slowly than its market possibly due to higher margins and a weak sales effort.

So, the divisions apparently operate in different markets but there does appear to be scope to share practices between them in order to improve. Looking at the individual metrics in more detail:

- Inventory days is the same across the divisions reflecting the new company-wide inventory management system. This indicates that some aspects of integration are working.
- Order book growth is an important measure of the growth and sustainability of profits in the business. Beeland with its effort to see customers every two weeks on average is seeing high levels of growth and the other divisions might learn from this.
- Teeland is seeing the highest proportion of sales of new products but this may reflect the fact that they operate in a more developed market. This could only be controlled by obtaining external data such as industry averages for each country.
- Veeland has shown a significant reduction in safety incidents and its training and operating procedures should be shared with the other divisions in order to see if similar improvement can be replicated there.
- Not surprisingly, the market with the largest proportion of revenue from new products is also the one which makes greatest use of training. The low training score in Veeland may reflect little sales training as the number of sales interactions shows the most dramatic difference of all the metrics.

Examiner's comments

Part (a) required an evaluation of the performance reporting system at the company. This part was generally well done with most candidates rightly focussing on the question of whether the report measures the achievement of the organisation's stated objectives. Candidates did show a tendency to have learnt a set response to such questions and repeat points regardless of their relevance to the company. While it is encouraging to see those who have made efforts to prepare, they need to use this preparation more thoughtfully in order to avoid wasting time on irrelevant matters in the examination. One detailed issue with the company's objectives worth noting for future was a tendency to apply the concept of 'value for money' as if the scenario was directed to a public sector company rather than to a for-profit entity.

A notable minority of candidates continue to respond incorrectly to such a requirement with an evaluation of the performance of the company. Sadly, this can only reflect a failure to look at past examinations, their examiner's reports and the various approach articles and videos where this error of understanding has been pointed out on many occasions.

Part (b) required an assessment of criticisms of a press release on a customer survey. Prior to the examination, the examining team considered that this would be the difficult part of question 1. Therefore, the team were pleased to see that this part was generally fairly well answered. Candidates made good use of the three broad areas of concern, suggested in the scenario, in order to structure their answers. They also made good use of the detail mentioned in the scenario to pick out appropriate specific areas of concern and discuss these.

Future candidates would do well to follow such an approach of using the detail in the scenario to structure their answers and then to respond to the detailed evidence there in supporting their own analysis.

Part (c)(i) required the candidates to discuss methods of benchmarking the three divisions and to evaluate the one proposed for the company. Candidates responded fairly well to this question demonstrating a fair level of knowledge of these methods. However, they tended to divide their answers equally, between the all possible methods and this did not reflect the (stated) concern of the board of the company which was focussed on their particular choice of method. As a result, answers often scored just over half marks for this requirement when the marker felt that the candidate had the ability to score higher.

Part (c)(ii) required a benchmarking of the three divisions of the company. Firstly, the candidates had to complete the benchmarking exercise with some simple calculations of given metrics. These were surprisingly poorly done. The calculations were all simple and the data provided was not extensive. Nevertheless, candidates did not often score above half of these marks due to their inability to perform basic arithmetic calculations, such as a percentage change between two figures.

The second part of the requirement requested a commentary on the metrics used in the exercise and its results. This part was surprisingly poorly done. Many candidates offered little commentary which it ought to have been obvious was worth a considerable part of the answer to this 14 mark part. It was also surprising as this type of commentary is regularly asked at both APM and the lower level PM examinations. Where there were substantive answers to this commentary, they often made two further misjudgements by ignoring the request to comment on the metrics used and by only offering a description of the results (e.g. Beeland had higher growth than the other divisions) without any attempt to explain why or explore the implications of this fact.

ACCA marking scheme	
	Marks
(a) 1 mark per point – must be based on scenario information Breaking down mission e.g. identify priority of objectives, pick out strategies – 1 mark per point , up to 2 marks Assessment of whether report meets mission – 1 mark per point , up to 8 marks Other points – 1 mark per point , up to 3 marks e.g. Lack of targets Lack of information on capital and liquidity General presentation (lack of narrative)	
Maximum	**10**
(b) Average calculations – up to 2 marks Calculation weightings – up to 2 marks Sampling issues – 1 mark per point, up to 6 marks Overview – 1 mark	
Maximum	**8**
(c) (i) Identify type proposed – 1 mark External benchmarking – up to 2 marks Functional benchmarking – up to 2 marks Internal benchmarking for Rezillos – up to 5 marks	
Maximum	**8**
(ii) Calculations – 5 marks in total, 1 mark for each of the following: Inventory days Order book growth % revenue from new products introduced in the last three years Reduction in incident rate Utilisation of learning and development programme Comments on choice of metrics: 1 mark per point, up to 4 marks Comments on results: 1 mark per point, up to 8 marks	
Maximum	**14**
Professional marks **Communication:** • Report format and structure – use of headings, sub-headings and introduction • Style, language and clarity – appropriate tone of report response, presentation of calculations, appropriate use of CBE tools, easy to follow and understand • Effectiveness of communication – content of the report is relevant and tailored to the question scenario **Analysis and Evaluation** • Comprehensive evaluation of the performance reporting system with discussion that is relevant to the scenario rather than more general in nature • Reasoned assessment of the analyst's criticisms of the customer survey, focusing on the three broad areas of concern in the scenario • Appropriate use of the data to perform relevant calculations to complete the benchmarking exercise and support discussion on metrics and results **Scepticism** • Recognition of the failings of the performance reporting systems in adequately measuring the achievement of the stated objectives • Recognition that there are challenges with the method of benchmarking used in the exercise and that other benchmarking methods exist that have relative advantages but also drawbacks • Demonstration of the ability to probe into the why the analyst's criticisms are justified	

Commercial Acumen • Effective use of examples drawn from scenario information and other practical considerations related to the context to illustrate points being made throughout the report • Recognition that the analyst's criticism seems to be merited with supporting evidence	
Maximum	10
Total	50

8 FEARTIES (SEPT 18) (AMENDED)

Key answer tips

Requirement (i) is worth 22 marks so plan your answer to ensure you have enough relevant points and that you cover the three areas requested by the CEO.

Requirement (ii) relies on book knowledge but you need to apply your points to Fearties and, more specifically, use customer surveys to illustrate your points.

In requirement (iii) start with the definitions before discussing the pros and cons of the existing approach and then recommend and justify an appropriate alternative.

To: The board of Fearties Security (Fearties)

From: An Accountant

Date: September 20X5

Subject: Performance reporting and management issues

This report evaluates the current choice of indicators within the financial perspective of the balanced scorecard and recommends new indicators to cover the additional perspectives of the scorecard. Additionally, the problems of measuring non-financial indicators are discussed. Finally, current management style is evaluated, and a new approach is recommended to match the strategy of the business.

(i) Key performance indicators

The balanced scorecard has four perspectives: financial, customer, internal business process and innovation and growth. Indicators are needed for each perspective. The indicators suggested here are for the use of the board at a strategic level and not detailed operational management.

Financial perspective

The overall business objective is to grow profit without taking excessive risks. This is focused on the financial aspects of the business and so it is consistent that the current key performance indicators (KPIs) are all financial, being taken or calculated from the accounting information supplied with them. However, they are open to criticism.

The figures provided are the absolute values where it may be more useful to provide the year on year change in order to show growth.

	20X5	20X4	Growth
	$m	$m	
Revenue	686	659	4.1%
Operating profit	36	34	5.9%
Cash flow from operating activities	64	64	0.0%
Dividends paid	14	13	7.7%

The operating profit figure is less helpful for control purposes than the operating margin which allows for the effect of increased sales activity. The figures above show operating profit improving but, in fact, this just reflects the increased sales, as the operating margin is constant at 5.2%.

The ability to generate cash from operations is one which should indicate if the company is at risk of failure and so it is a valuable measure of risk to the owners.

The dividend growth figure is only for one year and, given the family's long-term involvement in the business, it might be more helpful to have a five-year average of growth, which can be calculated as 7.0%. This smooths out the fact that dividends are often only changed every few years once an increase appears sustainable.

The return on capital employed (ROCE) ratio is incorrectly calculated. The ratio calculated in the draft report is the return on equity (profit after tax/equity). This may be useful to a family owned business where share values are critical but it does not reflect the efficiency of the use of capital overall. The correct value is 31.3% (operating profit/average capital employed = 36/(21 + 94)). However, this ratio is not of much value to Fearties as it does not have a significant capital base. It requires relatively little capital investment as its activities are mainly about the hiring out of its employees' time.

The existing KPIs do not adequately reflect the new plan to grow more rapidly by developing new markets. Figures for revenue growth and operating margin should be broken down as they are unlikely to be similar in the different markets.

Customer perspective

The customer's views are important for growth and so the scores of a customer survey may be used to indicate their satisfaction. However, as discussed later, there are difficulties in measuring customer satisfaction and so customer retention (through percentage of revenue generated from existing customers) may be a better objective measure.

Reliability is listed as a key selling point and some investigation may be required to identify on what aspects of the service the customers are basing this view. Possible measures could be the percentage of times that a security team of adequate size and experience are sent to each job or number of times when police have to be called to the customer's location (indicating a problem which the Fearties' team could not handle).

Internal business process

The operating margin indicator suggested in the financial perspective will supply useful information about the overall efficiency of internal processes.

Based on the issues facing the company, KPIs for this perspective should reflect employee recruitment and retention, so the average number of unfilled vacancies at the company over the year would be a relevant measure.

The success of the company's training process could be measured by the number and average size of the legal claims against its staff.

Innovation and learning

Training is a key issue for Fearties, so the percentage of staff who are qualified is an appropriate indicator. The time taken for this training and its costs may also be measures of the organisation's ability to learn and improve this process.

The operating margin changes over time which are generated in the new markets entered by Fearties would show the organisation's improvements in these new markets.

Obviously, revenue generated from new services offered would also measure innovation at Fearties. However, there appears to be little appetite for this at present as growth is to be driven from selling existing services in new markets.

Tutorial note

A common theme in APM questions is 'what gets measured gets done'. This is the focus of requirement (i) since Fearties needs appropriate financial and non-financial performance indicators to ensure it achieves its goals and addresses any issues faced.

There are many possible KPIs which can be suggested for this scenario and these would be given credit based on the justification offered.

(ii) Problems of non-financial performance indicators

Problems of non-financial indicators can stem from the lack of familiarity of management with them. This is a particular problem for Fearties given its history of using financial indicators. Such non-financial indicators can have issues in the different areas of recording/processing and then interpreting the information.

Customer satisfaction is a good example of an indicator with such difficulties. Customer satisfaction is often surveyed and the results are expressed in language. It can be difficult to tell if a complaint which describes service as 'poor' is more or less serious than one which describes service as 'unacceptable'.

The most common way to try to overcome this problem is to turn the data into quantitative data. For example, surveys often use scoring systems to capture data on service. A scoring system will often ask the customer to rank their satisfaction at the service provided on a scale of 1 to 5 with '1' representing 'completely satisfied' and '5' representing 'totally dissatisfied'.

However, the problem remains that such scoring systems are still subjective, and it has often been found that there is a tendency to score toward the middle as people tend to feel uncomfortable using the extreme scores of 5 or 1. However, Fearties may suffer from an over-reaction response as the events it deals with are dramatic. For example, if there was a burglary at a factory, then the loss is all blamed on Fearties' failure and a bad score given.

Also, there is the difficulty in interpreting qualitative data, such as customer satisfaction. It is essentially subjective since it is based on people's opinions. For example, in assessing quality of service, people have different expectations and priorities and so are unlikely to be consistent in their judgements. At Fearties, customer complaints will be driven by such opinions. Some customers may expect there will never be a security incident but this is out of Fearties' control since it is criminal actions which will generate some of these cases.

One way to reduce the effect of subjectivity is to look at trends in performance since the biases in opinion will be present in each individual time period but the trend will show relative changes in satisfaction.

(iii) Management style

The current style at Fearties would appear to be budget-constrained. The targets set are all financial and are short term in that they are only for the next financial year. This style of management leads to a focus on cost control and often staff are not rewarded if they take actions which will require investment or the foregoing of short-term profit, such as marketing to build a reputation for reliability as an outsourcing partner.

The profit-conscious style evaluates managers on their ability to build long-term profits for the business. This style would appear to suit Fearties' strategic goals but it does not emphasise non-financial issues such as recruitment and retention. It would not fit with the increased importance of these non-financial factors under the balanced scorecard approach to management.

In the non-accounting style, budgetary information plays a less important part of staff's performance evaluation. It suits an emphasis on quality and on operational factors. It would fit with many of the new non-financial indicators being proposed from the balanced scorecard. However, it may not be strategically suitable for Fearties due to the importance to the family of the financial returns from the business.

Overall, a profit-conscious approach is recommended but one which uses both financial and non-financial indicators from the balanced scorecard to support the long-term financial goals of the company. The profit-conscious style will suit the financial needs of the family and its long-term goal of growth while a supporting non-accounting approach will suit some of the operational arms of the business, for example, dealing with legal compliance and employee issues.

Examiner's comments

Part (i) asked candidates to respond to a request of work from the chief executive officer (CEO) which specifically was to assess whether the current KPIs covered the financial perspective of the balanced scorecard, to recalculate ROCE and then suggest reasoned KPIs within each of the other three perspectives. Note that this requirement meant that candidates needed to refer to the scenario to find out exactly what the CEO was requesting and this style of requirement will continue to feature in APM. Many candidates failed to refer to the work that was specifically asked for in the scenario, and instead spoke generically about what the balanced scorecard was, including advantages and disadvantages, neither of which were asked for, and ignored the request as to whether the current KPIs covered the financial perspective. Similarly, candidates were required to suggest two reasoned KPIs for each of the other three perspectives, but many candidates ignored these specifics – some gave only one KPI each, some gave more than two. Several candidates simply stated the KPI with no justification behind it. For example, it can be useful to have staff turnover as a KPI for any organisation but without a candidate stating that for this organisation it is useful because it is struggling to attract and retain staff they can score little credit.

Worryingly, many candidates simply did not appear to understand what a KPI is, and instead provided advice on what the company should do to improve performance.

Part (ii) focused on the problems of measuring and managing performance using non-financial performance indicators (NFPIs). Overall, this was the best part of the examination for many candidates, and it was clear that many essentially understood the main issues and discussed them well. However, the requirement specifically asked for examples relating to using customer surveys. This was missed by several students who generally discussed NFPIs as being difficult to define or measure but made no reference to customers or surveys. Candidates should be aware that their answers should relate specifically to the requirement in order to score well.

Part (iii) was about Hopwood's management styles. Again this part of the examination was answered relatively well by most candidates. Those who were well prepared on this topic scored well. The question specifically asked for a recommendation of an appropriate style, and it was pleasing that the majority of students attempted to give a recommendation, even if the recommendation was potentially incorrect. The examining team would like to stress the importance of attempting all parts of the question. Recommendations are often based on ambiguous information, and candidates can be awarded credit even if the recommendations differ to those in the model answers, as long as they are sensible and well argued.

ACCA marking scheme			
			Marks
(i)	No marks for naming the perspectives (done in question) Current KPIs focus on financial aspects only; absolute figures less useful than relative figures; not covering the long-term perspective; not referencing external data – up to 3 marks Financial indicators: Revenue growth, operating margin, cash flows generated, dividend growth (long and short term) – up to 8 marks ROCE – 1 mark for calculation, 2 marks for discussion New indicators – up to 4 marks for each of the customer, internal and innovation perspectives. Marks are for justification and discussion of two new indicators		
		Maximum	**22**
(ii)	Problems of NFPIs – 1 mark per point	**Maximum**	**8**
(iii)	Up to 4 marks for each heading (budget-constrained, profit-conscious, non-accounting): 1 mark for identifying current style 1 mark for definition of each style Up to 2 marks for discussion of relevance of each style for Fearties Up to 2 marks for a reasoned recommendation		
		Maximum	**10**
Professional marks **Communication:**			
•	General report format and structure (use of headings/sub-headings and an introduction)		
•	Style, language and clarity (appropriate tone of report response, presentation of calculations, appropriate use of the tools, easy to follow and more than a negligible amount of content)		
•	Adherence to the CEO's specific request to provide only two indicators and only for the three balanced scorecard (BSC) elements		

Analysis and Evaluation • Appropriate use of data to perform suitable calculations for the financial perspective of the BSC • Problems of NFPIs are clearly supported with examples from the use of customer surveys • Demonstration of explanation of all three management styles at Fearties **Scepticism** • Recognition of the need for both absolute and % growth figures in reporting • Recognition that ROCE is not useful for Fearties • Recognition that although the KPIs reflect Fearties' focus on financial results, the KPIs do not reflect the new goal of growth **Commercial Acumen** • Recommendation of performance indicators for the BSC are practical and plausible in the context of the company situation • Recommendation of the management style for Fearties is practical and plausible in the context of the company situation	
Maximum	**10**
Total	**50**

9 CHIVEN STORES (MAR/JUN 18)

Key answer tips

In requirement (i) an answer plan is essential. Planning will ensure an appropriate structure and that you do not repeat the same points or miss points out. Although there are many negative points to discuss, such as the lack of alignment to the mission and aims, information overload or no external information, there are some positives to be included also.

Requirement (ii) may typically follow on from a requirement similar to that in (i). Numerous measures could be recommended and would be given credit if they tie back to the mission and aims of the organisation. It is worth noting that it is much more useful for the organisation to use ratios rather than to calculate absolute figures.

Requirement (iii) examines the value chain and, more specifically, how the approach can be used in simplifying the supply chain. The value chain is rarely examined but it's in the syllabus so do make sure you are comfortable with this area. In this requirement the examining team is more concerned about how the value chain can be used to enhance performance rather than a simple regurgitation of book knowledge.

In requirement (iv) you need to apply your book knowledge of Big Data and this requirement should be manageable if you have this knowledge in place.

To: The board of Chiven Stores (Chiven)

From: An Accountant

Date: June 2018

Subject: Performance reporting and management issues

This report evaluates the current performance report used for the annual board review and suggests three additional important performance indicators. The performance measurement aspects of the use of the value chain to help to streamline the supply chain is considered. Finally, the impact, risks and challenges of Big Data for Chiven are discussed.

(i) Performance report for annual board review

The basic role of the performance report is to allow the board to see if the mission is being achieved along with the subsidiary aims and strategically important initiatives set by the senior management.

The mission of Chiven breaks down into two parts:

- becoming the largest clothing retailer in Beeland which is measured by Chiven's market share, but without an indication of the market leader, it is not possible to see if this is achieved; and
- delivering exceptional value to its shareholders which is measured through a number of measures (dividends, EPS, economic value added and ROCE). However, it is often the growth of these indicators year-on-year which would be more useful to assess performance rather than the absolute amounts. Additionally, market average information would be important for investors so they can compare their investment in Chiven with others in their portfolios.

The subsidiary aims and initiatives based on the CEO's comments are:

- maximising opportunities from new technology
- increasing web presence
- making use of 'Big Data' in relation to Chiven's web sales
- simplifying the supply chain

There are no measures of web sales or the impact of technology on the activities of Chiven which would allow measurement of the first three aims. The basic data does not appear to be collected as sales are reported in total and not for stores and for the website separately.

The final aim does appear to be measured by looking at the number of suppliers and also the number of product lines sold (no. of suppliers x average no. of product lines per supplier). Reduction of these numbers would indicate a more streamlined supply chain. This would also indirectly improve the probability of stock obsolescence and so reduce inventory write-downs.

General comments about the current report

The current report is likely to confuse the board as it presents too many indicators and so overloads the board with information. This could be improved by reducing the number of indicators. For example, it should be considered if there is a need for both economic value added and ROCE in the report as they perform similar functions.

The report does not appear to group or appropriately prioritise the indicators presented. Suggested headings for an improved report might be:

- shareholder value performance
- market leadership
- impact of new technology
- efficiency in the supply chain

For example, the main company aim relating to shareholder value should appear at the top of the report and include dividends, EPS, economic value added and/or ROCE. As already noted, the growth of these indicators year-on-year would be more useful rather than the absolute amounts.

There is a lack of external information (especially competitor information) such as the market leading market share.

There is a lack of forward looking information which given the aim of innovation through new technology would be important. Expected growth of web sales in the market generally would allow measurement of Chiven's performance in this area.

There is a lack of a summary of property costs which could be especially useful for comparison with web operations.

There are a number of indicators which are about the detailed operation of the stores (such as average time between customer entry and employee greeting or average queueing time for customers). These are of a more operational nature and may be distracting and unnecessary in the board report, as it ought to focus on the strategic indicators.

However, the board may take the view that such customer-experience centred indicators are strategically important as they are commonly used in retail. In this case, there ought to be equivalent indicators for the web-based sales, for example, relating to number clicks or pages needed in order to make a web sale.

(ii) Three new performance measures for Chiven

There are three performance measures, which currently do not appear on the report, which would improve presentation of Chiven's results. As noted above, the current report contains many absolute figures and some ratios would simplify the work of interpreting these results.

Key issues in the current report and from the perspectives of running the physical stores are the number of employees and the floor space of the stores. Therefore, it is suggested that the revenue and operating profit per unit for each of these variables would be helpful and are also common indicators used in the retail trade.

	Total 2017	**Total 2016**
Revenue per employee ($000)	65.0	66.1
Revenue per sq metre ($)	3,096.5	3,147.3
Operating profit ($m)	434.3	430.0
Operating profit per sq metre ($)	510.9	519.3

Operating profit per employee has not been calculated as the general body of employees are more concerned with sales rather than cost control and hence profits.

(iii) Streamlining the supply chain using the value chain

The value chain divides the value activities of a business into different types and then examines the links between these in order to more efficiently build value within the business.

The supply chain simplification may involve reducing the number of suppliers and making the chain more efficient. It impacts on three types of activity in the value chain: the main activity area is procurement (dealing with suppliers) but it could also include technology development (information systems) and inbound logistics. There may be other types of activity affected if these are outsourced.

The performance measures associated with this simplification are the number of suppliers and number of product lines supplied by each supplier (both areas are part of the existing reporting). They include the time taken to source new products and the revenue and profits obtained from these (new measures).

The information systems which would be involved would be those with contact to the suppliers obtaining product details and prices and also those liaising over delivery of these items. For example, these could be part of a just-in-time delivery system to reduce stock holding at Chiven.

(iv) The potential impact of Big Data for performance management at Chiven

Big Data refers to the very large amounts of data which are now available through the increased use of technology and can be used to develop predictive information about human (customer and supplier) behaviour.

There are three characteristics of Big Data: volume, velocity and variety.

The large volume of data obtained. This is best understood by considering the relevant information gathering systems for Chiven. In stores, loyalty cards being swiped at checkouts allow the details of all products purchased, the time, amount and method of payment used. On the website and on Chiven's social media pages, in addition to the data which could be collected as for stores, every page visited and every product examined or commented upon would be recorded. This information would require system hardware to store and retrieve it.

The velocity of Big Data refers to the short timescales for information developed to affect decisions. The information could be gathered in nearly real time and this might be necessary in order to react quickly to information about customers who are considering a purchase. For example, it would be much less effective to text a customer with price-comparison information after they have left the store.

The software must be present to allow the kind of data mining and predictive analysis required to perform these tasks.

Big Data is 'big' due to the variety of types of information collected. Chiven could be looking at transaction data and browsing activities, as already mentioned, but also more unusual data types such as social media reactions (text and photographs) and geographical information from customer phones.

This data is both structured and unstructured and these require different responses from the information recording and processing systems.

Risks and challenges

Systems which can record and process the volumes of data being produced are expensive, both the hardware and software. The costs are falling but as already noted, the volumes of data available are rising and Chiven's competitors will be active in this area too. It will be a process which requires large spending in order to catch up with and pass those competitors and then, constant ongoing spending to maintain an advantageous position.

The storage of personal information (e.g. about customers) is an active area of new laws and regulation. Breaking these rules can be punished both in the legal sense but also in a reputational sense resulting in lost business. In particular, theft or loss of personal data can lead to civil legal action and bad publicity.

The data obtained from qualitative sources (such as social media) can be imprecise or inaccurate and lead to inaccurate conclusions. Some data collected may be incorrect. This is sometimes referred to as the veracity problem. Also, in large volumes of data, some data may become out-of-date quickly especially about a customer's precise location and so constant monitoring of the database will be required to avoid this.

Examiner's comments

Part (i) was disappointing and candidates could have scored much better had they related their response to the aims and critical success factors of the company. Several candidates did indicate that the company had two aims and evaluated whether the report addressed these aims. However, there were four subsidiary critical success factors and very few candidates addressed whether the report measured these factors. This is the fundamental skill that is being tested in the evaluation of any performance report and it is something that candidates should realise is one of the main learning outcomes of the APM examination – put simply, are the measures in this Report appropriate and fitting for the company to help it achieve its critical success factors and its overall aims? Any analysis should be related back to these aims and critical success factors to make a proper response.

Some candidates also offered quite lengthy description on what a report should contain. Whereas this may gain a mark for recognising the purpose of the report, the ideals of what a report might contain must be discussed in light of the company in the scenario. Candidates have to offer analysis and justification as to whether the report they are looking at in this question has the content, presentation and construction of a high quality report. If so, candidates should be able to justify why the content, presentation etc. are appropriate and of high quality. If not, then, in the same manner, they should be able to justify why the report, in its current format, is not helping the company achieve its aims and critical success factors.

Part (ii) was generally poorly done. Candidates often ignored the requirement to consider the data in Appendix 1 and offered other measures based on a broader consideration of the business. Justified suggestions are rewarded wherever possible but such an approach made calculation impossible as answers like this were offered without calculation. Candidates should also be aware that it is the justification that is being tested in a question such as this, much more than the mere calculation. The skill that candidates should demonstrate is an understanding of the company, its situation, and a justified suggestion as to where a different measure would improve upon those already being utilised in the report. Any improvement has to be justified in terms of helping the company better achieve its aims/critical success factors. Candidates often did not suggest measures, only improvements to performance, or measures which clearly had not been logically or rationally thought through. Again, candidates can improve their performance in this area if they assess the measures' usefulness from the perspective of helping the company achieve its aims/critical success factors.

Candidates should also try to avoid giving examples of aspects such as customer satisfaction which are unjustified in terms of how they improve already existing measures. The reasoning of making such a suggestion is in the force of the justification – how would it help the company better achieve its aims and critical success factors? There does appear to be a perception that candidates can cite measures that appear to have been rote learned such as "customer satisfaction" without explanation or justification and such responses will always score very little (if anything) at APM level as it is the justification that is being tested.

Some candidates also gave an often lengthy list of measures, unjustified and in bullet point format. This is a technique that was not unique to this part of question 1 and was used in 1(iii) also. Candidates should avoid this practice if at all possible as the essence of APM is justification and the examining team are looking for reasons as to why candidates feel that the measures they suggest are appropriate for this company in its current situation. Such responses receive very little, if any, credit at APM level.

In part (iii) many candidates spent time explaining the value chain and offered detailed definitions of each part of the nine components. Such responses clearly did not address the question asked. Few candidates appreciated that the focus of this question was on the supply chain and that a question such as this is testing candidates' ability to evaluate the effect of one thing upon another. Therefore, the value chain was only relevant insofar as it might help simplify the supply chain which ensured that the focus was on the specific parts of the value chain that related to supply. Most candidates failed to appreciate this and offered generic, bland and unspecified measures for different components of the value chain that did not relate to the scenario. A useful self-check for candidates undertaking APM is to continually ask themselves – have I related this to the scenario? Have I used the company's situation in my response? If not, then it is likely that they have not addressed the demands of the question as the essence of this examination is about the application of theory to practice.

Another concerning aspect with regard to how this question was answered was the number of candidates who had, perhaps due to having rote learned the value chain, discussed how the company might use it to help its production process. It is very clear in the scenario that the company is in the retail sector and therefore do not manufacture any of the goods they sell.

In part (iv) candidates tended to score well here, particularly in the risks and challenges part where they outlined with some justification the difficulties that might be involved in the company using Big Data. There was evidence of a lack of technical knowledge with regard to Big Data in some responses as several candidates outlined the challenges that collecting data generally might present. This is something that can easily be overcome by candidates understanding the techniques/systems in the syllabus. Likewise, explanation of terms such as the "3Vs" of velocity, variety and volume were not always done in the context of how they related to Big Data.

ACCA marking scheme		
		Marks
(i)	Identifying the aims – up to 4 marks Picking out the topics and prioritising these Identifying if the aims are measured – up to 10 marks General comments – up to 10 marks E.g. repetition of measures, grouping, external info, forward looking info, focus on the strategic not operational, need for web measures as well as store based measures. Marks for general points and also specific examples.	
	Maximum	**20**

(ii)	KPIs Justification in context – 1 mark each Calculations – up to 5 marks Other relevant points up to 3 marks	
	Maximum	**8**
(iii)	Defining the value chain – 1 mark Identifying the activity types affected – up to 2 marks Measurement systems – up to 3 marks Information systems – up to 3 marks	
	Maximum	**7**
(iv)	Definition – 1 mark Impact on performance management using volume, velocity and variety to discuss examples for Chiven – up to 9 marks Risks and challenges – up to 6 marks	
	Maximum	**11**
	Professional presentation up to	**4**
Total		**50**

10 THYME (SEPT/DEC 17)

Key answer tips

This question is consistent with previous sittings in terms of the content and structure of the scenario, the standard of the requirements, the breadth of syllabus examined and the discursive marks available.

Requirement (i) asks for an evaluation of the given performance dashboard. This is a commonly examined area but in this requirement you are expected to focus on the positive (rather than the negative) aspects of the report.

Requirement (ii) directly examines the syllabus requirement on integrated reporting. Previously unexamined but, as part of the syllabus, its inclusion as a requirement should have been anticipated.

In requirement (iii) 6 marks are available for calculations; a clear and logical layout is required here. Another 6 marks are available for linking the target cost with TQM. Linking different syllabus areas will be expected in the exam.

In requirement (iv) be careful to answer all parts of the requirement. This is broken down into three parts.

Report

To: CEO of Thyme

From: A. Accountant

Date: September 2016

Subject: Reporting performance and quality issues at Thyme Engine Products

This report analyses the positive features of the award winning dashboard identifying some areas which specifically apply to Thyme. The role of the management accountant in providing information for integrated reporting is explained. Then, the target cost gap for the new engine is calculated and an evaluation is provided of the use of this target cost within the TQM approach. Finally, issues associated with the costs of quality at Thyme are addressed.

(i) Positive features of award winning dashboard

The following are features of the dashboard which will have weighed in the assessors' minds when making the award. They are placed in a priority order of most important first and then there are a few specific comments about the possible use of such a template at Thyme.

Achievement of the objectives and strategies of the business

The critical measure of whether the dashboard is fit for its purpose is whether it answers the question: has the business achieved its key objectives?

The dashboard measures all of the key objectives of the business growth of the firm:

1 shareholder wealth and returns through EVA™ and TSR; and

2 growth through revenue and market share growth.

It also measures the strategies used to achieve these results:

1 world-class engineering to design engines through the class leading design specifications;

2 high quality production through fault rates in manufacturing and delivery; and

3 customer service through those same fault rates and market share (an indirect indicator).

Balanced view

The report presents a balanced view of the business's performance. It deals with various perspectives (shareholders (TSR), customers (market share), internal business (fault rates) and innovation (design position)) which are used in the balanced scorecard approach. This is also achieved using both internal and external data (fault rates and average sector growth). It presents both the results and the determinants of those results by giving financial and non-financial indicators. For example, revenue growth will be driven by the customers' view of product and service, so design and manufacturing quality measures are important. Short and longer term measures are given such as profit margin and economic value added.

Planning and control

The dashboard should allow the board to perform both its vital functions in planning and controlling the business. The forecasts for next year (budgets) are given and also, as noted above, there are non-financial determinants of performance such as design and customer service which will drive the future short-term competitive position of the business.

The control activities of the board are served by providing historic trends and also current budget variances. The major headings are provided for under the financial headings with activity measured by revenue, profit by the margin and shareholder wealth by economic value added.

Presentation

The dashboard is kept brief as the board will have an opportunity prior to the board meeting to use it to identify issues requiring further analysis at the meeting. There is a short narrative commentary which deals with the major commercial points arising from the dashboard and also, gives further external market data as context for the figures (e.g. average sector growth). It is also worth noting that the narrative picks up on strategic issues of risk and opportunity which can more difficult to capture in numerical form. Hence, the commentary appears appropriate to assist in an annual review of the business.

Specific issues at Thyme

There are certain issues particular to Thyme which may be added to the example dashboard, though if these are deemed short term, then they may not necessarily appear on this main dashboard view. The example dashboard does not show measures of cash flow performance (such as free cash flow generated) nor gearing ratio, both of which would be important for future fund raising. There are no measures associated with governance and ethics which in the light of the bribery scandal may have a higher priority at Thyme. Ethical training costs may give a measure of this area.

(ii) Integrated reporting

There is no standard format for integrated reporting. However, there are changes in focus of the company's reporting which will require the input of the management accountants of that business. Integrated reporting has a focus on opportunities and risk, how resources are allocated and performance both recent historic and expected in the future. There are six capitals involved in value creation including traditional tangible and financial assets but also including human, intellectual, environmental and social assets.

For the management accountant, these newer forms of capital will require information systems capable of capturing and processing such non-financial measures. The forward-looking nature of such reporting will require more information of a forecast nature (with the accompanying requirement to understand their estimating assumptions). The more strategic view which integrated reporting intends to give also requires reporting on factors which drive long-term performance. A key part of the integrated report is linking performance to strategic goals and the ability to create value. This will require a less structured and more contingent approach to reporting. In other words, proforma reporting must be better tailored to the specific business's situation. However, it is considered a key requirement of such reporting that it is concise and so the management accountant must help to ensure that only the key information is reported. It can be seen that the dashboard discussed in the above section of this report achieves many of these requirements.

(iii) New jet engine: target costing and TQM

Workings:

	$000
Target cost	2,125
Production costs	1,825
Design and development	100
Sales and marketing	500
Current cost	2,425
Target cost gap	300 (12% of current cost)

The target cost for the new engine is $2.125m and the current estimated cost is $2.425m. Therefore, there is a need to cut costs by 12% to achieve the target profit margin. It is common for the initial costs to be higher than the target cost and for cost savings to be achieved as the product reaches maturity in its lifecycle. It should be noted that even at this higher initial cost, the engine will be making a small $0.075m profit per unit (a 3% margin).

Target costing involves setting a selling price based on what will be competitive in the market then deducting a target profit margin to obtain the target cost. An estimate is made of the cost of the engine based on the current design specification. The gap between this cost and the target cost is the target cost gap and opportunities to bridge this gap are sought by amending the product design or cutting costs in production.

Total quality management (TQM) is a management approach which seeks to have no defects in resource or relationship management. It aims to have a culture of continuous improvement in the organisation.

In this new engine project, the TQM philosophy will fit well with the need to cut a relatively small amount of costs in order to meet the target. By small but frequent improvements as the production team climb the learning curve associated with such a new product, it would be expected that such cost savings would be made.

Given the size of the cost gap, it does not seem that a major redesign of the engine is required.

(iv) Quality costs

There are four categories of quality costs:

- Prevention costs are costs to prevent the production of engines which fail to meet specifications;
- Appraisal costs are costs incurred in inspecting products to ensure that they meet specifications;
- Cost of internal failure are costs associated with making good products which are identified as sub-standard before delivery to the customer; and
- Cost of external failure are costs associated with making good products which are identified as sub-standard after delivery to the customer.

Working:

	$m
Prevention	139 (= 11 + 92 + 36)
Appraisal	138 (= 110 + 28)
Cost of internal failure	95
Cost of external failure	279 (= 223 + 56)
Total	651

Comments of results

The total quality costs are 5.7% of revenue which seems surprisingly low for an organisation which recognises this as a key competitive advantage; notable is the large size of the external failure costs of 2.4%.

Possible other relevant costs

Overall, there are likely to be administrative costs associated with many of these categories and some attribution of overhead should be undertaken beyond the customer complaint handling mentioned.

Appraisal costs include performance testing of final assembly and performance testing of subcomponents from suppliers. There may also be costs associated with inspection of raw materials inward since these make a difference to quality (shown by the higher purchase costs).

Internal failure costs include costs of re-inspection after repairs after final assembly testing. There must also be costs associated with repairing faulty goods identified at final testing and possibly also scrapping failed products. It is possible that there is idle time costs due to work held up by internal identification of faulty products.

External failure costs include customer complaint handling and replacements under warranties. There is also the cost of damage done to Thyme's brand by such problems although many customers will accept that these are inevitable and provided they are infrequent and covered by warranty, they need not be important.

New products such as the new jet engine will likely generate additional failure costs while production methods are optimised.

Relative importance of categories

Given the high cost of external failure and the importance of reputation for Thyme, the most important category is prevention. It would be appropriate for Thyme with a TQM approach to be spending heavily in this area. This will still need to be combined with warranty spending in order to protect the reputation of Thyme when problems do occur. As prevention succeeds, so the importance of the other categories will decline. It is worrying that external failure costs are more than twice internal failure costs, which suggests that final testing is not identifying a significant number of the faults in production.

Examiner's comments

Part (i). Similar questions to this have been examined in previous diets and as such candidates tended to score relatively well here. It is worth noting though that a significant number of candidates provided very superficial answers. For example, stating that there is not a lot of detail could be an advantage or a disadvantage depending on the users of the information, so it is essential to explain why something is good or bad. Candidates should clearly explain their logic behind such statements. Also, this particular question required candidates to detail the elements that were particularly good, and as such, parts of answers that discussed negative aspects scored little credit.

Part (ii). It was essential here for candidates to relate their answers to integrated reporting. Many candidates did not seem familiar with this type of report and simply discussed the role of a management accountant generally and how that role has changed in recent years.

Part (iii) was about costing and quality methods. The calculations in this section were performed particularly well by most candidates. Care should be taken to present calculations in a logical order to allow the marking team to award marks for method even if the final answer is incorrect. Good candidates also went on to discuss the results well.

Part (iv) was based around quality aspects of manufacturing. Similar to part (iii), many candidates performed well on the calculations, although some candidates were not able to correctly categorise the costs. Also, candidates should pay close attention to all the verbs within a requirement – this part of Question 1 specifically asked for four things (categorise, calculate, suggest and evaluate) and therefore candidates' performance would be improved if answers addressed each of these separately.

ACCA marking scheme			
			Marks
(i)	1 mark per point with additional marks for development of these issues Specific issues at Thyme not measured – up to 3 marks		
		Maximum	**15**
(ii)	Description of IR – up to 3 marks Impact on management accountant – up to 6 marks		
		Maximum	**6**
(iii)	Calculations: 1 mark for each of the following ($000) Target cost 2,125 Production costs 1,825 Design and development 100 Sales and marketing 500 Target cost gap 300 (12% current cost) Current profit margin $0.075m or 3% Discussion of cost savings – 1 mark Definition of target costing – 1 mark Definition of TQM – up to 2 marks Fit of TQM with target costing approach – up to 6 marks		
		Maximum	**12**

(iv)	Definition of quality costs – up to 2 marks Calculations: 1 mark for absolute ($m) or as a % of revenue Prevention 139 (1.21%) Appraisal 138 (1.20%) Cost of internal failure 95 (0.83% Costs of external failure 279 (2.43%) Total 651 (5.66%) Discussion of results – up to 2 marks Identification of other quality costs omitted which are appropriate for Thyme – up to 6 marks Relative importance of the categories – up to 4 marks	
	Maximum	**13**
Professional marks		
	Maximum	**4**
Total		**50**

11 DARGEBOARD SERVICES (MAR/JUN 17)

Key answer tips

This is a clear question with no surprises and is comparable to other recent Section A questions in terms of difficulty and scope. Do be careful not to write too much. Use the mark allocation when deciding how much time to spend on each requirement.

Report

To: The board of DS

From: An Accountant

Date: March 2017

Subject: Strategic performance reporting and reward systems at DS

This report assesses the coherence of the choice of key performance indicators (KPIs) with the mission of DS followed by the assumptions used in their calculation. Other aspects of the presentation of the dashboard report are then evaluated. Finally, an overview of the operation of the building block model and an assessment of two proposed reward schemes are provided.

(i) Linking the mission to the current KPIs

The mission statement can be broken into several parts. The principal aim is maintainable, profitable growth which is supported by three further goals: developing the best talent; providing world-class services; and being efficient.

The KPIs are linked to elements of this statement as follows:

- Operating profit margin shows that the organisation is profitable and also as a margin, it indicates efficiency in cost control.
- Secured revenue indicates the amount of revenue which is contracted and so has greater likelihood of being earned. Contracts give an indication of maintainability though here only in the short term.

- Management retention links to the need for best talent though it does not measure the developing of that talent.
- Order book shows the maintainability into the future of the business though it does not show the average length of the contracts.
- Organic revenue growth shows historic growth and may indicate what the management are capable of into the future.
- ROCE demonstrates the efficiency of profit-generation from the capital base of DS.

None of the measures are external, looking at the competitive environment and so it is not possible to indicate if DS has 'world-class services'.

Tutorial note

This is a highly examinable area. Review each KPI in turn and examine whether it helps to achieve all aspects of the mission.

(ii) Assumptions underlying the current KPI calculations

Every KPI will involve some assumptions in its calculations. The aim of this section is to highlight how each indicator could be manipulated to show a better picture so that the business can avoid this in the future and the subsequent bad image portrayed in the investing community.

Operating profit margin is a standard performance measure and the only area which can be questioned is the categorisation of costs below this line, for example, the movement of operating costs into 'exceptional costs' below this line in order to artificially inflate this indicator. If the $55m reorganisation cost was included in overall operating profit which was $91m (=5.9% of $1,542m) then the business would show an operating margin of 2.3%. The catering business would show a loss of $39m.

Secured revenue represents long-term recurring revenue streams. A good picture will show a high percentage of secured revenue but will be below 100% so that management can indicate that budget targets are being exceeded. It is worrying that the budget is completed well after the year start as this may indicate such manipulation. If the original budgeted revenue figure is used then the secured revenue for 2016 was 82%.

Management retention only includes retention of employees on full-time contracts which at 65% of all managers excludes a material number. Poor treatment (and thus retention) of part-time managers is therefore ignored. This may be a particular issue for managers with young children who often take advantage of such contracts.

Order book is a 'total 'value' figure but is this the cash or present value figure? By choosing cash value of the contract, this will give a much larger figure than the discounted present value, especially where some revenues will not be received for 10 years.

Organic revenue growth is calculated by using the total revenue figure as reported in the accounts. The main purpose of stating organic is that it is growth from within the organisation as it stands and so acquisitions should be ignored. The current figure would fall from 7.2% overall to a less impressive 3.9%.

Return on capital employed (ROCE). Capital employed is being calculated using the statement of financial position figures which may exclude many intangible assets. As such it may overemphasise the tangible capital base which is not as important in a service business such as DS. The focus on this measure can lead to suboptimal decisions.

Tutorial note

A clear layout is required. Look at each KPI in turn and assess how the assumptions and definitions may serve to artificially boost the measure (and hence DS's share price).

(iii) Evaluation of the strategic performance dashboard

The current information used by the board is both financial and non-financial allowing different elements of the mission to be measured. However, none of the measures are external, looking at the competitive environment and so it is not possible to indicate if DS has 'world-class services'. Also, the measures do not focus on shareholder concerns although the mission statement indicates that they are the principal stakeholders. Other measures beyond ROCE might have been expected given that priority, such as EPS or dividend per share. No breakdown of ROCE is provided for each business unit, this may be due to the lack of availability of capital employed figures for the units but it does seem an odd inconsistency since ROCE is the best KPI provided for shareholder use.

No revenue figures are given and as most figures are ratios it is not possible to gauge the absolute scale of the business. It is particularly surprising that an absolute profit measure is not included on the dashboard given the importance of profitable growth to shareholders.

Generally, there is a lack of external figures to allow benchmarking or the assessment of the competitive position of DS.

The breakdown of results into business sectors will help in the judgement of performance of the managers of those units but they may not be comparable, for example, comparing building services and security, it seems that building services is growing more rapidly but with weaker margins. Also, it may be that the employment market is different between each sector and so no comparison of management retention figures is sensible. Again, it may be helpful to provide either an external benchmark through industry averages or an internal one through a historic trend for these sector specific indicators.

The report does have good qualities as it is brief and clearly presented. The use of ratios makes for easy understanding.

(iv) The building block model

The model takes the important step of distinguishing within the dimensions of performance between what is the desired outcome (results) and what are the drivers of those results (determinants). It then highlights the need to measure both within the performance reporting systems of an organisation.

The standards are the target level for the specific measures chosen for each dimension appropriate to an employee's performance. Employees must take ownership so they need to be persuaded to accept the target and be motivated by the targets. Targets must be achievable and so challenge the employee without being viewed as impossible to achieve and so be demotivating. For example, they must take account of external market conditions which will be beyond the control of the employee, but this can be managed by benchmarking against an industry average. Targets must be fair, for example, different businesses within DS must be measured against their sector (catering, security, etc).

(v) Assessment of the proposed reward scheme

As the board is already considering using the building block model, it is appropriate to outline the main criteria in the model for reward schemes.

Rewards must be

- clear, that is, understood by the managers
- motivating, that is, of value to the employee; and
- controllable, that is, related to their area of responsibility.

Scheme 1

The scheme has the benefit that it continues with the successful policy of offering an equity share in DS. It continues to utilise the knowledge of the line manager in performing the appraisal. It attempts to address a problem of the current scheme which is that the breadth of the categories gives the line manager scope to continue to show favouritism to specific employees. This is addressed as the bonus for line management will be affected by their appraisal according to performance on this new scheme and it will be helped practically by giving them an expectation of the distribution of bonus shares. This will also mean that forecasting staff costs will be simpler.

However, this scheme does not address the problem that the appraisal categories are vague and do not reflect the KPIs of DS. It also could create a problem as line managers will give bonuses according to the stated expectation, for example, even where all staff are, in absolute terms, performing brilliantly only 20% will get the maximum. Also, there is no mention of the scale of the scheme bonuses as there is for Scheme 2, where the maximum is stated as 50% of basic salary.

Scheme 2

Scheme 2 loses a key benefit of the current scheme in not rewarding in shares but cash is an acceptable alternative. Cash may well be a preferred option for the managers as it offers a certain value to them. This form of benefit also reduces the desire to manipulate share prices. It sets standards based on the KPIs and so should lead to greater focus by each employee on the goals of DS. Involvement of both strategic and line management in this process should lead to a better set of measures being used.

It is not clear, however, why five targets are being chosen. This seems an arbitrary figure and it may be more sensible to suggest a range from three to six (the number of strategic KPIs) to be decided by the managers in consultation. The size of the maximum reward seems likely to motivate but the equal weighting for each heading may not be effective. It requires that, say, operating profit margin has the same importance as management retention.

Tutorial note

You are expected to recognise that there are drawbacks, as well as attributes, to each of the two reward schemes.

Examiner's comments

Part (i) required a common APM task of identifying the mission from the scenario. Candidates were good at repeating the mission statement from the question but few showed appreciation of the structure of the mission and how certain goals were subsidiary to an overall aim. However, most scored reasonably well as they linked the indicators given to the parts of the mission.

In part (ii) the responses were limited with many candidates only scoring a single mark per indicator but with 6 indicators and 12 marks on offer, they failed to develop their answers. For example, it was often clear that a candidate had correctly identified that there was a problem with the calculation of a particular indicator but very few attempted to quantify the impact of this problem. Many candidates showed that they did not understand how to calculate return on capital employed, which is an important financial indicator and one that they should be very familiar with.

Part (iii). Candidates often scored some marks by making general points but then missed out by not expanding their answers using the specifics of the scenario.

Part (iv). Responses to this question were generally poor as many candidates ignored the detailed requirements of the CEO and provided a rote-learned answer that irrelevantly described the whole model.

Part (v) was generally well done with many candidates using the Building Block model concepts to good effect by illustrating how the two schemes demonstrated the ideal features from the model.

ACCA marking scheme			
			Marks
(i)	Breaking down the mission – up to 2 marks 1 mark per point		
		Maximum	**8**
(ii)	Up to 3 marks for comments on each indicator: Operating profit margin Secured revenue Management retention Order book Organic revenue growth ROCE		
		Maximum	**12**
(iii)	1 mark per point	**Maximum**	**8**
(iv)	Results and determinants Standards: ownership, achievable targets, fair		
		Maximum	**6**
(v)	1 mark per point Up to 2 marks for general assessment of reward scheme 6 marks per scheme		
		Maximum	**12**
Professional marks		**Maximum**	**4**
Total			**50**

12 FLACK (MAR/JUN 16) (AMENDED)

Key answer tips

In part (i), as with previous past exam questions of this nature, make sure that you evaluate (i.e. examine the good and bad parts of the report in detail) the performance report and not the performance.

In parts (ii)-(iv) you are expected to discuss the appropriateness of different performance measures. This is a commonly examined area and is core to APM. Remember, 'what gets measured gets done'.

Report

To: Board of Flack

From: A. Accountant

Date: 1 September 20X5

Subject: Performance reporting and management issues at Flack

Introduction

This report evaluates the current performance report for Flack and the introduction of two new performance measures. Then, the effect of a proposed change in divisional performance measure is assessed. Finally, the use of expected ROCE for new store proposals is evaluated. Finally, the report explains how the proposed new information system can help to improve business performance at Flack.

(i) Performance reporting at Flack

The current report has a number of strengths and weaknesses. These will be discussed according to whether the report:

– addresses the mission,

– contains appropriate information for decision-making,

– shows signs of being short term and

– is well presented.

The current mission can be broken down into two parts:

– to be the first choice for customers and

– to provide the right balance of quality, service and price.

There are three strategies for achieving this mission, reflecting stakeholder concerns:

– earning customer loyalty,

– utilising all resources and

– serving shareholders' interests.

The report does not address the first part of the mission. This can only be measured using external data but the report is utilising only Flack's internal data. This part of the mission relates to the first strategy to gain customer loyalty. Customer loyalty could be gauged through repeat purchases or market share information but neither is supplied. This is clearly important to a retailer and may be more easily gathered once the data from the new information system are available for inclusion in this report.

The report provides no measures of the balance of quality, service and price other than through the historic growth in revenue. It would only be through comparison with competitors or customer survey data that a picture of the mix of these qualities could be gained.

The second strategy of utilising resources requires that the key resources be identified. Clearly, the stores themselves (and thus the capital invested) are an important resource and the introduction of the revenue and profit per square metre and comparison with competitors will indicate the efficiency of their use. However, there are likely to be other important resources such as staff and no measure of their performance is offered. Staff costs are not shown in the trading account although a more sophisticated measure such as revenue per employee is a commonly used metric and would address this.

The report is much better on the third strategy of serving shareholder interests as it supplies two helpful measures: total shareholder return and return on capital employed. However, most shareholders will want comparison with benchmark returns within the retail sector and the market more widely, since these represent their alternatives.

The criticism of the company's management as being short term is reflected in the performance reporting. The report only contains for comparison budget information and the previous year's figures. There are no longer term forecasts or information on future capital investment. Also, there are few indicators which would be described as determinants of performance. These are often non-financial and focused on the external business environment (behaviour of customers and competitors).

As already noted, there is a significant gap in the information in the report as it contains no external information. Also, although revenue is broken down into broad product categories, no further information about growth within these categories nor the margins being earned is supplied. As a result, it could be questioned whether this break-down is worthwhile.

In terms of presentation, the data is clear and in a form which would be easily recognisable to those used to reading accounts. However, no narrative commentary is provided which would highlight the key features in the report such as major deviations from the budget or performance well outside industry norms. There should be a comment on each of the five areas within the mission and strategies as well as comments about specific, material issues arising in the period covered. The report could be made easier to read by reducing the volume of numbers present both by cutting out unnecessary measures (see earlier discussion of product categories) and also by rounding all figures to millions.

(ii) New asset utilisation indicators

Revenue and operating profit per square metre reflect the utilisation of the key capital asset used in their generation (the store). Therefore, they are directly addressing a major part of the aim of utilising all resources; however, they do not address all resources which the business uses. There are likely to be significant staff costs and so similar measures of revenue and operating profit per employee could also be introduced in order to reflect these human resources.

	Metro	**Hyper**	**Flack**
Revenue per sq. metre	13,702	13,165	13,251
Operating profit ($000s)	159,058	498,791	657,849
Operating profit per sq. metre	987	592	656

These measures reflect the importance of the use of the store's space which is an area which the business does not give sufficient attention as is reflected in the problems with divisional performance measures. Focus on these measures will require addressing issues of volume of sales and the profitability of those sales. The two types of store at Flack will have different impacts on these measures. For example, the smaller Metro stores may be capable of earning higher margins as they are convenient to customers while selling lower volumes. The Hyper stores may concentrate on selling in volume to customers who come to buy in bulk. However, in terms of the overall performance of the business it is essential that Flack sells in high volumes as it is a low margin business but it must not sacrifice profitability, in effect buying customers' revenue by selling at or near a loss.

(iii) Divisional performance assessment

The current measure of divisional operating profit reflects the trading in the period under consideration. Profit will link to the whole business's operating profit which is the correct level to reflect the efforts of the divisional managers. However, this measure only indirectly addresses the capital being used by the divisions (depreciation charged to operating profit). This is distorting the behaviour of the divisional managers.

The managers are not investing in refurbishing their stores which is causing the press (and presumably customers) to notice their run-down appearance. This may reduce the depreciation charge against operating profit. They are prioritising new store capital expenditure over the refurbishment since they are not being charged for the use of that capital (financing charges are deducted after operating profit is calculated). This may not be optimal since small spending on existing capital assets often yields higher returns than new spending (which may be subject to greater risks).

The proposal to change the divisional performance measure addresses the issue of not reflecting the capital used since residual income (RI) deducts an imputed interest charge. Divisions can then be set targets in terms of their RI. The difficulties in calculating RI lie in correctly setting the imputed interest rate and calculating the capital being employed by the division. However, since both divisions are types of stores they will have similar assets and so the same rules can be applied to each to fairly calculate the capital used. An advantage of RI is that the imputed interest rate can be changed to reflect the different risks of the divisions. The two divisions here do not seem to have significant risk differences unless the geographical locations introduce these (city centres and city edges). However, it is worth noting that using RI can discourage investment. As net book values of assets fall over time, RI automatically increases and 'do not invest' could become an attractive option to the managers.

Overall, the proposed change addresses existing problems and would be considered a normal solution to measuring divisional performance in this industry.

(iv) Use of expected ROCE in new store appraisal

The expected ROCE is calculated as:

Demand scenarios	**Low**	**Medium**	**High**
Revenue ($m)	12.5	13	13.5
Probability (%)	20	50	30
Forecast operating margin (%)	4.1	4.3	4.4
Forecast operating profit ($m)	0.5125	0.559	0.594
Expected operating profit ($m)	0.5602		
Expected ROCE	13.34%		

The expected ROCE is above 13% which is Flack's required ROCE, so this should be an acceptable investment.

The use of expected values in the calculation of ROCE is appropriate if the probabilities used can be reasonably estimated and the decision is likely to be one which is made a number of times. Since Flack has opened many stores, it is likely to be able to predict volumes and margins with reasonable accuracy. Since Flack is going to continue to open stores, this decision will occur a number of times which makes using a probabilistic approach viable. In general, ROCE is neither considered as accurate nor as direct a measure of shareholder wealth as, for example, net present value (NPV).

Examiner's comments

Part (i) was generally well done. Candidates performed well when they used the signposts given in the scenario for specific issues to look for within the report.

Part (ii) was often not done well as many candidates could not identify how the new measures fit with the specific strategy point that they were seeking to address. Also, candidates often did not pick up simple calculation marks by failing to recognise that they were working in $000s.

Part (iii) was usually reasonably well done with candidates structuring their comments into criticism of the existing measure and then, analysis of how the proposed new measure would address these issues. Unfortunately, a number of candidates decided to focus their answer on a different new performance indicator of their own choosing and so they missed many marks.

Part (iv) was often well done with many candidates scoring all marks available for the calculations although the commentary on the method was often lacking an appreciation of the circumstances in which 'expected' values are appropriate. Also, many candidates ignored the advice to focus their answer on the concept of an 'expected' value for the indicator rather than offering a general discussion of the indicator.

ACCA marking scheme

		Marks
(i)	Performance report	
	Breaking down the mission – up to 3 marks	
	Two main aims, three CSFs/strategies, noting how these are logically connected	
	Comments on how report addresses mission and strategies – up to 6 marks	
	Missing information – up to 3 marks	
	Lack of external info; margins by product category	
	Report is 'short-termist' – up to 3 marks	
	Comments on presentation – up to 3 marks	
	Lack of narrative; data overload; rounding	
	Maximum	**16**
(ii)	New asset utilisation indicators	
	Addressing the mission – up to 3 marks	
	Calculations – 3 marks	
	Use in managing business performance – up to 5 marks	
	Maximum	**8**
(iii)	Divisional performance	
	Discussion of existing behaviour and measure – up to 5 marks	
	Discussion of new measure – up to 5 marks	
	Maximum	**8**
(iv)	Decision-making under risk	
	Calculations:	
	1 mark for method	
	1 mark for correct profit under each scenario	
	1 mark for expected operating profit	
	1 mark for expected ROCE	
	Comments – 1 mark per point; up to 4 marks	
	Maximum	**8**

Professional marks	
Communication:	
• Report format and structure – use of headings/sub-headings and introduction	
• Style, language and clarity – appropriate tone of report response, presentation of calculations, appropriate use of CBE tools, easy to follow and understand	
• Adherence to the board's specific request to focus comments on the use of an expected value and not the use of ROCE	
Analysis and Evaluation	
• Appropriate use of the data in appendix 1 to perform suitable calculations for asset utilisation measures and to support a comprehensive evaluation of the existing performance report and the introduction of the asset utilisation measures	
• Appropriate use of the data in appendix 2 to perform suitable calculations of the expected ROCE for the new store and a reasoned assessment of the use of this tool	
• Reasoned assessment of the current divisional performance measure and the proposed measure	
Scepticism	
• Recognition of the failings of the existing performance report (including missing information) and measures and a recognition that the new asset utilisation measures, change to the divisional performance measure and the use of expected ROCE have their own merits but also come with challenges	
Commercial Acumen	
• Effective use of examples drawn from scenario information and other practical considerations related to the context to illustrate points being made throughout the report	
• Recognition that the press's criticisms of short-termism and the run-down look of a number of stores seems to be merited with supporting evidence	
Maximum	**10**
Total	**50**

13 MONZA (SEPT/DEC 16)

Key answer tips

In part (i) to score a good mark you need to include examples relevant to Monza.

In part (ii) you should have identified that the proposed system was limited and deviated little from the current system.

Part (iii) was a more difficult requirement. Make sure that you plan your answer so that you have enough relevant points. Do not focus too much on the calculations.

A well prepared candidate should have scored well in part (iv), correctly analysing the costs into the four categories and discussing how TQM would impact each category.

(v) – Remember the importance of reviewing the technical articles on the ACCA website. An article was released a short time before the exam on this area.

Report

To: The board of Monza

From: A. Accountant

Date: September 2016

Subject: Performance measurement and management issues at Monza

This report addresses the problems of using the balanced scorecard within Monza. The current and proposed performance measures are evaluated and the main current measure is discussed in detail. Quality costs and the new quality programme at the manufacturing division are analysed. Finally, the lean philosophy is applied to the new information system for the drug development division.

(i) Problems with using the balanced scorecard

The balanced scorecard (BSC) provides no aggregate or single summary measure of performance unlike the value-based approach. Also, there is no simple, direct link between shareholder value, the main objective of Monza, and the balanced scorecard measures.

The measures in the scorecard can conflict, for example, cost controls (financial perspective) can obstruct the investment needed in order to speed up manufacturing processes (internal business perspective). Overall, the measures should seek to align with the fundamental need to create shareholder value.

It can be difficult to select measures. In particular, there is the danger of losing sight of key information in a plethora of indicators. This may be an issue for Monza as it has only had three indicators in the past and this will now increase significantly (a potential of 12, if there is one for each level of management in the four perspectives).

There must be management commitment to the change to the scorecard. In particular, there must not be a return to a focus on the financial measures which have been used in the past at Monza. Management should acquire the expertise for understanding non-financial measures through training.

There are potentially significant costs in collecting the additional information which will be needed for the new performance measures. Many of the measures will be non-financial and so new information systems will be required to collect and record the data.

(ii) Choice of current and proposed performance measures

Current measures

The current measures are all historic, financial ones and so the BSC approach will bring a longer term view by using non-financial measures which consider those factors which might drive future growth, for example, those in the learning and growth perspective. The current measures do not directly link to shareholder value which appears to be the overall aim of the company. A measure such as economic value added would do this more effectively.

The three measures do give a broad view of financial performance. ROCE is a widely-used measure which it should be possible to benchmark against competitors. As far as the divisions are concerned, there is a measure of success in selling through revenue growth, though this may not be due to only the sales division but also the drugs brought to market by the development division. Average cost to develop a new drug is a financial measure of the development division's performance but this does not measure its aim of innovation in development. Indeed, this measure may conflict with that aim as cost control of development may hinder innovative thinking. It would appear more appropriate to have a cost control measure associated with manufacturing as its goal is to be more efficient. The performance of the manufacturing division is only measured indirectly through its effect on the financial performance of the company as a whole.

Consultants' proposed measures

The suggested measures do not seem to deviate much from the existing measures, though there may be an advantage in this as the new system would be using existing information systems and known measures in that case. However, this advantage is secondary to the need to find measures which will drive useful performance in the four perspectives.

The proposed measures from the consultants' interim report mostly fit within the standard four perspectives of the BSC, although revenue growth is more appropriate as a measure from the financial perspective. Customer perspective measures should focus on the strategies which will achieve success in the eyes of the customers rather than just measuring the results of those strategies. Examples of this would be measuring the efficacy of the drugs which are developed by Monza or the reputation of Monza's medicines among the medical community.

Taking the others in turn, ROCE does not seem to be directly linked to shareholder value as, for example, economic value added or net present value would be. ROCE considers the performance over the whole capital base while the shareholders will be more directly concerned with returns on their equity investment. As a profit-based measure, ROCE may also be failing to target cash-generation which is ultimately driving dividend payments and value creation for shareholders.

As already indicated, cost control in business processes is important but other measures of success such as time to market for the development of new products and quality initiatives should also be considered.

The fourth perspective is particularly relevant to a high-technology firm such as Monza. There will be considerable competitive advantage in having a highly skilled workforce; however, the measure proposed is imprecise as it values all training days, whether for knowledge workers or unskilled labourers, as equally valuable. Measures of the number of innovations within each division may be appropriate as these will be qualitatively different (new compounds developed, manufacturing quality improvements and sales techniques/initiatives developed).

Overall, the initial proposed set of measures does appear limited and does not address the overall aim of Monza or the problem of the narrowness of the existing set of measures.

(iii) Variation in calculating return on capital

	ROCE	ROE
Using operating profit	18%	
Using operating profit before restructuring	23%	
Using profit after tax		97%

Return on capital employed is normally calculated by dividing operating profit by capital employed (debt and equity). The calculations above illustrate the possibilities using the different return (profit) and capital figures available.

The ROCE figure should not use gross profit as this ignores the operating costs not directly attached to sales and at Monza these will include significant overheads from the drug development and manufacturing divisions which are relevant to overall performance. The return figure should match with the capital used to generate that return. As ROCE is calculated based on the return on total capital, it should not include financing costs and so profit before and after tax are not consistent with this view. The one area that could be argued is whether to include the one-off costs of restructuring in performance. It would probably be best to disclose both figures to the company's stakeholders and to identify how any competitor would perform such a calculation for benchmarking.

A suitable approach for Monza

Return on equity (ROE) may be a more suitable measure given Monza's focus on shareholder (not debt provider) performance. In this case, the relevant return figure is the profit after tax as this is the return available to shareholders after the debt providers have been paid. The figure here (97%) is very large. This is due partly to the fact that the capital figures used in these calculations are from the financial statements and are not market values. (Market values of equity and debt would give a more accurate measure of performance both for ROCE and ROE.) Another reason why the ROE is large compared to ROCE is that Monza is highly geared (88%). ROE, therefore, demonstrates the benefit of the chosen capital structure of Monza.

Overall, therefore, ROE is a better measure than ROCE as it fits with the prioritisation of shareholders as opposed to all capital providers.

(iv) Quality costs and total quality management at manufacturing division

Quality costs are usually broken into four categories:

- Prevention costs which relate to avoiding producing defective items in the first place
- Appraisal costs which relate to ensuring that the products produced meet an acceptable standard
- Costs of internal failure which relate to products which fail appraisal and how these are handled; and
- Costs of external failure which relate to products which fail the standard but are still shipped to customers.

At Monza, for the most recent period, the following quality costs have been identified:

Prevention costs – $8m (training)

Appraisal costs – $12m (product testing)

Costs of internal failure – $13m (batches rejected)

Costs of external failure – $27m = $5m (fines) + $22m (discounts for late delivery)

Total raw material costs might hide relevant quality costs if the company is buying higher quality material to prevent problems of quality, however, this cannot be quantified in this scenario.

It can be seen that there were $40m of failure costs in the period but only $8m was spent on prevention. A 10% improvement in the failures could generate $4m in cost savings and the budget for improvements to production which prevent such failures could be significantly expanded in light of this. The analysis of quality costs should help to emphasise the importance of prevention by showing its financial value and this is vital to motivate a total quality management (TQM) approach.

Impact of TQM on manufacturing division

Total quality management focuses on the customer perspective and the need for each part of the organisation to avoid defects in the chain of production. Prevention is the key to improvement and so management should focus on avoiding defects through training and improved process design rather than appraisal. All employees must accept personal responsibility for their work and act to remove defects from production. Quality certification programmes are often instituted in order to encourage the focus on 'zero defects'. Quality circles may be formed as small, autonomous groups aimed at devising solutions to quality problems.

(v) Making the new information system 'lean' in drug development division

Lean systems aim to get the right thing to the right place at the right time, first time. They aim to reduce waste while being flexible. The need for flexibility will be important for the drug development division as it is constantly working in a changing environment.

The information in the system should be organised so that it can be retrieved with minimum difficulty. The information will also have to be accurate so that time is not wasted in making errors. The information should be presented clearly and, in particular, should not be excessive given the needs of the users. The information should be able to be exchanged easily. This will be important in a collaborative environment such as a research group in the development division.

Tutorial note

The 5Ss (Structurise, Systemise, Sanitise, Standardise, Self-discipline) could also be used to structure an acceptable answer.

Examiner's comments

Part (i). In questions of this nature, candidates should focus on the theoretical areas where they believe the problems lie and then try to exemplify or illustrate these problems by reference to the entity. What many candidates do, however, is to address the question by discussing another technique that they have spent more of their time revising. Making a suggestion as to an alternative may be worth merit but nevertheless does not address the fundamental question asked. It is a fundamental requirement of any APM exam that candidates should know about performance management and control techniques and the challenges that may arise from their implementation.

Part (ii). This is an area where most candidates addressed the question asked though it is worthwhile emphasising as part of good examination practice in this exam that assessment of current measures in the light of their suitability as KPIs of the company's strategic direction is very different to asking for an assessment of performance. It is good practice to ensure that suggestions are justified and supported: it is very common for candidates to highlight, for example, that 'more non-financial indicators are needed' or 'they should measure liquidity' in a question of this type. A key focus of any analysis is the justification behind the points that are being made and it would be good examination practice for candidates to consider this in their revision and ask questions such as: why is that relevant?; how/why would it benefit the company?

Part (iii) was poorly done as candidates did not demonstrate the technical knowledge that is expected at this level with regard to the composition of the measures of performance. Too many candidates gave descriptions of measurements rather than an evaluation of usefulness. For future diets, candidates would be best suited to consider and reflect upon what the metrics and ratios they have learned might mean and consider how they might differ from each other. It is also, as with question (i) above, always best as a matter of good examination practice to respond about the metrics that the question asked candidates to consider.

Part (iv). Some basic technical knowledge was lacking in the analysis of costs. The implementation of a new technique was a part of the question that was generally well done as most candidates focused on specific areas around implementation and tried to relate these to the entity.

Part (v). This question was generally badly done as, again, most candidates did not apply the operation of the system to the production method. Most answers mentioned and explained only either the production method or the system when the requirement of the question was clear in that the two had to be considered in the light of the effect of one on the other.

ACCA marking scheme		
		Marks
(i)	Problems with using the balanced scorecard Up to 2 marks per point if made relevant to Monza	
	Maximum	**8**
(ii)	Choice of current and proposed performance measures Current measures – up to 6 marks Proposed measures – up to 9 marks	
	Maximum	**12**
(iii)	Variation in calculating return on capital Calculations – 3 marks for profit calculation of appropriate ROCE figures; 1 for doing ROE calculation; 1 for gearing Maximum 5 marks Discussion of ROCE – up to 5 marks Discussion of ROE – up to 3 marks Justified recommendation – 1 mark	
	Maximum	**11**
(iv)	Quality costs and TQM at manufacturing division Discussion of categories of quality cost – up to 2 marks Calculation/identification of quality costs – up to 3 marks Discussion of results – up to 3 marks Effect of TQM – up to 5 marks	
	Maximum	**10**
(v)	New information system Aims of lean approach – up to 2 marks Ways of achieving a lean system – up to 5 marks	
	Maximum	**5**
Professional marks		4
Total		**50**

14 BOLTZMAN (DEC 14) (AMENDED)

Key answer tips

The scenario in this question is reasonably succinct with clear explanations of exactly what is and what is not required.

(i) This requirement is a test of knowledge (the detail of the Performance Pyramid must be known) but you are also expected to relate these back to the information in the scenario. The answer below includes the diagram of the performance pyramid. This is included to assist with learning. You will not be expected to reproduce diagrams in the CBE.

(ii) You should use Mendelow's matrix to analyse the company's stakeholders. In the second part of the requirement you are asked to evaluate the performance measures – therefore a balanced answer is required with both pros and cons.

(iii) Some easy calculation marks are available here. An evaluation of the approach to benchmarking is required, so again you would be expected to discuss pros and cons.

(iv) You should feel relatively comfortable with JIT but make sure that you come up with enough separate points and/ or add the required depth to your points.

To: The board of Boltzman

From: A Accountant

Date: 1 September 20X5

Subject: A coherent approach to performance management at Boltzman

This report brings the different initiatives together using the performance pyramid framework. The suggested performance measures are evaluated and then used in a benchmarking exercise of Boltzman compared to General Machines. Finally, the quality improvement initiative is commented upon.

(i) Performance pyramid

The performance pyramid indicates how strategies to assist in the achievement of corporate vision may be cascaded down through four levels.

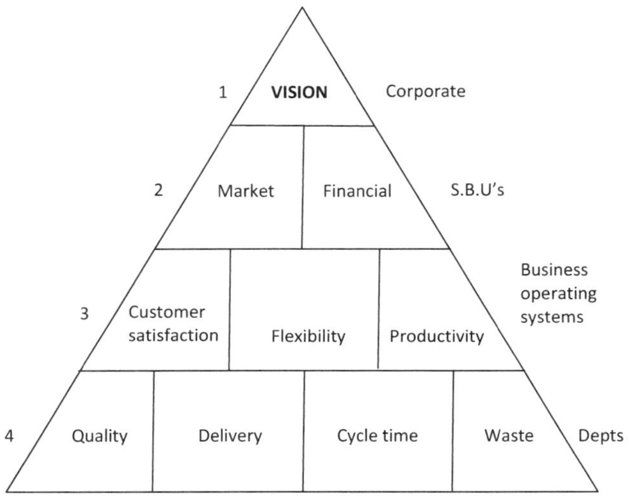

Level 1: At the top of the organisation is the corporate vision through which the organisation describes how it will achieve long-term success and competitive advantage.

Level 2: This focuses on the achievement of an organisation's CSFs in terms of market-related measures and financial measures. The marketing and financial success of a proposal is the initial focus for the achievement of corporate vision.

Level 3: The marketing and financial strategies set at level 2 must be linked to the achievement of customer satisfaction, increased flexibility and high productivity at the next level. These are the guiding forces that drive the strategic objectives of the organisation.

Level 4: The status of the level 3 driving forces can be monitored using the lower level departmental indicators of quality, delivery, cycle time and waste.

The left hand side of the pyramid contains measures which have an external focus and which are predominantly non-financial. Those on the right are focused on the internal efficiency of the organisation and are predominantly financial.

The analysis of stakeholder power will provide ideas on how the stakeholders can contribute to the success of Boltzman. For example, the relatively weak position of suppliers may lead Boltzman to be able to push them to make improvements to the quality of their components while maintaining the same selling prices. This impacts objectives for competitive strategy in level and will cascade down to quality measures in level 4.

The benchmarking exercise will help in setting strategies with which the business aims to achieve stakeholder satisfaction. It may identify strategies for improvement although here the data used will only give a strategic view, relevant for setting objectives and targets for level 2. However, as it is not operationally detailed, it is unlikely to supply much information for levels 3 and 4.

The quality initiative will impact primarily on level 3 – business operating systems. There will be a need to redesign processes in order to meet stricter quality standards. There will be a need to increase the capabilities of the organisation to manufacture with lower fault rates and at finer tolerances and this may come through greater emphasis on staff training to improve their capabilities or alternatively, through investment in the automation of processes to improve speed and accuracy of production. Each of these may impact objectives and KPIs set at levels 3 and 4.

(ii) Stakeholder analysis

The matrix suggests different management approaches are appropriate for each group of stakeholders, depending on their likelihood of engagement in decision-making and their ability to influence that decision-making.

Shareholders have considerable power but do not wish active involvement in decision-making (this is what they pay the management to handle). Therefore, they must be kept satisfied by ensuring their financial targets are met.

Employees have little power generally and so need to be kept informed. However, there is a sub-group of key employees with skills who the company must retain and this sub-group should be kept satisfied by the provision of opportunity to develop their skills through training and work on new technologies.

Customers are key players given the importance of our components to their business and the lost revenue if one were to drop us as a supplier. Therefore, they should be managed closely by having staff dedicated to liaising with them and involving them in product development. This type of close cooperation is likely to be necessary in high-technology industries such as ours.

Suppliers have little power and Boltzman should be in a position of strength in negotiation over the price and quality of their goods. They should require minimal effort and they would be expected to be doing the work to meet our needs as a major customer. However, suppliers are a common source of innovation, so keeping them informed of developments would be sensible. In particular, good supplier relations will be important for a move to JIT manufacturing.

Evaluation of suggested performance indicators

Performance measures should be focused on the influential stakeholders identified above.

It is appropriate that most of the indicators are directed towards the key players identified above. Return on capital employed, economic value added, revenue growth and net profit margin are all suitable measures for the shareholders as these measure financial returns across the organisation – its efficiency in deploying capital, its ability to grow sales and its efficiency in turning sales into returns for shareholders.

There are no indicators directed at customers who are key players. This is a major omission in the list of indicators suggested. It would be helpful to have indicators covering the price/quality mix of Boltzman's products and their innovative nature in such high-technology industry sectors. Also, there are no external measures of competitive advantage given in the list of indicators.

Average pay per employee is a poor indicator as this does not focus on the sub-group of key employees. It is appropriate to have an indicator for this group and it would be their average pay (possibly as a percentage of an industry benchmark) which would be valuable.

Suppliers do not have significant power or importance to Boltzman, being easily interchangeable. Therefore, it is appropriate that there is no indicator directed at them, although this will have to change as JIT is introduced.

(iii) **Benchmarking against General Machines**

Benchmarking method

The benchmarking exercise is an external one where comparison is drawn with a major competitor. This is valuable in identifying areas of the competitor's competitive advantage and also areas for improvement with a similar business. However, although this method can suggest areas where Boltzman can catch up with its major competitor, it will not identify how to gain advantage over General Machines.

Another fault in this method of benchmarking is that it will only indicate strategic improvements not operational ones, as such detailed information is unlikely to be in the public domain. It may be sensible to consider functional benchmarking with a world-class company from another business sector. Boltzman could share detailed operational data without the worry of loss of confidential information directly to a competitor. This is commonly done where quality initiatives, such as at Boltzman, are being introduced. Boltzman may find that its customers are already collecting process quality data and would be willing to share with a top tier supplier.

Benchmarking results

	Boltzman	**General Machines**
Return on capital employed	15.5%	9.2%
Economic value added ($m)		
Operating profit	2,907	1,882
Less tax charge	(663)	(718)
Less tax benefit of interest	(81)	(88)
NOPAT	2,163	1,076
WACC	11%	11%
Capital employed	18,785	20,373
Economic value added (= NOPAT – rC)	97	(1,165)
Revenue growth	6.4%	1.0%
Average pay per employee ($ p.a.)	54,618	52,299
Net profit margin	8.2%	3.3%

Tutorial note

ROCE figures are based on year opening figures although year closing figures are acceptable. Credit was also given if adjustment of EVA for product development costs was considered.

The results suggest that Boltzman is doing better than General Machines financially (ROCE, economic value added and profit margin) and has better current and possibly future growth prospects (revenue growth being driven by higher product development spending). The one area of weakness identified relates to size where General Machines has a higher revenue and more top customer accounts but with the higher growth of Boltzman, this may not last long.

(iv) **JIT initiative**

The JIT initiative will bring great benefits to Boltzman but will also place new demands on management in the business. It will fit well with the move to lean manufacturing.

The difficulties involved in introducing just-in-time manufacturing begin with the need to forecast demand accurately in order to time manufacture as required. This requires close links to our customers which should be possible given our status as a top tier supplier.

If we are only producing to order, then we can suffer if our own suppliers fail to make deliveries of sufficient quality and on time. The suppliers used at present are bulk suppliers and may not be used to the level of quality and ability to deliver on time which JIT requires. We will need to perform a detailed review of our supply chain in order to identify those suppliers who can meet our needs now, or else be brought up to that standard. We may then partner with a few suppliers in order to help them to improve their standards of service and quality of components.

By restricting the number of suppliers, we will be more open to disruption of our supply chain. We may wish to keep our suppliers local to the manufacturing sites but, of course, this restricts further our choice of supplier and so increases their bargaining power with us.

A further challenge will be the change in mind set which will come from moving to JIT where the focus of effort is no longer just on cost reduction but also on appreciation of the value of non-financial factors associated with quality. This change will have to occur throughout the organisation and is often most difficult at the operational level, where, for example, the basic layout of the factory must be redesigned and the workforce need to be flexible on working patterns and multi-skilled to avoid bottlenecks.

ACCA marking scheme		
		Marks
(i)	4 marks for the general description of the pyramid levels. Up to 3 marks for the discussion of each initiative and how it fits within the pyramid	
	Maximum	**8**
(ii)	Up to 2 marks for analysis of each of the four stakeholders Up to 10 marks for evaluation of the five indicators suggested	
	Maximum	**13**
(iii)	Up to 6 marks for evaluating the method of benchmarking Calculations: 1 mark for each indicator calculated (up to 4 marks) except economic value added 3 marks for calculation of economic value added Up to 3 marks for a reasonable conclusion	
	Maximum	**14**
(iv)	1 mark for identifying each difficulty of implementing JIT – additional marks where this is developed for Boltzman's situation.	
	Maximum	**5**
Professional marks **Communication:**		
•	Report format and structure – use of headings/sub-headings and introduction	
•	Style, language and clarity – appropriate tone of report response, presentation of calculations, appropriate use of CBE tools, easy to follow and understand, more than a negligible amount of content	
•	Adherence to the CEO's request not suggest a long list of additional indicators and to limit the benchmarking calculations to the five measures suggested	
Analysis and Evaluation		
•	Comprehensive discussion of the levels of the performance pyramid with a reasoned discussion of how the initiatives relate to these levels	
•	Appropriate use of the information in appendix 1 to complete the work started on stakeholder analysis	
•	Appropriate use of the information and data in appendix 1 and 2 to perform suitable calculations for the measures given and to support discussion of the benchmarking approach	

Scepticism • Recognition that there are potential failures or problems with the suggested performance measures, the benchmarking approach used and a move to JIT manufacturing **Commercial Acumen** • Effective use of examples drawn from scenario information and other practical considerations related to the context to illustrate points made throughout the report • Assessment, justifications and problems identified are practical and plausible in the context of the scenario information	
Maximum	**10**
Total	**50**

15 CANTOR (JUN 14)

Key answer tips

This question is broken down into five requirements testing a number of syllabus areas. The examining is very clear about what they require.

(i) A common requirement asking you to evaluate the performance report. Be careful – you are expected to discuss the pros and cons of the report and not to evaluate the company's performance.

(ii) Not a commonly examined syllabus area but you should be able to come up with a handful of relevant points here. Review the answer in detail if you are unsure of this requirement.

(iii) A typical EVA question – a reasonably straightforward calculation with only a handful of adjustments. Make sure you discuss your result and any assumptions.

(iv) This requirement asks for an explanation and evaluation of VBM. You need to have your knowledge in place but be careful to tailor your answer to the question rather than simply writing down everything that you know about VBM.

(v) In this requirement you are expected to work through the calculations quickly and focus on the difficulties in measuring the treatment of employees and in interpreting the results.

To: CEO

From: A Accountant

Date: June 2014

Subject: Performance reporting and value-based management at Cantor

This report evaluates the current performance reporting and cost structures of Cantor. It evaluates the impact of value-based management at Cantor calculating its current economic value added. Finally, recommendations for new performance measures for the new ethical area in the company's amended mission are made.

(i) Current performance report

The current report has a number of strengths and weaknesses. These will be discussed according to whether the report:

- addresses the overall aims of the group
- assists the individual subsidiaries
- is well-presented
- contains appropriate information for decision-making.

The current mission of the group can be broken down into three parts:

- to maximise shareholder value
- supplying good value food and drink; and
- providing appealing environments for our customers.

The report does not directly measure shareholder value which could be done through considering net present value or economic value added (EVA™) or share price and dividends. This problem has been recognised and is addressed in a later section of this report. The current report uses period profits as its main measure of performance. This can suffer from being short term unlike the shareholder value measures mentioned. The report does compare budget and actual performance which gives an indication of whether plans are being followed and is helpful in controlling the organisation.

There is an indirect measure of the customer value being offered by the group through the gross profit which, when compared to the industry average, gives a partial measure of value but without data on the price/quality mix compared to competitors, it is difficult to be conclusive about this. Revenue growth compared to industry growth would aid in giving an impression of the attractiveness of our offering to the customer. However, no historic information is given which would allow trends to be calculated.

Measuring the appeal of the sites to customers will be difficult and involve subjective non-financial measurements. Customer loyalty and price elasticity of demand will give some indication of the appeal but it will be difficult without directly surveying customers to untie this from the issues of price/quality mentioned above.

The main board would probably find it easier if less detailed figures were given and a clear statement of the key measures of subsidiary performance provided.

The report seems to treat the subsidiaries in the same way as the group, using profit and comparison to industry average margins and budgets as the main assessment tools. As already mentioned, the reporting of performance against budget is a helpful control tool. However, as the subsidiaries will have more detailed issues than the group, it does not seem appropriate to be using the same high-level overview as for the group board. For the subsidiaries, it would be expected that there would be a more detailed breakdown of revenues and gross margins by product line. Marketing, which is a significant cost, is not attributed to specific sites/products which would help to explain the changes in these categories. The subsidiary managers would probably benefit from the inclusion of a breakdown of profit by geographical region as well. It would seem that the measure being used to assess subsidiary performance would be the operating profit, which is appropriate as it contains the elements of performance controllable by the subsidiaries' managers. The annual reporting period would also appear to be too lengthy to allow the detailed control of operations required by the subsidiary boards.

In terms of presentation, the data is clear and in a form which would be easily recognisable to those used to reading accounts. However, it is common to provide a narrative commentary with such a report in order to highlight the key features in the report, such as major deviations from the budget or performance well outside industry norms. The report could be made easier to read by rounding all figures to thousands and thus removing unnecessary detail.

To summarise, additional information which could be supplied in the report also includes:

- historic information to demonstrate trends (especially important at Juicey with its fast growth)
- greater detail by product or site to aid the managers of the subsidiaries
- competitor information relating to their performance in the three areas of Cantor's mission (shareholder value, product value, site appeal).

(ii) Cost structures

The costs at Cafes and Juicey are a mix of fixed and variable. Fixed costs represent a risk to Cantor since if there is a fall in the general economy, these must still be covered by revenues. So, a breakeven analysis would be helpful in this situation. The difficulty with such an analysis is that some costs are partly fixed and partly variable.

Staff costs are likely to be part-fixed and part-variable. As these represent a significant part of the cost base, it will be necessary to establish what element is fixed (how many staff are the minimum required to run a site?) and what element is variable (how many staff can be used as needed when the sites are busy?). This cost area will be managed through decisions over the balance of the numbers of permanent and casual staff with casual staff being used to manage fluctuations in business.

Rent costs affect each subsidiary differently. At Cafes, rent is fixed and this is appropriate for a mature, established business where revenues ought to be predictable and so the fixed nature of the cost should not threaten the survival of the operation. At Juicey, the rent is a percentage of revenue and in a new operation this is appropriate as the rent will grow with the business.

However, the percentage demanded will reflect the risk which the landlord is taking on the success of Juicey and so will be higher than a fixed rent such as negotiated by Cafes. As Juicey becomes established, it may be worth considering beginning to move to negotiating fixed rental deals for Juicey in order to cut this cost.

This last point illustrates the dilemma which many businesses face in thinking about the balance of fixed and variable costs. Variable costs are more desirable as they do not threaten the survival of the business but they are often higher than a fixed cost deal.

(iii) Economic value added

	$
Operating profit	10,852,970
Add back	
Marketing capitalised	3,819,000
Less	
Tax paid	2,100,000
Lost tax relief on interest	200,250
NOPAT	12,371,720
Capital employed	
At 2014 year start	53,400,000
Marketing spend capitalised	3,819,000
Adjusted capital employed	57,219,000

WACC = (1/1.3 × 15.7%) + (0.3/1.3 × 6.5% × (1 – 25%))

= 13.2%

EVA™ = NOPAT – (WACC × Capital employed)

= 4,818,812

The EVA™ of Cantor for 2014 was $4.82m, showing this was added to shareholder value over the period by the group. The result reflects the fact that the group is comfortably exceeding its cost of capital.

This calculation is limited by the information available and a number of approximations and assumptions have had to be made. One approximation is that the accounting depreciation charge represents the economic depreciation suffered by the company. A more detailed examination would be required in order to check this against the full version of the EVA™ calculation. The marketing spend is partially capitalised to the extent that it represents a long-term investment in the brand name of Cantor. Further work should be done to identify if this long-term marketing spending requires to be amortised and so charged back against NOPAT; the capital employed calculation gives an illustration of how the year start figure might be affected but all prior years with their related amortisation would need to be considered for a full answer.

It may prove useful for the subsidiaries' performance management to collect data and calculate their individual EVA™s.

Tutorial note

Credit would be given for narrative comment or illustrative adjustment for marketing spend on capital employed. The calculation of EVA™s is discussed in a two-part article entitled 'Economic value added versus profit-based measures of performance'.

(iv) Value-based management

VBM begins from the view that the value of a company is measured by its discounted future cash flows. The idea being that value is only created when companies generate returns which beat their cost of that capital. VBM then focuses the management of the company on those areas which create value. A key to this process is the identification of the drivers of value and then a concentration of effort at all levels (strategic, tactical and operational) on these drivers in order to increase the value of the firm.

The implementation will broadly involve four steps:

1 A strategy is developed to maximise value.

2 Key value drivers must be identified and then performance targets (for both the short and long term) are defined for those value drivers.

3 A plan is developed to achieve the targets.

4 Performance metrics and reward systems measurement and incentive systems are created compatible with these targets.

At Cantor, these steps might include a strategy of acquisition and disposal to go alongside the organic growth of Juicey. The key value drivers for each operating subsidiary would have to be identified from strategic to operational levels and these could include gross margins (strategic) and site service levels (operational). Targets must then be developed from these measures – possibly by benchmarking against competitors.

The impact for Cantor would be the introduction of new performance measures based on the drivers and a reward system to motivate staff. There will be the need to develop such measures, targets and reward at the group level, then at the subsidiary level and, finally, at the individual site level in order to ensure full coordination of the system across Cantor. In order to align the interests of employees and management with shareholder value, a feature of the new reward system is often a share-based payment scheme.

The key benefits of VBM are the focus on value as opposed to profit, so reducing the tendency to make decisions which have positive short-term impact but may be detrimental in the long term. VBM thus will help to make Cantor more forward looking.

A danger of the VBM exercise is that it becomes an exercise in valuing everything but changing nothing. It is important that the detailed operational issues of the organisation are addressed through the new measures/targets. A further difficulty in implementation is that the measurement of the key value drivers can often involve non-financial indicators and these can represent a significant change for accounting-based management information systems.

(v) Measurement of treatment of employees

The measurement of treatment of employees is difficult due to its subjective nature. The organisation will constantly be in negotiation with the employees as they have conflicting aims, for example, over pay rates and workloads. The information in the appendices allows a number of measures to be calculated which could provide some indication of employee satisfaction and treatment.

	Cafes	**Juicey**	**Group**
Average employee numbers	1,498	106	1,624
Employee turnover rates	9.7%	14.2%	9.9%

Using staff costs and employee numbers, the average pay at Cantor is $13,143 (= 21.345m/1,624) and this could be compared to competitors. The comparative information is not given in the reports at present, although an indication is given through the staff cost margin which shows Cantor paying a slightly higher proportion of revenue than the industry average. However, caution must be taken with such a measure as it is an average and does not necessarily reflect the position of many individual employees.

The staff numbers data also allows calculation of staff turnover rates as 9.9% (= 161/1,624) at the group as a whole and 9.7% at Cafes and 14.2% at Juicey. This indicates staff satisfaction and the variation between Cafes and Juicey should be investigated. It may be due to the learning curve which managers are experiencing in the fast growing and newer operation.

Tutorial note

Using year-end figures is acceptable too in this case.

Examiner's comments

In part (i), most candidates performed reasonably well. There were a number of candidates who provided an irrelevant evaluation of the performance of Cantor. Those who attempted the question asked scored most of the marks associated with such reports in general but few scored marks that were present in appreciating the scenario surrounding Cantor.

In part (ii) most candidates knew what fixed and variable costs were and had some ability in applying these to the scenario information. However, very few showed sensitivity to the performance management aspects of operational gearing.

Part (iii) was generally well done. Two areas that demonstrated weak performance though were calculations of WACC and in selecting the capital employed. Finally, many candidates stated the assumptions rather than 'justifying' them.

In part (iv) the problem for the majority of candidates was lack of knowledge with many vaguely talking of value without an understanding of it in the context of the scenario.

In part (v) a number of points were not understood; firstly, comments about the existing mission statement were irrelevant. Secondly, the requirement asked for justified performance measures and so a list of points was of limited value. Finally, the requirement stated the answer should use the 'information in the appendices'.

ACCA marking scheme

			Marks
(i)	1 mark per point – must be based on the scenario information		
	For example:		
	Assessment of whether report meets mission		
	Appropriateness of the level of detail for the three boards		
	Use of budgets		
	Use of industry averages		
		Maximum	**15**
(ii)	1 mark per point	**Maximum**	**6**
(iii)	EVA		
	Calculation:		
	Marketing		1
	Tax		2
	Capital employed – marketing		1
	WACC		1
	EVA result		1
	Comments:		
	Result		1
	Assumptions	**up to**	3
		Maximum	**9**
(iv)	VBM		
	General description of VBM up to 2 marks		
	Description and impact of implementation of VBM up to 10 marks		
		Maximum	**10**
(v)	Calculations – up to 3 marks		
	1 mark per point on areas such as		
	difficulty of measuring		
	pay rates		
	staff turnover		
		Maximum	**6**
Professional marks:			
Introduction and report headings			1
Use of suitable subheadings in report			1
Clarity and language use			2
Conclusion (not required here but given if reasonably attempted)			1
		Maximum	**4**
Total			**50**

16 JHK COFFEE MACHINES CO (JUN 11)

Key answer tips

In part (i) make sure you focus on *divisional* performance measures and their relative strengths and weaknesses. Try to include a discussion of the different profit figures that could be used and issues such as controllable v uncontrollable costs.

In parts (ii) and (iii) ensure you back up your commentary with adequate supporting calculations.

In part (iv) make sure you focus on making comments about the impact of the new system on performance management not the specific difficulties in initial implementation of the system.

(i) **To:** Finance Director

From: A Accountant

Date: June 2011

Subject: Divisional performance issues at JHK and the introduction of a new information system

This report examines recent divisional performance issues. It begins by evaluating the performance of each division and offering a general consideration of the different measures of divisional performance.

The nature of transfer prices and suitable methods of transfer pricing the work of the service division back into the main manufacturing and sales division are reviewed. Finally, the impact of a unified corporate database and improved information systems are considered.

Divisional performance evaluation

	Manufacturing & Sales	**Service**
Controllable return on investment	30%	16%
(Operating profit/Capital employed)		
Residual income ($m)	270	3
(Operating profit less notional interest charge)		
Non-controllable return on investment	23%	13%
(PBT/Capital employed)		
EVA™ ($m)	158	1.1
NOPAT – WACC*Capital employed		
Operating profit	386	6.0
Add: other non-cash expenses	4	0.3
Less: Tax	116	1.8
NOPAT	274	4.5

WACC – used notional interest rate

Both divisions are performing well. They make a healthy return on investment although we have no target rate with which to compare them. Also, both divisions make a positive residual income and economic value added which again implies healthy returns.

Divisional performance measures

The appropriate return on investment (controllable ROI) is calculated on profit before interest and tax divided by capital employed at the division. The profit figure excludes allocated head office costs as these are not controllable at divisional level. The residual income takes the same profit figure but subtracts a notional interest charge based on the capital employed by the division. Both divisions are offering good returns with positive RI and high controllable ROI, although there would normally be a target ROI set in order to compare to actual performance. The target would have to exceed the 9% cost of capital as it does not take account of necessary head office costs.

ROI is a simple, commonly used measure of divisional performance. However, it can encourage divisions to delay investment in new assets since this measure improves as assets are depreciated with age. RI offers the possibility of applying different costs of capital to divisions with different risk profiles. However, RI does not allow a clear comparison of performance between divisions since it is an absolute measure of performance.

Both ROI and RI have the disadvantage of being based on profit measures of performance rather than cash. Measures such as NPV use cash flows which are less subject to the interpretation of accounting rules and are more directly aligned with shareholder interests.

It is unclear that either of these measures will align with the overall performance measure of TSR, since it depends on share price and dividends paid.

EVA™ is an absolute performance measure like RI. It involves a more complex calculation than RI with many adjustments to the accounting figures of profit and net assets, such as the use of replacement costs for asset values and economic depreciation rather than accounting depreciation. (Here, the calculated figures are an estimate using the available information.)

Many of the EVA™ adjustments are intended to avoid distortion of results by accounting policies that are present in ROI and RI. Thus, EVA™ is more directly aligned with the objective of increasing shareholder wealth and so should help to ensure that there is congruence between the divisional and corporate goals. EVA™, like RI, has the advantage that by treating certain costs as investments it encourages appropriate capital expenditure.

However, EVA™ depends on historical data while shareholders will be focused on future performance. Unlike ROI, EVA™ and RI would not help to judge relative divisional performance at JHK as the divisions are not of similar size and so an absolute measure is not comparable.

(ii) Transfer pricing

The transfer price is the price that the service division would charge to the manufacturing and sales division for its warranty servicing for which it would otherwise not receive any income. The objective of a transfer pricing system is to allow divisional management to be assessed on the basis of divisional profit and so provide them with motivation while retaining their autonomy.

The transfer price should be set so that the decisions of the divisions individually are beneficial to the company as a whole but still represent a fair position for both divisions. If divisions are in different tax regimes then the transfer price should minimise the overall company tax liability within the law.

The general rule for goal congruent decision-making is that transfer prices should be set with reference to the opportunity cost of sale to the selling division (service division) and the opportunity cost to the buying division (manufacturing and sales division). There are different situations if there is surplus capacity or a capacity constraint in the service division or if there is an external market for the service, since these affect the opportunities available to the divisions.

(iii) The two different methods of pricing the service division's work are now considered.

Market based pricing

The service division could consider an external market price since there is the opportunity to outsource and therefore, its managers would charge $200. This would generate a reduced divisional profit to the company of $0.59m from the warranty work as opposed to the profit from the current agreement of $2.67m (see appendix for working). Thus it would still provide motivation for the service division to take the warranty work.

However, there would be savings if the work were kept internal to JHK, such as the overhead of negotiating and managing the contract with the local engineering firm. Doing the work internally would save these costs and so, a market price adjusted down for these savings would be appropriate. There is also the danger of outsourcing the service function in that the company loses control of a strategically important part of its offering to customers. It is clear that the warranty is a key selling point for JHK and it may not be able to control the quality of the repair work if this is outsourced.

A market price will guide the service division to the right decision on whether to continue to do the warranty work in-house or whether to outsource it and free capacity for other opportunities. If external work offers a better contribution than warranty work, the service division will automatically do external work. It will also measure profits at market-based prices. Thus, this method will provide motivation without a price being imposed by head office.

The volume and profitability of external work that may be available to the service division should also be investigated. If this were more profitable than internal work then this would suggest that the service division should prioritise this work and outsource if there is a lack of capacity to cover the internal work. It should be noted that the current quote from the outsourcer demands a minimum volume of work and so their work may need to be repriced.

Cost based pricing

The work could also be charged on the basis of the cost to the service division. The variable cost is $135 on average per repair and so the $10m contract represents a contribution for the division of $4,654k (based on the expected 39,600 repairs per year). This represents a divisional profit of $2,674k (see appendix for working).

The work could be charged at variable cost but then there would be no contribution to the service division's profits and so no incentive for the service division to do this work. It would, therefore, prioritise external sales over internal ones.

If a breakeven divisional profit was desired then a price of $185 per repair should be charged as this covers fixed overheads in the division. Although it would not contribute to head office costs, service division managers would still be motivated to perform the warranty work. M/S division managers would accept any cost below the alternative of $200 per repair for outsourcing the work.

It may be worth comparing a cost plus approach with the existing agreement. The service division would have to charge $253 per repair in order to make the same divisional profit as it enjoys under the current agreement.

Current pricing method

The current fixed price charge provides a contribution to the division's fixed costs which will incentivise the service division. However, this may cause problems in quality since it is not related to the volume of work done by service and if there were a much higher number of repairs than expected then the service division might compromise quality in order to control costs.

(iv) New information system

The executive information system (EIS) will bring a number of benefits in decision-making at the strategic level at JHK but at certain costs and with certain problems.

The benefits relate to improved decision-making as the EIS should allow drill-down access to the more detailed operational records but the initial presentation of data should be based on the key performance indicators for the company. This system should also be linked to external data sources so that senior management do not fall into the trap of only looking inwards in the organisation at the risk of ignoring wider issues in the business environment (for example, the demand for external servicing work and market prices of this work).

The new system will increase the amount of information and analysis that it will be possible for senior managers to perform. It will present opportunities for better decision-making using the more up-to-date information. However, it may present the problem of information overload for managers. Therefore, the system will need to be designed to give access to only those areas that it is appropriate for any given manager to see.

The data used in decision-making will be more robust as a single database will reduce the problem of redundancy where multiple copies of the same data are held on different systems. This will remove the danger of inconsistencies and reduce the storage required by the company.

The EIS would allow access to decision support systems such as large spreadsheet models built in order to pull data out of the database for use in forecasting and appraising projects (for example, warranty repairs forecasting is important for the current fixed fee contract between the sales and service divisions).

The EIS will also give access to tactical information such as budgets in order to help the executive control the business.

In order to gain the maximum benefit from the new system, executive managers will need to be trained and this training should occur just before the new system is available so that they are in a position to use it immediately.

Overall, the new system should provide valuable information if used correctly but the cost of the system must be weighed against the benefits of the system which will be mostly intangible and so difficult to measure (e.g. improved decision-making).

(v) It is important that the new Executive Information system captures both internal and external information in order to allow appropriate business decisions. The types of external information may include details on competitor offerings such as machine features as well as information about the service provided, for example extended warranties.

It would also be useful to collate customer feedback about the products and services offered by JHK and incorporate this information into the system to track any changes in customer requirements. This would enable JHK to modify their machines if necessary.

As JHK is looking into providing warranty repair services for other companies, they should also collect information on other service providers in this area. It would be particularly important at this stage to understand the industry pricing to ensure the price offered by the local engineering company remains competitive. This would need to be combined with information regarding the cost of performing this service.

In conclusion of the report, the two suggested divisional performance measures do not align with the overall corporate strategy and it is recommended that the company use EVA™ as a more appropriate measure of performance. The current method of transfer pricing gives a good contribution to fixed costs in the service division but may not encourage both divisions to perform optimally from the perspective of the whole company. Further work needs to be undertaken to investigate the possibility of obtaining an additional stream of outside revenue for the service division.

Appendix:

	$
Labour (per repair)	36
Variable divisional overhead (per repair)	24
Fixed divisional overhead (per repair)	50
Parts	75
So	
Variable cost (per repair)	135
Total cost (per repair)	185

Number of repairs per year 440,000 units where 9% need repairing every three years. Given continuous production, this means in total 39,600 will need warranty repairs each year.

	Current recharge agreement	**Market pricing**
	$000	$000
Revenue	10,000	7,920
Variable costs	5,346	5,346
Contribution	4,654	2,574
Fixed costs	1,980	1,980
Divisional profit (before head office costs)	2,674	594

Cost plus prices

To give equivalent contribution to current recharge agreement	10m/39,600 = $252.53
To cover variable costs	5.346m/39,600 = $135.00
To give breakeven contribution to the division	(10m – 2.674m)/39,600 = $185.00

ACCA marking scheme

			Marks
(i)	7 marks for calculation of ROI, RI and EVA.		
	4 marks for ROI and RI: 1 for use of controllable profit; 1.5 for ROI and 1.5 for RI.		
	3 marks for EVA:		
	Other non-cash expenses		0.5
	Tax		0.5
	Depreciation treatment		0.5
	NOPAT		0.5
	WACC used		0.5
	EVA		0.5
	Up to 2 marks for assessment of performance from the calculated numbers.		
	Up to 3 marks for comments on each measure.		
		Maximum	**15**
(ii)	Transfer pricing system		
	Up to 5 marks on transfer pricing system, 1 mark per point.	**Maximum**	**5**
(iii)	Calculations, up to 8 marks		
	Number of warranty repairs pa		1
	Costs per repair		2
	Contribution under current agreement		1
	Contribution with market price		1
	Prices for breakeven under cost plus		3
	Transfer pricing commentary		
	Up to 5 marks on evaluating transfer pricing at JHK		
		Maximum	**12**
(iv)	Up to 5 marks for benefits. Up to 6 marks for problems	**Maximum**	**10**
(v)	1 mark per point	**Maximum**	**4**
Up to 4 professional marks			**4**
Total			**50**

17 LOPTEN INDUSTRIES (DEC 13)

Key answer tips

Make sure that you answer the question set (e.g. discussing KPIs in part (c) not CSFs) and ensure that you can complete basic calculations quickly and accurately.

Also be prepared you argue your case – in particular, justifying each indicator under consideration in the question requirement.

To: Board of Lopten

From: A. Accountant

Date: December 2013

Subject: KPIs for Lopten in Beeland

Introduction

This report calculates the KPIs suggested by the board and evaluates their effectiveness in addressing identified external environmental issues, their ability to cover the CSFs chosen for the Beeland operations and how they address the key functions of senior management to plan and control Lopten. Finally, the report evaluates whether the two suggested marketing strategies enable Beeland to achieve its target profit.

(i) Summary of KPIs

	Cheerful	**Posh**
Profit for each product ($m)	42	45
Average price per unit ($)	400	700
Contribution per unit ($)	145	375
Market share	12%	33%
Margin of safety	26%	27%
ROCE	13%	18%
Total quality costs ($m)	28	19
Consumer awards	1	4

Details of calculations are given in Appendix 1.

(ii) Issues in the external environment

The issues in the external environment can be identified using the PEST acronym, which stands for political, economic, socio-cultural and technological.

The political environment is characterised by government actions which here included the giving of grants to a competitor to set up manufacturing operations in Beeland. This is not Lopten's mode of operation which is to manufacture outside Beeland and only create a selling operation within the country. None of the KPIs directly address this issue which could lead to increased profit available to develop the competitor's products or government action against Lopten by, say, increasing import tariffs.

The economic environment is characterised by growth as the populace of Beeland becomes wealthier. There is no measure of this included in the KPIs. There is no measure of competitor activity, although market share does provide some measure of the relative strength of Lopten and its competitors. It is notable that none of the KPIs measure current rates of growth in their area. Also, the given KPIs do not reflect the foreign exchange risk which Lopten could encounter in repatriating profits from Beeland.

The socio-cultural factors include demographic trends and changes in customers' tastes. The increasing wealth mentioned earlier will be a factor in driving the consumers' taste towards the more expensive Posh products. These would justify the large potential growth indicated in marketing Plan B. There are several measures which will bear on this area but, as noted above, all will require trends to be given, for example, the inflation of average price per unit and consequent improvement in profit and contribution indicators.

Technology can impact on Lopten in two ways. First, the development of new features for the products themselves will require continued product development at Lopten as a whole, although it will be less relevant to the operation in Beeland which may not have the market for cutting-edge technology yet. Therefore, it is appropriate that this area is not covered by the existing KPIs. Second, new technology in manufacturing could improve further the contribution per unit as costs are cut from the manufacturing process by, for example, increased automation in production. The use of contribution to measure this impact is indirect as it is also influenced by the selling price, so a measure of manufacturing cost per unit would better capture the change.

(iii) Linking the KPIs and CSFs

The first CSF is to obtain a dominant market presence. This will be measured by the market share and it can be seen that Posh has obtained about a third of the market and so can be said to be a major presence. In order to judge whether this is dominant, Lopten will need to have its competitors' market share. Other KPIs (average price per unit, ROCE, consumer awards) can be used in measuring market position but again, only if comparable data for the competition is supplied. In trying to achieve dominant market position, Lopten could chose to cut prices in order to drive up volumes and the contribution per unit shows how far the selling price can be cut before breakeven is reached (= average price – contribution).

The second CSF is the maximisation of profit within the risk appetite of the business. The absolute level of profit is given as a KPI and so a trend analysis of this will indicate optimisation. The trends in average price per unit and cost per unit (not a KPI but indirectly indicated through the contribution) will show the effectiveness of the marketing and production activities in contributing to profit. ROCE will provide an indication of the efficient use of capital in generating profit. The risk taken is measured by the margin of safety which shows how far current sales would have to fall to result in a breakeven profit situation.

The third CSF looks at maintenance of brand through product quality. The most direct measure of brand can be gained through the consumer awards as they show the impression being made on the customers by the products. The total quality costs figure gives an indication of the spend on quality but without an internal trend and external benchmarking, this figure is difficult to interpret. There is no KPI on the marketing spending which would be a common support for the brand.

(iv) Planning and control at Lopten

Planning is carried out at Lopten where there is a top-down structure to the mission, objectives and CSFs leading to the KPIs. The KPIs which will be reflected in this activity are those which are forward looking. Margin of safety addresses the risk of making a loss going forward and the size of the margin will give the board comfort that they can afford to take strategic risks without risking the survival of the Beeland operation. Another forward looking indicator would be the awards won which should give the company ability to build volume and also margins in the future. The other indicators are of general financial health which will provide the capital base for future plans.

The control activity measures actual results against plan and then takes necessary action to correct activities back to plan. In order to be used in this way, the KPIs calculated above will need their benchmark comparators to be given. Most of the indicators given would be used in this way if benchmarks were provided.

At board level, much of the decision-making is planning while at the operational level, there is more control than planning activity. Therefore, the balance among the suggested KPIs is unusually towards control. This issue could be addressed by including measures such as revenue and market share growth which establish trends useful for financial projections.

(v) Target operating profit

Using the calculations for profit already completed in Appendix 1, we have the following projected profits for the two plans:

PLAN A	**Most recent**	**Yr 1**	**Yr 2**
Contribution	$m	$m	$m
Cheerful	162	169	176
Posh	165	172	178
Fixed costs	240	240	240
Profit	87	100	114
PLAN B	**Most recent**	**Yr 1**	**Yr 2**
Contribution	$m	$m	$m
Cheerful	162	162	162
Posh	165	190	218
Fixed costs	240	240	240
Profit	87	112	141

Therefore, we can see that if we continue with the current marketing strategy and so maintain our product mix (Plan A), then Beeland will fall short of the target profit in two years' time by $21m.

However, if Lopten adopts Plan B, then the company can achieve its target profit in two years. The success of Plan B depends on the achievement of a high growth rate of 15% p.a. This growth rate will depend on the continued improvement of the general economy, as this will create the wealth to generate the demand for the higher contribution Posh product. It will also depend on the success of the increased marketing spend on promoting Posh. It would be wise to consider whether the increased marketing spend will be effective, as the current spend of $80m may be saturating the market at present and so additional spending will not generate proportionately more sales.

Conclusions

The current KPIs do not cover many of the external factors in Lopten's business environment and link weakly to the CSFs. The balance of the KPIs is towards control when the balance of the board's work will be forward looking towards planning the future of the business. A revision of the KPIs used should be undertaken in order to address these concerns.

The current marketing plan for Beeland will fall short of the target profit and so it should shift to emphasising the higher margin Posh products (Plan B) which will achieve the target provided the growth assumptions are realistic.

Appendix 1

	Cheerful	**Posh**
Units (millions)	1.12	0.44
	$m	$m
Revenue	448	308
Variable costs:		
Labour	67	35
Variable overheads	45	22
Materials	101	53
Distribution	50	20
Quality	22	13
Contribution	162	165
Fixed costs:		
Administration	18	18
Distribution	16	16
Quality	6	6
Marketing	80	80
Total fixed costs	120	120
Profit	42	45
Breakeven sales units (millions)	0.83	0.32

(= total fixed costs/contribution per unit)

Tutorial note

Minor rounding differences in the calculations will not be penalised.

Examiner's comments

In part (i) most candidates performed well. The main weaknesses shown in this work were in the basic profit calculations and the margin of safety calculation. For such a basic set of calculations, it was disappointing that more candidates did not take the opportunity to score all 11 marks. A relatively common error which appeared here and in part (v) of this question was the treatment of fixed costs as volume related. Future candidates should be aware that breakeven and the associated analysis is something that they will be considered to be expert in by the time they reach APM.

Part (ii). Most candidates identified a number of issues in the external environment using PEST (a SBL model) but were notably weaker in the application of it to the KPIs suggested. Two issues became apparent in marking: firstly, a minority of candidates did not use the PEST model and so were only given some credit as the question was about application of this model and; secondly, many candidates discussed their own set of KPIs ignoring the ones under consideration by the board. The second fault was particularly notable in answers which offered lists of new indicators with scant justification of their relevance and their impact on the proposed KPI set to be used by Lopten.

Part (iii). This part was mostly well done. However, as in part (ii), candidates had a tendency to ignore the suggested KPIs and produce lists of new KPIs to address the issues which were not justified in context. There was also a tendency to discuss problems with the CSFs rather than the KPIs which was not requested by the question. For example, a suitable response to the concept of 'acceptable risk' was to look at how it could be measured within the existing KPIs rather than just comment that the target level of acceptable risk was not clearly specified in the scenario.

In part (iv), candidates often drifted away from the question requirement which was an assessment of the extent to which the suggested KPIs could be used for planning rather than controlling the business. The purpose of the question was to offer candidates the chance to show that they appreciated the difference in these activities. Sadly, this question was poorly done with answers discussing control activities to the exclusion of planning. Candidates should not be afraid to say that there is poor coverage in an existing system provided that this opinion is justified in their answer.

Many candidates seem to think incorrectly that setting and monitoring of targets is a planning activity. The distinctions were more that suitable KPIs had to be forward-looking and focussed on the external environment of Lopten. Again, in this part, there was insufficient focus on the suggested KPI list.

Part (v) was either done well or badly with little in between. Where a candidate addressed the fixed costs correctly and realised that the target profit was given as the profit in two years' time thereby, producing calculations for the two plans, then they tended to easily score above pass marks. Therefore, there were two common and fundamental errors in the calculations. Firstly, already noted above, was the failure to recognise the 'fixed' costs in the estimate of future profits, e.g. by taking the previously calculated profit per product and multiplying it by 1.042 in Plan A. Secondly, many candidates attempted to answer the question by doing only a calculation of profit in one years' time or else not doing any calculation work at all. (For those candidates that cannot see how poor such an answer is, we would suggest that you imagine the response of your boss when, having requested a forecast for next year's profit, you come to the meeting with either a forecast of the first 6 month's profit only or else a statement that things look okay based on the fact that you made a profit last year.) Such answers scored some marks for the discussion of the assumptions in the strategies but did not tend to collect many marks.

ACCA marking scheme		
		Marks
(i)	Variable costs	2
	Fixed costs	1
	Profit	1
	Average sales price per unit	1
	Contribution per unit	1
	Market share	1
	Breakeven	1
	Margin of safety	1
	Return on capital employed (ROCE)	1
	Total quality costs	1
	Maximum	**11**
(ii)	Using the PEST headings: Up to 2 marks for discussion of the relevant issue in the scenario and up to 2 marks for commenting on the relevance of the suggested KPIs to the issue	
	Maximum	**11**
(iii)	Up to 4 marks for comments on each CSF **Maximum**	**10**
(iv)	1 mark per point made **Maximum**	**5**
(v)	Calculations Plan A Contribution, 2 marks Profit, 1 mark Calculations Plan B Contribution, 1 mark Profit, 1 mark Shortfall, 1 mark Comments: 1 mark per point up to 4 marks	
	Maximum	**9**
Professional marks will be awarded for the format, style and structure of the discussion of your answer.		**4**
Total		**50**

Section 4

ANSWERS TO PRACTICE QUESTIONS – SECTION B

A – STRATEGIC PLANNING AND CONTROL

18 SGOLTAIRE (SEPT/DEC 21) (AMENDED)

Key answer tips

(a) It is important to address the two areas of the requirement separately, looking at the impact of ethical issues on both strategy formulation and on business performance. The points included on each area will be similar but there is some distinction between the two and it is important to demonstrate this. Although most of the answer will advise on why ethical issues will impact the decision, it is also important to provide a balanced answer to briefly discuss some of the reasons why ethical issues may not impact the decision.

(b) Start with a definition of EMA and then include a sub-heading for each of the four areas.

(a) Strategy formulation

Business ethics relates to behaviour expected by society, but not codified in law. Developing strategies which demonstrate high standards of ethical behaviour, for example, towards the environment, will help create long-term, sustainable competitive advantage. This is because stakeholders may react negatively to poor ethical behaviour.

For example, Sgoltaire's biggest shareholder only invests in ethical companies. This stakeholder has high power and interest and will strongly influence strategy formulation to ensure that this is consistent with its own principles and objectives. Ultimately, the pension fund could sell all of its shares, which may reduce Sgoltaire's performance by making it harder to raise finance. The creation of long-term, sustainable economic competitive advantage is consistent with Sgoltaire's main objective, which is to maximise the long-term wealth of its shareholders.

Apart from the business and economic consequences of the investment in Kayland, ethical issues need to be considered. Although Kayland's environmental regulations allow the discharge of diluted WPA into rivers, it would clearly be unethical to take action which could harm human health in the long term. Significantly, the discharge of WPA into rivers is not permitted in Jayland.

The use of scarce river water to dilute WPA, in order to conform to Kayland's limited environmental regulations, is also an ethical issue. Using scarce water in such a way may cause harm to the local population and their livestock.

The board has not yet estimated the costs of cleaning up the proposed site at Kayland once production ceases. This could be a deliberate strategy as the board could think this is unnecessary due to the less strict environmental regulations there. Leaving the site contaminated with harmful chemicals, after decommissioning the plant, could affect the company's reputation in the long-term and is unethical.

Conversely, the board does have a duty to develop strategies which benefit internal stakeholders such as shareholders and employees. For example, incurring costs to find safe ways of disposing of WPA, which could eventually turn out to be harmless, could reduce long-term shareholder wealth. Also, while many employees may want to work for a business with ethical strategies, the financial costs of these may reduce their job security by making the business less profitable.

Business performance

Poor ethical behaviour can have a big impact on Sgoltaire's reputation, leading to customers boycotting its products and a reduction in financial performance. For the proposed project in Kayland, Sgoltaire's reputation could be damaged in the short-term if it were found to be paying local workers unacceptably low wages.

A strategic decision to discharge WPA into rivers or not clean up the site could increase the interest of environmental campaigners, who may join forces with other stakeholder groups such as consumers and the government in order to increase their power. This will increase any possible damage to Sgoltaire's reputation. Managing these groups will incur cost and management time and possibly risk fines and penalties for poor environmental performance. These costs could, in the long term, exceed the costs of disposing of WPA in an environmentally safe manner. The use of water, which is a scarce resource, could also increase the interest of environmental campaigners.

Poor ethical behaviour could also reduce long-term financial performance, if people were to become ill as a result of contact with WPA; as well as the impact on reputation, there could be fines and lawsuits, the value of which is hard to quantify. Formulating an alternative strategy for the safe disposal of WPA may therefore be beneficial to long-term performance, even if there were a short-term cost to this.

Behaving ethically can have a positive effect on business performance, for example, by creating brand loyalty.

This already appears to be the case, as Sgoltaire is a well-known and trusted brand. Its household detergents and cleaning products command premium prices because they use ingredients and processes which cause less harm to the environment than those of competitors.

The publication of the annual CSR report will communicate how ethically Sgoltaire behaves towards a wide range of interested stakeholders. The stakeholders who value ethical behaviour will react positively to ethical behaviour by Sgoltaire. Customers may choose to buy its products, or investors to buy its shares because of this.

> ***Tutorial note***
>
> *Notice how the answer has discussed the level of power and interest of different stakeholder groups. Mendelow is not directly examined here but it is an appropriate model to use to illustrate your points and the examiner will give credit for the relevant application of this book knowledge.*

(b) EMA relates to the production and analysis of financial and non-financial information to help a business identify environment-related costs and manage its performance in respect of the environment.

Calculating costs

As Sgoltaire is listed in Jayland, it must produce an annual CSR report which demonstrates its performance in environmental and other social and ethical matters. The company will need to measure environment-related costs to compile this. The sophistication of the company's information systems is unclear, but traditional information systems do not capture environment-related costs, such as the costs to dispose of WPA, which may be hidden in overheads.

EMA helps to capture these hidden costs as well as contingent costs, for example, in cleaning up contaminated sites after production ceases. Of all the environment-related costs, the reputation and relationship costs which may occur, for example, if discharged WPA harms the health of large numbers of people, may be the largest cost.

By the use of techniques such as environmental activity-based costing, input / output analysis and lifecycle costing, EMA can be used to develop a clearer understanding of costs, particularly environment-related costs, meaning that budgets will be more realistic. This will make them more useful for planning purposes. Managers appraised using these budgets, which could include budgets specifically relating to environment-related costs, would be more motivated to achieve any targets set.

Sgoltaire may have to invest in more sophisticated information systems in order to capture environment-related costs which are currently hidden within overheads. The cost of this needs to be compared against the benefits of doing so.

Investment appraisal

EMA helps to ensure that all environment-related costs are included in an investment appraisal. For example, the board's calculations of NPV of the proposal to manufacture Chemical K in either Jayland or Kayland did not include estimates for the present values of decommissioning the plant or of cleaning the sites when production ceases.

If investment appraisals do not include all relevant costs such as these, business performance may decrease as Sgoltaire may start to manufacture products that will have a low, or even negative, NPV which will not generate long-term shareholder wealth.

If the project were to take place in Jayland, these costs would reduce the NPV of the project by 40% (W1), which is a large amount. The board has not estimated the present value of the costs to clean up the site in Kayland. As a result of logistical difficulties due to Kayland being 8,000km from Jayland, decommissioning costs would be 50% higher than in Jayland and so for the same reason, clean-up costs in Kayland might also cost 50% more.

On this assumption, the NPVs of both alternatives would be $120m. The board would probably choose to manufacture in Jayland, as there are lower risks by operating in the home country. If the environment-related costs of decommissioning and clean up were not taken into account, the board may have chosen to undertake the project in Kayland because the NPV of the project was $40m ($240 – $200) more than in Jayland.

Tutorial note

Don't overcomplicate the calculation here. An estimated NPV is appropriate, assuming the clean-up costs in Kayland will be 50% higher than in Jayland. The examiner is more interested in your commentary around the revised NPV, rather than a demonstration an ability to carry out detailed or difficult NPV calculations.

Setting performance measures and targets

EMA can be used to set targets for improving performance in respect of the environment, for example, by reducing environment-related costs, fines or taxes. This is important as Sgoltaire publishes an annual CSR report, so its environmental performance is clear to a range of stakeholders, many of whom have an interest in environmental matters.

Performance targets could be financial or non-financial, for example, physical quantities. If the production of Chemical K were to commence in Kayland, a non-financial target could be the volume of water taken from the local river. This is because water is a scarce resource in Kayland and taking too much of it may have a harmful effect on the local environment, the human population, and their livestock.

Environmental performance measures could be internal or external. Targets could relate to both short-term and long-term performance. The number of cases of ill health due to contact with WPA is an external measure relating to long-term performance.

Product pricing

Using EMA to develop a clearer understanding of costs also helps Sgoltaire in setting a price for Chemical K. EMA will help Sgoltaire to understand all of the costs in the product's lifecycle and what drives them. These will include environment-related costs which are incurred before or after production begins or after it ends, such as decommissioning or clean-up costs. Sgoltaire can price the product to ensure that all of these costs are covered. This should ensure that the company can make an acceptable profit on the sale of the product over its lifecycle and can choose not to make products which are likely make losses. This will improve long-term financial performance.

Environment-related costs occurring after production ceases may be incurred in many years' time. Predicting these costs will be difficult and may be significantly affected by inflation, changes in the cost of capital and the possible introduction of stricter environmental regulations in the future.

By demonstrating that production of Chemical K is made in such a way as to minimise harm to the environment, Sgoltaire may be able to charge a premium price to customers to whom this is important. Though the use of Chemical K is unclear, many of its household products already command premium prices for this reason.

Tutorial note

It is not essential to include the working below but it is a useful summary for the board. Make use of the CBE tools available in the exam to cut and paste the table from appendix 1 into your answer and then alter the numbers and add the other rows as required.

Working 1

NPV of the two possible proposals after including decommissioning and clean-up costs

	Jayland	**Kayland**
	$m	$m
NPV of project estimated by the board	200	240
Decommissioning cost	(20)	(30)
Cleaning cost	(60)	(90)*
NPV after decommissioning and cleaning	120	120
Decommissioning and cleaning costs as a % of the estimated NPV	40%	50%
(80 / 20 : 120 / 240)		

***Cleaning costs of Kayland estimated at 50% higher than in Jayland.**

Examiner's comments

Answers to part (a) generally lacked a sensible structure, with many candidates simply restating the ethical issues which had been highlighted in the scenario. The requirement asked for advice on how these issues may affect the decision [by the board] to manufacture the new product in Kayland. It is a sensible approach to start with the issues highlighted in the scenario, but candidates must then discuss how these would influence the decision. It is worth noting by candidates that business ethics relates to behaviour expected by society, but not codified in law. Therefore, the board may not be legally obliged to behave in a manner that is 'ethical' but failure to do so would be noticed by stakeholders which could ultimately lead to negative consequences for the business. There were several ethical issues highlighted in the scenario, and those candidates who systematically discussed each, tended to score well. It is always recommended to base an answer around the issues that are specifically mentioned as opposed to introduce hypothetical issues which may arise but have not been mentioned.

Answers to part (b) were generally better than those for part (a). The key to this was the fact that the advice required was broken down in four sections in the scenario. Candidates who followed the structure and gave sensible advice scored well here. That being said, many candidates wrote very superficially under each heading and failed to score high marks. Those candidates who simply ignored the four headings detailed in the scenario and instead wrote generally about how EMA can improve performance still scored marks where their points were relevant. Unfortunately, several candidates did not attempt to use and/or adjust the figures which were provided.

ACCA marking scheme		
		Marks
(a)	Impact of ethics on strategy formulation – 1 mark per point, up to 6 marks Impact of ethics on business performance – 1 mark per point, up to 6 marks	
	Maximum	**10**
(b)	1 mark per point: Calculating costs – up to 3 marks Investment appraisal – up to 3 marks Calculations – up to 2 marks Setting measures and targets – up to 3 marks Product pricing – up to 3 marks	
	Maximum	**10**
Professional marks		
Analysis and Evaluation		
•	Problems of not paying sufficient attention to ethical issues clearly supported with examples	
•	Comprehensive advice on how EMA will help the four stated areas including appropriate use of data in appendix 1, together with appropriate assumptions, to recalculate the NPV to support discussion and draw an appropriate conclusion on the new investment	
Scepticism		
•	Recognition of the need to consider the challenges of investing in Kayland and an ability to probe into why the investment decision should not be based purely on lower labour costs, less strict environmental regulations and a higher estimated NPV	
Commercial Acumen		
•	Effective use of examples drawn from the scenario information and other practical considerations related to the context to illustrate points on how ethical issues may affect a decision in a question	
•	Demonstration of an understanding of how EMA will help in each of the four separate areas identified, rather than how EMA could help in general	
	Maximum	**5**
Total		**25**

19 STOKENESS ENGINEERING (JUN 13) (AMENDED)

(a) Porter's five forces analysis

Threat of new entrants

The threat of new entrants will be dictated by barriers to entry into the fuel cell market. These appear to be high, given the long timescale and the high levels of technical expertise required to develop a viable product. Also, the developer will need to have cultivated a strong relationship with the major vehicle manufacturers who will be the customers for the product.

A suitable performance measure would be percentage of revenue derived from patented products to measure the legally protected revenues of the business and so indicate the barrier to entry. Stokeness will need to ensure that all technology developments are written up and assessed for their patent possibility.

Tutorial note

Other measures could include ratio of fixed cost to total cost (measures capital required) or customer loyalty (through long-term contracts to supply fuel cells to manufacturers).

Threat of substitutes

The substitutes mentioned in the question are electrical batteries, compressed natural gas and improved existing diesel/petrol engines. However, it is clear that improved diesel/petrol engines would potentially have many lower barriers to cross as the technology is known to the car industry and the infrastructure exists to deliver the fuel to the end-users of the cars.

The threat of each of these substitutes would be measured by an analysis of the comparative cost of creating a viable alternative to the fuel cell. The performance in terms of power output of the engine and emissions reductions compared to price would be critical. Management of this aspect will entail monitoring fuel prices in the market, reviewing the appropriate technical journals and attending conferences in order to identify these threats and their progress. This will require the input of both finance and engineering staff at Stokeness.

Power of suppliers

The suppliers have considerable power. There are rare raw materials used in production and the price and availability of these will dictate possible output levels for fuel cell producers. This is especially important, given the possibility of increased production which could flow if fuel cells become the dominant way to power vehicles in the future. There is a danger that the market in these materials is controlled by a few suppliers who can then dictate price. The engineering subcontractors will also have power through their knowledge of the design elements of Stokeness' product. It will be important for Stokeness to protect this by legally enforceable non-disclosure agreements. There is a danger that this knowledge will lead the suppliers to consider pre-emptive forward integration by taking over Stokeness.

The power of suppliers could be measured by estimating the cost of shifting to an alternative supplier, which could be considerable, given the innovative nature of the technology. These costs would have to include the damage to value from the delay that such a shift would cause.

Tutorial note

Other measures could include cost of suppliers' product compared to total cost of the fuel cell, which indicates the importance of this component in production, and the number of suppliers as it indicates the level of competition in that market.

Power of customers

The customers are the major bus and truck manufacturers. Again, the customers will have a large degree of influence, given their size and limited numbers if Stokeness wants to access the world market. There will need to be a partnership between the fuel cell maker and the vehicle manufacturer in order to ensure that the technologies are compatible. There is the threat that these powerful customers will seek to take over Stokeness if its products prove successful; however, this may be an attractive exit for the shareholders depending upon the price offered.

The power of customers can be measured by estimating their switching costs which are likely to be high, given the technological compatibility issue. However, these costs will only occur once the vehicle manufacturer has agreed to source from a particular supplier (e.g. Stokeness) and until an agreement is reached, the fuel cell supplier will be in the weaker position. The vehicle manufacturer will also have the commercial power to be able to become a new entrant to the market if it appears more profitable to do so.

Stokeness could seek to manage these problems in two ways:

(a) Quickly enter into an exclusive arrangement with one partner by emphasising the technological lead which they hold over the competition. This will be lower risk but will cut returns as the partner will then have pricing power; or

(b) Seek to develop a product which will be attractive to multiple vehicle manufacturers and then maximise price by playing them against each other. This appears less plausible in this scenario, given the limited number of large manufacturers.

Tutorial note

Other measures could be the number of alternative customers, the level of discounts customers demand and the number of alternative suppliers customers can choose from.

Power of existing competition

The power of existing competition appears low as Stokeness has a two-year lead in development. It will be important to protect this legally by patenting innovations as soon as possible and, also, ensuring the strictest commercial confidentiality is maintained within Stokeness and their commercial partners.

The power of existing competitors can be measured by market share once the market forms. However, at this development stage of the industry, a measure such as time to market (the expected commercial launch date of a viable fuel cell) would be more appropriate. This will aid management focus on delivering the product as rapidly as possible, thus maintaining Stokeness' competitive advantage and avoiding time over-runs in development which will strain the cash flows of the company and may lead to unwelcome further calls for funding from the VCs.

Tutorial note

Other measures could be partnership agreements (with car manufacturers) signed or projected revenues/volumes under such agreements.

The use of ideas such as patent protection, time to market and partnering with a vehicle manufacturer are relevant under several of the headings and credit is given provided the point is suitably justified to the particular force being discussed at that point of the answer.

(b) The CEO's concerns over the definition of market in market share are justified, as there are a variety of possibilities.

If Stokeness were to take an ambitious view, then they could measure the market as the total commercial vehicle market and measure the number of vehicles powered by Stokeness' fuel cell compared to the total number of vehicles. This would be a measure of competitive performance against all existing engine technologies including existing petrol/diesel. It would be more realistic to use the number of new vehicles sold rather than all vehicles in existence in this measure. A second possibility exists in this scenario for comparing the number of vehicles with Stokeness' fuel cell compared to the number using any of the alternative engine technologies (fuel cells, electrical, compressed natural gas).

However, Stokeness could take an even less ambitious view and consider just the market for fuel cells, therefore measuring Stokeness' performance against only other fuel cell makers.

The board must make a choice as to the market they are competing in or maybe decide the firms which they see as their main competitors, and then use this to define the market and so the performance measure.

(c) The VCs are likely to be rational investors seeking maximum return for minimum risk. However, they will have invested in a number of companies and so are prepared for investments to fail, provided that some of their investments perform very well. Therefore, they will be risk seeking in technology start-ups such as Stokeness.

The VCs have placed employees within the management team and so have a high degree of influence on Stokeness. They will be looking at medium/long-term returns, given the nature of the project, through net present value based on projected revenues. Of more immediate concern will be the worry that Stokeness runs out of cash before it has a viable product to sell and so cost control measures (variances from budget) and cash outflow will be key measures at present. They will have stated a rough timescale to exit the investment on provision of the initial funds and they will monitor performance to plan on this basis. Progression towards an exit will require Stokeness to pass various milestones (e.g. to file patents, to sign contracts with customers); timely achievement of these would be useful performance indicators, as well as purely financial ones such as meeting the cash flow projections.

ACCA marking scheme

			Marks
(a)	Up to 3 marks for performance measure justified and performance management implications for each force		
		Maximum	**12**
(b)	1 mark per suitable point made	**Maximum**	**4**
(c)	Assess risk appetite up to 2 marks Impact on performance measures up to 3 marks		
		Maximum	**4**
Professional marks			
Analysis and Evaluation			
•	Appropriate use of scenario information to perform a reasoned assessment of the impact of the external environment, including a justified performance measure for each of the five forces		
•	Problems in defining a market and measuring market share clearly supported with examples		
•	Reasoned assessment of risk appetite of VCs, using the information provided to support discussion of impact on performance measurement		
Commercial Acumen			
•	Effective use of examples drawn from scenario information and other practical considerations related to the context to illustrate points being made throughout the answer		
•	Recommendation of performance measures are practical and plausible in the context of the company situation		
•	Demonstrate an understanding of the impact of risk appetite on performance measurement		
		Maximum	**5**
Total			**25**

20 CLONYARD AND ELRIG (SEPT/DEC 20) (AMENDED)

(a) Skills

With regard to the skills element, it is clear that Clonyard and Elrig train and develop their staff in different ways. Clonyard has placed an emphasis on detailed product knowledge and on ensuring that the individual's needs are met. Such training and development is very much aligned with a company that has a specialist niche. It is also clear that Elrig's focus is less on meeting individual requirements than in pursuing a sale and it is likely that Elrig's staff have been trained and developed more in terms of sales techniques than with regard to product knowledge. This means that the staff from Clonyard have a different skill set and it is clear, from their reaction to the Elrig staff working in Clonyard shops that no attempt has been made to develop the skill set of either group of employees in order to align them with each other.

Staff

It is clear, especially given the point above, that staff are treated in a different way in both organisations. It is also evident from the scenario that Clonyard staff are leaving the organisation. It is likely that staff have been given responsibility for inventory and shop management in Clonyard and that the focus in the company has been on developing the individual to enhance their range of specialist knowledge. Elrig's singular focus on market share would suggest that Elrig's staff are more likely to be trained and developed in the areas of financial performance measures and be aware of costs, margins and the financial implications of the decisions being made. Indeed, the fact that Elrig's staff are seeking to make a sale quickly suggests that they are aware of the cost of the time they spend with each customer and it is likely that there is an ideal time per sale that they will work towards.

Style

Style usually represents the corporate culture of the organisation and it is clear that the cultures are very different within Elrig and Clonyard. The issue of the takeover being hostile in the first instance is perhaps an indicator that the styles of the organisations are very different.

Style is also indicative of how an organisation presents itself to the outside world and again it is clear, through the interactions with customers, which Clonyard would seek to satisfy the customer's specific requirements whereas Elrig would try to sell a product to the customer with the minimum time spent on the transaction. Such a contrast in styles would inevitably be reflected in the customer experience and it may prove to be very damaging for Clonyard if its style is aligned with that of Elrig. Customers may feel that there is no longer any reason to visit Elrig if its main differentiators of individual service, product specialism and time spent with the customer are removed.

Tutorial note

The fourth soft element, shared values, is not required in this answer. However, for learning purposes it is worth reviewing the below:

Shared values

All of the above elements illustrate that the companies have very different values. The element of shared values should reflect the guiding beliefs of people in the organisation as to why it exists and it is clear in Elrig and Clonyard, even at the level of their mission statements, which they exist for quite different reasons. It is clear that the attitudes and behaviours which reflect these differing strategic approaches are reflected in the differing shared values of the staff in the scenario.

Elrig, for example, expects that it should be able to impose its own business model upon a very different type of business. This is because its underlying objective is that its business only exists to return as much value for shareholders as possible and that the people in the organisation should all be focused on making that happen. There should be no reason, in terms of Elrig's values and beliefs, as to why this structure should not be accepted in Clonyard.

Clonyard's values are very different to this, however, and rely on individuals taking responsibility, and making decisions accordingly; to pursue things which they feel would benefit both the customer experience and Clonyard. Clonyard's lack of pursuit of shareholder value in its mission is reflected in it achieving modest growth, which has most likely ensured that most stakeholders in the organisation have been satisfied.

Each company does appear to have shared values within its own organisation – for example, staff in both Elrig and Clonyard appear to have a set of shared values for the organisation they work for. This makes the alignment of values for the new organisation very difficult. From the scenario, Elrig does not appear to have tried to do anything to help in this regard.

Conclusion

It is clear that there is overlap and interconnectivity between each soft element of the 7S model. Elrig appears to have made no attempt to align these differing elements and as a result there is no sense of shared values, different styles of operation and different skill sets in the respective staff.

The 7S model has been useful in addressing this lack of alignment and provides evidence to Elrig that it must revert to the mission of Clonyard and decide if this now needs to change in the light of the takeover. If not, and as the 7S model has shown, Elrig might be best advised to allow Clonyard to operate as it was doing quite successfully beforehand and consider integration and alignment as a long-term rather than a short-term goal.

Tutorial note

A 10 mark question on the McKinsey 7S model would have been a surprise for many students since this is a rarely examined area. However, you can score well here by having a broad appreciation of the use of the model in business integration and of the three soft elements. There is plenty of information to use in the scenario also, so don't panic! This is a good lesson that the examining team are willing to test all parts of the syllabus; there is no such thing as an unimportant, minor or unexaminable syllabus area.

(b)

Key answer tips

An evaluation of the introduction of a new system (for example, an ERPS) is a reasonably common requirement. However, you must be careful to not simply discuss a generic set of advantages and disadvantages. This sample answer is a great example of how the scenario information should be used in your answer. Almost every point relates back to the specifics of the scenario with only a minor inclusion of more generic advantages/disadvantages.

Advantages

An ERPS would help alleviate the problems detailed with regard to inventory control in that the current inventory levels would be very clear on the ERPS and any sale would register immediately, thereby showing the effect on the inventory overall. Minimum inventory levels may be set within the ERPS and an order to the supplier automatically triggered when inventory reaches that level. An ERPS will also allow details of the delivery to be tracked and the ERPS will enable staff at the appropriate level to discover how long deliveries are taking and to manage the supplier relationship accordingly.

The discounting of product lines in certain areas is clearly a key part of Elrig's strategy to enhance its market share and the sales manager is correct in that it is impossible to impose this strategy on Clonyard with such old data. An ERPS would ensure that the sales manager has access to immediate sales of each product and could compare this with both planned sales of the product and past sales of the product. The ERPS may also permit the inclusion of some external data which could inform the company of any changes in the market for particular products or distinct product lines. This would certainly enable the sales manager to take real time decisions with regard to which products might be discounted and to what level. The ERPS would be of great benefit to him in this endeavour.

The ERPS, as highlighted above, has the ability to remove the responsibility for the ordering of inventory from the employee and undertake this function based on the minimum inventory levels that have been input. This would certainly solve the problem of Clonyard employees not entering the purchase order into the computer system and would ensure that the relevant people in the organisation are fully aware of the inventory both on order and in store.

Disadvantages

However, the view of the director of Elrig appears to be that he can use the introduction of an ERPS to impose Elrig's strategy on Clonyard and this is something which should be avoided. The strategies of the two companies should be aligned initially and any shared computer system, and the information that it might generate, should be agreed thereafter.

There are other significant potential negative effects of introducing the ERPS based on the director's view. For example, it may further enhance the feeling of alienation that many Clonyard employees appear to be feeling if another system is imposed on them without discussion and agreement. Their motivation would suffer and Clonyard's ability to maintain its position in the market may be affected. This market position is, after all, the main reason for Elrig's purchase of Clonyard in the first place.

There is evidence from the scenario that Clonyard is delaying the information that it offers Elrig as even manual systems could offer more up-to-date data than that detailed by the operations manager and the sales manager. This sub-optimal behaviour has perhaps been a reaction by Clonyard staff to the imposition of Elrig's systems. Much as the removal of any sub-optimal behaviour should be encouraged, the introduction of the ERPS without discussion and agreement may enhance those feelings of Elrig imposing its operations upon Clonyard. This stresses again the dangers of introducing a computer system to integrate one company's operations into another and further highlights the need to come to a common approach with regard to the future strategic direction of Clonyard.

It is also naïve of the Elrig director to assume that Clonyard employees will be enthusiastic about the introduction of a new computer system. Aside from the potential negative aspects associated with control that are highlighted above, there is evidence from the scenario that Clonyard employees are not engaging fully with their own computer system. This may be because they have not been properly trained and the prospect of the introduction of a new and much more complex system may be very threatening for them.

Alongside the difficulties associated with the introduction of the ERPS into the Elrig/Clonyard operation, an ERPS has other well-established and more generic disadvantages such as its cost, its difficulty in adapting to the specifics of some individual business operations and the time taken to implement the system.

Overall, the introduction of an ERPS would certainly help with regard to some operational aspects detailed in the scenario. The overall benefits are likely to be much wider than this with, for example, the access to real-time information being very useful to Elrig/Clonyard in their current environment. However, the introduction of the ERPS should not be used as a way of integrating Clonyard within Elrig's operation. This needs to be done at a much more fundamental level where strategic direction is agreed. Using an ERPS to integrate without this agreement first is likely to lead to more problems with regard to integration than it will solve.

Examiner's comments

Part (a). The examining team provided the diagram of the model so that candidates would have a good starting position for their evaluation. A detailed scenario was provided, and candidates were expected to discuss each of the three soft elements in relation to the issues raised regarding the two companies. Candidates generally performed well on this part of the question, many correctly identifying the issues raised and explaining the consequences for the new combined entity. Most candidates also correctly used the soft elements as headings in their answer which allowed them to structure their points more effectively.

The examining team were aware that certain issues could be discussed under more than one of the 'soft' elements and awarded credit where such answers showed how the points being made related to those elements.

Candidates who failed to use the soft elements to structure their answer often lacked focus to the points they were making and made it difficult for the examining team and marking team to determine what they were trying to say. A significant minority, also, spent time discussing all seven sections of the model and this was a waste of examination time.

Part (b) was generally well answered by candidates, which has been reflective of the upward trend the examining team are seeing in relation to questions about technology and systems. Candidates clearly demonstrated a good understanding of the characteristics of an ERPS, including generic advantages and disadvantages, with many successfully developing these points by applying them to the scenario. Answers that simply discussed any advantages and disadvantages without application however scored minimal marks.

ACCA marking scheme		
		Marks
(a)	Skills – up to 3 marks Staff – up to 3 marks Style – up to 3 marks Conclusion – up to 2 marks	
	Maximum	**10**
(b)	Advantages of ERPS – up to 6 marks Disadvantages of ERPS – up to 6 marks	
	Maximum	**10**
Professional marks		
Analysis and Evaluation		
•	Reasoned assessment of the three soft elements of the McKinsey 7S model in relation to the alignment of Elrig and Clonyard	
•	Balanced and reasoned appraisal of the ERPS proposal	
Scepticism		
•	Recognition that the McKinsey 7S model has overlap between the elements and the company has not attempted to align them	
•	Recognition that the ERPS won't integrate the two companies beyond initial operational benefits	
Commercial Acumen		
•	Recommendation of the introduction of an ERPS clearly demonstrates an understanding of the issues facing Clonyard and Elrig and is commercially sound	
	Maximum	**5**
Total		**25**

21 JOLT (SEPT 18) (AMENDED)

Key answer tips

BPR has been examined in depth in several recent exams and you must prepare adequately for this possibility. Notice the link of BPR to another syllabus area, namely ethics. Being able to link different syllabus areas is essential for good performance in APM.

(a) BPR

BPR is the fundamental and radical redesign of business processes to achieve dramatic improvements in performance. For Jolt, the BPR proposal aims to meet the retailers' demands for lower prices and the requirement to meet performance targets relating to lead times and quality.

Lower prices

To be able to sell swimwear at lower prices, Jolt proposes reducing costs by outsourcing production to an overseas supplier. The current average production cost of manufacturing is \$5.00 per unit. The cost of purchasing from an external supplier is \$4.00, which is \$3.50 purchase cost, plus \$0.50 (\$5,000/10,000) shipping costs. This 20% (\$1.00/\$5.00) saving is a significant improvement in financial performance, but not a dramatic one, and may not fit the definition of BPR.

Exchange rate movements could reduce the cost saving significantly. In the near future, expected changes to international trade tariffs will increase the unit cost to \$4.35 (\$4.00 + 10% of \$3.50), and reduce the cost saving to just 13% (\$0.65/\$5.00).

Unless Jolt decides to outsource the remaining 50% of production and close its factory completely, factory overheads of \$0.95 per unit may still be incurred and just be re-allocated to Jolt's other sportswear products, possibly totally eliminating the cost saving.

Tutorial note

This is one approach only. Marks will also have been given for excluding the ***(fixed) factory overhead****.*

Combining several jobs into one is a characteristic of a re-engineered process. As such, reorganising staff into multidisciplinary teams may create overhead savings, such as by reducing the number of staff employed by the automation of purchase invoice processing. These savings will be offset by additional costs, such as investment in new information systems, retraining staff to work in unfamiliar roles, or incentivising them to work overseas.

Re-engineered processes often allow workers more autonomy to make decisions. Giving teams more autonomy to set prices may allow Jolt to set prices reflecting the customers they serve and to prevailing market conditions.

Meeting performance targets

Lead times

Current lead times for customer orders are unknown. As the proposed supplier is 17,000 km away, goods will take several weeks to be transported by sea. This may increase lead times significantly, though may be offset by faster production times in larger factories. As Jolt's sales are seasonal, retailers may pre-order in advance, reducing the importance of long lead times. To minimise shipping costs, shipping containers must be full, which may mean deliveries will be in larger quantities and which may increase the lead times.

Quality

Jolt is already known for producing high quality products. The quality of the new supplier's products needs to be ensured. Any deterioration in the quality of Jolt products would undermine its reputation and reduce long-term business performance as fewer consumers would buy them. Monitoring of quality standards is more difficult when using external suppliers, especially at long distances, than when manufacturing in Jolt's own factory. In re-engineered processes, work is performed where it makes most sense to do so. In this respect, having staff responsible for quality and supplier audits working close to the manufacturing site will help Jolt maintain performance in supplier relationship management.

(b) Impact on workers

Jolt is known for its high ethical standards towards workers. Following the BPR, at least 500 (50% of 1,000) manufacturing workers are likely to be left without jobs. As Jolt's competitors have already closed their factories, these workers may be unable to find new jobs doing similar work, though jobs may be created in the new supplier's factory.

Staff who remain in work may become demotivated if they think that BPR will be extended to all of Jolt's products. This may reduce financial performance by reduced productivity, increased staff turnover or difficulties recruiting new staff.

Staff may also be demotivated if they are placed in unfamiliar roles, or may be unwilling to learn new skills. Other staff may welcome, and be motivated by, the opportunity to perform new types of work, learn new skills or work overseas. This will probably increase their individual performance.

Suppliers

Any association with unethical practices, for example, if the new supplier were found to be using unacceptable working practices, could seriously harm Jolt's reputation for high ethical standards. This could reduce financial performance, as consumers may not buy Jolt's products, or potential investors could be discouraged from providing capital. Part of the team located close to the manufacturing site is responsible for supplier audits, which may help to reduce this risk.

Environment

Jolt should consider the environmental impact of shipping goods long distances. The environmental credentials of the new supplier are unknown. This will be amplified if Jolt decide to ship containers that are not full, increasing the carbon footprint generated per item. As Jolt voluntarily publishes a corporate sustainability report, any deterioration in its performance on environmental issues will become widely known. This could lead to reduced financial performance if consumers switch to competing products.

Examiner's comments

Overall, candidates who specifically answered what the requirements asked for scored well. The examining team would again like to draw attention to the fact that the requirements are specific, and those candidates who chose to answer a 'different question' did not score well.

Part (a). The key to answering this question was to focus on the two key demands of the customers which were to have lower prices to pass on to the consumers and for suppliers to meet performance targets relating to lead times and quality. Candidates who then discussed the implementation of the BPR proposal in relation to the above key demands scored well. Unfortunately, some candidates explained the concept of BPR, which was awarded some credit, but then went on to discuss generic advantages and disadvantages of the BPR process with little or no reference to the scenario or the stated key demands.

Part (b). For some candidates, there appeared to be some confusion regarding the difference between ethical considerations, such as the impact on the employees' welfare and potential pollution of long distance transportation, and operational considerations, such as reorganisation costs and logistics. However, it was very clear that candidates who structured their answer well also performed well on this question. Again, it is advised that all candidates ensure that they adequately attempt all parts of the requirement. Many candidates correctly discussed ethical considerations as stated above, and then developed their points by discussing how this could impact the BPR proposal, for example, negative publicity can affect sales, or by increasing costs to try to counter the effects on welfare or pollution. This was pleasing to see, and is a good approach to use on all questions.

ACCA marking scheme	
	Marks
(a) 1 mark per point: Explanation of BPR – 2 marks Lower prices – up to 6 marks Performance targets – up to 6 marks	
Maximum	**12**
(b) 1 mark per point: Ethical standards relating to workers – up to 4 marks Ethical standards relating to suppliers – up to 3 marks Ethical standards relating to the environment – up to 3 marks	
Maximum	**8**
Professional marks **Analysis and Evaluation** • Use of the data in Appendix 1 to determine relevant calculations to analyse the outsourcing proposal • Comprehensive evaluation of how the BPR proposal could improve performance of the customers' two key demands is undertaken **Scepticism** • Recognition that the BPR proposal will bring additional challenges to Jolt, not just potential improvements • Identification that information related to customer lead times is missing **Commercial Acumen** • Comprehensive assessment of the possible ethical consequences of the BPR proposal	
Maximum	**5**
Total	**25**

22 CUTHBERT (MAR/JUN 16)

Key answer tips

A fantastic question for ensuring you have the depth of knowledge that is required on BPR.

In part (a) be sure to discuss the influence on operational performance rather than performance in general.

Part (b) demonstrates how the examiner views APM as an entire subject rather than a number of individual topics – in this case a link is being made between BPR and changes to the reward system.

(a) Business process reengineering (BPR) involves radical and fundamental changes in the way processes in organisations are designed. A focus on the needs of the customer, and customer satisfaction, are key to BPR. BPR aims to improve key performance measures such as reducing costs, improving quality, service delivery and customer satisfaction.

The proposal is to move away from the existing functional structure where staff are attached to only one stage of the production process, or even to one type of machine within each function, to team working. This is a radical change for Cuthbert and as such, is an example of BPR.

Reorganising into teams

Currently, there is very little multi-skilling of production staff at Cuthbert. This was seen where there were insufficient trained zip machinists available for the emergency order for the Ceeland army, even though there were enough machinists to sew buttons. This led to the emergency order failing to meet the customer's requirements as it was not delivered on time.

Furthermore, it seems that machinists also prefer to work on one particular type of machine. This is probably because they are currently rewarded according to the speed of production, rather than the quality of production, and can work faster when using just one machine.

A change to team working would imply job enlargement for machinists, who would need to be trained so that they were multi-skilled in different parts of the production process. They could then perform the roles of other members of their team, to ensure that there were no bottlenecks in production.

The cost of reorganisation and the costs of training the machinists should be outweighed by the resulting improved efficiency and flexibility of production. In this way, there is more focus on the outcome (goods of the correct quality produced on time) and less focus on the individual tasks within the process, which is a key principle of BPR.

Production teams are responsible for quality

Cuthbert's brand has a strong reputation, and the use of its products for protection in harsh environments and by the armed forces means that quality is a key element of customer satisfaction. Cuthbert must be able to manufacture goods which are free of defects, unlike the emergency order for the Ceeland army.

Reorganising the production into teams of machinists, sometimes known as production 'cells', would make machinists responsible for decisions about quality of a particular product type. This should lead to improvements in quality and therefore to meeting the needs of the customer.

Reducing the number of processes for checking is typical of a reengineered process, and the quality checking currently performed by the supervisors would no longer be necessary. The production teams will be managing themselves in this respect, and the distinction between supervisors and machinists will be removed, which is again typical of organisations which have undergone BPR.

Encouraging machinists in each team to suggest improvements in the production process should bring about improvements in both quality and efficiency, and hence a reduction in costs. It is the machinists who are closest to the production process and may be able to see how it can be improved. Cuthbert could also consider a more formal system of incremental continuous improvements such as Kaizen costing.

Tracking with RFIDs

Typically, organisations with reengineered processes end up having a flatter hierarchy. It seems that the supervisors' current roles will no longer be required if the proposal is adopted. Quality checks will no longer be undertaken by them, nor will recording of batches, which will become automated using RFID tags. This should save salary costs and improve lines of communication in the business.

The use of RFID tags would capture the information required to manage the production process at source, and there would be no distinction between the gathering of information and processing it. This is in contrast to the current system of inputting batch data into a spreadsheet, and is a feature in organisations which have undergone BPR.

Practical and cultural aspects of the proposal

New performance measures related to quality rather than just quantity produced will have to be developed and processes and systems developed in order to record and report these. New rewards systems will also have to be developed and introduced as a result of the changes proposed.

The proposal by definition represents a significant cultural change for Cuthbert, and may meet resistance by staff who may perceive it is a threat and a one-off cost cutting measure rather than a fundamental long-term change in the business. It will also impact the organisational hierarchy, relationships between employees and the roles within Cuthbert. There will be significant costs with training staff and with the disruption the transition may cause.

(b) The current reward system

The machinists are currently paid a basic hourly wage plus an amount depending on how many items they sew. This will encourage them to work quickly, which will reduce product costs. However, as they are not directly rewarded for the quality of the work which they produce, they may not be motivated to produce high quality work. Furthermore, in order to work quickly, machinists prefer to work on only one type of machine. This reduces Cuthbert's overall flexibility to respond to customer needs such as with failure to deliver the emergency order for the Ceeland army.

The production supervisors also receive a bonus according to how many items machinists in their team are able to sew. This too does not reward the production of high quality work, and supervisors may also neglect quality in order to increase the speed of production. The machinists in their teams could also see it as unfair that the supervisors obtain a bonus based on what they see as their efforts.

The production manager does not receive a bonus for production or quality. It seems that the he has currently no direct motivation to improve on either of these two aspects of the process.

At 5% of salary, the bonus related to Cuthbert's overall profits is relatively small and it is unclear whether it is a significant motivator to any of the employees. Furthermore, machinists in particular may perceive their own efforts as too remote from the company's overall profit for them to bother to achieve it. Even if they were to be motivated by this, it is unclear what proportion of the total costs are related to direct labour as Cuthbert incurs many other costs such as advertising to maintain the brand. If the costs of direct labour were relatively low, even a large improvement in production efficiency by the machinists may have little effect on overall profit.

Under the new proposal

The existing reward systems would likely need to change if the move to team-based production were to be adopted.

It may still be appropriate to reward machinists with volume related bonuses, but as they worked in teams, a team-based performance bonus would be more appropriate. In that way the rest of the team would ensure that any underperforming machinists would improve their performance.

Rewards based on other factors such as quality, innovation, on time delivery and the ability to work as part of a team would also be appropriate and consistent with the machinists' enlarged job role. This would be a significant change for Cuthbert, where machinists are now being encouraged for the first time to bring about improvements in the production process. Rewards based on direct costs of production, or for the number of suggestions made by each machinist may be appropriate here.

New performance measures would need to be developed against which to align rewards to ensure that employees work towards the overall objectives of the organisation. New reporting systems will need to be put in place to feedback information regarding quality to each cell. This may incur additional costs in the development of existing or new information technology systems.

The commitment of senior management to these changes would be required, as well as communication and training of employees at all levels. This may again incur additional costs and divert management time away from existing activities.

Examiner's comments

Part (a) was generally well done, with those candidates that broke their answers down into a detailed discussion of the impact of each part of the BPR project scoring most highly.

Part (b) was reasonably done, with those candidates that addressed the specific issues with each level of employees scoring most highly.

Answers to this question which used the detailed structure of the question (BPR proposals and existing employee hierarchy) generally made points that scored easily since they directly addressed relevant issues for the business that was seeking advice. APM is about specific application not just generic points that could apply to any business and those candidates that do this often shift their marks materially into the range of a good pass.

ACCA marking scheme

			Marks
(a)	Explanation of BPR – up to 2 marks Each element of BPR proposal – up to 4 marks Other practical issues – up to 4 marks		
		Maximum	**14**
(b)	Evaluation of current system – up to 8 marks Recommendations – up to 6 marks		
		Maximum	**11**
Total			**25**

23 FRAMILTONE (SEPT/DEC 16) (AMENDED)

Key answer tips

Part (a) was a slight deviation from the normal style of the examining team but was very manageable. Good candidates will have worked methodically through each line of the budget, setting up workings to show the changes expected.

In part (b), good candidates will have examined, in detail, the suitability criteria for each type of budgeting, supporting their discussion with reference to the scenario.

(a) Recalculate the budget for Luxury division to the end of the current year (20X5)

C$000	Q1 (Actual)	Q2	Q3	Q4	Total
Revenue (W1)	10,400	12,240	11,388	7,247	41,275
Cost of sales (W2)	(6,240)	(7,020)	(6,370)	(4,654)	(24,284)
Gross profit	4,160	5,220	5,018	2,593	16,991
Distribution costs (W3)	(624)	(734)	(682)	(434)	(2,474)
Administration costs (W4)	(2,296)	(2,243)	(2,186)	(2,132)	(8,857)
Operating profit	1,240	2,243	2,150	27	5,660

Recalculating Luxury division's budget for the year to reflect current conditions gives a more realistic target for the division managers. For the coming year, the effect of this is very significant and represents a much more challenging target for managers as it increases the expected total annual operating profit by 42% (5,660/4,000) over the original budget.

Workings (C$000):

(W1) Revenue	Q1 (Actual)	Q2	Q3	Q4	Total
Original budget	10,400.0	12,000.0	11,000.0	7,000.0	40,400.0
2% sales volume		240.0	220.0	140.0	600.0
1.5% sales price			168.3	107.1	275.4
Total	10,400.0	12,240.0	11,388.3	7,247.1	41,275.4

(W2) Cost of sales	Q1 (Actual)	Q2	Q3	Q4	Total
Original budget	6,240.0	7,120.0	6,460.0	4,720.0	24,540.0
2% sales volume		142.4	129.2	94.4	366.0
6.67% Exchange rate*		(242.2)	(219.7)	(160.6)	(622.5)
Total	6,240.0	7,020.2	6,369.5	4,653.8	24,283.5

*6.67% = 1 – (1.4/1.5), applied to 50% of COS.

(W3) Distribution costs

	Q1 (Actual)	Q2	Q3	Q4	Total
Original budget	624.0	720.0	660.0	420.0	2,424.0
2% sales volume		14.4	13.2	8.4	36.0
1.31% Fuel tax increase*			8.8	5.6	14.4
Total	624.0	734.4	682.0	434.0	2,474.40

* 1.31% = 70% × (3/160)

(W4) Administration costs

	Q1 (Actual)	Q2	Q3	Q4	Total
Original budget	2,296.0	2,300.0	2,300.0	2,300.0	9,196.0
2.5% compound savings		(57.5)	(113.6)	(168.3)	(339.4)
Total	2,296.0	2,242.5	2,186.4	2,131.7	8,856.6

Workings for savings in administration costs:

Q2 2,300.0 × 2.5% = 57.5

Q3 57.5 + (2,242.5 × 2.5%) = 113.6

Q4 113.6 + (2,186.40 × 2.5%) = 168.3

(b) Incremental budgeting

Framiltone currently uses this type of budgeting, the starting point of which is usually the previous year's actual performance or budget. This is then updated for any known changes in costs, or for inflation. The budget would normally remain unchanged for the remainder of the year.

Incremental budgeting is suitable for use in organisations which are stable and not undergoing significant changes. This is the case for Dairy division, which operates in a saturated market and has little opportunity to grow.

Production volumes in Dairy division have only increased by 0.5% over a full five years, so it is a very stable business. Dairy division has stability of both revenues and costs. It has long-term fixed cost and volume supply agreements with its supermarket customers. It also has similar fixed contracts with its suppliers of milk, the most significant raw material ingredient used in its products.

Though the third party distribution company is able to pass on some increases in fuel costs to Dairy division, these are capped at only 0.5% per year. This is significantly less than the tax increases which will increase Luxury division's fuel costs after the start of Q3. It appears that Dairy division has relatively little exposure to rising fuel prices.

Furthermore, these increases are agreed prior to the setting of the current year budget, so there is no need to update these costs on an ongoing basis throughout the year.

As the dairy foods market is saturated and stable, there is little opportunity for the division to incur discretionary costs such as research and development of new products.

Incremental budgeting is only suitable for business where costs are already well controlled. This is because a big disadvantage of incremental budgeting is that it perpetuates inefficient activities by often simply building inflation into previous year results or budgets. It appears that Dairy division, having been in existence for a relatively long time, does have good cost control as it has modern production plant and is recognised as having the most efficient production processes in the industry.

Incremental budgeting may, however, build in budget slack. Managers may spend up to their budgeted amounts in one year, so that their budget is not cut the next, which may affect their appraisal and reward in the future. It is unclear whether this is occurring at Dairy division, though for many years (while Dairy division was the only division at Framiltone), the budgets set following consultation with divisional managers have just been achieved. This may be consistent with the stability of the division, but could also indicate that budgets were not set at a challenging enough level, even though Dairy division had the best performance of the two divisions last year.

It is not therefore advisable that rolling budgets are introduced in Dairy division, as the current incremental process appears satisfactory. This is especially so since divisional managers have little experience of setting their own budgets, and the time and cost of using rolling budgets would exceed the value of them to the division.

Rolling budgets

Rolling budgets are continually updated to reflect current conditions and are usually extended by budgeting for an additional period after the current period, for example, a quarter, has elapsed. That way, the budget always reflects the most up to date trading conditions and best estimates of future costs and revenues, usually for the next four quarters.

Rolling budgets are suitable for businesses which change rapidly or where it is difficult to estimate future revenues and costs.

Luxury division was only set up two years ago, and is therefore a relatively new business. It also operates in quite a different sector of the industry to that in which Dairy division operates and where Framiltone has most experience. There is likely to be considerable uncertainty as to future costs and revenues as Framiltone has little direct experience on which to base its forecasts.

Whereas Dairy division operates in a saturated and stable market, Luxury division uses rare ingredients which are subject to variations in availability and cost, for example, as a result of poor harvests. There is no indication that Luxury division has fixed price and volume contracts with its customers or suppliers and is therefore likely to suffer from instability of supply as well as demand resulting from changes in consumer tastes.

The frequent changes in the product range are also likely to make forecasting for a year ahead difficult. The fact that a large proportion of ingredients are imported from Veeland, makes costs susceptible to changes in the C$:V$ exchange rates which can quickly make an annual budget out of date, though managers may use methods such as forward contracts to reduce these movements. If managers are appraised on a budget which is out of date or unrealistic, they are likely to give up trying to achieve the budget, which will negatively affect the performance of Framiltone.

Rolling budgets will provide a more accurate basis on which to appraise managers at Luxury division as they incorporate the best known estimates of future costs and revenues. It can be seen by the recalculation following Q1 results that Luxury division's revised budgeted operating profit for the year has increased significantly by 42% (5,660/4,000), most of which is due to exchange rate changes. Where costs and revenues are likely to change during the period, rolling budgets give a much more realistic basis on which to appraise divisional performance and appraise and reward divisional managers. Budgets are likely to be achievable, which will motivate managers to try and achieve them.

Though the regular updating of the budget required in rolling budgeting is costly, time consuming and possibly a distraction for divisional managers, it does seems that rolling budgets are more suitable for Luxury division than the current incremental approach, particularly as being realistic and achievable, they will increase managers' motivation to achieve the budget and so improve the performance of the business.

Examiner's comments

Part (a) was attempted well by many candidates, and the layout of the answers was generally excellent. Although some of the calculations in this part of the question were tricky, candidates at the Strategic Professional Level, who read the requirement carefully should have had few problems here. The examination team was disappointed to see how many candidates could not adjust forecasts by a set percentage, or struggled to compensate for a change in an exchange rate. As mentioned above, candidates must ensure that all relevant workings are shown. Too many incorrect answers were presented without supporting calculations, and thus marks for method were potentially lost.

Part (b) was generally well done and most candidates who attempted this question scored at least half marks on this part. It was pleasing to see many candidates adopting a sensible structure to their answers here – explaining the budgeting system, discussing advantages and disadvantages of the system with regards to each division, and then making a suitable recommendation. It is recommended that candidates identify a clear structure for their discursive answers to ensure that all areas of the requirement are covered, and relevant examples to the scenario are used.

ACCA marking scheme

		Marks
(a)	Calculations:	
	Use of Q1 actual as starting point – 1 mark	
	Sales volume increase on revenue – 1 mark	
	Sales price change from Q3 – 1 mark	
	Sales volume increase on COS – 1 mark	
	Exchange rate percentage – 1 mark	
	Application of exchange rate change – 1 mark	
	Sales volume increase on distribution costs – 1 mark	
	Fuel tax percentage – 1 mark	
	Application of fuel tax change – 1 mark	
	Administration savings – 1 mark	
	Conclusion – up to 2 marks	
	Maximum	**10**

(b)	Use of incremental budgeting in the divisions – 1 mark per point, up to 6 marks Use of rolling budgeting in the divisions – 1 mark per point, up to 6 marks	
	Maximum	**10**
Professional marks **Analysis and Evaluation**		
•	Appropriate use of the data in the appendices to recalculate the current year budget, considering the most logical layout for the budget, with clear and referenced workings to explain how the recalculated figures have been arrived at and to explain any assumptions made	
•	Balanced and reasoned evaluation of the advantages and disadvantages of both types of budgeting, ensuring points made are tailored to the specifics of the two different divisions	
Commercial Acumen		
•	Demonstration of an awareness of the environment the organisation operates in and of the differences between the Dairy and Luxury divisions, ensuring discussion and recommendations are relevant and feasible.	
	Maximum	**5**
Total		**25**

24 ALFLONNSO (SEPT/DEC 16)

Tutorial note

There is a reasonably large amount of information to absorb in this question. You should anticipate this and practise a broad range of questions before the exam so that you feel comfortable in reading, interpreting and using the scenario.

Key answer tips

Part (a)(i) – there are only 5 marks available here so briefly explain why ABC allocates costs more accurately before focusing on the two costs in the scenario. A detailed explanation of ABC and its advantages is not needed and would waste time.

Part (a)(ii) – hopefully a straightforward 3 marks on core ABC calculations.

Part (b) – a methodical approach to the calculation is required here, working through each item in the scenario in turn. Good candidates will have identified the huge benefit of taking a lifecycle approach in terms of accuracy.

Part (c) – the key to scoring a good mark here is being able to relate your EMA knowledge to the particulars of the scenario.

(a) (i) Activity based costing

Activity based costing (ABC) allocates costs to products based on the activities which actually drive the cost to better allocate the costs.

At Alflonnso, the group accounting policy is to allocate waste treatment overhead costs on the basis of revenue, which is arbitrary. From the analyst's calculations, R&D costs do not seem to be allocated to specific product costs at all. This may be appropriate elsewhere in the group, where different products may consume similar levels of overheads, but the three new products being evaluated consume quite different amounts of R&D and waste treatment overheads.

It is therefore inappropriate to charge these costs to the products on the basis of revenue. Charging these costs on the basis of the activities which drive them, which are research hours and volume of waste by-products for R&D costs and waste treatment costs respectively, will give a more accurate costing. This will provide a better basis on which to evaluate the new products and set appropriate prices.

(ii) Calculation of waste treatment cost

	ALF7	**Red**	**Green**
Quantity of waste by-product (m litres)	8.0	34.00	0.75
[m litres produced/no. of m litres to make 1 litre of waste]	[100/12.5]	[85/2.5]	[75/100]
Allocated total $300m according to quantity of waste as proportion of total 55m litres:			
Annual waste treatment allocated ($m):	43.6	185.5	4.1
	[8 × 300/55]	[34 × 300/55]	[0.75 × 300/55]
R&D cost			
Allocated total $60m according to required hours of research as proportion of total 30,400 hours:			
R&D treatment allocated ($m):	1.6	16.8	7.9
	[800 × 60/30,400]	[8,500 × 60/30,400]	[4,000 × 60/30,400]

(b) Average unit cost of each product over total lifecycle

$m	ALF7	Red	Green
Revenue [given]	800.0	1,105.0	825.0
Direct material, labour and energy [given]	(524.0)	(724.0)	(565.0)
Factory overheads [given]	(80.0)	(122.0)	(74.0)
Waste treatment [from part (a) (ii)]	(43.6)	(185.5)	(4.1)
Total annual net profit	152.4	73.5	181.9
Lifecycle duration (years)	3	15	8
Total net profit over lifecycle (before other lifecycle costs)	457.2	1,102.5	1,455.2
Scientific study [$4m × 20 years]	–	(80.0)	–
Decommissioning cost	–	(45.0)	–
R&D cost [from part (a) (ii)]	(1.6)	(16.8)	(7.9)
Total net profit over lifecycle	455.6	960.7	1,447.3
No. of litres produced over the lifecycle (m)	300	1,275	600
Average profit per litre over lifecycle	$1.52	$0.75	$2.41

From the analyst's calculations in Appendix 1, Red has the highest profitability per litre of the three products at $2.26, but this only covers a single period. As such, it does not consider costs which occur before production commences or after it ceases. When the costs of the products over their entire life cycles are taken into account, Red has the lowest average unit profit, the highest being Green at $2.41. This change has occurred as the R&D costs, the cost of the study which will span 20 years and the decommissioning costs have now been recognised. Knowing the costs over the entire lifecycle of a product will help the agrochemicals division to better evaluate its investment decisions, determine appropriate prices and generate an acceptable margin.

(c) EMA

Environmental management accounting (EMA) involves the production of non-financial and financial information to support internal environmental management processes. This could involve measuring the physical movements of inputs to a production process, such as materials and energy, and outputs such as waste.

The agrochemicals division could also record financial data on costs and savings related to the environment. It appears that, in common with most other businesses, these costs are not currently identified by Alflonnso's accounting system and they lie hidden within overheads.

Managers have no incentive to reduce these environment related costs as they are not even aware of them, or the costs of poor environmental practices. EMA allows an organisation to identify environment related costs and take steps to control them. Such costs are often categorised into conventional costs, contingent costs and reputation costs.

Conventional costs

These costs include the cost of energy and raw materials, and may remain hidden within overheads. The energy costs of the three new products in the analyst's income statement are simply combined with raw material and direct labour costs. This does not, for example, highlight the relatively high energy cost to produce Green. Being unaware of this cost, managers are unable to take steps to redesign the specification or production process for the product in order to reduce the cost.

Contingent costs

These are costs which are incurred in the future, for example, the decommissioning costs of plant used to manufacture Red. This cost is significant at an estimated $45m, but occurs 15 years in the future and so the estimation is unlikely to be accurate.

Identification of these contingent costs will at least allow the agrochemicals division to more accurately estimate the cost of each of the three new products. Also, by identifying these costs at an early stage, this may allow managers to redesign the specification or production process for the product in order to reduce the cost and help prevent managers from focusing only on short-term performance.

Reputation costs

Reputation costs are incurred where an organisation acts in a way which may cause harm to the environment, and include sales lost as a result of loss of reputation. These costs are hard to quantify. For example, the accumulation of the existing product, ALF6, in the soil is said to have a potential effect on crop yields which may lead to future claims from users of the product or to loss of sales due to its potential harm to the environment.

Similarly, Alflonnso's failure, by producing Green, to improve crop yields in countries where food production is already scarce is likely to arouse disapproval by public and governments in the 25 countries where it operates. This again may result in lost sales or refusal by governments to grant licences for Alflonnso to operate.

Making managers aware of these reputation costs should focus their attention on the need to manage the risks of them occurring.

Examiner's comments

Part a) (i) was generally poorly done as candidates did not address the demands of the question. Most candidates gave a developed definition of the costing technique which, whilst technically correct on almost every occasion, did not address the specific question demands as to how it may help the entity determine the specifics of product profitability. This relates to the point made previously with regard to definitions and rote learning: a maximum of 25% of the marks can be gained in this way and candidates should also be aware that full marks could be obtained for this part of the question without any definitions being given and purely application being undertaken.

Part a) (ii) was a brief question on a specific calculation and was well done by those who undertook it.

Part b) was generally passed by those who undertook it but most candidates showed a fundamental lack of technical competence by being unable to distinguish between costs that occurred on an annual basis and those that related to the product's overall life. It is also worth highlighting to candidates that when a question asks for comment on the results that what is being sought is more than 'this figure is larger than another.' In the context of this type of question, the commentary being sought is with regard to the implications of the figures: would they change a decision, has the use of one technique as opposed to another fundamentally changed the product cost and what significance should be attached to that? Commentary on the figures here should add more than can be seen from the figures themselves.

Part c) asked for candidates to relate environmental management accounting to the entity. Several answers gave a brief response which only defined and/or explained EMA. The question is assuming that some technical competence in the area of EMA exists and asked for how the principles of it would potentially benefit the entity. Once more, and consistent with the demands of the exam and its level, it is the application of the technique to the entity's practices that is being assessed. Would practices change? How? What might be involved? These are useful trigger questions for a candidate to consider when faced with a question of this nature.

ACCA marking scheme

				Marks
(a)	(i)	Generic explanation of purpose of ABC – 1 mark Application to scenario – 1 mark per point		
			Maximum	**5**
	(ii)	Waste treatment costs – 2 marks R&D costs – 1 mark		
			Maximum	**3**
(b)		Revenue, direct costs, overheads (given) – 1 mark Waste treatment costs – 1 mark Total net profit over LC (before other LC costs) – 1 mark Scientific study – 1 mark Decommissioning cost – 1 mark R&D cost – 1 mark Total litres – 1 mark Average profit per litre over LC – 1 mark Comments – up to 3 marks		
			Maximum	**9**
(c)		Description of EMA – up to 2 marks Each cost category – up to 3 marks		
			Maximum	**8**
Total				**25**

25 CORTINAS RETAIL CLOTHING (CRC) (MAR/JUN 19)

(a) Advantages of the current budgeting system

CRC managers use the previous year results as a starting point when drafting their budgets and increase the variable costs according to any anticipated growth in volumes. This is an example of incremental budgeting.

An advantage of incremental budgeting is that it is quick and easy to prepare. The budgeting system at CRC has remained unchanged for a long time and it is unlikely managers will have experience in any other method of budget setting. While CRC was growing steadily, and relatively slowly at approximately one new store approximately every two years (approximately 18 years/10 stores), the use of incremental budgeting may have been appropriate. But as CRC is now entering new locations, such as out of town shopping centres and possibly food retailing, incremental budgeting is unlikely to be appropriate.

Incremental budgets can also be flexed according to anticipated activity levels. The manager of the central warehouse has done this, rather simplistically, by increasing costs of running the warehouse to reflect the anticipated increase in volumes in 20X6.

Disadvantages of current budgeting system

The use of incremental budgets can encourage slack. This includes incorporating extra costs into the budget to make it more achievable, or spending up to the budgeted amount to ensure that a larger budget is set next year. This may be particularly so at CRC, as managers are appraised based on achieving their budget. The manager of the central warehouse appears to be building in slack by increasing the budget for heating and lighting when the general rate of inflation is zero. This will make it more likely that the manager will receive a positive appraisal next year as it will be easier to achieve the budget.

Incremental budgeting does not encourage CRC to look for new and innovative ways of doing things. The level of automation in the warehouse is lower than in competitors and CRC appears to have just increased the budget for more staff to manually handle items in response to increased volumes. The introduction of the RFID system is, though, an example of the use of technology to increase efficiency in the warehouse.

Incremental budgeting is only appropriate where costs are already well controlled and operations are efficient. Otherwise, poorly controlled costs and inefficiencies are just incorporated into the next period's budget. Staff resistance to the introduction of the RFID system, and their difficulties in using it, suggest that this might not be the case.

Advantages of activity-based budgeting (ABB)

The principle of ABB is that it is activities, such as the goods inwards and goods outwards in the central warehouse, which drive costs. By understanding what drives the cost, such as the number of receipts from suppliers and the number of despatches to stores, CRC can take action to control the drivers of the costs and eliminate activities which are not value adding. ABB is particularly useful where overhead costs form a large part of total costs.

ABB can help identify critical success factors which CRC must do well, such as being able to put items away in the warehouse quickly and accurately and to retrieve them efficiently. This is more likely to be done right first time as ABB focuses on the whole of an activity.

ABB is useful as CRC is changing the nature of its operations. It is undergoing rapid expansion by opening four new stores a year. There is also likely to be a change in the nature of its business, with the opening of its first out of town store and possible acquisition of a food retailing business. The incremental approach to budgeting may no longer be appropriate given the scale and nature of these changes. ABB may be more suitable as the business becomes more complex.

Disadvantages of activity-based budgeting (ABB)

One of the main disadvantages of ABB is the time and resources which are needed to implement it, for example, by identifying activities and their costs drivers. In the short term, overheads may not be controllable which will reduce the benefits of implementing ABB.

CRC has used all its financial resources to fund its expansion and has only old and basic IT systems compared to its competitors. Its current systems are not enterprise resource planning systems (ERPS), unified databases or networked systems. Significant investment in CRC's IT systems will be needed to collect and process large volumes of data on cost drivers and activities which would be required to implement ABB. There may also be resistance to the change from staff, who may also require extensive training, as they will be unfamiliar with the ABB approach.

Conclusion

CRC should adopt ABB, mainly as a response to the significant changes in the business and its increasing complexity.

The out of town store and the food retailing business will both be supplied from CRC's existing central warehouse. The nature of these businesses may be different from the existing business. For example, out of town stores may require despatches each containing a larger number of items from the goods outwards section. Food retailers may require smaller, more frequent despatches to prevent spoilage. The current approach of incremental budgeting, in the central warehouse at least, is unlikely to be appropriate. The benefits of implementing ABB do, however, need to be compared to the financial cost and disruption of doing so.

(b) Activity-based budget for the central warehouse for YE 30 June 20X6

	Total	Goods inwards	Goods outwards	Other
	$	$	$	$
Warehouse manager's salary*	55,000	–	–	55,000
Lease of RFID system*	75,000	45,000	30,000	–
RFID tagging (W1)	72,000	72,000	–	–
Warehouse staff wages (W2)	315,000	157,500	157,500	–
Heating and lighting (W3)	10,000	–	–	10,000
Total	527,000	274,500	187,500	65,000
Annual number of receipts into goods inwards expected		9,000		
Cost ($) per receipt into goods inwards		30.50 (274,500/9,000)		

*As already calculated by the analyst

Comments on variance analysis

The total expected cost for receipts into goods inwards for July 20X5 was $19,825 ($30.50 budgeted cost per receipt x 650 receipts). The actual cost was $18,000 giving a favourable variance of $1,825. It cannot be identified, on the basis of the information available, the cause of the $1,825 variance, as the breakdown of the $18,000 actual cost would be required.

100,000 items were processed in July 20X5 which is the same as the budgeted amount. However, the number of receipts budgeted was 750 (9,000/12), whereas the actual number of receipts was only 650, equivalent to $27.69 ($18,000/650) per receipt. This is a favourable variance of $2.81 per receipt.

It appears that the favourable variance may be due to the receipt of larger quantities of items from suppliers in each delivery. If some of the goods inwards costs are variable with the number of items this would result in a cost saving. This could be because of the reduction in the number of suppliers, with fewer suppliers individually supplying more items.

(W1) RFID tagging

Expected volume of items received in the month = 100,000

Each member of staff can tag 35,000 items per month, so 2.86 (100/30) staff are required – say 3

Annual wages cost is 3 × $24,000 = $72,000

(W2) Warehouse staff wages

Number of staff required in budget year = 14 (12 + 2) Total warehouse staff wages = 14 × $22,500 = $315,000

Of which $157,500 (50% of $315,000) relate to each of goods inwards and goods outwards

(W3) Heating and lighting

As inflation is zero the cost included in the budget should be $10,000.

Tutorial note:

This is a good example of how a numerical ABB question may be included in APM. Do spend some time working through this ensuring you are comfortable with the approach to the workings.

Examiner's comments (extract)

Part (a) – Candidates generally performed well in this part. The answer required a consideration of the advantages and disadvantages of both the current system (incremental) and activity based budgeting (ABB) before offering a justified conclusion as to what the company should do. Candidates would rarely undertake all of these requirements. "Evaluate" means that candidates should assess the strengths and weaknesses of the arguments that arise, in relation to the scenario that is detailed, before coming to a justified conclusion as to what the company should do. It is always worthwhile offering a very brief definition of any technique or technical term to demonstrate comprehension but candidates should be aware that such comments are not worthy of many, if any, marks. Candidates also tended to bring in other techniques that were not relevant to the requirement of the question here, for example zero-based budgeting (ZBB) or rolling budgeting.

Part (b) was worth 12 marks and was not well done with many candidates not undertaking it at all. Those candidates that did undertake it tended to score most of the calculation marks. Candidates who did not score well did not appear to realise that they had to work out how many manual workers were needed to be employed by the company. It was perhaps an inability to calculate this figure that confused some candidates as the rest of the calculations, as with the one above, were straightforward. Most candidates gained comment marks for the insights they offered even if their initial calculations were incorrect.

Candidates also tended to err with regard to the heating and lighting costs in this part of the question, not realising that the proposal for an increase in cost in an environment of zero inflation should not be accepted in an activity based budget. This was a key part of demonstrating the difference between the inefficiencies that the traditional system would allow to be carried forward from year to year and the new system which required justification for the figures used.

ACCA marking scheme		
		Marks
(a)	1 mark per point: Advantages and disadvantages of current system – up to 8 marks Advantages and disadvantages of ABB – up to 8 marks Conclusion – up to 2 marks	
	Maximum	**13**
(b)	Calculations:	
	RFID tagging	2
	Warehouse staff wages	2
	Heating and lighting	1
	Cost per receipt	1
	Total variance	2
	Variance per receipt	2
	Commentary on the variances – up to 4 marks	
	Maximum	**12**
Total		**25**

26 GODEL (JUN 14)

Key answer tips

Part (a) requires a discussion of the implications for performance management of splitting variances into planning and operational elements. This area has been examined in the past and it demonstrates the importance of your brought forward knowledge from PM.

Part (b) asks for an evaluation of the budgeting system. Ensure that you include a full discussion of both the pros and the cons and relate your points back to Godel.

Part (c) on ZBB is core knowledge and should not cause too many problems. Try not to focus too much on the benefits – there are a number of reasons why ZBB is inappropriate for this business.

(a) Planning variances are those which arise due to inaccurate forecasts or standards in the original budget setting. Operational variances are then the remainder due to the decisions of operational managers. A planning variance is the difference between the original standard and a revised one set with the benefit of hindsight. An operational variance is the difference between this revised standard and actual performance.

The total variable cost variance considers all costs together and so it is unlikely that gains or problems can be attributed to one individual. It is of limited value and should be used to point to more detailed analysis to identify the specific source of the variance. Currently, at Godel, the standard costs have been set too high and it appears that the bulk of the cost improvements can be attributed to this. The operational managers have had limited impact in driving down costs overall in May 2014.

The sales price variance indicates how far sales prices were misestimated in the budget (planning) and how well the sales managers have done in negotiating high prices with customers (operational). It appears that the budget was overoptimistic in setting too high an initial price but the sales managers have done well in negotiations with customers. The best individual sales managers could be identified and their techniques communicated to the rest of the sales team. The initial price setting process should be examined as it may have been due to faulty market intelligence about the price setting of competitors or the commercial situation of the customers (supermarkets).

(b) **Purpose and benefits of budgeting**

Budgeting is a key control tool for management and of particular importance in controlling costs in businesses such as Godel which is seeking to be a cost leader. At Godel, it is succeeding in this as total costs show a favourable variance. Budgets help to communicate and coordinate all the management activities within the company towards a single plan. The budget helps to attribute responsibility for performance, for example, the favourable material usage variance indicates that fewer raw materials are required than was planned and this reflects the work of the production manager in cutting waste and, possibly, the purchasing manager in buying good quality raw materials. The participatory nature of the budget process will help to motivate managers to achieve budget figures which they themselves have helped to set. It is important for this purpose that the budget is achievable or else it is demotivating.

Budgets assist the evaluation of performance by identifying variances and then point to areas for corrective action or future learning. At Godel, sales are clearly under-performing the plan both in terms of the quantity and price achieved. On the positive side, the managers in charge of labour and the workforce are working efficiently and cheaply.

There are several problems with budgeting at Godel:

1 The time-consuming nature of the process which is unusual as the business is mature and stable and so budget-setting should not be a complex process. The exasperation of the managers probably results from the fact that they see little benefit coming from work involved in forecasting. The operating variances given are relatively small.

2 The planning variances explain the bulk of the variances at Godel and so the operational managers have good reason to be concerned as their performance affects the operational variances only.

3 The operational and planning variance analysis is limited in scope. Performing more detailed operating and planning variance could also assist in addressing the complaint that operational managers are being asked to explain variances which are not their fault, for example, by doing this analysis for all the different cost headings in the operating statement and not just the total cost variance.

4 The use of standard costs in budgeting could discourage a system of continuous improvements which would help a cost leader in making efficiency gains. However, Godel's senior management may view that it is unlikely that there will be a need to make such changes on a regular basis and that a review of the costs once a year is sufficient.

(c) Zero based budgeting (ZBB) is a method of budgeting that requires each cost element to be specifically justified, as though the activities to which the budget relates were being undertaken for the first time. Without approval, the budget allowance is zero.

There are four distinct stages in the implementation of ZBB:

1 Managers should specify for their responsibility centres those activities that can be individually evaluated.

2 Each of the individual activities is then described in a decision package. The decision package should state the costs and revenues expected from the given activity. It should be drawn up in such a way that the package can be evaluated and ranked against other packages.

3 Each decision package is evaluated and ranked usually using cost/benefit analysis.

4 The resources are then allocated to the various packages.

The approach of ZBB is considered appropriate in industries where there are rapid changes in the business environment, new product developments and/or where there are very higher levels of overheads, especially discretionary costs such as research and development.

This approach at Godel would appear to be inappropriate for a number of reasons:

1 There does not appear to be the need to have to justify every cost from scratch. There is little evidence of budget slack or excessive spending and the work generated in having to prepare decision packages may increase the complaints about time-consuming exercises from the operational managers.

2 The lower level managers would now need to prepare their own decision packages and would require training in this. They do not appear to have the appetite for such development.

3 There is no indication that there are rapid changes in Godel's business and little innovation, so the ZBB approach would not appear to yield many benefits.

Overall, then, there are insufficient benefits and many barriers to switching to ZBB at Godel and it is not recommended.

Examiner's comments

Part (a). Most candidates did not know the definitions of these and so talked about all the other variances in the appendix thus avoiding the question.

Part (b) was also inadequately attempted. As in the past, too many candidates only saw the negatives of the existing system and few identified the positives for a traditional company like Godel.

ACCA marking scheme

			Marks
(a)	Definitions	up to	1
	Total variable cost variance	up to	3
	Sales price variance	up to	3
		Maximum	**6**
(b)	Benefits of budgeting for Godel including:		
	Planning and coordination – meeting overall strategy		
	Responsibility		
	Integration		
	Motivation		
	Evaluation		
	1 per point made up to 6 marks		6
	Problems with budgeting at Godel including:		
	Time-consuming and unnecessary		
	Lack of recognition of planning failures		
	Insufficient planning and operational analysis		
	Impedes continuous improvement		
	1 per point made up to 6 marks		6
		Maximum	**11**
(c)	Description	up to	3
	Appropriateness at Godel	up to	5
	Recommendation		1
		Maximum	**8**
Total			**25**

27 BOOXE (JUN 14)

Key answer tips

In part (a) a cost/benefit analysis is required. This should be reasonably straightforward but be careful to not spend too much time of the calculations here.

In part (b) do not just write everything you know about BPR. Take a few minutes to plan your answer ensuring that both areas of the requirement are addressed, that there are a sufficient number of points and that these points are prioritised.

Part (c) focuses on the HR aspects of performance management. Use your own experience to offer advice on the appraisal process at Booxe.

(a) **Annual costs of new system:**

	$
Hardware for warehouse and purchasing depts (depreciation)	27,500
Software total cost (depreciation)	34,375
On-going servicing cost	22,500
	84,375

Benefit of new system (cost savings):

		$	
Staff costs			
	Warehouse	125,000	= 10 × $25,000 × 50%
	Purchasing	54,400	= $32,000 × 8.5/5
		179,400	
Net benefit	$95,025		

The BPR project will yield a net benefit of $95,025 p.a. and so the project is financially successful. However, there are other costs not included in this analysis such as redundancy/retraining of the staff whose workload has been reduced and the training costs for staff on the new system.

(b) Business process re-engineering (BPR) is described as the fundamental rethinking and radical redesign of business processes to achieve dramatic improvements in critical contemporary measures of performance, such as cost, quality, service and speed.

It cuts across traditional departmental lines in order to achieve a more efficient delivery of the final product. At Booxe, this is evident in the effect which the BPR project has had on both warehousing and purchasing departments.

This change to a process view will require a change towards process teams rather than functional departments. Employees will need to retrain in order to gain additional skills. The organisational hierarchy will flatten with the employees being given more responsibility to make decisions. This is often aided by the introduction of a unified corporate database accessed through an ERP system. These will represent major changes at Booxe which appears to have become set in its ways. The change will require much communication and leadership from senior management as a result.

The implications for accounting at Booxe are that performance measures must be redesigned around processes rather than departments. The aim is to identify where value is being added and eliminate where resources are employed to no valuable outcome. An activity-based approach might be used to model the processes in the business as part of the BPR restructuring and this could be carried on in the accounting systems. The ABC system of costing is a more detailed method of allocating overheads in order to achieve a more accurate product cost and, therefore, a more accurate idea of the profit each product generates. It is more time-consuming and expensive to set up compared to traditional overhead absorption methods but in the context of the intended changes to processes at Booxe due to BPR, it will fit well. Financial reports will have to be redesigned around process teams and any variances to budget used may need to be reconsidered in the light of the activity-based approach.

Tutorial note

Other analysis models (for example from SBL) could be relevant to this answer and would be given appropriate credit within the mark limitations of the requirement.

(c) Appraisal is the process of collecting and reviewing data on an employee's work which will provide an assessment of their capabilities and potential in order to improve performance, for example, by training. It also presents an opportunity to deal with other HR issues, such as discipline, career management, motivation and determining rewards.

There is a general need for some kind of performance assessment; however, appraisal systems are often criticised as irrelevant to the work of the organisation. Indeed, the current system at Booxe has arguably become too informal, possibly as a result of neither side of the process taking it seriously. In order to make the process relevant, appraisal is seen as a means of control of staff and linking their activities to the overall organisational goals such as driving down costs. It will lead to improved development of appropriate skills and greater motivation on the part of the staff, especially if linked to a suitable reward system.

The balance between control and development within the appraisal process will link to the culture within the business. At Booxe, there is a culture of craft appreciation which implies the importance of development of skills and thus it may be that there has been a loss of the sense of control and this has led to the increased costs which the CEO is trying to drive down.

Examiner's comments

Part (a) was generally well done although many candidates muddled a per annum view of cost/benefit with a project lifetime view which left answers difficult to interpret.

Part (b) was again generally well done. Most candidates realised there were two areas to discuss and split their answers appropriately. A large number took the hints in the scenario to consider how this might link to activity-based approaches and the introduction of ERPS. The one weakness demonstrated was a simplistic grasp of what 'culture' might be.

Candidates who performed well in part (c) usually discussed the purpose of an appraisal system, considered the issues at Booxe and then suggested solutions to the problems identified. Those candidates that gave text-book answers did not score marks very efficiently.

ACCA marking scheme

				Marks
(a)	Costs:	Depreciation		1
		Total		1
	Savings:	Warehousing		1
		Purchasing		1
		Net benefit		1
	Comments:	1 mark for suitable comment on the calculations		1
			Maximum	**6**
(b)	Definition of BPR – 1 mark per point		up to	2
	Culture – 1 mark per point		up to	5
	Impact on accounting systems – 1 mark per point		up to	5
			Maximum	**11**
(c)	Definition of process – 1 mark per point		up to	2
	Purpose – 1 mark per point		up to	4
	Balance of control and development – 1 mark per point		up to	3
			Maximum	**8**
Total				**25**

28 GANYMEDE UNIVERSITY (JUN 12)

Key answer tips

This question concerned a university (Ganymede) which was in the process of undertaking a benchmarking exercise with two other universities in its country. This was easily the most popular question in section B.

Overall, answers were disappointing to what ought to be a straightforward question in a APM examination. Make sure you understand the steps involved in a benchmarking exercise as well as how to interpret the results of such an exercise.

(a) Benchmarking process

The benchmarking process is often described using seven steps. The following are the steps with the current state of the exercise:

1 Set objectives and decide the areas to benchmark

GU has set the objective of improving efficiency and is benchmarking all of its administration operations relating to teaching and research.

2 Identify key performance drivers and indicators

The performance drivers have been provided and the indicators are based on the activity per driver. The drivers might be improved by distinguishing between teaching staff and administrative staff.

3 Select organisations for benchmarking comparison

The government selected the three largest universities for benchmarking which excludes five other smaller universities. This can be justified if the large universities cover similar teaching and research areas while the smaller ones are narrower in focus (for example science and engineering subjects only). However, it may be that there are examples of good practice in university administration that will be missed as a result of restricting the exercise. It might be sensible to include foreign universities in the exercise. Differences in the mix of subjects researched and taught might also affect the results (e.g. managing teaching facilities in engineering and law will be different).

4 Measure performance of all organisations involved in benchmarking

The basic data has been gathered as required by government. This step would normally be more complex in a private sector situation as commercial secrecy would hinder the sharing of information.

5 Compare performances

This is the stage that has been reached. See answer to part (b) for results.

6 Specify improvement projects

The results of the comparison should lead to identification of areas for improvement. If GU is not demonstrating leading performance then it should send staff to the top performer to identify their best practice processes and devise projects to implement these at GU.

7 Implement and monitor improvements

Management should perform a post-project review in order to identify if the improvement has achieved or exceeded its goals and consider lessons that have been learned from the project.

(b) The benchmarking has been completed as follows:

	GU	**AU**	**BU**
	$	$	$
Research			
Contract management	78	87	97
Laboratory management	226	257	281
Teaching facilities management	951	1,197	920
Student support services	71	89	73
Teachers support services	506	532	544
Accounting	204	204	197
Human resources	156	156	191
IT management	817	803	737
General services	2,153	2,088	2,286

Research categories are considered per $000 of contract value supported.

Teaching facilities and student support are considered per student.

Other categories are considered per staff member.

From the results, it can be seen that GU is best at controlling costs associated with research contracts and it has the highest research funding ($185m). This may indicate that the government monitors such cost control and that GU should ensure its continued good practice in this area. AU spends most per student on its teaching facilities and student support although it has the smallest number of students. It might be expected that this would lead to higher student enrolment which may imply that student enrolment is not significantly dependent on these factors. However, lower dropout rates and higher student pass rates and future success in gaining employment may reflect the more expensive teaching environment at AU. These quality measures are not being reflected in the benchmarking exercise.

In accounting services, all the universities perform broadly in line. BU has achieved a small 3.5% advantage over the others.

In human resources management, BU is 22% more costly which is surprising given the larger staff numbers at BU over which to spread such a central cost.

In IT management, there is some variation of performance with BU costs being 10% lower than GU's. These variations may well be due to the subjects being taught (for example, universities that are more orientated to science and technology will probably demand larger computing resources).

In general services, all the universities perform broadly in line. AU has achieved a small 3% advantage over GU.

It is necessary to give a warning about the difficulty of comparing the performance of the universities due to differences in location and the mix of subjects taught and researched.

Examiner's comments

Part (a). Answers were generally unstructured with those that laid out a set of steps in the benchmarking process scoring best. Nevertheless, a general understanding of the method was present but this had to be combined with suitable comments about Ganymede's current progress in order to gain a pass mark.

Part (b) ought to have been a straightforward analysis of the data table given. However, as mentioned earlier, candidates displayed a disappointing lack of judgement over what constitutes useful advice in this scenario and failed to use the indicated drivers in order to calculate suitable relative measures. Also, as in Question 2 (a), the commentary was often restricted to the unnecessary writing out in a sentence the output of the table, e.g. 'GU has the highest research contract value', with no value-adding (and mark-scoring) comments attached.

ACCA marking scheme

		Marks
(a)	1 mark per point up to 8 marks. (Note only 2 marks are available for identifying the headings in the process.)	
	Maximum	**10**
(b)	Up to 8 marks for calculations applying the appropriate drivers. Up to 8 marks for commenting on the results.	
	Maximum	**15**
Total		**25**

29 MAXWELL (DEC 14)

Key answer tips

Part (a) asked for an assessment of two given plans. You are expected to carry out some calculations here but note that the level of detail in the model answer goes beyond what is needed. Leave time to conclude on your calculations.

In part (b) it would be useful to explain the different categories of environmental cost. This will help to give your answer structure and depth.

Part (c) requires a discussion of lifecycle costing issues. Make sure that you adequately focus on the issues here.

(a) The environmental goal of Maxwell is to reach the CO_2 emission reduction target of 20% in five years while increasing capacity to cope with an expected rise of 10% in demand over that period.

The changes in mix of generating stations have the following effects:

Plan 1a

		Details for each type of station			**Totals for Maxwell**		
Power station type		**Maximum generating power (MW)**	**Operating cost of electricity ($/MWh)**	**Capital cost ($m)**	**Number of stations**	**Total capital invested ($m)**	**Total CO_2 emissions (million tonnes)**
Coal	(small)	300	25	1,320	3	3,960	2.36
	(large)	600	25	2,640	3	7,920	9.46
Gas	(small)	300	50	300	7	2,100	2.76
	(large)	900	50	900	2	1,800	7.10
Nuclear		1,200	20	6,000	3	18,000	0.75
						33,780	22.43

The new nuclear station will cost $6,000m. The total power output of Maxwell is maintained at 10,200 MW and the total CO_2 emissions falls by 15.4% to 22.43 million tonnes. The operating cost of electricity will fall on average as a nuclear station is the cheapest one to operate. Therefore, Maxwell will have maintained its capacity and reduced CO2 emissions but it will not have covered the rise in demand nor met the government's target for CO2 reduction. (Plan 1b will provide the same generating capacity as Plan 1a and it will be less expensive in capital terms but it will not reduce CO2 emissions.)

Plan 2

The addition of a second new nuclear station would cost a further $6,000m and would increase power-generating capacity by 11.8% to 11,400 MW. This would cover the expected rise of 10% in demand for electricity due in the next five years. It would increase the total CO_2 emissions by only 1.1% (0.25/22.43, assuming it is done in combination with Plan 1a) and would, therefore, further reduce the average CO_2 emitted in the operation of the stations.

We do not have the detailed figures for actual power output for each station but if we use maximum power capacity, then currently, Maxwell produces 0.0026 tonnes of CO_2 per max MW (= 26.51/10,200).

If the company pursues plan 1a and plan 2 in combination, then it will produce 0.0020 tonnes of CO_2 per max MW (= 22.68/11,400). This is a 23% reduction and indicates the government's target may be achieved.

If the company pursues plan 1b and plan 2 in combination, then it will produce 0.0023 tonnes of CO_2 per max MW (= 26.76/11,400). This is a 12% reduction and indicates the government's target may not be achieved.

(b) Management accounts provide us with an analysis of the performance of the business. However, traditional accounting systems are unable to deal adequately with environmental costs. As a result, managers are unaware of these costs and have no information with which to manage or reduce them.

Specific areas include the following:

- Conventional costs, such as energy costs will not be prioritised by management since they often hidden within overheads.
- Contingent costs such as future compliance costs or remediation costs when a power station is decommissioned are often incurred towards the end of a project so are ignored by managers who focus on short- term performance. This aspect is addressed within environmental lifecycle costing below.
- Relationship costs such as the cost of producing environmental information for public reporting are often ignored by operational managers who are unaware of their existence. It is likely that a separate PR department within Maxwell will deal with communications to the local community to reassure them about safety, for example.
- Reputational costs such as costs associated with failing to address environmental issues may be ignored by managers who are unaware of the risk of incurring them.

(c) Lifecycle costing records the costs of a product 'from cradle to grave', taking into account the environmental consequences across the whole life of the product. In order to appraise a project correctly, cost recording systems must capture all costs.

In particular for a nuclear power station, these must include:

- those costs incurred prior to production such as costs of handling regulatory difficulties and design choices, and also
- those costs incurred after production ceases such as the clean-up costs of decommissioning and decontaminating the site and safely storing all waste.

It is important that these costs are identified and included in the initial project appraisal. In the case of Maxwell building a new nuclear power station, there are the uncertain costs up front associated with the regulatory process which could include the financing costs associated with delays in the project while regulatory approval is sought. There is the normal uncertainty over the building cost when a project costs $6bn and takes five years to complete. Finally, there is the estimated $1bn in decommissioning costs which again carry uncertainty. If Maxwell is to be able to claim to be financially and environmentally responsible, then it must have plans in place to cover these costs.

ACCA marking scheme

			Marks
(a)	2 marks for identifying the detailed environmental goal 1 mark for choosing suitable ways to assess the goal (choice of indicators) Up to 4 marks for each plan		
		Maximum	**10**
(b)	Up to 2 marks for describing lifecycle costing Up to 6 marks for discussing issues associated with Plan 2		
		Maximum	**8**
(c)	1 mark for each well explained point or example	**Maximum**	**7**
Total			**25**

30 ENT ENTERTAINMENT CO (JUN 11)

Key answer tips

This question uses the BCG matrix which is also covered in SBL. In APM you are more likely to have to calculate key inputs such as market growth and share and, more critically, evaluate its use for performance management.

(a) The BCG matrix breaks a business into its component units and then considers their performance in terms of the growth of the unit (usually measured by revenue) and the relative market share of each unit.

The sector growth and market share for each of ENT's divisions is as follows:

	2010	**2011**	**2012**	**2013**
Growth in sector				
Restaurants		1.0%	1.0%	0.0%
Cafes		9.0%	11.0%	9.0%
Bars		–2.0%	–3.0%	–3.0%
Dance clubs		6.0%	6.0%	9.0%
Market share				
Restaurants	0.5%	0.5%	0.5%	0.6%
Cafes	1.0%	1.0%	1.1%	1.2%
Bars	3.5%	3.5%	3.5%	3.6%
Dance clubs	11.0%	11.0%	10.9%	11.0%

Relative market share	2010	2011	2012	2013	Mkt leader
Restaurants	0.17	0.17	0.18	0.19	3.0%
Cafes	0.33	0.34	0.37	0.39	3.0%
Bars	1.17	1.17	1.18	1.22	3.0%
Dance clubs	0.73	0.73	0.73	0.73	15.0%

(Relative market share calculated as a ratio of division's market share to market leader's share. Figures calculated to nearest 0.1%.)

Additionally,

	Market growth (2011 – 2014) % pa	**ENT divisional growth (2011 – 2014) % pa**
Restaurant	0.67	4.67
Café	9.66	15.28
Bars (Shrunk)	–2.67	–1.34
Dance clubs	6.99	6.98

Tutorial note

There are more calculations given here than are needed for a good answer. They are intended to illustrate useful analysis of the data given.

(b) The restaurant and bar sectors are slow growth or in decline while the clubs and cafes appear to be growing at a pace well above the general economic expansion of 2% pa. ENT has a strong position in the bar and club sectors but is relatively small in the restaurant and cafe sectors.

Consequently, the restaurant division would be seen as a dog with low growth and poor market share which would make it a poor candidate for investment. A disposal could be considered unless there are other reasons to keep it (such as it acts as a feeder to dance clubs). The cafe division is a problem child where there is the possibility of good growth in the sector but the division lacks market share in such a fragmented market. The sector appears ripe for consolidation and so either the division should be financed to grow by acquisition or else sold on to another consolidator. The bar division is a cash cow as it has a strong share of a low growth sector. It will be managed for its cash generative capabilities and will be heavily cost controlled. Finally, the dance clubs represent another problem child with strong growth and a large market share (near the market leader). They would not be considered a star as they lack market leadership but would be considered an excellent candidate for investment to achieve that position.

This portfolio of divisions represents a good spread of businesses with the cash generative bar business supplying the financial resources for the development of the cafe and club businesses. It is unclear from this analysis how creative the company as a whole is at developing new businesses to replace the poorer performing entities.

(c) The BCG matrix can be beneficial as it allows the company to view the prospects of its different divisions. A different style of management should be applied to each division based on this analysis. Those businesses which are in faster growing sectors will require more capital to be invested and may not generate cash as efficiently from profits. However, those businesses in slower growing mature markets should have a focus on cost control and cash generation. Business units identified as cash cows and, particularly, dogs should not be dismissed since if they are properly managed they can provide a rich source of cash as they are run down.

The performance management systems and metrics used by the divisions should therefore be adjusted to reflect this analysis. The metrics for high growth prospects of cafes and clubs will be based on profit and return on investment, while those in lower growth, such as the bar division, will be focused on margins and cash generation.

However, the BCG matrix is a very simple method of analysis. For example, using relative market share measured against the largest competitor, where a value of 1·0 is used as cut off between large and small, means there is only one star or cow per market. It was designed as a tool for product portfolio analysis rather than performance measurement.

As a performance system, it seems to downgrade traditional measures of performance such as profit and shareholder wealth and therefore may not be well aligned with all of the key stakeholders' objectives. It should be seen as a starting point for considering the appropriate performance management for a business unit but not the final result.

Additionally, it may be that different products with each business unit may not fit the unit's classification. For example, the newly launched wine bar format seems to be in a higher growth sub-sector and so applying the performance systems and management style of a dog business would not be appropriate. It may also be difficult to distinguish the sectors from each other as, for example, it may be difficult to define the difference between a cafe and a restaurant. The model also fails to consider the links between the business units, for example, where the bars or cafes may serve as feeder businesses for late night dance clubs.

(d) The existing remuneration system is primarily based on the division's performance compared to budget. It is likely that the management style will be highly cost conscious and conservative as a result. This would be appropriate for the bar and restaurant divisions which foresee low growth. However, this could present particular problems for the divisions that are or could be grown (cafes and clubs). They will require a more entrepreneurial managerial approach and, therefore, should be using long-term profit measures of performance in order to align the manager's motivation with the business unit's needs.

The chairman is also correct to be concerned about the broad measure of divisional performance (EVA™) and whether this is coherent with the budgetary approach to management reward in the divisions. There is the possibility that if the budgets are not set in order to maximise EVA™ then the overall objectives are not reflected in the reward system at divisional level.

Examiner's comments

With part (a) many candidates did not know that the growth element of the analysis referred to the growth of the market sector and either ignored this element or calculated the growth of the division instead. This lead to poor marks as half of the analysis was therefore missing and the conclusions compromised as a result. Also, some candidates chose to ignore most of the forecast numerical data and only calculate the current position of the company. This wasted an opportunity to score marks on the historical trends and also, the expected future position which is relevant if giving strategic advice.

Requirement (b) was also affected by this lack of knowledge of the method. However, there were a number of excellent answers in which, better candidates demonstrated good confidence in exposing the weaknesses of the BCG model and suggesting possible alternative solutions to performance management at ENT.

Requirement (c). The answers to this part often represented the candidate's best work on this question although few candidates displayed a clear grasp of the scenario. Better candidates noted the problem of applying a uniform package based on cost performance where they noted from the BCG analysis that some divisions showed growth or growth prospects that required a different style of management. They also commented on the lack of alignment of the divisional performance measure with the cost-based bonus element of the package.

ACCA marking scheme

			Marks
(a)	6 marks for appropriate calculations.	**Maximum**	**6**
(b)	Up to 5 marks for an appropriate classification with reasons.	**Maximum**	**5**
(c)	Up to 2 marks on general benefits of BCG analysis. Up to 2 marks on how BCG can be applied in performance systems. Up to 5 marks on limitations of the BCG approach. To score well the comments must be illustrated by application to the scenario.		
		Maximum	**8**
(d)	1 mark per point. Maximum of 6 marks.	**Maximum**	**6**
Total			**25**

31 PLX REFINERY CO (PILOT 10)

Key answer tips

A useful question on the core areas of the environmental management accounting topic. This is a fantastic revision tool. Make sure you have the necessary knowledge in place and that you can apply it to the particulars of the scenario.

(a) Environmental cost categories

PLX will need to identify existing and new cost information that is relevant to understanding its environmental impact.

There are conventional costs such as raw material costs and energy costs which should be broadened to include the cost of waste through inefficiency. These and other conventional costs (such as regulatory fines) are often hidden within overheads and therefore will not be a high priority for management control unless they are separately reported.

There are contingent costs such as the cost of cleaning industrial sites when these are decommissioned. These are often large sums that can have significant impact on the shareholder value generated by a project. As these costs often occur at the end of the project life, they can be given low priority by a management that is driven by short-term financial measures (e.g. annual profit) and make large cash demands that must be planned at the outset of the project.

There are relational costs such as the production of environmental information for public reporting. This reporting will be used by environmental pressure groups and the regulator and it will demonstrate to the public at large the importance that PLX attaches to environmental issues.

Finally, there are reputational costs associated with failing to address environmental issues when consumer boycotts and adverse publicity lose sales revenue.

(b) Explanation and evaluation of techniques

A lifecycle view consists of considering the costs and revenues of a product over the whole life of the product rather that one accounting period. For an oil refinery, this might be taken to be the useful life of the refinery. A lifecycle view may take profit or discounted cash flow as the principal measure of performance. This is particularly relevant for PLX given the planned redevelopment programme at the refinery which will highlight the decommissioning costs of such plant. This will aid future long-term investment planning at PLX.

Activity-based Costing (ABC) is a method of detailed cost allocation that when applied to environmental costs distinguishes between environment-related costs and environment-driven costs. At PLX, related costs would include those specifically attributed to an environmental cost centre such as a waste filtration plant while driven costs are those that are generally hidden in overheads but relate to environmental drivers such as additional staff costs or the shorter working life of equipment (in order to avoid excess pollution in the later years of its working life). This will assist PLX in identifying and controlling environmental costs.

Input/output analysis (sometimes called mass balance) considers the physical quantities input into a business process and compares these with the output quantities with the difference being identified as either stored or wasted in the process. These physical quantities can be translated into monetary quantities at the end of the tracking process. Flow cost accounting is associated with this analysis as it reflects the movement of physical quantities through a process and will highlight priorities for efficiency improvements.

These techniques are not mutually exclusive and all can assist PLX in improving performance. However, cost/benefit analysis will need to be undertaken for each of the systems. This will be difficult, as benefit estimates will prove vague given the unknown nature of the possible improvements that may accrue from using the techniques. The non-financial benefits will include a better public image and reduced chance of protest by environmental groups and an improved relationship with the government who is likely to be a key supplier of crude oil to the business. Additionally, ABC and flow cost accounting will require significant increases in the information that the management accounting systems collect and so incur increased costs. As a result, the decision to use these techniques is likely to be based on the balance between known costs and estimated benefits of non-financial factors.

(c) Lifecycle costing

A traditional analysis of the costs of Kayplas might yield the product profit given in the original data. However, this ignores capital costs, environmental costs and the cost of decommissioning. A lifecycle analysis aims to capture the costs over the whole lifecycle of the product and it would show

Costs	**$m**
Production costs	82.3
Marketing costs	17
Development costs	8.6
	107.9
Environmental costs	**$m**
Waste filtration	8.1
Carbon dioxide exhaust extraction	5.3
	13.4
Other costs	**$m**
Decommissioning costs	18
Total costs	139.3

This should be compared to revenues of $149.4m and leaves only a small overall return on investment (surplus of $10.1m). It should be noted that the decommissioning costs are estimated at $18m in five years. It is likely that given the difficulty in dealing with specialised equipment and the fact that environmental legislation may get stricter, this could easily be a significant underestimate. This could destroy all of the added value of the product.

The value of lifecycle costing often lies in the visibility it gives to costs that are determined in the early stages of the design of the product and in this case, it emphasises the need to minimise the cost of decommissioning. This should be done in the design phase of the refinery extension.

The traditional product profit analysis shows a surplus of $41.5m over the life of the product failing as it does to capture the environmental and decommissioning costs.

Additionally, if volumes of production can be ascertained then a cost per unit of Kayplas could be calculated and this would assist in price setting.

ACCA marking scheme		
		Marks
(a)	Up to 2 marks per cost area discussed. Points must include examples of relevance to the scenario to score full marks.	
	Maximum	**8**
(b)	Up to 2 marks per technique – an explanation and its link to environmental performance. 3 marks for an evaluation of the techniques.	
	Maximum	**9**
(c)	2 marks for calculation of lifecycle costs. Up to 2 marks for calculating the product profits of the two approaches. Up to 4 marks for discussion of improvements and issues identified by lifecycle costing.	
	Maximum	**8**
Total		**25**

32 FGH TELECOM (FGH) (DEC 10)

(a) Government regulations relevant to FGH's environmental strategy include requirements to recycle materials, limits on pollution and waste levels along with new taxes such as carbon levies to add additional costs. Performance indicators would be additional costs resulting from failure to recycle waste, fines paid for breaches and the level of environmental tax burdens.

The general economic climate is relevant to the strategy including factors such as interest, inflation and exchange rates. For FGH, the general economic environment is not good and cost savings from reductions in energy use would help to offset falling profits. Also, the difficulties indicated in raising capital could be monitored through the firm's cost of capital. This would be especially relevant if the environmental initiatives lead to significant capital expenditure for FGH.

Trends and fashions among the general public appear to be relevant for FGH as the public will be end-users of its services and environmental action could improve the brand image of FGH. Suitable performance indicator would be based around a score in a customer attitude survey.

Technological changes in the capabilities available to FGH and its competitors will affect its environmental strategy. New environmentally efficient technologies such as hybrid cars and solar recharging cells would be relevant to the cost and product sides of FGH. Performance indicators would involve measuring the impact of the use of new technology on existing emission data.

(b) The company has a target of cutting emissions by 60% of their 2001 values by the year 2017. Overall, it has cut emissions by 38% in the first nine years of the 16-year programme. There was a reduction of 16% in the last year of measurement. If this rate of improvement is maintained then the company will reduce its emissions by 82% (62% × (84% ^ 7)) by 2017. However, it should be noted that it is unlikely that there will be a constant rate of reduction as it normally becomes more difficult to improve as the easy actions are taken in the early years of the programme.

The initial data are rather complex and so to summarise, three categories for the three types of transport were considered (Road, Rail and Air). The largest cut has been in rail related emissions (63%) while the contribution from road transport has only fallen by 38%. The road emissions are the dominant category overall and they are still falling within the programmed timetable to reach the target. However, it is clear that air travel is not falling at the same pace but this may be driven by factors such as increasing globalisation of the telecommunication industry which necessitates travel by managers abroad to visit multinational clients and suppliers.

One unusual feature noted is that the mix of transport methods appears to be changing. Rail travel appears to be declining. This is surprising as rail is widely believed to be the lowest emitting method from these forms of travel. However, caution must be exercised on this conclusion which may be due to a change in the emissions technology relating to each category of travel rather than the distance travelled using each method.

The major change that is apparent from the basic data is the move from petrol to diesel-powered motor vehicles which in the commercial fleet appears nearly complete. It will be more difficult to move company and private cars to diesel-power as there will be an element of choice on the part of the car user in the type of car driven.

Working:

	2001	**2009**	**2010**	**Change on base year**
Measured in millions of kgs	**Base year**			
Commercial Fleet Diesel	105.4	77.7	70.1	–33%
Commercial Fleet Petrol	11.6	0.4	0.0	–100%
Company Car Diesel	15.1	14.5	12.0	–21%
Company Car Petrol	10.3	3.8	2.2	–79%
Other road travel (Diesel)	0.5	1.6	1.1	120%
Other road travel (Petrol)	3.1	0.5	0.3	–90%
Rail travel	9.2	9.6	3.4	–63%
Air Travel (short haul)	5.0	4.4	3.1	–38%
Air Travel (long haul)	5.1	7.1	5.4	6%
Hire Cars (Diesel)	0.6	1.8	2.9	383%
Hire Cars (Petrol)	6.7	6.1	6.1	–9%
Total	172.6	127.5	106.6	
Index	100%	74%	62%	
	YoY change	–16%		

Simplifying categories

Road travel	**Base year**			
	153.3	106.4	94.7	–38%
Air travel	10.1	11.5	8.5	–16%
Rail travel	9.2	9.6	3.4	–63%
Total	172.6	127.5	106.6	–38%

Mix of travel method in each year

	Base year		
Road travel	89%	83%	89%
Air travel	6%	9%	8%
Rail travel	5%	8%	3%

(c) The analysis could be improved by collecting data on the total distances travelled so that employee behaviour can be tracked. This would allow measurement of the effect of switching away from physical meetings and using teleconferencing facilities. This may be particularly effective in cutting air travel which has been noted as a problem area.

It would also allow assessment of the homeworking scheme which should reduce total distance travelled. Although, the full environmental benefit will not be apparent as much of the travel would have been a regular commute to work which an employee will not be able to claim and so is unlikely to record.

Finally, the collection of distance travelled data will allow a measure of the effect of changing modes of transport by calculating an average emission per km travelled.

Tutorial note

Requirement (a) could be answered using any sensible set of headings for example, PEST.

The working given in this solution is more detailed than would be required to produce a good answer to this question. It is here to give detailed explanation of the calculations.

Examiner's comments

Part (a) was generally well done although a number of good candidates ignored the request for illustrative performance indicators.

Part (b) showed up basic weaknesses in some candidates' skill set. It was well-answered by only a minority of candidates.

Many candidates wasted their time by limiting their comments to only writing out lists of statements such as

'Commercial Fleet Diesel use has fallen from 105.4 to 70.1' or even 'Commercial Fleet Diesel use has gone down'. First, this is stating the obvious to anyone who read the table but also, this is far too detailed for most reporting purposes.

An appropriate plan of attack for this part might have been:

1 consider the 'big picture' – whether the overall target for emission reduction be met

2 break down the data into smaller but meaningful (and manageable) chunks – Road, Rail and Air transport; and

3 discuss the individual lines of the data table focussing on the data that explains the overall picture of emission changes, for example, the switch from petrol to diesel powered motor vehicles is complete in commercial vehicles and has led to large reductions in emissions but such a change may be more difficult in company cars as employees may resist such a change.

Good candidates analysed the numerical data given in the scenario. They created information from the data given and provided the reader of their answer with new insight into the key factors driving the reduction in emissions.

Part (c) was often poorly done as a result of the failure to address the requirement which asked for the data to be related to the reduction initiatives mentioned in the scenario. Many candidates got a mark for general suggestions of further useful data but few related this to the reduction initiatives.

ACCA marking scheme

		Marks
(a)	1 mark per factor identified as relevant for each section of the broad sections of the analysis (PEST or PESTEL sections are appropriate and competition could be an additional area considered). Up to 1 mark for each performance indicator relevant to the factors identified. Maximum of 8.	
	Maximum	**9**
(b)	Up to 4 marks for analysis of basic data, commenting on overall picture and achievement of target Up to 4 marks for simplifying data into broad categories and commenting Up to 4 marks for analysis of mix of methods of travel and commenting (Another acceptable categorisation could be related to fuel type: petrol, diesel and aviation – rail is problematic as it is a mix of diesel and electricity but reasonable assumptions will be acceptable)	
	Maximum	**12**
(c)	1 mark per point reasonably **made up to**	**4**
Total		**25**

33 FILM PRODUCTIONS CO (FP) (DEC 10)

Key answer tips

This should be a reasonably straightforward question focussing on the core areas of CSFs, KPIs and their use. Unfortunately many students did not know the difference between CSFs and KPIs and/or were unable to apply their knowledge to the scenario.

(a) Information for establishing CSFs

The company can use information about the internal and external environment to set its CSFs. Relevant external information would include the structure of the industry and the strategy of FP's competitors. The geographical location of production and the main sales markets may also be relevant. Film is a hit driven industry where word of mouth can lead to success, therefore, recognition of the product and the brand ('Film Productions') by the public would lead to success. For example, the Walt Disney Company has achieved a high level of brand recognition that has enabled it to expand into other entertainment areas using characters from its films.

Relevant internal information would include measures of seasonality on sales which will dictate the timing of film releases and effectiveness of marketing campaigns. By forecasting the size of the market along with likely levels of competition, profit can be optimised.

However, these forecasts will be subject to uncertainty and so the information systems will need to be flexible and allow probabilistic analysis. A CSF based on the quality of these forecasts would therefore be appropriate. Other internal sources could include measures of the cost per film and the time taken to produce a film.

Other possible information could include contingent factors (those that depend on specific threats or opportunities facing FP).

(b) Performance indicators linked to the CSFs

Audience satisfaction – performance indicators are:

- Sales per film – currently the company releases an average of 6·4 films per year and makes about $31·25 million on each one. These figures should be compared to industry averages. Trends on sales per film should be monitored for indications of changes in consumer taste.
- Brand recognition – consumers should be surveyed to identify if the FP name is known and used as an indicator of quality when selecting films. If FP regularly uses certain artists (directors or film stars) then positive consumer recognition of these names will indicate satisfaction.
- Repeat viewings – with TV showings, it will be possible to measure viewers for each showing of the film and monitor the decline in viewing over repetitions. The level of DVD purchases following a cinema release will also indicate customer satisfaction with customers actively wanting to own their own copy of a favourite film.
- Awards won – number of awards won will indicate success. However, the level of recognition of any award must be brought into account as major ones such as those voted on by the public or those whose ceremonies are widely reported have the greatest impact.
- Response of the media – scores by film critics often appear in the media and these give a measure of satisfaction although this category must be treated carefully as critics often look for artistic merit while FP is seeking commercial success and broad audience acceptance.

Profitability in operations – performance indicators are:

- Industry average margin – collect data on competitor companies to set an appropriate benchmark. This will require care to ensure that appropriate comparator companies are chosen, for example, those with a production budget similar to FP's of $18 million per film.
- Time in production – the cost of a film will depend on the length of time it takes to produce. If the film is intended to meet a current customer demand it may require to be produced quickly, in order to meet revenue targets. Therefore, the time in production will affect both sales and cost levels so altering the gross margin. Again, it would be helpful to identify if films meet their production schedule and if these schedules compare favourably to those of other film companies.
- Costs – the costs should be broken down into categories such as those for artists, production technicians and marketing. The cost structure for each film should be compared internally, to others that FP produces and also externally, to available figures for the industry.

(c) Impact on FP's information systems

The company website can collect audience survey results and comments posted on the site.

Consumers can be drawn to the site with clips and trailers from current films and those in production. The site can log the frequency with which films are viewed and if audience members create accounts then further detail on the age, gender and location of the audience can be collected. This will allow a more detailed profile of the customer base for FP to be created and will be used to help in decisions about what films to commission in the future. The account members can be given the opportunity to score each film providing further information about satisfaction.

The company could also consider scanning the websites of its competitors to identify their performance – especially their published results which will provide benchmark information on gross margin levels.

A management information system (MIS) will collate the information from individual transactions recorded in the accounting system to allow middle level management to control the business. This system will allow customer purchases to be summarised into reports to identify both products that sell well and the customers (such as cinema chains and TV networks) who provide the main sources of revenue (indicators of satisfaction). The level of repeat business on a customer account will give an indication of the satisfaction with FP's output. The system will also produce management accounts from which gross margins will be drawn and it should be capable of breaking this down by film and by customer to aid decision-making by targeting FP's output to the most profitable areas. This will aid decision-making about the performance of the production team on a film and can be used to set rewards for each team.

An executive information system (EIS) is one that will supply information to the senior management of the organisation allowing them to drill down into the more detailed transaction reports where necessary. The EIS will provide summarised information, focused on the key performance indicators in order to allow the directors to quickly judge whether the company is meeting its CSFs. It will draw on internal sources such as the MIS and also external sources such as market data on revenues that different films are earning at the box office.

Examiner's comments

Requirement (a) was poorly attempted. This part asked for the information used in setting CSFs and then, using their reading of the scenario and general business knowledge, suggestions of suitable CSFs. Many candidates were unable to address this part of the question due to lack of knowledge of the definition of a CSF and devoted their answer purely to KPIs, as a result scoring no marks. Those candidates that read the question requirement and responded to it were quickly rewarded.

Requirement (b) was generally well answered with many candidates getting 7 or 8 out of 10. The best answers were those that used the question requirement to give a methodical structure to their answer. Those candidates who did not score well tended to provide bullet point lists of many KPIs when the question asked for four.

Requirement (c) was generally adequately attempted. The better answers clearly linked the KPIs to changes that would be required in the design and use of the information systems mentioned. Thus, they could demonstrate knowledge of how such systems operate and the use to which the information produced is subsequently put.

ACCA marking scheme		
		Marks
(a)	2 marks for the sources of information. 2 marks for each example including demonstration of why it is appropriate for FP.	
	Maximum	**6**
(b)	2.5 marks for each suggested performance indicator with 0.5 for identification and 2 for discussion of use and relevance to FP. Maximum of 10. (Students may also discuss different margin measures such as operating and gross profit but these must be related to actual operations in order to gain much credit.)	
	Maximum	**10**
(c)	3 marks for each relevant information system indicating how it links to the PIs.	
	Maximum	**9**
Total		**25**

34 DALDORN (SEPT/DEC 19) (AMENDED)

(a) Board

The board members are key players who have a high level of power and interest. It is important that they understand and approve of Daldorn's strategy. It is vital that they are kept motivated in order to drive Daldorn's performance. The VC has recently implemented a new reward system, where the board will receive a very large annual performance-related bonus for the achievement of targets on return on capital employed (ROCE).

ROCE may be an appropriate measure as it will be familiar to the board. It does have some drawbacks as a performance measure, for example, by discouraging investment in new assets. Alternative measures such as economic value added (EVA^{TM}) may overcome some of these drawbacks.

Employees

Employees have a high interest as they depend on the company for their income in an area of high unemployment. Most employees are relatively unskilled, and individually have low power, as they could be easily replaced. As Daldorn operates in a strict regulatory environment, employees' rights are likely to be legally protected which may increase their power.

Employees should be kept informed to prevent them joining forces with more powerful stakeholder groups, such as the regulators or trades unions. Training costs are probably not a suitable measure for the mostly low-skilled workforce, as the manufacturing process does not required a high level of skill. Measures relating to employee productivity may be more useful, because, for example, higher productivity may increase their job security.

Some employees' roles are more highly skilled and, for them, training costs will be a suitable measure of how well their skills are increased or maintained. The cost of training may not, however, indicate whether the training is appropriate or effective. A more precise measure, such as the percentage of employees achieving a particular relevant qualification or skill level, may be more appropriate.

Government and regulators

There are currently no measures relating to the government and regulators. As Daldorn operates in a strict regulatory environment, this seems inappropriate as breaches in regulations could lead to fines or loss of reputation.

The government and regulators have a high level of power but low interest. To prevent them becoming key players, they should be kept satisfied. This could be done by introducing measures relating to environmental performance, such as the level of toxic pollutants in the soil close to Daldorn's factory. This would allow Daldorn to take action to reduce the level of pollutants if these approached levels likely to breach environmental regulations.

Tutorial note:

A good example of how 'stakeholders' may be examined. There are three stakeholder groups and three areas to address for each one. Therefore, your points can be succinct, as long as they relate to the scenario and cover each area.

(b) The board now has very large performance-related bonuses. This will mean that they have a risk seeking attitude to risk, in order to maximise their bonuses. The board would use the 'maximax' decision rule, that is, they would choose the price which maximises the maximum contribution. This price is $95,000 which would give a maximum contribution of $55,100,000.

The main drawback of using the maximax decision rule is that it may encourage the board to take excessive risks, as opposed to their previous attitude which was too cautious. The maximax rule also does not take into account the probabilities of each outcome and these probabilities are difficult to determine.

(c) The VC is an almost entirely risk neutral investor. The expected value (EV) approach is appropriate as they will accept the project with the highest expected NPV.

A problem with the EV approach is that it is a long run average which assumes a decision is repeated many times and is inappropriate for one-off decisions. The EV is unlikely to be the actual outcome of the project.

The VC has undertaken many similar projects and, hence, it would be appropriate to use EV. The estimations of the probabilities and the cost of capital are subjective and could be inaccurate. This would limit the effectiveness of the EV approach. The VC is experienced in estimating these probabilities, which would make the results of the calculation more reliable. The EV calculations for the two projects only consider two important exogenous variables. In practice, there are many different internal and external factors which could affect the NPV of the projects.

The calculations indicate that both projects have the same NPV of $1,347 million. As a risk neutral investor, the VC would be indifferent to which project to undertake.

The outcomes of project A have a slightly lower standard deviation (103) than those of project B (106). The spread of possible outcomes is therefore greater for project B, which means that it is riskier. The VC may therefore choose project A. Given that the NPV of the two projects are the same, further work such as sensitivity analysis, or an analysis of the external environment (PEST), could be done to help the VC make their choice.

Examiner's comments

Part (a) was reasonably done. However, many candidates wasted time by focussing their answer on performing a jargon-laden, Mendelow analysis when the question requirement focussed on the performance measures appropriate to the stakeholders.

Future candidates should read this question and then test themselves by asking whether they consider a valuable response is either (a) 'keep informed' to one of the stakeholders or (b) indicate which measures should be used and why for a given stakeholder. If the answer is (b) then the candidate has grasped the main point of the question.

Part (b) was either done well or badly depending on the basic knowledge of the methods. Many candidates could neither name the correct method to use nor describe their method for selecting the appropriate selling price.

Part (c). Performance on this part was weak reflecting poor basic knowledge of how to calculate expected values and the appropriate conditions for the use of this method.

ACCA marking scheme

			Marks
(a)	Each stakeholder – 1 mark for power/interest commentary and up to 3 marks for advice on performance measures		
	Maximum		**9**
(b)	Justification of maximax approach		1
	Identifying the maximum contribution of $55,100,000		1
	Stating price chosen		1
	Drawbacks of decision rule		2
	Maximum		**5**
(c)	Comment on indifference between two projects based on EVs		1
	Comment on standard deviation as indication of risk and influence on decision	up to	2
	Evaluation of EV method	up to	4
	Comment on further work	up to	1
	Maximum		**6**

Professional marks

Analysis and Evaluation

- Reasoned assessment of the power/interest of the different stakeholder groups and relevant advice on the existing performance measures and recommendation of an appropriate new measure for each stakeholder
- Appropriate use of the data in appendix 2 and appendix 3 to recommend the price for the new product and the project to invest in, together with relevant discussion of the risk technique used

Scepticism

- Recognition that the existing performance measures do not adequately measure the company's performance in managing the concerns of the three stakeholder groups
- Recognition that the risk techniques discussed have associated drawbacks

Commercial Acumen

- Recommendation of the alternative performance measures and risk techniques clearly demonstrates an understanding of the issues facing Daldorn and acumen in offering advice and arriving at appropriate and commercially sound recommendations

	Maximum	**5**
Total		**25**

35 SWEET CICELY (SEPT/DEC 17) (AMENDED)

Key answer tips

If you are comfortable with PEST and risk then you should find this a manageable question.

(a) This is a good example of how PEST may be examined. Rather than simply listing the various PEST factors, you are expected to evaluate how the PEST factors may lead to risk and uncertainty and how they could be managed effectively by SC.

In (b) and (c), relevant comments for minimax regret, maximax and expected values are required.

(a) Importance of incorporating risk and uncertainty in making long-term decisions

Risk relates to the variability of outcomes, the probabilities of which are known, or can be estimated. Uncertainty occurs where the outcomes and their probabilities are unknown. The variability of demand for SC's chocolate bars is a risk, and the probabilities of different levels of demand can be estimated. The outbreak of conflict in a cocoa growing region affecting cocoa prices cannot be assigned a probability, and so is an uncertainty.

The market price of cocoa and the demand for chocolate bars are examples of exogenous variables which significantly affect the performance of SC. Exogenous variables arise from outside the business, but over which the business has no control. Climatic conditions, soil erosion, for example, all affect the price of cocoa, and therefore the performance of SC.

When investors evaluate businesses, they take into account prospective returns and the level of risk involved. Therefore, managers should consider risk and return when evaluating projects on their behalf. Long-term strategic planning requires forecasts to be made about future events, such as the price of cocoa. These future events are by definition unknown, and subject to risk and uncertainty. Risk and uncertainty must, therefore, be considered when making long-term plans, such as opening the new factory. The further into the future the plans project, the riskier, and more uncertain, events are likely to be, as it is harder to predict what conditions will be. This mean consideration of risk and uncertainty is even more important when making long-term decisions than for short-term decisions.

Use of PEST analysis

To incorporate risk and uncertainty into long-term strategic planning, SC must identify and monitor the most important exogenous variables, taking action to manage the risks they present. As a traded commodity, the risks of rising cocoa prices could be managed (hedged), for example, by using cocoa futures. The board member's comments suggest planning for the cake business was poor, and did not adequately consider the importance of exogenous variables. Risks in the macro environment could be identified using a PEST analysis.

Political factors

The market price of cocoa is affected by conflicts and political uncertainty, so consideration of these external factors is needed to incorporate risk and uncertainty into long-term planning. By identifying factors such as political instability or conflict, SC can improve its long-term performance by sourcing cocoa from more stable regions. The political situation in a region can change rapidly, which might make it difficult to incorporate these risks into long-term planning, as there is a high degree of uncertainty.

The introduction of increased taxes on products containing sugar is a political factor affecting the long-term demand for SC's products. Once introduced, this factor is likely to operate in the long term and be more predictable. Identifying this, SC could develop products containing less sugar and so reduce the amount of these additional taxes on its products.

Economic factors

Economic factors such as the variation in long-term interest rates can influence SC's performance by affecting exchange rates or overall consumer demand. By identifying these factors, SC could hedge against currency exchange rates. In the longer term, SC could locate its operations in a country where the risks from exchange rate fluctuations are lower, or diversify geographically to spread the risk.

Social factors

Overall demand for chocolate products will be influenced by social factors such as consumer tastes or increased awareness of healthy eating. SC can improve its long-term performance by not investing in a chocolate factory at all, if it believes demand for its products will fall sufficiently to make the venture unprofitable.

Technological factors

The increased cocoa yields from genetically modified crops may reduce long-term cocoa prices and SC could incorporate this into the net present value calculations for the factory. There may be unpredictable consequences which are harder to plan for, such as the acceptance by consumers of genetically modified foods.

Tutorial note

Ensure you add enough depth to your answer in (a) rather than focusing too heavily on (b) and (c).

(b) Board

The board wants to minimise the opportunity cost of making the wrong decision about the size of the new chocolate factory, which means to minimise the regret of making the wrong decision. The minimax regret rule would be the appropriate method to use so they would choose the project with the lowest maximum regret.

Option 1 is the option with the lowest maximum regret ($11m), and that would be the option preferred by the board according to their risk appetite. A drawback of using the minimax regret rule is that the probabilities of the outcomes are not considered.

New shareholders

The new shareholders are keen to increase the long-term performance of the business and are prepared to accept a high level of risk to achieve this. They will choose the option with the maximum possible outcome, which is option 3, with a maximum possible net present value of $17m. This is known as the maximax rule. This also takes no account of the probabilities of the outcomes, and also tends to be over-optimistic. It also ignores the fact that even risk seekers have a risk–return trade off.

(c) The risk neutral investor's choice, for year 1 only, would be option 3, with an expected value of $2.1m.

Problems of using an expected value approach

A risk neutral investor would use the expected value approach to choose between the three options. The expected value is a long run average, and is only appropriate where a decision is repeated many times. This does not appear to be the case at SC which has made only one attempt at strategic expansion in the last several years. For the same reason, the expected value will not equal the actual outcome.

Determining the probabilities, of the market price of cocoa for example, is subjective. Even analysis of historical market prices is not necessarily a guide to what will happen in the future. The expected value approach is suitable for a risk neutral investor. This does not apply to the key stakeholders at SC, and hence this approach is inappropriate for use in the decision on the three options. Determining the payoffs is also difficult when demand is subject to uncertainty. SC should not make a decision on the factory based only on the first year's operating profits, and should take a longer term view, for example, based on discounted cash flows.

Examiner's comments

Part (a) was generally reasonably well done. Good answers illustrated the use of PEST analysis with reference to risks for this manufacturer. Part (b) was usually well done although the minimax regret table caused some difficulties. Part (c) was generally well done with the limitation of the expected value method in context of this business reasonably discussed.

ACCA marking scheme		
		Marks
(a)	Consideration of risk and uncertainty – 1 mark per point, up to 8 marks Discussion of use of PEST analysis – 1 mark per point, up to 8 marks	
	Maximum	**12**
(b)	Comments on board's preference – 1 mark per point, up to 3 marks Comments of new shareholders' preference – 1 mark per point, up to 3 marks	
	Maximum	**5**
(c)	Conclusion and drawbacks of expected value approach – 1 mark per point	
	Maximum	**3**
Professional marks		
Analysis and Evaluation		
•	Reasoned advice on why risk/uncertainty should be considered with a comprehensive evaluation of the use of PEST in managing this, considering the scenario information available and why this is important	
•	Appropriate use of the data in appendix 2 and appendix 3 to determine which chocolate factory to build, including a reasoned assessment of the risk techniques used and recognition of the drawbacks of the techniques	
Scepticism		
•	Recognition of the need for caution when using relevant risk techniques to recommend which size chocolate factory to invest in	

Commercial Acumen • Effective use of examples drawn from across the scenario to support the discussion of the consideration of risk/uncertainty and the use of PEST • Recommendation of which chocolate factory to build are practical and plausible, showing insights and perception in understanding the various risk appetites	
Maximum	**5**
Total	**25**

36 TURING (JUN 14) (AMENDED)

Key answer tips

This question shows the examining team's desire to focus on more complex business structures.

In part (a) a discussion of the different risk appetites of the two joint venture partners was required together with a recommendation of an appropriate method for decision making and an evaluation of the choice of turbine design. This area has been examined a number of times and it is important to feel comfortable with the ideas discussed in the answer.

In part (b) make sure that you have enough relevant points and that you relate your points back to the scenario – general book knowledge will score few marks.

(a) Risk appetite – Turing

The risk appetite of Turing will be dominated by the VCs who own 90% of the company. They are risk-seeking as they hold a portfolio of high-risk investments where they accept the failure of some investments provided others generate high returns. The other key stakeholders mentioned are management who has been given an equity stake in the business and so is likely to be comfortable with this high-risk approach.

Method of decision-making – Turing

Overall, therefore, Turing is likely to be risk-seeking and so a maximax approach to decision-making under uncertainty will be appropriate. In the maximax approach, the design selected will be the one which maximises (over the three designs) the highest profit for each design among the three demand scenarios.

Risk appetite – Riemann

The risk appetite of Riemann will be dominated by the financial investors, both the shareholders and any debt providers, as they have recently had to provide new funds to keep Riemann afloat. These investors will be concerned about the immediate survival of the business as will the management who could lose their jobs. The need for short-term cash flow gains from TandR emphasises this point.

Method of decision-making – Riemann

Overall, therefore, Riemann is likely to be risk averse, focusing on the survival of the business and so a maximin approach to decision-making under uncertainty will be appropriate. In the maximin approach, the design selected will be the one which maximises (over the three designs) the lowest profit for each design among the three demand scenarios.

Tutorial note

Some credit will be given for a minimax regret solution as it is risk averse, although it is not as clearly focused on obtaining a minimum level of return needed to aid the survival of the business.

Choice of turbine design type

Demand	**1,000**	**1,500**	**2,000**		
Profit				**Max payoff**	**Min payoff**
8 MW	2,900	8,100	13,300	13,300	2,900
3 MW	3,980	6,380	8,780	8,780	3,980
1 MW	3,090	4,815	6,540	6,540	3,090

Maximum of the maximums	8 MW	13,300
Maximum of the minimums	3 MW	3,980

Therefore, the risk-seeking decision makers at Turing will select the 8 MW design with the possibility of earning $13.3bn from the project. The risk-averse decision makers at Riemann will select the 3 MW design with the likelihood of earning at least $3.98bn from the project.

Other comments

The management at Turing will also be motivated to choose projects with an innovative edge such as the 8 MW unit proposed.

The high fixed costs of the 8 MW unit are unlikely to deter Turing's management as they represent a large investment in their education in potentially world-leading technology.

The wide range of demand forecasts (1,000 units to 2,000) will make Riemann nervous. The likely long timescale for development of the 8 MW unit, where $7.5bn will be invested, may not be attractive in meeting their short-term cash needs.

(b) Considering first the problem of measuring performance in joint ventures, the primary difficulty is establishing the objectives of the joint venture (JV). The different JV partners may have different goals; in this case, Riemann wants fairly immediate cash flows while Turing wants the possibility of large returns (possibly over a longer time-frame). Performance metrics are likely to include a variety of financial indicators, such as profit, growth and cash flows. However, there may be different emphasis put on these metrics by each JV partner and there will be difficulties in attributing accountability for these different elements of performance where each partner in the JV is bringing different skills and knowledge to the venture.

The different timescales which Riemann (short term) and Turing (longer term) will emphasise will also lead to conflict in the choice of metrics: quarterly cash flows for Riemann to report to its shareholders and discounted cash flows over the project life for Turing.

At TandR, the different risk appetites of the key stakeholders will lead to conflict in the choice of key performance measures and these problems will be difficult to resolve as the ownership is split 50:50 between Turing and Riemann. The possibility of deadlock can only be avoided by having clearly laid out a path for resolution at the outset of the JV (possibly in the JV legal agreement).

This high level conflict can also appear in day-to-day co-ordinating and controlling the JV. The management of the JV must be given clear direction at the outset, otherwise this deadlock problem will appear whenever there is a disagreement between the managers selected by the JV partners. Therefore, the compatibility of the management styles and cultures of the JV partners will have an important impact on success.

Another potential issue in joint ventures and specifically at TandR is that, as well as sharing offices, assets and staff, the partners must also share information and intellectual property. It appears that Turing are bringing significant advantage for the JV with their blade design skill. However, it is often difficult to measure the contribution of such intangible assets to the performance of the JV and a suitable method of extracting these assets at the end of the life of the JV will need to be agreed at its outset.

It is likely that the venture partners will be reluctant to share too much information about their own businesses with their JV partner. It will be important for the success of the JV that a climate of trust exists which will again depend on issues such as management style and culture.

Examiner's comments

Part (a) was generally well done. It was especially cheering to note that most candidates understood that decision-making 'under uncertainty' is different to 'under risk' or else, they realised that the lack of information on probabilities meant that expected values were not an optimal approach. One point for future candidates to note is that the companies involved cannot choose to produce a certain number of units as this is the uncertain factor.

Part (b) was adequately answered with many candidates able to identify the problem areas but few could discuss the causes and impacts of these problems in anything other than vague terms.

ACCA marking scheme	
	Marks
(a) **Turing:** Risk appetite; 1 mark per point, up to 3 marks Method of decision-making, up to 2 marks: 1 for properly selected method 1 for description of method **Riemann:** Risk appetite; 1 mark per point, up to 3 marks Method of decision-making, up to 2 marks: 1 for properly selected method 1 for description of method **Choice of turbine design** Maximax result and conclusion; 1 mark for each, up to 2 marks Maximin result and conclusion; 1 mark for each, up to 2 marks	
Maximum	**12**
(b) 1 per point made up to 8 marks, points such as: Different goals and performance metrics at JV partners Handling different risk appetites Deadlock in decision-making Handling different time horizons for results Different management styles and cultural differences Information sharing Intellectual property	
Maximum	**8**
Professional marks **Analysis and Evaluation** • Reasoned assessment of the risk appetites of the two firms, with appropriate use of the scenario information and data in appendix 1 to provide justified recommendations of the risk method and choice of design. Recognition that expected values could not be used due to the absence of probabilities • Comprehensive evaluation of the problems in managing joint venture performance, identifying the problems but also going on to discuss causes and impacts **Commercial Acumen** • Effective use of examples drawn from across the scenario information and other practical considerations related to the context to correctly assess the risk appetite of the firms and to provide a comprehensive assessment of the problems in managing joint venture performance	
Maximum	**5**
Total	**25**

B – PERFORMANCE MANAGEMENT INFORMATION SYSTEMS AND DEVELOPMENTS IN TECHNOLOGY

37 LUVIJ (MAR/JUN 18) (AMENDED)

Key answer tips

Requirement (a) – Some book knowledge is required but you should be able to apply some common sense and professional judgement to use the information given in the scenario to adequately answer the question. A good answer can be achieved by spending time planning; brainstorm five or six key issues to use as headings and then consider how a database could address each of these.

Requirement (b) can also be approached well through careful planning to come up with a relevant structure including a handful of headings.

(a) **Relevant**

For the external information to be useful, it should be relevant to the needs of the users. The information in the quarterly spreadsheet contains both sales data and information on market trends in designs. All of this information may not be relevant for all of the departments to which it is circulated. For example, data on design trends may not be relevant to the production department using it to plan production capacity.

A unified database, integrating data from different sources, would make data more relevant to users by giving users only information and reports which are relevant to them and sharing data from all relevant departments. Users would not waste time interpreting data which is irrelevant to them.

Timely

For external information to be useful, it must be available when needed. This is particularly so in the fashion industry where designs change quickly and where competitors may offer short-term discounts. The external information at Luvij is only sent at the end of each quarter, which is likely to be too infrequent in the fast moving industry in which Luvij operates. Additionally, as the information is prepared by one staff member, there could be delays in producing it if they were on sick leave, for example.

A unified database would ensure that data was available instantly, especially if linked to retailers' own systems' real-time sales data. This should improve the speed of decision making.

Accurate

To be useful, information must be accurate. Entering large volumes of data into a complex spreadsheet is prone to error, as well as being time-consuming. Inaccurate data may lead to poor decision making. A unified database would process all data automatically with minimal human intervention, and would thus be less prone to inaccuracies. All departments would share identical data.

Communication

Though the spreadsheet of external information at least ensures that all departments have access to the same data, the large volume of data may be difficult to understand. Managers may be overloaded with data, much of which they do not need. A unified database would allow users access only to information which they need. This would be in an easy to use format, perhaps with the ability to drill down to more detailed information held in the database.

Emailing data to a large number of staff may mean that confidential or commercially sensitive information, such as on design trends, is shared with staff who do not require it. A unified database would restrict access to information, using passwords, only to staff who are authorised to receive it.

Cost

The cost of producing the external information should not exceed the benefits of doing so. Costs of the current system include not only the costs of employing the team to compile the information but also time spent collecting, processing or interpreting data which may be inaccurate, irrelevant or out of date.

Using a unified database would incur costs of buying, maintaining and developing the system, as well as staff training. An evaluation must be made whether these costs are justified by the benefits. Some adaptation of the existing system, such as increasing the frequency of reporting the information, or sending different sets of information to different departments, may be more cost effective.

Tutorial note

The use of the characteristics of good information is one way this answer can be structured. There are many other approaches which would be acceptable.

(b) Problems of performance measurement

Measuring the performance of the joint venture may require Luvij and Shirville to share confidential information, which they may be unwilling to do. Luvij's innovative designs for children's footwear and Shirville's knowledge of advanced production techniques are both likely to be commercially sensitive.

It is unclear exactly what is each of the parties' contributions to the joint venture. Luvij is providing innovative designs, and Shirville is providing advanced manufacturing machinery and production techniques. As each party is providing different things to the joint venture, it may be hard to measure the contribution, to profit for example, from each party.

Luvij and Shirville will have their own information systems. These may be incompatible, or it may be difficult or costly to integrate them. Each party may measure or collect information in a different way, which will mean information used to measure the performance of the joint venture is not prepared on a consistent basis.

Problems of performance management

Luvij's objective for the venture is to become the market leader in high-quality children's footwear. Shirville's objective is to utilise spare production capacity in a factory where the lease is due to expire in three years. As the parties have different objectives, it may be hard to develop performance metrics for the joint venture. The share of the chosen market may be a key performance metric for Luvij, and return on capital employed may be appropriate for Shirville. The metrics chosen may conflict, and their relative importance may be unclear. This will make it difficult for managers to manage the joint venture according to each party's objectives.

Luvij's objectives for the joint venture are long term, whereas Shirville may choose to end the joint venture upon expiry of the factory lease in just three years. Establishing timescales for performance objectives may be difficult as each party has different time horizons for the venture.

Luvij is entering a new market and has already invested heavily in market research and product design. Shirville seems to have a much lower risk appetite, as it only wants to utilise spare capacity. Managing performance may be difficult because Luvij may wish to make decisions which involve a higher level of risk than Shirville may wish to accept.

The parties have may have different expectations of the level of quality of products arising from the joint venture. Luvij manufactures high-quality footwear and will want its range of children's footwear to be of a quality consistent with its women's footwear range. Shirville supplies supermarkets and high street stores, probably with lower quality products. Disagreement about acceptable levels of quality may reduce the performance of the joint venture.

Examiner's comments

Part (a) was generally well done. Candidates identified the missing areas of information needed by the company and then connected these to the benefits of a unified corporate database.

Part (b). Candidate performance on this part was also generally good with many answers effectively describing the differences between the two organisations and how this would impact on the joint venture.

ACCA marking scheme		
		Marks
(a)	1 mark per point: Limitations on usefulness of the external data – up to 6 marks Evaluation of the use of a unified database – up to 6 marks	
	Maximum	**10**
(b)	Problems of performance measurement – up to 6 marks Problems of performance management – up to 6 marks	
	Maximum	**10**
Professional marks **Analysis and Evaluation**		
•	Consider information from the scenario to help determine and discuss the limitations of the external data and to comprehensively and logically evaluate how the use of a unified corporate database could address the limitations	
•	Appraise information objectively with a view to advising on both the problems of performance measurement and performance management	

Scepticism	
• Recognition that there are failings with the external data and a demonstration of the ability to probe into these failings	
• Challenge and critically assess the information presented to advise on the problems of performance measurement and management	
Commercial Acumen	
• Demonstrate an understanding of the benefits of a unified corporate database in addressing the limitations of the external data whilst also using judgement in proposing and recommending that a full evaluation should be carried out to ensure it is commercially viable	
• Show insight and perception in understanding different organisational and external factors which will affect the performance measurement and management of the joint venture	
Maximum	**5**
Total	**25**

38 NELSON, JODY AND NIGEL (NJN) (MAR/JUN 17)

Key answer tips

Overall, this is quite a challenging question but if you have your knowledge and exam technique in place then you should be able to score a pass.

(a) Other than a broad knowledge of lean, little knowledge is required here. Instead you need to use the scenario information and should be able to identify the shortcomings of the existing system.

(b) There are only 6 marks available here so keep your answer brief. You should be able to identify the shortcomings of each proposal in terms of addressing the issues faced.

(a) Manual input

At NJN, at least some of the inputs to the WIS are manual, and that means they are prone to error. This is time consuming and costly.

The packing lists which are received in the shipping containers are input manually. If incorrectly input, the quantities of items in the locations in the WIS will also be incorrect. Incorrect information in the WIS wastes time by needing teams to investigate the discrepancies, reconcile inventory records with those held by the manufacturer, and correct the information held on the WIS.

Furthermore, customers will not receive the items they have ordered, as in 8% of picking notes, items are not in the location they should be, or are in insufficient quantities. This is a high proportion of errors. Staff will waste time looking for items stored in the wrong locations. This will cause customer dissatisfaction and mean that larger quantities of inventory will need to be held, which is a wasteful use of storage space. Fewer complete orders can be fulfilled per unit of warehouse space, than would otherwise be the case. Both of these are sources of waste.

In the longer term, this means NJN staff must undertake a series of cyclical inventory counts in order to correct the information held in the WIS. This is wasteful activity which does not add value to customers, and should be eliminated.

The provision of accurate inventory information will also be of value to the retailers who can place orders only for items which are available, rather than only finding out about unavailable items by receiving an email from NJN. This would lead to increased customer satisfaction by avoiding having stock outs of particular items by ordering alternatives.

NJN should consider the use of barcodes or radio frequency identifiers (RFIDs) on products, to ensure that accurate data is input into the WIS. Using these devices, the product numbers and quantities of goods entering and leaving the warehouse could be automatically read into the WIS, without any intervention from warehouse staff. This would reduce the time taken to manually input the data and improve its accuracy.

An effective information system may interface directly with the manufacturer's and retail customers' information systems through electronic data interchange (EDI). This would increase service levels by ensuring that all parts of the value chain had access to accurate and timely information.

Time delays

The packing list batches are not available until up to 48 hours after receipt of the goods. The information held in the WIS will therefore be out of date. Items which are required for sales orders may be unavailable for picking. The use of automated input, where possible, will increase the timeliness of the information input into the WIS. This will reduce the labour cost of correcting the system and improve the number, accuracy, and completeness of orders despatched to customers.

Currently, all picking notes are printed in the warehouse office, which may be some distance from the area where items are picked. This also implies the existence of a bottleneck in the provision of information to the staff picking the items and wastes staff time moving to and from the warehouse office to pick up the reports. An improvement would be to ensure that information is available when and where it is needed, using terminals in the warehouse, or portable devices such as tablets. This would reduce time spent collecting picking information.

Similarly, in order to investigate discrepancies, staff have to obtain special reports which the warehouse manager extracts from the WIS. Again, this is a bottleneck which could delay staff getting the correct information, and may mean that the reports are inconsistent depending on the parameters set to run them. An effective system would eliminate these problems by providing standardised reports when requested, and in an optimal location.

Complex presentation of information

Effective systems add value to information when they organise and present the information in a clear way, without excessive detail. This allows the users to easily and quickly identify the information they need. It prevents wasting time obtaining the information in the first place, and correcting errors caused by interpreting it incorrectly.

The picking sheets show the 12-digit product codes which can easily be misread and increases the likelihood of errors. A better system would present the information in a more accessible way and prevent information overload, for example, showing product descriptions, or product codes, only for the items to be picked.

(b) There are two main types of waste at NJN which can be identified using lean principles: waste which does not add value to the customer and waste which occurs due to variations in demand and demands on staff.

Reorganising the warehouse to place high volume items near to the despatch area will help reduce the type of waste where the movement of staff to pick goods is more than should be required. Less movement, which means less staff time and cost, will be required by staff to pick these items and bring them to where they are to be despatched. It may be, however, that large and bulky items should be placed nearer to the despatch area instead, to save on the time spent transporting them to the despatch area. This may also address the increased seasonal demand for certain types of product as products which are popular for that specific period could be stored more closely to the despatch area.

The cost of absenteeism is a waste caused by demanding too much of staff at busy times to compensate for inefficient organisation in the warehouse and errors in the WIS. The cost of searching for items which have been put in the wrong physical location at busy times is a waste due to variation in activity levels.

Another type of waste which does not add value to the customer is holding excessive inventory, for example, the additional warehouse space which NJN has rented. By not making efficient use of the warehouse space it has, NJN is reducing its level of output, and revenue, relative to the resources available to it. In addition, the extra warehouse space means more time spent by staff moving through the warehouses trying to locate goods.

The cyclical inventory counts which the management consultant has suggested do not add value to the customer and are also more demanding for staff. This is a wasteful activity, correcting the errors which have occurred in the WIS. NJN should instead concentrate on ensuring that errors do not occur in the first place, which will cost less than correcting them.

(c) The 5Ss in the adoption of lean principles during the warehouse reorganisation are Structurise, Systemise, Sanitise, Standardise and Self-discipline.

Structurise

This involves introducing order where possible, for example, by ensuring that items in the warehouse are arranged so that they are easy to find. This would also include segregating damaged or obsolete inventory, or discarding it from the warehouse.

The management consultant has suggested the measure of the proportion of inventory not stored in order of its alphabetical description, with 'A' nearest the despatch area and 'Z' furthest away. This may measure how easy to find each product is, but would not necessarily make best use of all available space or make the picking process more efficient. It may also be subjective and prone to errors caused by the interpretation of the product description, for example, in deciding if cricket balls be measured under 'C' or 'B'.

Systemise

This principle involves organising items so that they are easy to use. At NJN, this means being able to accurately pick the correct items in the shortest possible time. It could also cover access to other resources, such as having computer terminals close to where they are needed.

The measure relating to the storing of goods alphabetically seems to conflict with the consultant's recommendation to place the high volume lines close to the despatch area. Whereas storing goods alphabetically may make items easy to find, it does not necessarily make them easy to use (pick). By storing the high volume items near to the despatch area, the average time taken to pick orders would be reduced.

Sanitise

This principle means to be tidy and avoid clutter. This helps make things easy to find, allows easy access of staff around the warehouse, and helps make a safe working environment. The warehouse manager's daily assessment of tidiness is a suitable measure of this principle, which is a subjective assessment.

There is the possibility that the assessment will be biased, especially if the warehouse manager who is undertaking the assessment is also having his performance evaluated on the tidiness of the warehouse. The characteristics of what constitutes a tidy warehouse, compared to an untidy one, will need to be defined. There is the possibility of inconsistent measurement if someone other the warehouse manager does the assessment, or the assessment is done at different times of the day.

Standardise

This principle involves finding the best way of undertaking a process or task, and applying it consistently. The suggestion of the number of accidents caused by goods which have not been stored or picked in the correct way would measure this. As NJN should aim to have no accidents, this should be a performance measure with a target level of zero.

Self-discipline

This principle relates to sustaining the other Ss by motivating employees. Motivation is subjective, and hard to measure. None of the performance measures the management consultant has suggested directly measure this principle. The consistency in which specific tasks or processes are performed could be a measure of how well they are being sustained.

Tutorial note

Ensure you have all of your APM knowledge in place. The examining team are willing to test any part of the syllabus. A key concept in APM is 'what gets measured gets done'. Here you need to explain each 'S' in the context of NJN and then evaluate the metrics used in relation to that 'S'.

Examiner's comments

Part (a) required an assessment of the existing information system and was generally well done with candidates able to identify and discuss the problems from the scenario. The better candidates then tied these problems to the operation of the information system and often made good suggestions for improvements.

Part (b) asked for advice on whether three specific changes to the systems at the warehouse would reduce waste. The candidates were asked to view this as an application of lean principles. Few candidates structured their answers using lean ideas about waste but, by keeping their answers focused on the specifics on the scenario and the proposals, they nevertheless scored well.

Part (c). This part offered a mixed performance by candidates as many candidates did not know the meaning of the lean principles given but could offer some useful evaluation of the indicators from first principles.

ACCA marking scheme

			Marks
(a)	1 mark for each valid point	**Maximum**	**10**
(b)	1 mark for each valid point	**Maximum**	**6**
(c)	Each S discussed – up to 3 marks	**Maximum**	**9**
Total			**25**

39 INTEGRATED REPORTING

Key answer tips

Integrated reporting (IR) is a relatively new area, so make sure you are aware of the different concepts and terms and keep an eye open for relevant articles for further guidance on how it may be examined.

This question is not a past exam question but has been included because there are only a small number of past exam questions on this area. The Section B questions in the exam would contain a longer scenario. However, this question is useful for revision purpose and for consolidating knowledge on IR.

(a) In its simplest form, integrated reporting can be understood as the merging of the sustainability report and the financial report into a single 'narrative', as described by the Marketing Director.

However, the International Integrated Reporting Council (IIRC) does not use the word 'sustainability' in its definition of the concept.

According to the IIRC's 'International IR Framework,' an integrated report is 'a concise communication about how an organization's strategy, governance, performance and prospects, in the context of its external environment, lead to the creation of value over the short, medium and long term.'

The key emphasis of this definition is the idea of sustainable **value creation**, which makes the report and the processes underpinning it far more valuable than simply a compliance or reporting exercise.

Furthermore, this framework is intended as **guidance** for all businesses producing integrated reports, rather than compliance with a set of rules.

(b) The IR Framework recognizes the importance of looking at financial and sustainability performance in an integrated way – one that emphasizes the relationships between what it identifies as the 'six capitals':

Financial capital

This is what we traditionally think of as 'capital' – e.g. shares, bonds or banknotes. It enables the other types of Capital described below to be owned and traded.

Manufactured capital

This form of capital can be described as comprising of material goods, or fixed assets which contribute to the production process rather than being the output itself – e.g. tools, machines and buildings.

Intellectual capital

This form of capital can be described as the value of a company or organisation's employee knowledge, business training and any proprietary information that may provide the company with a competitive advantage.

Human capital

This can be described as consisting of people's health, knowledge, skills and motivation. All these things are needed for productive work.

Social capital

This can be described as being concerned with the institutions that help maintain and develop human capital in partnership with others; e.g. Families, communities, businesses, trade unions, schools, and voluntary organisations.

Natural capital

This can be described as any stock or flow of energy and material within the environment that produces goods and services. It includes resources of a renewable and non-renewable materials e.g. Land, water, energy and those factors that absorb, neutralise or recycle wastes and processes – e.g. climate regulation, climate change, CO_2 emissions.

The fundamental assumption of the IR Framework is that each of these types of capital – whether internal or external to the business, tangible or intangible – represents a potential source of value that must be managed for the long run in order to deliver sustainable value creation.

(c) The objectives for integrated reporting include:

- To improve the quality of information available to providers of financial capital to enable a more efficient and productive allocation of capital
- To provide a more cohesive and efficient approach to corporate reporting that draws on different reporting strands and communicates the full range of factors that materially affect the ability of an organisation to create value over time
- To enhance accountability and stewardship for the broad base of capitals (financial, manufactured, intellectual, human, social and relationship, and natural) and promote understanding of their interdependencies
- To support integrated thinking, decision making and actions that focus on the creation of value over the short, medium and long term.

(d) As well as external reporting to a range of stakeholders, the principles of IR can be extended to performance management systems. This is sometimes referred to as 'internal integrated reporting'.

An emphasis on these types of capital could result in more focussed performance management in the following ways:

- KPIs can be set up for each of the six capitals, ensuring that each of the drivers of sustainable value creation are monitored, controlled and developed.
- These can be developed further to show how the KPIs connect with different capitals, interact with, and impact each other.
- The interaction and inter-connectedness of these indicators should then be reflected in greater integration and cooperation between different functions and operations within the firm.
- This should result in greater transparency of internal communications allowing departments to appreciate better the wider implications of their activities.
- Together this should result in better decision making and value creation over the longer term.

40 BLUEFIN SCHOOL (DEC 11) (AMENDED)

Key answer tips

Make sure you answer the question set. In part (b) you were asked to evaluate the usefulness of the pack provided, rather than assess the performance of the school. Also, try to link your discussion to the organisation's mission and ethos to earn full marks.

(a) The controls necessary over management information would involve the use of standard templates and definitions for all information that has to be collated. This will be important at Bluefin where the information processing is decentralised to the departments. The department heads are preparing information in different formats using different methods of presentation. This could be potentially confusing to the governors if they were trying to compare departmental performance. Comparison will also be made more difficult if different performance measures are used by each department (such as average class marks and exam pass rates). These controls are important to ensure that time is not wasted in understanding the different formats or in devising different formats.

The reports should be examined periodically to ensure that they are actually being used. For example, the governors should be asked if the reports are read or the minutes of the board meeting should be reviewed for references to the reports.

The cost of producing the reports should be compared to the benefit that they supply. It will be difficult at Bluefin to quantify the benefits as it is not financially driven. The reporting will be to satisfy the major stakeholders such as the government who fund the school. Costs of the system would also be difficult to identify as this would require the measurement and costing of department heads' time.

In order to safeguard data, there should be a policy on regular backups. Bluefin has a decentralised information system where controls relating to the backup of records are more difficult to enforce.

The security concerns at the school will relate to the sensitive, personal nature of individuals' exam performance and the school's financial information. In a decentralised system, there are more locations from which sensitive data can be accessed. Security protocols are more difficult to enforce, for example, it is necessary to ensure that PCs are not in publicly accessible areas. It will also be important to ensure that password controls are observed (such as regular changes to passwords) and that they are not easy to guess or in a written form beside the relevant computer.

The current system of passing information by memory stick could easily lead to misplacement or loss of data. If memory sticks are to be used then data should be encrypted. It will also mean that there may be different versions of the data files on the department PCs and the administration system which will require to be controlled. It can also lead to virus infection being passed around the computers in the school. All files should be screened by anti-virus software that is installed across the school's computers.

(b) The positive aspects of the current governors' pack are that it addresses the financial and educational performance of the school; it provides the raw numerical data on which judgements about the quality of teaching and financial management can be made; and it utilises the skill of the department heads in giving them the choice of how to present data on pupil performance.

However, the current governors' pack for the annual review suffers from a number of basic flaws. Firstly, there is too much information being provided and that information is too detailed for a non-expert audience such as the governors. The financial information may well be too detailed and since this is a review rather than an executive control meeting it would be more helpful to provide a summary of the financial highlights. The information on exam performance is also too detailed. The governors will not cope very easily with 11 department reports, each possibly listing about 20 sets of individual class average marks (if the mathematics department report is of average length).

Secondly, there appears to be a lack of narrative in the pack to explain the data given. For example, the class averages themselves are not explained in any commentary, although the previous year's comparative figure is provided.

Thirdly, the school's ethos provides a guide to the overall mission of the school. However, the governors' pack does not attempt to measure the performance of the school in areas such as citizenship and self-confidence. The current pack only provides information on the financial and examination performance of the pupils. Possible measures of citizenship could be number of pupil hours spent in community service.

The additional information on self-confidence will be difficult to collect as it is qualitative and the measurement will be subjective.

Fourthly, no statement of financial position information is given which might allow an understanding of the school's investment in its buildings and equipment. This could be important in making a decision over the proposed IT improvements.

Finally, although not mentioned in the school's ethos, it would be expected that external comparisons of the school's performance would be appropriate, so this benchmark data should be provided along with the school's performance.

(c) The suggested improvements will bring the benefit of removing possible duplication of files and reducing storage requirements by unifying the data in one database. The network should facilitate the transfer of information between the departments and the school office making errors in transfer less likely. The centralising of the data in the school should make control over security tighter, it will be easier to enforce a policy on the backup of data and it should facilitate the standardisation of departmental report formats. By connecting the network on the internet, communication with key stakeholders such as the government will be improved. It may be possible to share data with other schools which could assist in a benchmarking exercise in order to identify best practice in the region.

However, the changes could lead to problems. The opening of the school network to the internet will provide additional opportunities for the spread of viruses and possibly open the network to hackers. The centralising of all data may make a loss more catastrophic although backup procedures will reduce this risk. The costs of such an upgrade may not be outweighed by the benefits as the benefits are all non-financial.

Examiner's comments

Requirement (a) was generally well done with candidates scoring highly by picking controls that were relevant to a school such as Bluefin.

Requirement (b). Performance in this part was variable in quality. Good candidates often used the school ethos as a tool for judging whether the pack met the board's needs. Some weaker candidates dwelt extensively on the performance of the Mathematics department which failed to address the value of the information being supplied.

Requirement (c). Again, there many good answers to this part with those who identified how these improvements addressed the problems noted in the earlier parts of the question scoring most highly.

ACCA marking scheme

			Marks
(a)	Controls and security, 1 mark per point	**Maximum**	9
(b)	Positive aspects, 1 mark per point up to 2 marks Information overload, 1 mark per point up to 2 marks Information confusing and unexplained, 1 mark per point up to 2 marks Failure to cover overall objectives, 1 mark per point up to 3 marks Other – 1 mark per point made		
		Maximum	6
(c)	Benefits, 1 mark per point up to 4 marks Problems, 1 mark per point up to 3 marks		
		Maximum	5

Professional marks **Analysis and Evaluation** • Appropriate use of the scenario information to provide a reasoned and relevant discussion of the controls and security procedures • Appropriate use of the data and information in appendix 1 to support the evaluation of the pack provided • Balanced and reasoned evaluation of the information system improvements in the context of the scenario and, importantly, addressing the problems identified earlier **Scepticism** • Demonstration of the ability to effectively challenge the effectiveness of the current information systems and information provision, identifying failings in a courteous and professional manner **Commercial Acumen** • Effective use of examples drawn from scenario information and other practical considerations related to the context to illustrate the points made • Points are practical and plausible in the context of a school and, more specifically, Bluefin School and its ethos	
Maximum	**5**
Total	**25**

41 QUARK HEALTHCARE (DEC 13)

Key answer tips

Make sure you answer the question set. In part (a) you were asked to assess the impact of the RFID system using the input from the CFO. This should have given you a clear set of points to structure your answer around.

In all parts of the question it was vital to relate your points to the specific context given, rather than relying on generic comments.

(a) The new information will not be without cost to Quark. The costs of hardware and software to set up the system and then ongoing operation of the system in terms of maintenance, consumables and employee time are often considerable. However, these costs can be offset against the efficiency savings of lost employee time in searching for tagged items and quality improvements in patient care which will result from that quicker access.

The information now being collected is non-financial in the location and quantities of equipment and drugs. However, these are forms of information which exist in the current systems and so there need not be dramatic change. The significant difference from the old system will be the real-time nature of the information and also its accuracy as it is collected and updated automatically. The tags are attached to batches of high-value drugs and if one of these batches is opened, then the count of inventory will not be entirely accurate if only the RFID information is used. A physical count will still be required for accuracy but the locations of these items from RFIDs will speed this.

Performance reporting will change as weekly inventory check reports will no longer be filed for the high-value drugs and instead there will be real-time, screen-based information. The relevant staff will need to be trained to access and use the information in this new system. It would appear that many medical staff will need access and so terminals will need to be available throughout the hospital – if the speed gains in finding items are to be obtained.

Improved control will result from the knowledge of location of high-value drugs. It will be easier to ensure that they are all in secure locations which will reduce the opportunity for theft. Additionally, knowing the date of delivery it will easier to identify items which may become obsolete and so they can more easily be used first, thus reducing wastage. Regarding the items of equipment, identification of location will reduce staff time in searching and also allow the items to be placed in the stores where they are most often accessed, thus further reducing searching time. This will improve quality of patient care due to a faster response. It will also be simpler to check and ensure that these items are in secure locations and so reduce the risk of theft. Management will also be able to check if processes of tidying up and locking away are being observed by doing daily checks on this through the system.

(b) Lean systems are based on the Toyota production system whose overall goal was to get the right things to the right place at the right time, the first time. Additional aims were to minimise waste and be open to change. These objectives match closely with the RFID system at Quark.

The location information will allow assets to be in the right location or at least a more optimised location and so speed ('right time') delivery of the service. The reduction in obsolescence and staff time help to minimise waste while the introduction of such a different process will require a culture of change in the organisation.

The five Ss concept is often associated with lean principles and has the aim of creating a workplace which is in order. It should sit well with the high status of work in Quark as it engenders employees' pride in their work and results in higher quality performance.

The five Ss are:

- Structurise – Introduce order where possible. Thinking about optimal locations for storage of the tagged items will help to do this at Quark.
- Systemise – The new RFID system will help to arrange and identify items for ease of use.
- Sanitise – Be tidy. There is danger that the easy availability of the knowledge of the location of items may lead to a lack of care with them. However, by training staff that they will be judged on storing items in useful locations, this information can be used as a control tool by management.
- Standardise – Be consistent in the approach taken.
- Self-discipline – Maintain through motivation. The system should report by exception to management on a daily basis about any items misplaced and so corrective action can be taken.

In order to be successful, lean techniques must be more than just housekeeping and should be treated as signs of theimportance of quality at Quark.

(c) The attitude of the medical staff to the system will be important. As they are high-status individuals, it will be necessary to persuade them to accept the new system rather than impose the change. There will be the danger that they see the system as spying on them and take this as an insult to their professionalism. They will need to see the benefits both in terms of reduced frustration in their own job and patient care. This will motivate them to change their current way of storing assets.

The new system will be screen-based but the use of information technology should not be shocking in Quark as it has the reputation of being advanced in this area. The reports will need to be carefully designed with input from the medical staff in order that they find the system easy to learn and use, as this is often a major barrier to the uptake of a new system. The design of the new method of recording drug administration by nurses may have been part of the problem with its implementation.

Promotion of responsibility and accountability will come through the management use of the new information. It may be possible to make specific staff (e.g. nursing staff) responsible for the storage of drugs and specific specialist doctors responsible for the storage of equipment related to their field of expertise. Regular checks on the position of assets will act as a control test of this staff activity. It may be necessary to break the hospital into departments or wards in order to identify the relevant responsible individuals. The managers must think carefully about how often to do their control reporting but daily exception reporting of any items not properly stored would appear appropriate, given the need to use the assets at short notice.

It will be important to select the correct individuals and groups to be responsible as there will be a demotivating effect if a staff member is being criticised for not securing an item when a higher status member of staff (e.g. medical specialist) has over-ridden their decision.

Tutorial note

Do not be frightened by this question. RFID may appear to be a small syllabus area and you may feel you have little knowledge to use here. However, there is a lot of information in the scenario that can be used to support your answer and to boost your mark.

Examiner's comments

Part (a). The scenario listed a number of areas of concern for the CFO of Quark and those candidates that used this hint tended to provide more complete and better structured answers. Most candidates did well in identifying the control benefits of the system but in not addressing the CFO's concerns often found that they ran out of ideas for further comment to reach the 12 marks available. Very few chose to comment on the nature of the information supplied and the changes to performance reporting and as a result, there were many passing answers to this part but few that scored highly.

Part (b). Few candidates had a clear idea of the definition of 'lean' in this context though most realised that it related to waste reduction/efficiency/accuracy. Most candidates scored some marks for their illustrations from the scenario of how the new system created these benefits. (Candidates should note that they were not required to mention the 5Ss in order to score full marks here, though it may have been useful in structuring an answer).

Part (c). The rigid hierarchy of the staff and previous information system problems were described in the scenario and those that made use of this as illustration of their general points scored well. The question asked for the influence that staff attitude would have on design and implementation and better candidates used these two phases (design and implementation) to discuss their answer. The final part of the requirement asked about the impact on responsibility and accountability and, as in previous diets, candidates only displayed a very vague grasp of what these terms might mean in the context of the RFID information system.

ACCA marking scheme

			Marks
(a)	Costs and benefits	up to	3
	Type of information supplied	up to	3
	Performance reporting	up to	3
	Improved control	up to	6
		Maximum	**12**
(b)	Definition of lean system	up to	2
	Analysis of impact of RFID system	up to	7
	Up to 2 for definition of five Ss		
		Maximum	**7**
(c)	Medical staff's behaviour will influence the design	up to	4
	Promotion of responsibility and accountability	up to	4
		Maximum	**6**
Total			**25**

42 ALBACORE (PILOT 10)

Key answer tips

This is a really useful revision question on the evaluation of a performance report and management styles. The theory here is reasonably straightforward but this theory needs to be applied to the specifics of the scenario. Once you have attempted the question, have a thorough read through the answer and marking scheme. Would you be able to replicate something similar in the real exam?

(a) The branch information appears to be inadequate on a number of levels to appraise the shop manager's performance. The manager should only be held responsible for those areas of performance that they can control.

The branch manager should be appraised on a realistic sales budget. The overall market fall of 12% suggests that the original budget of no change on previous year was not realistic. It is possible to analyse this by calculating planning and operational variances as follows:

	$
Revised budgeted sales given market fall	234,080
Budgeted gross margin	60%
Revised budgeted gross margin	140,448
Original budgeted gross margin	159,600
Planning variance	19,152 A
Actual sales	237,100
Revised budgeted sales	234,080
	3,020 F
Budgeted gross margin	60%
Operational variance	1,812 F

The operational variance reflects more accurately the manager's work and from this we can see the manager has done well by limiting the fall in gross profit by $1,812.

This analysis could be extended to other areas of the performance report. For example, if the breakdown of sales prices and volumes for individual product lines were given together with details of market volumes and price movements then the sales price variance could be broken down into operational and planning elements to reflect the manager's use of the limited discounting power that she has. Overall at the Tunny branch, the gross margin has remained constant (at 60%) which indicates that the manager may not have made use of the sales price discounting authority.

There are a number of other non-controllable costs in the branch information. It is unlikely that the branch manager can affect the price variance of heating and lighting costs as the prices are set through central purchasing although they will have some control over usage. The rental cost will reflect head office property management and is not controllable. The manager's own wages are not controllable although the staff costs will reflect the fact that the manager can choose to work longer hours and so save on part-time staff, therefore a labour efficiency variance would be appropriate.

A revised report would split the costs into two groups (controllable and on-controllable) so that a controllable profit would be shown as well as the overall shop profit. This would be the basic measure of performance of the store. A more detailed understanding of responsibility for the variances would be given by a breakdown of the operational (controllable) and planning (non-controllable) elements of each variance. It might look like this:

Revised performance report for Albacore Chess Stores

Tunny branch – Year to Sept 2011

	Budget	**Actual**	**Variance**	**Planning variance**	**Operational variance**
	$	$	$	$	$
Sales	266,000	237,100	–28,900	–31,920	3,020
Cost of sales	106,400	94,840	11,560	12,768	–1,208
Gross profit	159,600	142,260	–17,340	–19,152	1,812
Controllable costs:					
Marketing	12,000	11,500	500	0	500
Staff costs: Part-time staff	38,000	34,000	4,000	0	4,000
Controllable profit	109,600	96,760	–12,840		
Non-controllable costs:					
Staff costs: manager	27,000	27,000	0	0	0
Property costs	26,600	26,600	0	0	0
Shop profit	56,000	43,160	–12,840	–19,152	6,312

Notes:

Property costs includes heating, lighting and rental.

Positive variances are favourable.

Summary

The manager's performance has been good in difficult general economic circumstances since if we exclude the gross margin planning variance ($19,152A) and allow that the part-time staff costs and marketing costs are controllable then we see that there is a favourable variance in controllable profit of $6,312 ($19,152-$12,840).

As indicated, additional variances that could be reported include operational and planning price variances for sales; part-time labour efficiency variances in operational variances; part-time labour rate variances in planning variances; and some price and usage variances for property costs. There is insufficient data to calculate examples of these variances here.

(b) The management style at Albacore is highly budget-constrained (Hopwood). It is driven by financial performance to meet the needs of the venture capitalist owners who have probably highly geared the business at the time of purchase. The cost control attitude is illustrated by the focus on achieving budget in the reward system and the enforcement of staff pay rates. This management style leads to stress for employees and difficult working relationships – as illustrated by the unhappiness of the shop managers. It also can motivate manipulation of performance reports although given the centralised nature of Albacore this appears unlikely at the shop level. It does however focus attention on achieving budget. This could be desirable in difficult economic circumstances.

Alternative styles are:

- profit-conscious where the performance is evaluated on longer-term effectiveness of the business unit in question (plausible here given Albacore's aim of profit maximisation)
- non-accounting where the budget is of low importance in performance evaluation

The performance appraisal system at Albacore reflects this cost-conscious, budget constrained approach. The shop managers are instructed as to their objectives and there appears to be no discussion of this target between the appraiser and the shop manager. For the branch given, it is striking that the failure to make budgeted profit (by $12,840) has led to no bonus being paid although the shop made an operating profit of $43,160 and the operating margin of the shop has held up at 18% compared to 21% per the budget.

The branch information needs to reflect the areas that the manager can control as mentioned in part (a) to this answer. Using the analysis of revised controllable profit, we have seen that the manager has returned a good performance $6,312 ahead of budget. The increased use of operational and planning variances should help to motivate the managers and reduce the friction with senior staff.

The current contract between the manager and Albacore could be described as coercive as it is imposed. The budget should be agreed between the manager and their appraiser using the detailed knowledge of both parties to improve the budget estimates. Although for Albacore, the likely budget will reflect the expectations of the senior management in order to achieve the business' overall financial objectives.

The reward system could move to a more calculative basis where the manager is paid a percentage of the profit above a certain level, usually this bonus is capped to a maximum as in the current system. The senior management will need to assess the trigger level based on head office costs (administrative support and financing costs). Therefore, the operational director's assessment would become more objective and this could remove lack of clarity in how performance is assessed.

Performance appraisal could also recognise longer-term and non-financial factors in the manager's performance such as innovative marketing ideas and customer feedback on their shopping experience. Additionally, as the branch manager handles the shop's staff development, recognition could be given for branch staff who progress from part-time to shop manager.

ACCA marking scheme

			Marks
(a)	**Variance calculations:**		
	Flexed budget		1
	Operation and planning (1 mark per point up to 4)		4
	Controllable profit		1
	Revised performance report	up to	8
	Comments:		
	Structure		1
	Revenue budget unrealistic		1
	Controllable costs (general 1, specific justifications 2)		3
	Controllable profit		1
	Other variances	up to	5
		Maximum	**13**
(b)	Management styles (1 mark per point up to 6)		6
	Performance appraisal system (1 mark per point up to 6)		6
	Improvements (1 mark per point up to 3)		3
		Maximum	**12**
Total			**25**

C – STRATEGIC PERFORMANCE MEASUREMENT

43 CHICORY (SEPT/DEC 17) (AMENDED)

Key answer tips

In part (a)(i) the calculation and evaluation of ROCE should be quite straightforward.

In (a)(ii) 7 marks are available for the calculation and evaluation of EBITDA. Do not view any syllabus area as 'fringe' or 'unexaminable'. This requirement demonstrates that the examining team are willing to test all syllabus areas.

In (b) a generic list of drawbacks will not be given much credit. Use of the scenario information to point out the large number of difficulties and differences in comparing the two companies is required.

(a) (i) ROCE

As can be seen in working 1, Chicory's ROCE is 13.6% and Fennel's ROCE is 14.9%. Fennel has apparently performed better than Chicory. One benefit of using ROCE as a performance measure in this benchmarking exercise is that it gives a percentage figure and can compare businesses of different sizes. ROCE does not, however, give the absolute level of return. In this case, Fennel has both a higher capital employed and a higher percentage return.

ROCE is easy to calculate and will be familiar to Chicory's management as it is currently one of Chicory's main financial performance indicators. The figures required to calculate ROCE are readily available from published data, which makes this a good financial performance measure for benchmarking.

ROCE shows a weak correlation with Chicory's objective to maximise shareholder wealth, which may limit ROCE's usefulness as a performance measure in this benchmarking exercise. ROCE may be distorted by accounting policies or where different businesses have different levels of intangible assets. This may lead to drawing incorrect conclusions from the exercise. A big disadvantage of using ROCE in this benchmarking exercise is that it may encourage managers not to invest in new non-current assets, which contradicts Chicory's strategy of investing in charging points.

Working 1

Chicory:

Opening capital employed (Total assets – Current liabilities)	\$78.0m (138.0 – 60.0)
Closing capital employed	\$59.0m (140.0 – 81.0)
Average capital employed	\$68.5m ((78.0 + 59.0)/2)
ROCE (Operating profit/average capital employed)	13.6% (9.3/68.5)

Fennel:

Average capital employed (170 × 0.25) + (176 × 0.75)	\$174.5m
ROCE	14.9% (26.0/174.5)

Tutorial note

In (a)(i), ideally the average capital employed figure should be used to calculate ROCE. However, do not get too distracted and waste time on this. A pass could still be achieved without using the average figure.

(ii) EBITDA

Using Chicory's main financial performance indicators of ROCE, Fennel has performed better than Chicory. When depreciation of non-current assets and the write-off of goodwill in Chicory are added back to operating profit to calculate EBITDA, Chicory's performance, with an EBITDA of $52.0m, is slightly better than that of Fennel, which has an EBITDA of $51.0m.

EBITDA as a proxy for cash flow

EBITDA is easy to calculate from published data, and easy to understand. It is a measure of underlying performance, as it is a proxy for cash flow generated from operating profit. As Chicory is having cash flow difficulties following the unsuccessful acquisition, EBITDA would be a relevant measure for this benchmarking exercise. EBITDA does not, however, take into account the cash flow effect of working capital changes, for example, by Chicory negotiating longer payment terms with its suppliers.

Excludes items which are not relevant to underlying performance of the business

Tax and interest are distributions from profits, unrelated to the underlying performance of the business. Excluding them from measures of performance, therefore, gives a better understanding of the underlying performance of Chicory and Fennel. This is important for the benchmarking exercise since Fennel appears to suffer much lower rates of tax, probably due to the tax incentives given by the Veeland government. Loans underwritten by the Veeland government may be at artificially reduced rates of interest and should also be excluded when measuring performance.

Similarly, depreciation, amortisation and write-offs such as goodwill are not relevant to the current year's underlying performance and may relate to previous years. For example, adding back the write-off of goodwill in Chicory means the two businesses have identical EBITDAs, albeit that Fennel has much greater capital employed.

EBITDA affects comparability of benchmarking data

Using EBITDA as a performance measure in the benchmarking exercise makes the data for the two businesses more comparable and removes one element of subjectivity, such as in determining useful economic lives of non-current assets. EBITDA does, however, ignore the replacement costs of these assets. This might limit the usefulness of comparisons between Chicory and Fennel if one were to lease non-current assets and the other to purchase them. The introduction of a new accounting standard on the treatment of leases may, however, remove this limitation.

Unlike Chicory's existing measure of ROCE, which is a percentage measure, EBITDA is an absolute measure and so makes it difficult to compare businesses of different sizes. As a profit based measure, its usefulness is also limited by subjective assumptions made in the calculation of profit, or by inconsistent accounting policies. Development costs may be capitalised in Veeland, but not in Deeland, which may make a comparison against the benchmark difficult.

Working 2

$m	**Chicory**	**Fennel**
Operating profit	9.3	26.0
Add back:		
Depreciation on non-current assets	18.0	25.0
Write off of goodwill	24.7	–
EBITDA	52.0	51.0

(b) Benchmarking the performance of Chicory against a similar business implies that there is a best way to operate. Though Fennel may be similar to Chicory, there is no indication that it is best in class and benchmarking against it may be inappropriate.

For example, Fennel has taken advantages of tax incentives and loan guarantees to finance new investments. These do not exist in Deeland, so Chicory may be unable to fund investment in this way. It may have to consider leasing assets instead, or accept a slower rate of growth if it wishes to set up charging points in Deeland.

Benchmarking is a catching up exercise. The financial data for Fennel is 18 months older than that for Chicory and may already be out of date. In 20X3, Fennel improved operational performance by investment in IT. The effect of this is not reflected in the financial data given. Benchmarking performance against historical data may not be relevant for current or future performance. The electric car market in Veeland has grown rapidly in the last two years. This growth is not reflected in the financial performance data given for Fennel, nor is the falling price of components for the charging points.

Though Fennel has agreed to share data, this data may be inaccurate or misleading. Though initially the benchmarking exercise is only against Fennel, it may be difficult to find other comparable businesses to benchmark against in the future. The data required for calculation of the three financial performance indicators used in the benchmarking exercise is likely to be readily available and audited, however, which means it is reliable.

A large part of Fennel's business relates to providing charging points for charging electric cars. Though this is a business model Chicory intends to follow in the future, it is very different to its existing business, and so benchmarking against Fennel may be misleading unless more detailed data relating to the two activities can be obtained.

Similarly, Fennel operates in a different country, where the economy is much stronger. Performance targets set following the benchmarking exercise may be unachievable for Chicory. Fennel's financial data has been converted into $ from its home currency. Movements in exchange rates may make the benchmarking data less comparable, especially if the economies in Deeland and Veeland are growing at different rates.

Examiner's comments:

In part (a), many candidates scored poorly on the calculations, with few being able to calculate these correctly for both companies, which is disappointing as these are ratios that one would expect an accountant to be fully able to calculate. The evaluation of the methods of was generally performed well.

In part (b), candidates generally scored well and demonstrated good knowledge. Several candidates lost the opportunity to score more marks here by not relating their knowledge to the companies described in the scenario. Also, some candidates wasted time discussing the use of benchmarking, and in some instances gave a detailed explanation of the process of benchmarking, despite the requirement specifically asking about problems.

ACCA marking scheme

			Marks
(a)	(i)	Calculation of Chicory and Fennel's average capital employed	2
		Calculation of both companies' ROCE	1
		Comment of the results of the ROCE calculation	1
		Evaluation of ROCE as a performance measure	3
		Maximum	**6**
	(ii)	Adjustments to operating profit	2
		Calculation of both companies' EBITDA	1
		Comment of the results of the EBITDA calculation	1
		Evaluation of EBITDA as a performance measure	4
		Maximum	**7**
(b)	Problems of benchmarking exercise – up to 2 marks per point		
		Maximum	**7**

Professional marks

Analysis and Evaluation

- Appropriate use of data to perform suitable calculations of ROCE and EBITDA to support the evaluation of the relative financial performance of Chicory against Fennel
- Comprehensive evaluation of the use of ROCE and EBITDA as performance measures
- Problems of the benchmarking exercise clearly supported with examples

Scepticism

- Recognition of the limitations of using ROCE and EBITDA as performance measures and also of the problems of using the benchmarking exercise as a way to improve performance

Commercial Acumen

- Effective use of examples drawn from scenario information and other practical considerations related to the context to illustrate the points being made

Maximum	**5**
Total	**25**

44 TOSEMARY AND RHYME HOSPITAL (TRH) (SEPT/DEC 17) (AMENDED)

Key answer tips

Overall, this is a manageable question with clear requirements and adequate time.

In requirement (a), a good answer will focus on the need for NFPIs due to the multitude and diversity of objectives at TRH.

In requirement (b), ensure you outline the meaning of each 'E' (from the 3Es) before justifying a relevant performance measure for each of these.

In requirement (c), if you have your knowledge in place then it should be reasonably straightforward to identify that the organisation is largely budget constrained and that this would have potentially negative consequences for TRH.

(a) Lack of profit-making objective

Not-for-profit organisations do not, by definition, have profit as an overriding motive. Patients are not charged for receiving treatment, so TRH does not have a revenue stream. It may also be difficult to define a cost unit as this could be cost per patient arriving at hospital or cost per patient successfully treated.

Not-for-profit public sector organisations, such as TRH, have strict constraints on the amount of funding they receive, such as a fixed amount of funding received entirely from the government. They cannot obtain funding from elsewhere, so financial measures cannot be ignored completely. TRH must exist within its financial means, and the use of budgets to control costs is critical.

TRH provides an essential public service. Political, legal and social influences would prevent it from closing down a service just because it became more expensive or uneconomic to provide it. For all of these reasons, financial objectives are less relevant than for most commercial organisations, and its objectives are mainly non-financial in nature.

Not-for-profit organisations also undergo more public scrutiny and have multiple stakeholders, so non-financial indicators will be necessary to manage expectations. For example, patients are stakeholders who will have relatively little interest in how TRH exists within its financial constraints. They will have much more interest in non-financial performance, such as how quickly and successfully they are treated.

Multiple objectives

Not-for-profit organisations have multiple objectives, and it may be unclear which are the most important. Except for some aspects of giving value for money to the taxpayer, TRH's objectives are all non-financial.

The outputs or benefits of the services provided are non-financial in nature, for example, giving prompt and high-quality treatment to patients. Therefore NFPIs are required to measure performance.

(b) Value for money in public sector organisations can be measured using the 'three Es': economy, efficiency and effectiveness.

Economy

Economy means obtaining resources at the lowest cost. Doctors' salaries will be a significant expense for TRH, and salary per doctor is a suitable measure of economy. Doctors at TRH have an average salary of $150,000 ($3.75m/25), compared to the national average of $175,000 ($4.20m/24).

The relatively lower salaries of doctors may be due to differences in levels of experience or that they work unpaid overtime. It may also be one of the reasons why the staff satisfaction is so much lower at 9% compared to the national level of 89%.

Efficiency

Efficiency relates to obtaining the greatest possible outputs from the resources available. Treating patients is a key objective of TRH, and the number of doctors is an important resource. The number of patients treated per year by each doctor is a good measure of efficiency. In TRH, each doctor treats an average of 975 (24,375/25) patients per year, 17% more (975 v 833) than the national average 833 (20,000/24). This may be because they work longer hours than their colleagues in other hospitals.

Effectiveness

Effectiveness means how well TRH achieves its objectives. TRH has multiple objectives, one of which is to provide high quality medical treatment for patients. Where patients are re-admitted to TRH because their treatment had failed, this represents a failure to provide high-quality medical care, so the rate of re-admission of patients is a measure of effectiveness. The rate of re-admission at TRH is 7.5% (1,830/24,375), much higher than the national average of 1.5% (300/20,000). TRH seems to have performed relatively very poorly in this respect.

Summary

Overall, the results from the measurement of the 3Es are consistent with the doctor's comments that they are working without being paid overtime and treating more patients than their colleagues in other hospitals. TRH appears to deliver better economy and efficiency than the national average. This seems to be reducing performance, however, in respect of providing high-quality medical treatment for patients, where TRH is less effective than the national average.

(c) **Extent to which management style is budget constrained**

A budget-constrained management style emphasises the need to achieve short-term performance measures, for example, the annual financial budgets.

The doctor said that TRH has always achieved its total financial budgets, and this is supported by the fact that the doctors' salaries for the year to 31 August 2017 equalled the budget set for the period. Though it is unclear what NFPIs are measured at TRH as a whole, doctors receive only a limited set of financial and non-financial performance data. The discussion about this data, however, is mainly related to financial targets. This implies greater emphasis is given to performance against financial targets, rather than non-financial ones.

All of this suggests that TRH has a budget-constrained management style. An advantage of this is that it ensures TRH operates with the financial constraints of the fixed amount of funding received from the government.

Implications of a budget-constrained approach at TRH

This management style encourages short-termism, by encouraging doctors to work long hours without being paid overtime, or not making funding available to recruit new doctors to alleviate the situation. An implication of this is that TRH may reduce its performance against its objectives, and this is already seen by the relatively high rates of re-admission as an indicator of a reduced quality of medical treatment. Job-related tension is a consequence of a budget-constrained management style, and the low staff satisfaction score could have resulted from this.

This management style encourages manipulation of results, or the way they are measured, to show better performance. At busy times, more patients are referred to the nearby larger hospital. There is apparently no medical need for this, which is inconsistent with the objective to deliver high-quality treatment. It appears to be a way to distort waiting times to demonstrate improved performance in treating patients promptly. From patients' perspective, though, this will mean they are treated less promptly than if treated at TRH.

Being unable to recruit new doctors reduces TRH's flexibility in reducing waiting times at busy periods, as the steps already taken seem to have had minimal effect. This management style does not encourage innovation, probably because doctors have insufficient time for this. Though this may have long-term benefits, it seems to be taken as less important than the other key objectives, to provide prompt, high-quality treatment.

Examiner's comments

Part (a) was generally fairly well answered with better answers targeting issues specific to this hospital.

Part (b). Although this has been a common topic in APM, some candidates seemed ill-prepared; with many unable to define the framework and so properly attribute an indicator to each of the three headings. Candidates who did not know the framework tended to only score tangentially as it was the application of this model that was being tested. Candidates who knew the model generally scored well.

Part (c). Strong candidates gave logical answers which firstly identified the style currently in use, evidencing this with proof from the scenario and then discussed the consequences in achieving the organisation's objectives. Weaker candidates offered short answers for a 10 mark part often ignoring the points on the implications for performance management and just giving lists of possible performance management improvements without reference to the management style.

ACCA marking scheme

			Marks
(a)	Importance of NFPIs - 1 mark per point	**Maximum**	4
(b)	Definition of 3 Es – 1 mark Each E – up to 4 marks	**Maximum**	8
(c)	Discussion of budget constrained style - 1 mark per point	**Maximum**	8

Professional marks **Analysis and Evaluation** • Appropriate use of data to perform suitable calculations of performance measures to support the evaluation of value for money • Importance of non-financial performance indicators clearly explained and supported with examples • Reasoned evaluation of the extent to which management style is budget constrained and problems of this style clearly supported with examples **Commercial Acumen** • Effective use of examples drawn from scenario information and other practical considerations related to the context to illustrate the points being made	
Maximum	**5**
Total	**25**

45 PITLANE (MAR/JUN 17)

Key answer tips

This is a reasonably challenging question and highlights the importance of having you PM knowledge in place.

(a) You should be able to have a good attempt at this calculation if you know that the cost gap is the difference between the target cost and expected cost.

(b) To obtain a good mark you need to compare the current system with the use of target costing and then examine each stage of the target costing process in detail, with a specific focus on how Pitlane could take steps to reduce the cost gap.

As always in APM, in requirement (c) application to the scenario is required. For example, you are expected to give advice on empowerment of employees.

(a)

	2018	**2019**	**2020**
Basic selling price	180.0	170.0	160.0
10% uplift for features/packaging	18.0	17.0	16.0
Estimated selling price	198.0	187.0	176.0
Less: 15% net profit	(29.7)	(28.1)	(26.4)
Target total cost per unit	168.3	158.9	149.6
Current expected cost:			
Estimated total direct cost per unit	134.0	134.0	134.0
Estimated fixed cost per unit (W1)	44.1	44.1	44.1
Estimated total cost per unit	178.1	178.1	178.1
Cost gap	9.8	19.2	28.5

W1 – Fixed overhead cost per unit

= Total fixed overheads/Number of units sold

= $10,000,000/227,000 units = $44.05

(b) Target costing

Pitlane currently operates a traditional cost plus pricing method, where customers pay a fixed mark up on Pitlane's standard cost. This has been appropriate because the components currently produced have been manufactured in the same way for some time and their cost structure is well understood. Actual costs of production are very close to the standard costs. There is little competition in the market for Pitlane's current products, as a long-term contract was recently renewed with its biggest customer.

In contrast, for the proposed Booster product, the market price is only estimated. To compete with similar products, the Booster will need to sell at a price reflecting that of competitors' products, taking into account the different benefits and quality which each product has.

Target costing begins with taking the price which the market will pay for the product for a given market share. From that, the required profit margin is deducted to arrive at a target cost. The difference between the estimated cost for the product and the target cost is the cost gap. Where the estimated costs exceed the target cost, steps are taken to reduce the cost gap. The product can then be sold at a price which the market will accept, and which generates an acceptable profit margin.

Determining the market price

Pitlane's marketing department has estimated the average market price of competitors' products and the likely market share over the three years of the scheme. The estimates are based on the success of a similar scheme in Veeland, and the assumptions used could be incorrect. Electricity prices may already be higher in Veeland than in Deeland, meaning consumers there would reduce their energy costs more by installing solar panels. Similarly, consumers in Veeland could save more on energy costs if there is more sunshine there than in Deeland, enabling solar panels to generate more energy. Both factors would, in this case, reduce the take up of subsidies by consumers in Deeland and the amount they would be willing to pay for solar panels.

The domestic solar energy market is new in Deeland, and Pitlane has no experience in estimating market share or price for this type of product. Pitlane's belief that consumers would be willing to pay a 10% premium for highest quality packaging, or for the Booster to communicate with consumers' mobile phones, may be incorrect.

Calculating the target cost using the required profit margin

Pitlane charges a 15% profit margin on its existing projects. The shareholders' financial objective indicates that they require the same profit margin to be earned on Booster.

For its existing products, Pitlane can set a selling price based on its own costs, whereas the Booster's price must reflect external market conditions more closely. Target costing will focus Pitlane on the external environment by considering prices and relative benefits of competitors' products.

Estimating total costs of Booster

The total direct costs of Booster have been estimated at $134.00. The fixed overhead per unit relating to Booster for the three years of the scheme is $44.05, making total estimated costs per unit of $178.05. The cost estimates may be incorrect, especially as Booster is new, and different from Pitlane's existing products. As Booster includes costs which are fixed, estimating sales volumes is also crucial in determining costs per unit.

Pitlane has no recent experience of developing new products or of estimating costs and sales volumes for them. This makes it more likely that the cost estimates for the Booster will be incorrect. Estimating the total costs is needed for the next stage in the target costing process, to identify the cost gap.

Reducing the cost gap

A big advantage for Pitlane of using target costing is that it is often easier to reduce costs of a product at the design stage rather than after it has entered production. As Boosters are not sold directly to consumers, the buyers of the product, who are professional installers, may not see value in the highest quality packaging. This could be a significant yet unnecessary cost, to be eliminated at the design stage. In deciding what costs to eliminate, Pitlane will have to take into account the effect of these on the quality and perception of the final product.

The features where the Booster can communicate with consumers' smartphones, and the use of highest quality packaging, are believed to enable Pitlane to charge 10% more than competitors' products. The $3.8m (W1) of estimated additional total revenue from the packaging and smartphone features may not justify the $2.8m upfront development costs for the smartphone feature alone, especially if the time value of money were to be taken into account. Consumers may not value these two features or be prepared to pay more for them. Eliminating them would therefore have little effect on sales volumes and would enable Pitlane to charge a more competitive price, or obtain higher gross profit margins.

Due to damage of sub-components when assembling the prototype, the estimated assembly labour cost assumes highly skilled labour will be used. This is 30% more expensive than other labour. By providing additional training, lower paid labour could be used to produce the Booster, and hence reduce the cost gap.

Pitlane plans to purchase the four main sub-components in bulk from six different suppliers. Consolidating suppliers, or using suppliers in lower cost countries, could help reduce the cost gap by reducing purchase costs. Moving to a just-in-time production system, rather than buying supplies in bulk, would help reduce costs of holding inventory as suppliers would only deliver sub-components when needed. This may increase other costs such as by requiring investment in information technology. It would also take time to develop the close relationship required with suppliers.

Another source of waste is due to internal transport and handling, which forms over 5% of the total direct cost of the Booster. This will also increase production cycle times, and is an unnecessary process which does not add value. It could be eliminated by changing the layout of the factory, or reorganising production into teams and ensuring all production was done at a single factory, rather than in both of Pitlane's factories.

W1 – Additional revenue from smartphone feature and highest quality packaging

2018 – 60,000 units × $198 = $11.880m

2019 – 75,000 units × $187 = $14.025m

2020 – 92,000 units × $176 = $16.192m

Total revenue = $42.097m (= $42,097,000 × 10/110 = $3,827,000)

(**Note:** This is a detailed solution. You would not be expected to produce an answer of this length.)

(c) Kaizen costing

Unlike target costing, which occurs at the beginning of a product's life, Kaizen costing is a process of long-term continuous improvement by cost reduction throughout the life of the product.

The Booster will be produced only for the three years during which the Deeland government offers subsidies and tax incentives. Generally, Kaizen costing is used over longer periods, and it is likely the full benefits of this approach will not be achieved in such a short timescale. The target cost is the starting point for Kaizen costing. After production begins, each period's target is based on the previous period's reduced costs.

Target costing can achieve large cost reductions at the design stage of the product, e.g. by choosing not to develop the smartphone feature. Kaizen costing, however, reduces costs in much smaller, incremental steps.

The need for continuous improvement

Even though Booster's share of the market rises over the three years of the project, the market price falls, as does the size of the market. Which means that in order to achieve the shareholders' financial targets, the direct costs of the Booster must fall over the three years. Continual incremental improvements using Kaizen costing, and measuring these improvements against targets from the previous period rather than the original estimated cost, could help to achieve this.

Ways to reduce waste using Kaizen costing

Traditional costing methods often see employees as the cause of high costs, whereas Kaizen costing sees the employees as a source of ideas on how to reduce costs. The manufacturing director's comments, that the damage caused by employees to delicate sub-components may mean it may not be possible to produce the Booster, indicates that Pitlane is currently following the traditional approach. Employees are seen as the source of the waste.

To benefit from Kaizen costing, Pitlane must undergo a culture change to encourage employees to suggest ideas, perhaps using quality circles, to reduce costs. That way, improvements could be made in the way sub-components are assembled during production, which would shorten the production cycle and lead to a reduced cost of scrapped items.

Examiner's comments

Part (a). Many candidates scored well on this part. However, a significant number chose to present their answers using absolute figures rather than per unit. This is both a failure to answer the question requirement and also, illustrates a lack of understanding about the application of the method, where per unit calculations are most helpful.

Part (b). Candidates scored reasonably well on this part but often failed to score marks as they did not analyse all the problem areas mentioned in the scenario. The scenario will often provide hints of areas to consider in an answer and good candidates use these to efficiently compile high marks in the longer parts of questions.

Part (c) of the question was fairly well answered with candidates demonstrating a fair understanding of Kaizen costing and its application.

ACCA marking scheme

			Marks
(a)	Estimated unit selling price – 1 mark Less: 15% net profit – 1 mark Target total cost per unit – 1 mark Less: Fixed costs per unit – 1 mark Target direct cost per unit – 1 mark Cost gap – 1 mark		
		Maximum	**6**
(b)	General description of target costing – up to 2 marks Advice on target costing for Pitlane – 1 mark per point Additional revenue generated from features – 2 marks		
		Maximum	**12**
(c)	General description of Kaizen costing – up to 2 marks Application of Kaizen costing to Pitlane – 1 mark per point		
		Maximum	**7**
Total			**25**

46 JENSON, LEWIS AND WEBB (JLW) (MAR/JUN 17)

Key answer tips

In part (a) the key concept being examined is 'controllability'. It is important to explain that the managers should only be appraised on performance they can control. In order to gain 7 marks, specific examples relating to controllability are required. However, it is also important to recognise that determining what is/ is not controllable can be difficult.

In part (b) you are expected to adjust the net profit and revenue figures for uncontrollable items and to draw a conclusion that the manager of the division should, in fact, be awarded a bonus.

In part (c) to gain a good mark you need to give relevant examples from the scenario and also need to recognise that only the Domestic division, as an investment centre, would be suited to using this measure.

(a) A key characteristic of divisional performance measurement is that divisional managers, and the divisions themselves, should only be appraised on performance that they control. For example, costs which are not controlled by divisional managers, such as JLW's apportioned head office costs, should be added back to profit when appraising manager's performance.

Similarly, as Export division is a profit centre, divisional managers are not able to make capital investment decisions and so depreciation is out of their control and should be added back to profit for their appraisals. Domestic division is an investment centre, so managers there can make investment decisions, and depreciation is a cost which they can control.

On 30 June 2015, the $KL weakened by 15% against the £SL. This meant Export division benefited from an increase in revenue which was not under the control of the divisional manager. This amount must be deducted from revenue when calculating the controllable net profit for Export division.

The net profit arrived at after items which are not under managers' control are added back is known as the 'controllable profit'. This is what divisional managers should be appraised on. This is because it is unfair to appraise them on factors outside their control, and may mean they become demotivated or give up trying to improve performance, which is not in the interests of JLW as a whole.

Divisional performance should be evaluated on all the items which relate directly to the division which is its 'traceable profit'. Allocated head office costs do not directly reflect the activity of the division and should be excluded when calculating the traceable profit.

The traceable net profit for Export division, after adjusting for allocated head office costs, was $KL905,000 (W1), and the traceable net profit margin was 11%.

A difficulty with calculating controllable and traceable profits in this way may be that it is difficult to determine which items are controllable or not. For example, though the new machine purchased for Export division by head office did lead to improvements in productivity, the extent of this increase must be attributed to good management, or otherwise, by the divisional managers. This increase in productivity is therefore due partly to controllable factors, and partly to uncontrollable.

W1 – Traceable net profit

	$KL000
Reported net profit	545
Add back: Allocated head office costs	360
Traceable net profit	905
Traceable net profit margin: (905/8,000)	11%

(b) **Conclusion on payment of Export division manager's bonus**

The controllable net profit is arrived at after items which are not under the manager's control are added back. The net profit margin controllable by the manager of Export division is 10%. Given that it is difficult to assess the effect of the increased productivity on controllable net profit, the manager should be awarded her bonus for the year. This is because the controllable net profit margin of 10% exceeds the target of 8%.

W1 – Controllable net profit margin for Export division year ended 31 December 2016

Controllable net profit	$KL000
Reported net profit	545
Add back non controllable items: Depreciation	
395	
Allocated head office costs	360
Deduct currency gain (W2)	(522)
Controllable net profit	778

Controllable revenue	$KL000
Reported revenue	8,000
Deduct currency gain (W2)	(522)
Controllable revenue	7,478
Controllable net profit margin: (778/7,478)	10%

W2 – Currency gain

Six months revenue from 1 July 2016 was increased by 15% due to currency gain. Six months revenue before currency gain 4,000/1.15 = 3,478

Therefore non-controllable currency gain is 4,000 – 3,478 = 522

As the exact increase in productivity resulting for the new machinery on Export division is unclear, it is difficult to accurately adjust the controllable net profit margin to reflect this. It would seem the divisional manager is benefitting from productivity improvements which are not entirely under her control. To reduce the controllable net profit margin to 8%, the threshold at which the manager is awarded her bonus, the net profit would have to fall by approximately $KL179,760 (778,000 – (7,478,000 × 8%)). This is equivalent to 3.7% of cost of sales (179,760k/4,800,000). It is difficult to conclude, therefore, whether the 'significant' improvement in productivity would make the difference between the manager of Export division receiving her bonus or not.

(c) **EVA™ as a performance measure for Export and Domestic divisions**

EVA™ makes adjustments to the financial profit to calculate the economic value generated by each division, and then makes a deduction for the cost of the capital invested in the division. A positive EVA™ indicates a division is creating value above that required by those who finance the business. It is therefore consistent with JLW's objective to maximise shareholder wealth. Appraisal of divisional performance on this basis would therefore align the interests of managers with those of JLW's shareholders.

EVA™ involves making many adjustments to operating profit and capital employed. These may be time consuming, and be poorly understood by managers. The manager of Export division has already commented that she finds the bonus calculations difficult to understand. Failure of managers to understand the EVA™ calculations would make it difficult for them to work towards targets set for the division.

EVA^{TM} avoids distortion from estimates and financial policies

EVA^{TM} avoids the financial results from being distorted by accounting policies and estimates made by divisional managers, for example, the $KL75,000 bad debt provision made in Domestic division, as increases in provisions are added back to operating profit in the EVA^{TM} calculation. Whilst this provides a consistent basis to evaluate performance of divisions within JLW, EVA^{TM} is not suitable for comparing divisional performance as it is an absolute measure and does not make allowance for their relative sizes.

EVA^{TM} encourages managers to take a long-term view

The advertising costs for the new range of paints would be capitalised as these generate future value. The use of EVA^{TM} would encourage managers to incur costs, such as these, which will benefit the business in the long term.

However, the calculation of EVA^{TM} is backwards looking, and based on historical financial information, whereas shareholders need information about future performance on which to base their decisions.

EVA^{TM} takes into account the cost of capital

The current performance measure of net profit margin is a poor measure as it takes into account neither the absolute net profit achieved, the capital employed in the division, nor the cost of capital. By making a deduction for the cost of capital employed in the division, the EVA^{TM} calculation makes managers consider both the capital employed and the cost of capital in their divisions.

Export division is a profit centre and managers do not have control of investment decisions and hence it is not a suitable measure for the evaluation of the performance on Export division because there is no controllable capital employed. Domestic division is able to control investment decisions, and does have controllable capital employed, so EVA^{TM} would be a suitable measure for evaluating Domestic division's performance.

However, to use the weighted average cost of capital (WACC) in the EVA^{TM} calculation requires a number of assumptions and estimates to be made, for example, in calculating the cost of equity or market value of debt. The WACC is normally based on historic data, which may not reflect circumstances in the future, and may not be accurate.

Examiner's comments

Part (a). In order to score well, it was important to pick up on the issues mentioned in the scenario and examine their impact on this question. Those that did this scored well in this part.

Part (b) was generally well done.

Part (c). Answers to this part were surprisingly weak, often due to the candidate believing that the question required a lengthy description of the method of calculation of the indicator rather than focusing on its suitability for use in the scenario.

ACCA marking scheme			
			Marks
(a)	Evaluation of manager's comments – 1 mark per point Traceable net profit calculation – 2 marks		
		Maximum	**7**
(b)	Depreciation and allocated head office costs – 2 marks Currency gain – 2 marks Controllable revenue – 2 marks Controllable profit margin – 1 mark Conclusion – 1 mark		
		Maximum	**8**
(c)	Evaluation of EVA™ – 1 mark per point	**Maximum**	**10**
Total			**25**

47 ESSLAND POLICE FORCE (DEC 13)

Key answer tips

This is a great question on league tables and should form a key part of your revision of this topic. If you struggle with some APM concepts, then try to apply them to a range of scenarios that you are more familiar with, such as school or hospital league tables in this instance.

(a) Logically, the Force Score (FS) should reflect the aims and objectives of the department. The overall aim has two basic parts: (1) value-for-money service; (2) community safety. The score does use variables associated with community safety but does not measure value-for-money. Value-for-money would be reflected by measures which take account of the economy, efficiency and effectiveness of the police forces. For example, the other indicators given in Appendix 1 allow calculation of the following measures which could be useful in measuring performance of this objective:

Other indicators:	**C**	**D**	**E**	**F**
Number of police per 10,000 population	49.6	48.9	50.0	52.7
Cost per population member ($)	323.2	331.1	336.5	340.0

The more detailed goals of the police forces are:

- Tackle the underlying causes of crime and achieve long-term sustainable solutions – which is measured by Rank 1 for the number of reported crimes.
- Bring perpetrators to justice – which is measured by Rank 2 which measures the detection rate of crimes.
- Provide protection and support for individuals and communities at risk of harm – which is measured through the user satisfaction score (Rank 3).
- Respond to community needs by being accessible and engaging with their concerns – which is measured through the user satisfaction score (Rank 3) and the responsiveness is measured by call handling speed (Rank 4).

None of these ranks will perfectly measure all aspects of each of the goals but there is a broad coverage present. For example, an improvement might be to include a measure of community engagement through the number of public meetings between police and the community or a measure of community-based policing initiatives.

The choice of weightings used in the FS formula must be considered. Force F is top ranked and Force C is bottom ranked. However, among the four variables used to calculate the score, no one force dominates with three different forces being the best in each of the four variables. Therefore, the weightings are important in determining the final FS.

The formula used is simple as it recognises only four input variables and weights these equally. No explanation of the logic of the choice of variables or weightings has been offered. Different weightings would produce very different results. To illustrate this, if a simple weighting system were used where weighting was given only to Rank 3 (on user satisfaction), then Force D would rank top and Force F would be bottom. Also, relatively small variations can have big impacts on the final FS.

For example, the difference between each force in their call answering is not great with three percentage points separating best and worst but this generates a difference of 0.75 in the forces' final FS.

There is a danger of over-complicating the formula (with more variables and complex methods of allocating weightings) and thus losing one of its main advantages, which is its simplicity.

(b) The use of league tables effectively benchmarks performance and can have a positive effect on behaviour. The sharing of data on performance can indicate areas of best practice and so improve performance across all forces. Additionally, the use of league tables gives a single figure which gives a clear, immediate answer to questions of performance.

However, the use of league tables only measures relative performance. The best force in the table could still be producing an unacceptable performance in absolute terms. In order to avoid this problem, tables will often try to include comparable bodies from outside the area of control of the government (foreign police forces). However, to get comparable data in order to calculate an FS for a foreign police force will be difficult.

On introduction, if the police staff do not feel that they can affect the FS, then they will not be held accountable by it. They may ignore it or actively undermine it in public through their union. This will present the government with difficulty as the police are considered the experts on this area of public policy and their criticism will carry weight with the electorate.

Once the system is in use, the FS can be used as a target for the leaders of each force; however, it can lead to over-focusing by employees on the variables in the FS to the exclusion of other relevant issues, i.e. only doing what gets measured. This means that the FS must encompass the key variables which will drive desired performance.

The police staff may be demotivated by the league tables if they feel:

(i) that the FS does not reflect the valuable work which they do (as noted above, the current FS formula does not take account of the value-for-money aspects of the police force's efforts); or

(ii) that the FS is driven by factors outside their control. (For example, there may be a link between the number of crimes reported and the economic conditions in the forces area which they do not have power to affect.)

The use of league tables has stemmed from their introduction for schools. However, the comparison between police forces and schools may not be valid, as school league tables are helpful where parents have some choice in the school to which they send their children while with only four forces covering the country, residents will have to move a long distance to be under the protection of a different police force. The schools' league table only used the single output of pupils' performance while the FS is more complex as it tries to encompass a number of different outputs. This will lead to greater debate about the value of the measure for the reasons given above and possibly its reduced effectiveness.

Examiner's comments

Part (a). Candidates did well when they structured their answer by taking firstly, the aims of value for money and community security then the four detailed goals and examined how the four variables in the force score would relate to these and then whether the formula weighted these appropriately. This again emphasises the helpfulness in taking a logical approach to question answering. Unfortunately, a minority of candidates discussed the use of league tables in this part although the requirement focusses on the force score. These candidates should have read the whole question requirement and they would have realised that this was subject of part (b).

Part (b) for 11 marks was split into two parts firstly, a general discussion of the merits of league tables which was well done followed by specific concerns on their use on these police forces. Again, it was worth noting that the scenario hinted at the specific areas to consider though many candidates chose only to address the staff issues while leaving unscored the marks on the comparable usefulness of tables in measuring schools and police forces.

ACCA marking scheme

			Marks
(a)	Calculations:		
	Other indicators	up to	2
	Comments:		
	Force score formula		
	Choice of variables used for weighting		
	– match to overall aim	up to	3
	– match to detailed goals	up to	5
	Allocation of weightings	up to	4
	Other	up to	2
		Maximum	**14**
(b)	General evaluation of league tables	up to	4
	Link of tables to targets and employee reaction		
	Introduction of tables	up to	2
	Behaviour under the system and sense of accountability	up to	5
	Comparison of use in schools and police sectors	up to	2
	1 mark each for other relevant points		
		Maximum	**11**
Total			**25**

48 BEESHIRE LOCAL AUTHORITY (BLA) (DEC 14)

Key answer tips

This question is based on a local authority. The scenario is reasonably long and contains some numerical information to absorb.

Requirement (a) asks for an explanation of why NFPIs are useful for public sector organisations, giving relevant examples. This is a test of core knowledge and as long as you make a decent attempt to relate your points to the scenario you should be able to score a pass/good pass here.

Requirement (b) tests performance indicators once again (a very popular area) but now in the context of value for money. The link between value for money and performance indicators should be anticipated.

Requirement (c) asks for difficulties in measuring qualitative factors. In addition to the difficulties outlined make sure that you offer relevant solutions.

(a) Public sector organisations have a number of problems which can be at least partially addressed with the use of non-financial performance indicators.

- **Lack of profit measure**

  BLA's waste management is not expected to make a profit. This is obvious from the fact that there is no specific charge for the service and so no clear revenue stream associated with it. The danger is that the only financial measure is cost and, in the current state of Seeland, this would mean that positive progress would only be seen in its reduction. This would be to the detriment of service and the three goals for the department (safe, clean, environmentally friendly).

- **Multiple objectives**

  It is difficult to say which is the single, overriding objective unlike in a profit-making organisation. This requires an approach which takes account of all the perspectives. BLA shows this in its three goals, none of which are financial.

- **Difficulty in defining a suitable financial measure**

  Many non-profit seeking organisations provide services for which it is difficult to define a cost unit. At BLA, should the cost unit be cost per tonne of waste collected or cost per household or cost per tonne of waste landfilled? Also, the benefits of the service are mainly non-financial such as clean streets.

The three goals of BLA's waste management department could be addressed by looking at health statistics, tourist/resident surveys and tonnage of recycled waste. These are all non-financial in nature.

(b) The standard criteria for analysis of the value-for-money of a service are:

- Economy – the optimisation of the resources which the organisation has; ensuring the appropriate quality of input resources are obtained at the lowest cost
- Efficiency – the optimisation of the process by which inputs are turned into outputs
- Effectiveness – how the outputs of the organisation meet its goals.

At BLA:

Economy could be measured by looking at the cost of buying equipment such as the lorries or fuel or the major cost of staff (44% of the total). The current average staff pay is $31,429. This is above the national average pay of $29,825. However, paying more for each member of staff could result in greater efficiency as staff members have improved skills.

Efficiency could be measured by the number of tonnes of waste moved per staff member (629 tonnes/staff member) or the cost of collection of waste per tonne ($114) or the staff cost per tonne collected ($50). Benchmarking these against national averages, the cost of collection of waste per tonne and staff cost per tonne collected are below the national averages of $123 and $51 respectively while the tonnes of waste moved per staff member (583 tonnes/staff member) is higher than the national average. This implies that BLA is showing good efficiency in its use of resources. The balance of capital and staff costs would also indicate how labour intensive the department's work was, for example, the value of the lorry fleet per tonne collected compared to the staff cost per tonne collected. No figures are given for lorry fleet value, so no quantification of this can be done.

Effectiveness has to be measured against the departmental goals:

1. Public health concerns – this is a vague objective and could be measured against many indicators such as level of vermin or levels of diseases related to waste. The lower frequency of collections (17% below national average) may present a public health problem.

2. Clean and attractive streets – this is a subjective goal as discussed above. The level of tourism and return visits may give a rough measure of this goal. The trend in complaints by residents will be a more reliable measure.

3. Increased recycling – the trend in tonnes recycled would be one measure but an imprecise one. If waste collected is generally going up, then this will rise too. A better measure of the effort to increase use of recycling would be the percentage of waste which is recycled compared to the government's target. (BLA is recycling 43% of its waste which is already ahead of the target of 40% by 2015. It is also ahead of the national average of 41%.)

(c) The major problem in interpreting qualitative data is that it is subjective since it is based on people's opinions. For example, in assessing quality of service people have different expectations and priorities and so are unlikely to be consistent in their judgements. At BLA, customer complaints will be driven by such opinions. Some customers may wish to see effort focused on recycling, while others may be more concerned about unsightly waste in the streets and others will focus on the frequency of waste collections. Some customers may not understand that improved waste collection is only possible with spending implications which may not be acceptable due to the current recession in Seeland.

One way to reduce the effect of subjectivity is to look at trends in performance since the biases in opinion will be present in each individual time period but the trend will show relative changes in quality.

The recording and processing of qualitative data can be difficult. Opinions are expressed in language and it can be difficult to tell if a complaint which describes service as 'awful' is more or less serious than one which describes service as 'unacceptable'. The current data for BLA does not contain any such information and this is often the result of these difficulties in collection.

The most common way to try to overcome this problem is to turn the data into quantitative data. For example, surveys often use scoring systems to capture data on service. A scoring system will often ask the customer to rank their satisfaction at the service provided on a scale of 1 to 5 with '1' representing 'completely satisfied' and '5' representing 'totally dissatisfied'.

However, the problem remains that such scoring systems are still subjective, and it has often been found that there is a tendency to score toward the middle as people tend to feel uncomfortable using the extreme scores of 5 or 1.

BLA waste management will suffer from these problems particularly in their goal of keeping the streets attractive as this will clearly require subjective judgement in its assessment.

ACCA marking scheme

			Marks
(a)	Up to 4 marks for general discussion Up to 4 marks for examples relevant to BLA		
		Maximum	**6**
(b)	Up to 3 marks for a description of a general approach to VFM 1 mark per point – discussing each heading at BLA		
		Maximum	**12**
(c)	1 mark per point made	**Maximum**	**7**
Total			**25**

49 TENCH CARS (DEC 11)

Key answer tips

The keys to scoring well on this question are (1) knowing the content and (2) being able to apply your knowledge to the scenario given. The latter skill was the main discriminator between good and weak scripts.

(a) The costs of quality will probably be hidden in overheads in the standard costing system at Tench. They relate to design, inspection and repair and reworking. The existing system will need to be modified to separate these costs.

The quality costs that will need to be collected will include the following:

- Costs of conformance: ensuring that cars produced are at the acceptable quality standard. This includes prevention costs such as training for staff, building quality into the design of the cars and the design of the business processes in order to avoid quality rejections. It also includes appraisal costs which include the inspection of components from suppliers before they are used and inspection of work-in-progress and finished cars.

- Costs of non-conformance: cost of dealing with cars that do not meet the prescribed quality standards. These costs include internal failure costs when a quality fault is noticed before the car leaves the factory and is rectified. External failure costs also arise when a customer finds a fault with the car which must be handled through customer complaints.

There are quality costs that an accounting system will tend to omit such as the opportunity cost of lost future sales resulting from customer dissatisfaction and the knock-on effects of faulty component purchases in lost time in the rest of the manufacturing process.

The identification and collection of these costs will probably lead to greater management focus on the quality issue as 'what gets measured, gets done'. This will help Tench to raise the quality of its products in order to compete more effectively with the new imports.

The issues discussed above represent the traditional view of quality costs where there is an optimal effort that minimises but does not eliminate quality faults. There is a trade-off occurring since the reduction of non-conformance costs requires an increase in conformance costs in order to prevent product failures and there comes a point where the cost of reducing the error rate further is greater than the benefit from preventing that additional fault. For a national manufacturer faced with multinational competitors, this may seem an appropriate approach as Tench will not have the resources to be able to drive out all quality faults.

(b) The Kaizen costing process focuses on producing constant, small, incremental cost reductions throughout the production process during the product's life. Kaizen can be translated as continuous improvement. Kaizen costing applies functional analysis in the design phase to create a target cost for each production function. These are totalled to give a product target cost which, after the first year of production, is used as the baseline for further on-going reductions. These reductions in turn reduce the baseline cost and so on as the production process improves. The cost reduction rate is set as a target and managed by exception throughout an accounting period often on a monthly basis compared to the annual setting of standard costs.

The effect of this on the standard costing system at Tench is significant since, in a process that is continually improving, standard costs have much less value as they are fixed over the relevant period. Therefore, Kaizen costing can respond more easily to a dynamic business environment. Standard costing is used to control costs while Kaizen costing focuses on cost reduction.

The management attitude to employees is different in the two systems, as in continuous improvement systems they are the source of the improvement solutions while in standard costing systems with its analysis of variances of labour rates and efficiencies, the employees are often seen as the source of problems. In the Kaizen system, the employees often work in teams and are empowered to make changes to production that would have to be cleared through a management hierarchy in a more static standard costing system. Changing the costing system would be likely to represent a major cultural change at Tench with its history of bureaucratic control.

The benefit of continuous improvement, which has been successfully followed at many multi-national car manufacturers such as Toyota, is that it will allow the company to address quickly the changing nature of Tench's competitive environment. It will increase staff motivation through empowerment. However, there may be significant management difficulties initially in getting workers who are used to a command and control structure to change their behaviour and speak out about possible improvements.

(c) Just-in-time (JIT) is a demand-pull system of ordering from suppliers which aims to reduce inventory levels to zero. It can be broken into two parts: purchasing and production. Each part has a similar goal to produce the components for the next stage of the production process only when they are needed (hence demand-pull). The system is often used in conjunction with the continuous improvement methods discussed earlier.

For Tench, this will bring benefits and problems. The benefits will be measured in lower working capital requirements, factory floor space savings and increased flexibility in meeting the customer's individual needs (faster response times to product specification changes).

There are a number of problems to be overcome. There will be an increased reliance on suppliers as any component quality failures are not necessarily rectifiable by going to inventory to pick a replacement. This can lead to costly stoppages to production. For Tench there could be difficulty in finding local suppliers who are capable of meeting the required component and delivery standards needed in order to run such a system. Quality systems are therefore a driver of the feasibility of JIT and the metrics associated with quality costs (mentioned above) will become important as a result.

Output must be matched to demand and each stage of the production process must match its output speed to the demand level. Teams must be formed to work by component or product rather than by the type of work performed. Staff will require training in order to work in these teams as they will have to be multi-skilled (able to operate and maintain the machinery in use by their team). This means that traditional functional divisions of costs become less appropriate, again requiring cultural change at Tench. Measures of spare capacity and bottlenecks in production will be critical to achieving these aims. Also, the amount and effectiveness of staff training will need to be measured during the implementation of these changes.

(d) Tench's existing performance reporting system uses standard costing and variance analysis for monitoring and control purposes. This is likely to have been adequate under the old regime when the focus was on production but will not necessarily drive the business forward. As the surrounding markets begin to see the effects of deregulation there is likely to be a greater rate of change in prices and availability of goods and labour and Tench may find it difficult to keep the standard costs up to date and appropriate. This could lead to significant variances being reported and time wasted on analysis and investigation. Tench may find it useful to analyse and report on a wider range of performance measures going forward and will need to consider performance relative to the competition as well as simply comparing against budget. The variance analysis system may also constrain managers as there may be insufficient focus on growing the business and taking advantage of the greater wealth enjoyed by the population. Tench could consider a system which incorporates a range of different measures and takes into account both internal and external factors. A system such as Fitzgerald and Moon's building blocks would achieve this and could also help the business consider the impact of quality management on performance.

Examiner's comments

Requirement (a). The better candidates began by realising and describing what is meant by the current standard costing method at Tench. Their subsequent comments then showed how it would be difficult to implement the collection and use of quality costing given this system.

Requirement (b). Again, good candidates addressed the detailed requirement by considering the difficulties and opportunities of taking Tench from its old command and control style systems and culture into performance management style that is common in the current car industry.

Requirement (c). Many answers wisely used the requirement to breakdown their comments into sections on JIT in purchasing and JIT in production. However, most answers were poorly connected to suitable performance measures.

ACCA marking scheme

			Marks
(a)	Describe quality costs		2
	Impact of quality costs	1 mark per point up to 4 marks	4
	Use of quality costs		
	And traditional view of quality costs	1 mark per point up to 5 marks	5
		Maximum	**6**
(b)	Describe Kaizen costing		4
	Comparison of standard and Kaizen costing	1 mark per point up to 3 marks	3
	Effect on management of employees	1 mark per point up to 3 marks	3
		Maximum	**8**
(c)	JIT		
	Description		2
	Benefits	1 mark per point up to 2 marks	2
	Problems	1 mark per point up to 3 marks	3
		Maximum	**6**
(d)	Issues with standard costing and variance analysis – 1 mark per point up to a maximum of 5		**5**
Total			**25**

50 THEBE TELECOM (JUN 12)

Key answer tips

While the use of templates and checklists can help structure an answer, they can also become a problem. For example, DMAIC is perfect for part (b) but if you tried to use it in part (a), then you may have struggled. If a checklist isn't working, then try something else.

(a) There are a number of broad ways in which the implementation of Six Sigma improves quality in an organisation. These include:

- an increased focus on customers illustrated at Thebe by the strategic need to improve customer service and the project objective of improving customers' bills
- management decision-making being driven by data and facts not intuitions such as the use of customer satisfaction scores or numbers of complaints as key performance measures
- the identification of business processes' improvement as key to success which is exemplified by the mapping of the processes and then their redesign
- the proactive involvement of management such as the CEO championing the billing improvement project. Six Sigma depends on leadership which is provided by various experts who interact with the various Six Sigma projects which will be improving processes in the organisation
- the increased profile of quality issues and the increased knowledge of quality management that comes from the use of different layers of trained experts in the project. There are green belts who will often be line managers, who in additional to their normal work will lead Six Sigma projects. There are black belts who will exclusively specialise on Six Sigma and lead specific projects and there are master black belts who are Six Sigma experts in statistical methods who consult across several Six Sigma projects; and
- Six Sigma implementation requires collaboration across functional and divisional boundaries so bringing the focus of the whole organisation to quality issues as illustrated at Thebe by the involvement of all the business units in the billing project.

(b) The DMAIC process is as follows:

1 Define customer requirements/problem

Here the problem is the complaints on bills that result in customer dissatisfaction and delayed revenue receipt or potential loss of business. Customer requirements can be divided into those that are the minimum that is acceptable (e.g. billing errors are corrected), those that improve the customer's service experience (e.g. billing corrections completed swiftly) and those that go beyond the customer's expectations (e.g. offering additional services as compensation). The customers could be surveyed in order to identify if different customers have different needs (e.g. based on the three business units).

2 **Measure existing performance**

The number of customer complaints or scores below a threshold level on customer surveys will have to be measured and targets set (e.g. number of complaints per million bills issued or average time to resolve complaints). Measurement should focus on areas where the customer will value improvement. A key issue at this point is ensuring that the measurement system is reliable and this may require redesign of the existing customer survey forms/procedures.

3 **Analyse the existing process**

This step involves data collection in order to identify the root causes of problems and then techniques such as Pareto analysis will improve the focus of action on the issues that give raise to the majority of complaints based on the idea that 20% of the categories of causes will give rise to 80% of the complaints. For example, the analysis at Thebe could look at causes of delays in complaint resolution such as staff motivation or processing time for rebilling.

4 **Improve the process**

This is the implementation stage for any changes that are suggested and it is important at this stage to check on the cost and resource consequences of any suggested improvement.

5 **Control the process**

The improvement project will be monitored after implementation to ensure that the benefits of reduced complaints are maintained. This can be done through exception reporting if complaint numbers begin to exceed the tolerance set or continued monitoring of the time taken to resolve complaints. The general performance measure of the success of the project will be the retention of customers which is commonly measured through the churn rate of customers (percentage of existing customers lost per year).

(c) One quality practice which Thebes could consider is Total Quality Management. TQM is a philosophy of quality management that is applied to the whole organization and aims for continuous improvement and prevention of all errors. In this sense it is consistent with the introduction of Six Sigma. TQM is more frequently used in manufacturing organisations where the impact of quality failures in the production process may be that goods are scrapped. However it is possible to apply the concepts to an organization such as Thebes and a focus on improvement to process and minimizing errors in all aspects of the business could enhance the customer experience which is a key aim of Thebes. A TQM approach would also provide support to the Six Sigma programme and ensure quality is maintained and improved in all aspects of the business.

Kaizen costing is another quality practice which Thebes could introduce. This practice focuses on small, incremental cost reductions throughout the production process. Again it is more commonly found in manufacturing but elements of the concept may be applied to service industries. One key aspect of Kaizen costing is the involvement and empowerment of staff. As Thebes is aiming to differentiate with respect to customer service, involving staff could be beneficial. However Kaizen costing does have the overall aim to make cost reductions which is not considered by the CEO to be the main focus for Thebes.

Target costing is something which also may be applied. This concept focuses on the customer and their requirements in terms of quality, service and price and takes into account all costs occurring in the product life-cycle. This is appropriate for Thebes in the sense that it starts with external factors and customer needs. However identifying and therefore analysing the appropriate costs may be difficult for Thebes due to the nature of the business.

It is recommended that Thebes consider a Total Quality Management approach which will support the Six Sigma programme. Kaizen costing and Target costing are not recommended for the reasons given above.

Examiner's comments

Part (a) was poorly answered with much evidence of candidates trying to use DMAIC as a template for an answer when the question was asking about the six sigma method (in general) and not a specific implementation method. Nevertheless, it was possible to score some marks with this approach although the themes of Pande and Holpp were more relevant and those who used these scored close to full marks in this part.

Part (b) was usually done very well by the candidates who attempted it. Many candidates scored full marks by describing each of the steps and then illustrating the step with a relevant comment for Thebe.

ACCA marking scheme

		Marks
(a)	Up to 3 marks per theme for each of three themes.	
	Maximum	**8**
(b)	Up to 3 marks per stage of the process with 1 mark for a general description and 2 marks for application to the scenario.	
	Maximum	**9**
(c)	Up to 4 marks per quality practice including: TQM Kaizen costing Target costing	
	Maximum	**8**
Total		**25**

51 LINCOLN & LINCOLN ADVERTISING (DEC 12)

Key answer tips

In parts (a) and (b) ensure you address your advice to the individual circumstances of the three offices instead only offering generic comments for the whole company. The scenario gives much detail on the three offices and each faces their own challenges requiring a tailored response – indeed, the CEO in the scenario specifically advises you to avoid 'a one-size fits all policy'.

(a) Regional office performance

Fundamentally, all three offices are doing well.

	North	East	West
	$m	$m	$m
Net income	20	65	80
Net cash flow in year	24	86	46

They have all delivered profits at its most basic level (net income) and positive cash flows. In addition, there have only been positive residual incomes and returns on capital employed of over 50%. However, these are not effective performance measures for a service company such as LLA. The intangible nature of many of the assets and services provided will make traditional measures based on capital employed less reliable. A more thorough analysis of performance would require data on customer satisfaction and retention.

However, the offices do show differences in their growth and liquidity prospects.

1. The North office has seen a decline in revenues over the three periods (by 1.9% in the most recent year). As a result, net income has fallen by 4.8% in the last year. The office has the lowest operating margins.
2. The East office has stable revenues growing slightly (although it would help to gain a clearer perspective on this figure by benchmarking against the wider market for advertising). The East office has managed to hold down cost of sales and this has driven a strong increase in net income (by 12.1% over 2011).
3. The West office has seen the highest growth in revenues (by 8.9% over 2011). But this has led to strains in working capital as receivable days has risen to 93 days (well above the 54–59 day range for the North and East offices). This, and a higher level of capital expenditure, helps to explain why West is seeing a fall in cash flows generated while driving its profits higher. It should be noted that West is obtaining significantly higher operating margins than North or East as well. This may be as a result of the large capital expenditure that seems to be going into that office.

(b) Suitable performance measures at LLA

Net income is not wholly the responsibility of the regional management as head office costs are allocated outside of their control. Therefore, measures based on operating profit are more appropriate for the regional managers at LLA. However, even using operating profit, residual income and return on capital employed are less meaningful for a service-based business, since the business will not use a great deal of tangible assets compared to a manufacturing business. More meaningful measures would be revenue growth and, in cost terms, the ratio of staff costs to revenue. If residual income were to be used, it may be more appropriate to use different notional interest rates for the different offices. This is justified as it seems that West may be in a different environment and with its higher capital spend, it may be taking more risks, for example, by investing in technology to aid the creative design process.

Specifically, at present, the following performance metrics match to the issues at each office:

1 At North, the need is to turn around the decline in revenue and so revenue growth would be set as a target. However, this must not encourage the 'buying' of revenue by slashing prices and so an operating margin measure would be an appropriate additional control.

2 At East, the business appears stable and therefore efficiencies should be sought. East should focus on staff costs as it is paying 37% of revenue to its staff compared to as little as 31% at West. There may be economic reasons for this – the East office may be in the richest and most expensive part of Veeland and so it costs more to attract good employees to work there. The East office could pass on to the other offices how it has driven such high gross margins (72% as opposed to 66% at West).

3 At West, the business needs to continue its growth at the best operating margins but it must maintain control of working capital and so turn profit into cash. Therefore, debtor days or current assets should be targeted.

It would assist decision-making if suitable benchmarks internal (office to office) and external (competitors) to LLA were also found and included in performance reporting. A further suitable external measure may be the market share that each office holds in its region.

Therefore, it is recommended that operating profit is a more appropriate general measure for the offices at LLA with revenue growth and staff costs ratio as subsidiary indicators of performance. There are additional detailed indicators noted above to address each office's specific problems.

(c) Remuneration packages

Generally, using industry norms as a basic benchmark will help to ensure that staff are kept broadly happy, although it will not motivate them to outperform their peers.

Taking each of the staff levels in turn:

Senior management

Their basic salary reflects historic norms and the bonus should motivate performance. It is notable that no account is taken of the different economic conditions that each office may find itself in and so there may be resentment from those in offices where the general economy is doing poorly to those who are in a region with good performance and so profits are growing easily.

It may be worthwhile trying to benchmark the performance of each office against its regional competitors, although it can be hard to obtain such detailed information.

Creative staff

The creatives' packages are set when recruited. This could lead to a loss of motivation, especially for those who get only a fixed salary. If a bonus is paid, then it is currently based on revenue and not profits and so there is no mechanism to control costs on projects with these employees. There will be tension between the need for imaginative ideas and cost efficient ones. Overall, it is likely that each staff member should have a personalised package with a performance element that would be based on the assessment of a superior manager. In order to maintain some sense of objectivity, the criteria that the manager might use to judge performance should be agreed across the firm and could include, primarily, winning new business in tender competitions and, secondarily, winning industry awards.

Buying staff

The packages for the buying staff appear to be based on appropriate performance, although the setting of such targets depends heavily on the expertise of the finance team and, as they are based in the East office, they may lack the local knowledge to set the budget accurately. It may be wise to maintain the bulk of the buyers' remuneration as a fixed salary element as a result.

Account management staff

It is surprising that this group of client-facing staff are not paid on performance. It would seem that their performance could be directly measured by client retention and new business won, so it would be common for such staff to have a high percentage of their remuneration based on performance and not be wholly fixed. Measures such as numbers of clients and total client revenues would be appropriate for these posts.

Administration staff

This is a common method of remuneration for these types of jobs and in line with the general market. A small bonus based on the overall performance of the firm may help to create a culture of loyalty throughout the business. It is unlikely to be efficient to set individual targets for such employees, given that there will probably be a large number of them.

Examiner's comments

In part (a) most candidates understood that there were differences between the offices but failed to bring them out in their answers. The marks in this question were for analysis of the data not its repetition. Therefore, those candidates who explained the implications of the data or succeeded in connecting trends in one indicator with another scored well (e.g. falling revenue plus fixed costs leads to larger falls in profit). The best answers offered a general overview of the three offices performance and then took each office in turn to bring out the commercial issues present there e.g. West's rapid growth but dangerous increase in receivables. Future candidates should consider the reader in writing their responses. In this situation, the board would have found an answer divided into sections by office much more helpful than split into sections based on the standard headings of an accountant's ratio analysis.

Similarly in part (b) candidates scored well if they appreciated the need to address the regional offices' specific requirements. Many candidates offered a reasonable set of generic suggestions for the company as a whole but missed out on the regional differences. The first part of the requirement sought an evaluation of the existing performance measure (net income) and a recognition of two key facts – this measure contained uncontrollable costs and it was too general to cover the issues across the company. Other criticisms of the measure were credited as well, however, these were the main areas.

The second part required justified recommendations of alternative metrics. Most candidates realised that non-financial indicators would be useful and those that made suggestions appropriate to LLA scored well. Those that offered lists of metrics that could apply to any company scored significantly less well. There were many answers that provided lengthy (possibly rote-learned) proposals of ROCE, EVA™ and RI although these were of limited use in this scenario. The better solutions made sure that their comments on these alternatives were consistent with their criticism of the existing measure.

Part (c) was typically well done. Most candidates addressed their comments to the five different grades of staff given in the scenario. However, many candidates assumed that all of the existing policies must be wrong and so only made negative comments – future candidates need to be aware that evaluate means to give a balanced assessment (including both the positive and negative aspects of an issue). On the suggested improvements, most candidates provided practical suggestions addressing the weaknesses previously discussed. For example, the best candidates suggested that the account management staff should have part of their remuneration based on measures of client satisfaction such as retention.

ACCA marking scheme

			Marks
(a)	Discuss overall performance	up to	1
	Evaluate measures calculated and offer suggested improvements	up to	3
	Discuss performance of each office	up to	7
		Maximum	**10**
(b)	1 mark per point	**up to a maximum of**	**8**
	(To obtain a good mark a candidate must address the issue of controllability and responsibility)		
(c)	1 mark per point	**up to a max of**	**7**
Total			**25**

52 LANDUAL LAMPS (JUN 13)

Key answer tips

The question required an assessment of the current transfer pricing system and then the consideration of two changes: one to the transfer pricing policy and one to the divisional structure of the company. To answer this question well it is vital that you consider the implications of any changes, recalculating the figures in part (a), if necessary.

(a) Current transfer pricing policy

A good transfer pricing system will ensure goal congruence and fair performance measurement between the divisions and maintain a suitable level of managerial autonomy within each division. Generally, the use of variable costs is helpful as it leads to optimal decisions for the company as a whole. The use of fixed production costs obscures these marginal costs and can lead to sub-optimal decisions by the divisions.

Electrical components

The use of a market price basis for electrical components makes sense, as these are generic products for which there is a ready external market. Therefore, the performance of the components division in their production can be readily compared to this market and the assembly division will accept such a price, as this is its alternative to sourcing internally. This activity does return a small contribution to head office costs, currently $383k (1,557 – 804 – 370). This small contribution reflects the generic nature of the products.

However, the assembly division could reasonably argue that the market price is too high, since an internal transfer of components does not require a number of costs (transport, marketing and bad debts). These should be deducted from the market price in order to get an adjusted market price. If this is done, then the contribution to head office costs from electrical components within the components division falls to $114k (1,288 – 804 – 370 or 383 – 269), as shown below.

Housing components

The housing components are currently priced using actual production costs. This makes sense, as these components are uniquely produced for the assembly division and there is no external market since this would give away Landual's competitive advantage. It could be argued that the unique work in housing components should be rewarded with greater divisional profit. The components division only covers its actual production costs and gets no contribution towards the allocated head office costs from these components. Thus, since housing represents the bulk of the division's revenue (84% = 8,204/9,761), it will be difficult for the components division to ever earn a significant profit. A mark-up on actual total production costs of 30% (say) would not seem unusual for such unique products and would lead to additional divisional profit of $2,461 (30% of $8,204k). This would significantly shift the location of the divisional profit from assembly to housing.

However, by using actual rather than budget costs, this means that there is no incentive to reduce on costs by the components division, as it will always receive these back from the assembly division. This lack of incentive could explain the failure to meet budget by $575,000 caused in the production of the housing components.

Applying all of these changes, divisional reports would be:

Data for the year ended 31 March 2013 Notes:

		Components Division	Assembly Division
		$000	$000
Sales	Electrical	1,288	
	Housing	9,918	
	sub-total	11,206	15,794
Cost of sales			
	Electrical	804	1,288
	Housing	6,902	9,918
Fixed production costs			
	Electrical	370	
	Housing	1,302	
	sub-total	1,672	1,268
Allocated HO costs		461	2,046
Profit		1,367	1,274

Notes:

1 Transfer price for electrical components is reduced by additional costs of external sales.

	$000
Previous market price for electrical	1,557
Less: additional costs for external sales	(269)
Adjusted market price	1,288

2 The transfer price for housing is now budgeted total production cost (7,629 = 6,902 + 1,302 – 575), marked up by 30%.

(b) The change in transfer policy has the effect of reducing the revenue/cost of sales of the components/assembly divisions by the fixed production costs of the housing components ($1,302k). It shifts this amount of divisional profit from the components to the assembly division. This change seems unusual since the competitive advantage of the business lies in the housing designs, and yet this change is further emphasising the importance of the assembly division which does not seem to be the value-adding element of the business.

There is a danger, here, that the company focuses on the work of the division with higher profits and so downgrades the unique work done by the components division. However, the clarity of using variable costs only in transfer pricing may assist the company overall in achieving optimal pricing and profit.

There is no change to the company's profit from such a change.

Working:

Data for the year ended 31 March 2013

		Components	**Assembly**	**Landual Lamps**
		$000	$000	$000
Sales	Electrical	1,557		
	Housing	6,902		
	sub-total	8,459	15,794	15,794
Cost of sales				
	Electrical	804	1,557	
	Housing	6,902	6,902	
	sub-total	7,706	8,459	7,706
Fixed production costs				
	Electrical	370		
	Housing	1,302		
	sub-total	1,672	1,268	2,940
Allocated HO costs		461	2,046	2,507
Profit		(1,380)	4,021	2,641

Note: Only change is that housing is now charged to assembly on variable cost only.

> ***Tutorial note***
>
> *This calculation is much more than required as the change is simple – it is presented here for clarity only.*

(c) Housing division

The housing division is now a cost centre and so it will be easier for it to focus on cost control (avoiding adverse budget variances) and quality of its output (as it makes the key components for the company's products). However, there may be an adverse effect on the motivation of divisional managers through losing profit centre status and this must be countered by altering their reward packages to focus them on costs.

Electrical division

The electrical division can be seen to be making a small divisional profit ($335k). Its treatment as a profit centre makes sense, as it can be compared to similar companies for benchmarking purposes and also so that Landual can consider easily the 'make or buy' decision for such generic components. Obviously, at present, electrical is making a contribution to HO costs, which means that it should continue to obtain the business from the assembly division.

Assembly division

The assembly division is unaffected by the changes, although the greater clarity of results in the electrical division will allow the managers of the division to ensure that the electrical division remains competitive.

Landual Lamps

The change has no effect on the company profit reported but it would be hoped that the change would bring the benefits noted above (cost savings in housing and greater motivation to compete in electrical) and so improve profits in the future.

Working:

Note: Head office costs have been reallocated *pro rata* with cost of sales.

	$000	$000	$000	$000
Sales			15,794	15,794
Electrical		1,557		
Housing				
Cost of sales				7,706
Electrical		804	1,557	
Housing	6,902		8,204	
Fixed production costs			1,268	2,940
Electrical		370		
Housing	1,302			
Allocated HO costs	413	48	2,046	2,507
	(8,617)	335	2,719	2,641

Examiner's comments

This question was generally poorly done with weak (often no) efforts at handling the quantification issues – recalculating the current transfer price, calculating the impact of the two proposed changes on the various entities in the scenario. Again, this meant that candidates often had very little to say in evaluating or giving advice in the commentary parts of their answers. Also, candidates did not focus their answers on the stated area of competitive advantage for Landual in making the housing components. This ought to have been a priority.

Part (a). The requirement emphasised the need for calculations. There were a number of faults in the existing system which needed to be pointed out with the impact that correcting these would have on the divisions in the company.

In part (b). A useful answer here would provide firstly, what this change would do to profit in the two divisions and for the company as a whole and then, from this, consider the likely reactions of the key stakeholders (the three sets of management). Unfortunately, if the (simple) quantification work was not done then very few candidates could see that this change lead to lower profits in the division that was the key competitive advantage of the company (the difficult process of design and manufacture of the housing components).

Part (c). The question provided an illustration of the impact of changing the emphasis of a division from profit centre to cost centre as well as increasing the number of divisions. Again as in part (b), the calculations were straightforward but where they were done at all, they were often done poorly. A common basic mistake was imputing a revenue stream to the new housing division when it was stated that it was to become a cost centre. Future candidates would be advised to consider, during their revision, the impacts that strategic changes such as designation of cost, profit and investment centres would have on the performance management of divisions or departments within a company.

ACCA marking scheme

			Marks
(a)	Electrical components Basic policy – up to 2 marks Use adjusted market price – 1 mark Housing components Basic policy – up to 2 marks Need for mark-up – up to 2 marks Use of budgeted costs – up to 2 marks Workings: New divisional profit – electrical policy 1 mark housing policy 2 marks		
		Maximum	**10**
(b)	New component revenue figure – 1 mark New profit figures, 1 for each entity – up to 3 marks Comments – 1 mark per point up to 4 marks		
		Maximum	**6**
(c)	New profit figures, 1 for each entity – up to 4 marks Comments – 1 mark per point up to 7 marks		
		Maximum	**9**
Total			**25**

53 BEACH FOODS (JUN 15) (AMENDED)

> **Key answer tips**
>
> Make sure you apply the models mentioned to the specific scenario in the question as much as possible.

(a) Economic value added (EVA™) as a divisional performance measure

The main benefit to EVA™ is its link to the overall corporate objective of adding shareholder value. It is an appropriate measure to use if the company is applying value-based management. Therefore, by using it as a divisional performance measure, divisional managers should also be motivated to work in the best interest of the company as a whole and this ought to be one of the main objectives of a divisional performance measure.

The other advantages of EVA™ are that:

- It gives an absolute measure so showing the overall contribution to the company.
- The basic test of performance is simple since if EVA™ is positive, then the division is generating a return above that required by the providers of finance. (ROI requires a target level to be set usually based on benchmarking to the industry sector.)
- The adjustments within the calculation of EVA™ mean that the measure is closer to cash flows than accounting profits and so is less subject to choices in accounting policies.
- EVA™ encourages investment for the future (for example, in advertising and development) by removing such costs from the performance period and treating them like capital expenditure. This will reduce the dysfunctional temptation for management to engage in some short-term decision-making, which can be a problem with the capital employed figure from the financial statements which is used in ROI and RI. This is likely to be particularly appropriate at Beach, where R&D is significant.

However, EVA™ does have disadvantages, some of which are common to the two suggested alternative measures and some which are specific.

All three measures are dependent on historical data and so are only of limited use in forecasting future performance.

The specific criticism of EVA™ that it is complicated is reasonable as the full version requires more than 100 adjustments to the information in the normal financial statements. RI and ROI are derived from headline information in the financial statements which would be more familiar to the board.

EVA™ (like RI) uses a charge for the capital employed in the division. EVA™ uses the weighted-average cost of capital for the company as a whole and may not reflect the risks of the division. However, RI uses a notional cost of capital based on the risk of the division, which will be subject to an element of judgement and estimate. Also, as an unlisted business, the estimation of WACC is difficult.

Unlike ROI, EVA™ would not help to judge relative divisional managerial performance at Beach if the divisions are not of similar size.

It is sensible to avoid consideration of the R&D division in this discussion as it is not a revenue-generating division.

(b) Workings:

Baby division

	20X5
	$m
Revenue	220
Divisional operating costs	121
Controllable profit	99
R&D costs recharged	11
Profit after R&D costs	88
Apportioned head office management fees	28
Divisional profit before tax	60

	ROI	**RI**
		$m
Based on controllable profit	23%	52.4
Based on profit after R&D	21%	41.4
Based on divisional profit	14%	13.4

The key assumption in the calculation of both metrics is which profit figure to use. Controllable profit relates to those revenues and costs under direct control of the divisional manager but this does not reflect the R&D costs, although it takes account of the revenues which new products are generating. It would be more appropriate to include these costs in an assessment of the divisional managers' performance, especially if the product development was at the request of the divisional management and the transfer price was widely agreed. The assessment of the division itself should include all relevant operating costs and so the divisional profit would be the appropriate figure to use.

The RI and EVA™ give the same assessment that the division is performing well (both figures are positive). It is not possible to do a simple comparison between RI and EVA™ as there are different tax and R&D cost treatments to take into account. The ROI figure should be compared to the comparator; however, this is not possible as the profit used in calculation of the comparator is not specified.

(c) Baby division

As the star of the Beach portfolio and with new products launching, it would appear sensible that Baby was an investment division with the autonomy to continue to develop its business successfully. However, it is unclear where the decision to commit to a new product rests as the R&D division actually does the development work. In that case, it may be appropriate to make Baby a profit centre and manage it according to its profit generating ability.

The business is rapidly growing and so a budget-constrained style would be inappropriate as it would stifle the creativity necessary for such a division. Alternatively, a non-accounting style where criteria other than profit such as revenue growth and new product development may be appropriate. Once the market sector has matured further then given a strong market share, the focus of the division will move to optimising profit.

Chocolate division

As the cash cow of the Beach portfolio, Chocolate should be run for the profit which it generates. It could be classified as a profit centre since its sector is mature and there are unlikely to be plans to make new investment. Alternatively, it could be classified as an investment centre so it does not have to wait for approval of limited capital expenditure such as happened with the production line upgrade. The management style should be budget-constrained with special emphasis placed on the ability of the division to generate cash not just profit.

R&D division

The R&D division has no source of revenue other than internal recharge of its services and so it should be a cost centre. However, the value of the division will only be appreciated if the overall profit generated from these new products can be demonstrated. This may be the cause of the problem with the Baby division managers. They only see the recharge cost appearing in their performance reports without the revenue which these new products are generating being specifically disclosed. It may be helpful to have a profit calculated for each product over its lifecycle to demonstrate the value of the division which is seen by Beach as vital.

A budget-constrained style of management would be appropriate where the budget is set separately for each new product development project. However, it would be important not to constrain the division within a fixed overall budget if there is a number of good product development ideas. The generation of ideas may be helped by using a non-accounting style, giving priority to more than just budget numbers (e.g. number of new product ideas/favourable press comments on new product launches).

A specific approach will therefore need to take account of all these factors in order to arrive at a style of management which meets the needs of the company as a whole.

Examiner's comments

Part (a). Generally, this was done reasonably well. Those candidates who attempted to show how EVA^{TM} could be affected by conditions in the two relevant divisions scored well. However, the question did not require any lengthy description of how EVA^{TM} is calculated. This should have been obvious as the company is already using this measure for its overall performance.

Part (b). Those candidates who realised the nature of the assumptions in their calculations, specifically the difference between divisional and managerial performance, scored highly. They considered the choice of profit to use in their calculations as central and calculated the profit from multiple perspectives. Many candidates realised that there were different profits to use but did not do the numerical work and so their answers lacked the evidential support that was clearly within their ability to produce.

Part (c). This part was poorly answered as many candidates clearly did not know the criteria for the choice of responsibility centre (the centre headings to choose from were given in the scenario). Lengthy descriptions of the three management styles were not helpful here as the candidate was expected to demonstrate that understanding through the application of the ideas to the scenario.

The general lesson for future candidates from this question is to learn not just the models or jargon but how to apply them in a specific scenario. Candidates should also make sure that they understand issues around responsibility accounting and the choice of responsibility centre for controlling a business unit.

ACCA marking scheme

		Marks
(a)	1 mark per point	
	Maximum	**6**
(b)	Calculations: Correct calculation of both RI and ROI for more than one profit figure – 1 mark per profit figure used, up to a maximum of 3 marks RI and 3 marks for ROI Comments, 1 mark per point up to a max of 4 marks	
	Maximum	**6**
(c)	1 mark per point, up to 3 marks for any one division – all recommendations must be justified within the answer to gain credit – high marks within the answer for any one division can only be scored by discussing both the type of centre and management style	
	Maximum	**8**
Professional marks		
Analysis and Evaluation		
•	Comprehensive evaluation of the use of EVA™, including a discussion of the relative advantages and disadvantages compared to RI/ROI	
•	Appropriate use of the data and information in the appendices to perform suitable calculations for ROI and RI, including recognition of the impact of the assumptions made, and to support discussion on divisional control and management style	
Scepticism		
•	Recognition that the directors' questioning of the value of using EVA™ is valid but there are also drawbacks to the alternative methods being considered	
•	Recognition that the RI and ROI have been calculated based on a number of stated assumptions	
Commercial Acumen		
•	Effective use of examples drawn from the scenario information and other practical considerations related to the context to illustrate the points made throughout the answer	
	Maximum	**5**
Total		**25**

54 POSIE FURNITURE (SEPT/DEC 15)

Key answer tips

Make sure you learn the DMAIC model and how to apply it, particularly focussing on the implications of each stage on the business.

(a) The DMAIC process is a technique used to implement six sigma to improve existing processes and is split into five phases as described below.

Define the process

The CEO is concerned that the increase in returns from customers is increasing costs and threatens to affect the Posie brand. Six sigma focuses closely on the requirements of the customer and it is important to be clear exactly what customers' requirements are and in this case specifically why products are returned.

The objective of the project needs to be clear, in this case to reduce the number of customer returns.

Customers will expect certain minimum requirements from the manufacturing and packaging process, for example, that the furniture is able to be properly assembled and all the necessary components are included in the box. They will also expect the goods to be delivered undamaged within a reasonable time and at the time and date promised when the order was placed. Customers' perceptions of quality should correspond to the price paid, though different customers will have different expectations of this.

Beyond this basic requirement, there may be aspects of the manufacturing product which further enhance the customers' experience of the product and presumably of the Posie brand. Customers may be particularly pleased with furniture which is delivered early or at a time especially convenient to them, or which is robust, durable and 'well-made'. These perceptions are subjective and may equally relate to design or the quality of raw materials as to the manufacturing process. By identifying where the products exceed customers' expectations, it may be possible to focus more on these aspects in the future. While products which significantly exceed customers' expectations will enhance the Posie brand, it may also indicate a quality of manufacture which is too high and allow Posie to reduce manufacturing costs in accordance with its cost leadership strategy whilst still having mainly satisfied customers.

Measure the existing process

The current returns figures do give some data to as to why products are returned, but its usefulness is limited as it is unclear which of the categories relates to defective manufacture, and which relate to activities of other divisions. The ambiguity of the data and category definitions will need addressing to enable the process to be measured effectively.

Returns in Category 1 could be because the goods were not manufactured or packed properly in the manufacturing division, but could also be due to poor design, customers losing components or simply being unable to assemble furniture.

Damaged goods in Category 2 probably do not arise because of defective manufacturing either, though customers may wrongly categorise defective goods as damaged. For the other categories it is less clear. Though goods may become damaged by the distribution company, it seems that only a small number of returns relate directly to them.

Returns in Categories 3 and 4 could be due to defective manufacture or if the customer had simply changed their minds and no longer wanted the product. In Category 3, the identification of 'defective' items is too broad.

Returns in Category 5 which arrived late are clearly not due to manufacturing defects and as this causes only 2% of returns, is relatively insignificant.

Currently 10% of Posie's sales are of products from other manufacturers. There is no indication from the data given how many of the returns relate to these products, nor of the total number of returns relative to the number of items sold.

Therefore the existing data are insufficient to reliably measure existing performance and take no account of inputs such as raw materials. Only items which customers value should be measured. The CEO has suggested more detailed data are required, for example, on overall customer satisfaction with the manufacturing, but this is at 93% which already seems high and there is little point in incurring costs to measure what customers are already satisfied with. In the context of the six sigma project at Posie, there is little that can be done to improve this particular area and such items should not be measured.

Analyse the process

This stage is where the root causes of the problems are identified. Additional information may be needed, for example, to analyse customer returns by type of product, by country of sale or with a clearer definition of what is meant by 'defective'. By doing so, Posie may identify areas of the business where customer returns are particularly high and so be able to focus on these.

Improve the process

At this stage the proposals for improving the process are implemented and availability of resources and likely costs of making the improvements need to be carefully considered. Posie may need to consider which aspects of the production or packaging process could be improved, for example, by better maintenance or calibration of machinery. Additional training of staff may also be required.

Control

This is the on-going monitoring that the reduction in customer returns due to defective manufacturing is being maintained. Reporting on the number of returns may be done by exception if they reach a particular level. In Posie, it seems likely that the data on customer returns used to manage this process will need to be redesigned to make it clearer in which responsibility centre the problems arise. The ongoing monitoring may indicate that some of the earlier stages in the DMAIC process need to be revisited.

(b) (i) The CEO wants to identify which responsibility centres are the root causes of the problem of customer returns. A responsibility centre is a part of the business where a manager has specific authority and accountability for its performance and so Posie will need information relating to aspects of performance specific to the centre. For example, performance data relating to the reasons for customer returns need to be clearly segregated between responsibility centres. Currently, the information compiled on customer returns does not do this and some categories of return may result from manufacturing defects but some will be from problems outside the manufacturing division, or even outside Posie itself, for example, from poor quality raw materials purchased externally, or because of late deliveries or damaged goods caused by the distribution company.

Once information has been analysed and responsibility has been identified, then the managers of those areas will need the information drilled down into even further, as in order to improve they need to know which specific areas they can control.

It would be unfair to make managers responsible for aspects of performance which they are unable to control, and the board member responsible for manufacturing quality has recently resigned because of this.

Posie needs to ensure it produces performance data to an appropriate level of detail so as not to overload the users with too much data. For board level reporting, the information in the current board reporting pack may be too detailed and it would be sufficient just to produce summary data on the overall level of returns relative to sales. Responsibility centres would need much more detailed information, perhaps even down to product or production line level.

However, Posie should also consider the costs and resources required to provide more detailed performance data. Given Posie's cost leadership strategy, the costs of data collection may outweigh the benefits of doing so.

Performance data should be provided at an appropriate frequency. For the Posie main board, monthly reporting may be sufficient to alert them to any problems. Responsibility centres will need much more frequent, even daily or weekly details of the levels of customer returns so that they can react quickly to any problems identified. At the moment, the returns data are compiled every six months, possibly due to the difficulties in obtaining data from the IT systems in the overseas businesses. Even for a board level report, this seems much too infrequent.

(ii) At the moment, the overseas subsidiaries are being designated as profit centres and managers will be held accountable for both revenues and costs. As they do not manufacture, it seems reasonable to designate them as revenue centres. As such, managers would be held accountable for just revenues as they have little or no control over costs as most goods for resale are purchased from the manufacturing division.

The performance data produced by Posie's subsidiaries' IT systems will therefore switch to focus more on revenues rather than costs. As revenue centres they may well have some freedom to change selling prices. Posie will need to ensure the subsidiaries have information to monitor the impact of different pricing strategies and will need to provide the management of these subsidiaries with information gleaned from the external environment. It will be important to evaluate competitors' pricing strategies when making pricing decisions.

A potential problem with providing only performance data relating to revenue is that managers could focus too much on achieving revenue targets rather than maintaining or improving profitability. As they are autonomous subsidiaries, there will be aspects of their own costs, such as staffing costs and other overheads, which they will be able to have some control over. It is important that Posie ensures the management still has sight of this information to ensure that such costs are still controlled effectively.

Furthermore, if the overseas managers are only held responsible for sales, this may mean they do not focus sufficiently on addressing reasons why goods are returned, and so levels of returns may increase. This means that once Posie undertakes the exercise to identify the root causes of the returns from customers, this information is shared and monitored.

Posie needs to be aware of these issues when determining information requirements if the reclassification of the subsidiaries goes ahead. It will not be as simple as assuming that they will now only need information on revenues.

Examiner's comments

Part (a). A key focus to the question was the use of DMAIC methodology and it was clear that a few candidates had little knowledge about how this methodology worked. Given that the use of the methodology was being tested, knowledge of it was essential and candidates who could not demonstrate this scored very few, if any, marks.

An explanation of the DMAIC methodology scored a few marks though the majority of credit in this question was to be gained from applying the methodology to the scenario. One of the main shortcomings in many responses to this question was a failure to recognise properly how to use the data given with each part of the methodology – Define, Measure, Analyse, Improve, Control and actually how all this connected to customer requirements and expectations. Answers were not provided in sufficient depth.

Part (b) (i). This part was badly done overall as many candidates did not read the requirement of the question and offered responses which considered the effect on the organisation's performance. Such responses scored few marks. The need to recognise the effect upon information requirements is fundamental with the introduction of a six sigma project and a DMAIC methodology. The data that has to be captured is significant and it is important for a candidate sitting APM to recognise the effects of the introduction of a major development such as this.

Part (b) (ii). Few candidates attempted this question in a meaningful way and a number failed to differentiate between the two types of responsibility centre.

ACCA marking scheme				
				Marks
(a)	Use of DMAIC			
		Define		
		1 mark per point	up to	4
		Measure		
		1 mark per point	up to	6
		Analyse		3
		Improve		3
		Control		3
			Maximum	**15**
(b)	(i)	Definition		1
		Impact on information requirements		
		1 mark per point	up to	6
			Maximum	**6**
	(ii)	Impact on information requirements		
		1 mark per point	up to	4
			Maximum	**4**
Total				**25**

55 UNIVERSITIES IN TEELND (MAR/JUN 16)

Key answer tips

Part (a) – Value for money (VFM) is a key tool for assessing performance in a not-for-profit organisation (NFPO). It is important to be able to explain VFM in terms of the 3Es, i.e. economy, efficiency and effectiveness.

Part (b) should be relatively straightforward if you have your core knowledge of the advantages and disadvantages of league tables in place. Make sure you reference your points back to the scenario.

Tutorial note

The solution given is very detailed and candidates would not have to provide an answer of this length to score maximum marks. It is provided to give an idea of the scope of the relevant points which could have been made.

(a) Public sector organisations such as the Teeland universities receive all their funding from central government and do not have the generation of profit as an objective. Furthermore, their objectives such as 'improving the standard of education of the citizens of Teeland' cannot be measured in financial terms. The value for money of the universities can be assessed using the '3Es' framework of economy, efficiency and effectiveness.

Economy

This involves obtaining the inputs to the service at the lowest possible cost, while still maintaining the quality of the inputs. In practice, this may be difficult to do, and a reduction in cost may lead to a reduction in quality.

From the performance data given, the average annual payroll cost per member of academic staff is highest in Northcity University at $62,286 ($109m/1,750). This is 51% higher than Eastcity University, which has the lowest cost at $41,237 of the four universities given. The high costs in Northcity University may reflect the fact that staff there may be more highly qualified or that highly skilled, trained staff are attracted to work there because of the high standards of teaching and academic research.

A higher payroll cost per member of academic staff may not necessarily mean a particular university is not giving good value for money. The relatively high salary costs in Southcity University of $62,083 may simply reflect the higher costs of living in the capital city and so comparison between the regions may be inappropriate.

As such, there may be a conflict between this performance measure and the ability of the universities to achieve their objectives, such as to improve educational standards in Teeland. The politician's proposal to reduce salary levels for new recruits may reduce the number of appropriately qualified and skilled staff who wish to work there. This may reduce the standard of teaching and academic research, and as a result, the universities' performance against their stated objectives. This means that focusing solely on economy would not ensure the universities achieve value for money.

Efficiency

Efficiency measures the amount of outputs relative to the amount of inputs. The number of academic staff per student may be a suitable measurement but there may be differences between universities which would make it hard to compare results.

For example, there are 10.1 (17,600/1,750) students per member of academic staff in Northcity University, which is ranked number one in the Teeland government's provisional league table. There are 17.9 in Westcity University which is ranked much lower at 21. It would seem therefore, that increasing the number of students relative to the number of academic staff as per the politician's proposal may reduce the performance of the universities against their stated objectives and as such will not increase value for money.

The politician's comparison with the number of students per academic staff in neighbouring Veeland may not be appropriate. Whilst the politician's assertion that educational standards are higher in Veeland may be correct, the undertaking of high quality academic research may not be a key objective of the universities there, or the quality of research may be lower than in Teeland.

Effectiveness

Effectiveness measures whether the objectives of the organisation are being met. The stated objectives of the Teeland universities are to improve the overall standard of education of citizens in Teeland, to engage in high quality academic research and to provide well-qualified university graduates to meet the needs of the graduate jobs market in Teeland.

Objective to improve the overall standard of education in Teeland

Currently, there is no direct measure of the performance of the universities' stated objectives to increase the level of education of the citizens of Teeland. The number of graduates entering graduate jobs and the results of the TSOR survey may indirectly measure the effectiveness of the universities in achieving this aim. More direct measures such as the number of students completing their studies, or obtaining good results in university exams may be more appropriate.

The effectiveness of the universities in improving the standard of education should really be related to the entry requirements of each university. Westcity University is the lowest ranking of the four universities in the provisional league table and has the lowest proportion of graduates entering graduate jobs at 50% (1,750/(11,200/3.2)). It also receives the lowest amount of research funding per student at around $1,250 ($14m/11,200), but it has the lowest entry requirements, which have been relaxed to encourage students from a more diverse range of backgrounds to study there. Therefore, the improvement in educational standards relative to students' attainment on entry may be higher than the position in the league table may suggest.

Objective to engage in high quality academic research

The stated aim of the universities to engage in high quality academic research is also not currently measured. The amount of research funding received from government and other organisations by each university may indirectly reflect the quality of the research there as providers of funds for research would probably look to fund high quality research.

This measure may, however, equally reflect that some types of research are more expensive than others. Southcity University, which is successful in science and technology subjects, receives $15,592 per student compared to $5,000 in Eastcity, which specialises in arts and humanities subjects. The funding received may be more indicative of the past quality of academic research rather than future quality, or may not even reflect the quality of the research and may be high due to wastage or inefficiency. The definition of 'quality' of research is unclear.

Objective to meet the needs of the graduate jobs market

The number of graduates from each university obtaining graduate jobs each year is an indirect measure how well each university is achieving this objective. However, the number of graduate jobs filled may simply reflect the number of students at each university and demand for graduate jobs in the economy.

Many graduates, including the most talented of them, may take graduate jobs overseas. In which case, the measure of graduate jobs filled may not be a clear measure of the objective to meet the needs of the graduate jobs market in Teeland. A more precise measure of graduates entering graduate jobs in Teeland may be more appropriate. Even this may be misleading, if graduates later return from overseas to enter graduate jobs in Teeland.

The definition of what is a 'graduate' job is subjective and likely to change over time, for example, as a result of changes in the economy. This again limits the usefulness of this measure in determining whether universities have met this objective.

The TSOR survey is a measure of effectiveness reflecting a basket of measures, one of which is students' own perceptions of their future job prospects. The measures in the TSOR survey are, however, highly subjective according to individuals' personal perceptions, for example, about students' job prospects and the quality of teaching at the university. Furthermore, the survey also covers a wider range of factors such as their overall satisfaction with university life. As such, this may not reflect the stated aims of the universities in Teeland. The TSOR score for Westcity University is considerably higher than for all the other universities, despite it having the lowest overall ranking.

(b) Effect of league tables on the quality of the Teeland universities

League tables encourage competition between universities

The publishing of league tables of the performance of the universities in Teeland should stimulate competition for high ranking between them. This should encourage them to find better ways to improve the quality of the service, achieve their performance objectives, and deliver greater value for money.

Sharing of resources may be discouraged

However, this may discourage knowledge or even resource sharing between the universities if they see themselves in competition for the best students and limited research funding. This could particularly be a problem if the university leaders were given performance targets and rewards based on their university's position in the league table. They may be encouraged to undertake 'gaming' and focus solely on their position within the league table to the detriment of other aspects of performance. This may mean the objectives for the universities overall in Teeland may not be achieved.

University leaders may focus on a narrow range of objectives

Students' overall experience of university life may be influenced by access to social, pastoral and sporting facilities. Management time and resources may be diverted away from these important areas by focusing on a narrow range of performance objectives such as improving educational standards and high quality research in order to boost the position in the league table.

Use of league table to ensure accountability of the universities

If the performance league tables are made publicly available, for example, on the internet as they are in Veeland, this should ensure the performance of the universities is transparent. This will mean that they are held accountable by the public for the quality of service and value for money which they provide.

League tables give choices to students and staff

To be really effective, league tables should provide users of the performance data, such as the public, with the ability to make choices based on the data given. Prospective students and staff will be able to make choices about which university to study or work at according to their position in the league tables. In addition, providers of funding such as the government will be able to identify where corrective action or additional funding may be required.

This could also be a disadvantage of using league tables, as the best students are likely to be attracted to the best universities, which are in turn likely to attract the most funding for academic research. This may cause a reduction in the overall performance of lower ranking universities, and therefore a failure of the universities as a whole to achieve the stated aim of improving educational standards in Teeland.

League tables may not reflect variation of standards at each university

There may also be considerable variation of the standards within one university, which a ranking in a league table will not address. For example, Southcity University offers courses in a variety of subjects and is particularly successful at science and technology subjects. This may mean that it achieves a high overall ranking in a league table, whereas its performance in other subjects may be weaker. For all of these reasons, the provision of league tables or performance data at a lower level, such as by subject area, may therefore be a better way to make the universities accountable to the public.

Regions may not be directly comparable

There may be inherent differences between universities which make comparison using league tables misleading or of limited value. For example, Eastcity University specialises in teaching arts and humanities. It may be inappropriate to compare it to universities offering a wide range of courses or specialising in science and technology subjects. Similarly, it may be misleading to compare universities of different sizes or in locations in different parts of Teeland. Universities which also attract students from outside Teeland, for example, those in capital or major cities, are likely to have more access to the most able students.

Due to its capital city location, Southcity University may incur additional costs of providing facilities and have to pay staff more to reflect the higher cost of living there. It may be more appropriate to produce league tables at a lower level, like within individual cities, to make the comparisons more meaningful and eliminate the effect of regional variations such as this.

There may be differences in the way different universities collect and report performance data. These problems can be reduced by the use of consistent and enforced policies for compiling performance data.

Resources required to produce league tables

Other problems relate to the targets chosen, external influences on results and cost of collating and measuring performance for the league table.

In Veeland, there is a sizeable government department dedicated to measuring performance. The cost of collecting performance data and compiling the league tables may therefore outweigh the benefits to be gained from doing so. It will use up resources which could be used, for example, in providing additional funding to the universities themselves.

Performance measures used to create league tables may be confusing and conflicting

By having a large number of targets such as in Veeland, this may cause confusion to managers, who may not know which to focus on. Similarly, it may be difficult to decide which performance measures are the most important.

Many performance measures chosen are likely to conflict. Reducing the salaries paid to academic staff may make it harder to recruit and retain experienced and well-qualified staff, which may lead to failing to meet the universities' key objectives. Similarly, increasing the number of students per member of academic staff is unlikely to help achieve any of the universities' objectives as staff will have less time available for teaching and for engaging in high quality research.

The use of league tables may demotivate staff and students

The Teeland politician's proposed target of a 5% annual increase in the number of students entering graduate jobs sounds very challenging and may be unrealistic. This will be especially so if accompanied by a reduction in the number of academic staff and a reduction of the salaries of new recruits. If the targets are felt to be unachievable by the university leaders, they may become demotivated, and give up on trying to achieve them altogether. This will especially be the case if this is an 'all or nothing' target. A more realistic target may at least ensure that some progress is made.

Students may also become demotivated if their university ranks poorly in league tables, even if the students themselves are satisfied with the standard of education they are receiving.

Similarly some performance measures, such as the number of students entering graduate jobs, which may be highly dependent on the economic conditions in Teeland, are not entirely under the control of the university leaders. The economic conditions in Teeland will be a key factor in determining the number of graduate jobs available there. University leaders may become demotivated by this measure as well and stop trying to improve.

The relative importance of different performance measures is subjective

The weighting of the different performance measures used by the Teeland government in arriving at the provisional ranking of the universities is subjective. It is difficult to determine which measures are the most important, and hence how each should be weighted. The opinions of different stakeholders on which are the most important measures will also vary. Academic staff and students may view different measures as important compared to the providers of finance (the Teeland government) and organisations who recruit university graduates.

Determining the relative importance of different performance measures in order to publish a league table is therefore difficult. Furthermore, the measures chosen, and their relative weightings, could differ from those in other countries. This would make it difficult to benchmark performance against universities in other countries, such as Veeland.

Examiner's comments

Part (a). Many candidates made good use of the 3Es to structure their answer. A good answer also utilised the data in the scenario to illustrate their points.

Part (b). This part was generally fairly well done with candidates breaking their answers into two parts (benefits and problems) and illustrating their answers with specific issues between the universities in the scenario.

ACCA marking scheme			
			Marks
(a)	Description of 3Es in public sector organisations – up to 3 marks Application of 3Es – 1 mark per relevant point		
		Maximum	**12**
(b)	Potential benefits – up to 6 marks Problems – up to 10 marks		
		Maximum	**13**
Total			**25**

56 LAUDAN ADVERTISING AGENCY (LAA) (SEPT/DEC 16)

Key answer tips

Part (a) – CSFs and KPIs are commonly tested. Make sure you practise a number of questions on this area.

Parts (b) and (c) cover transfer pricing and are entirely discursive. Make sure that you are comfortable with the discussion around transfer pricing and not only the calculations. The challenge here was to ensure the answer had enough relevant points and that there was some depth to these points. An answer plan should help with this.

(a) (i) **CSF of high quality design**

The directors of LAA have identified the importance of producing high quality creative designs as a CSF to ensure successful advertising campaigns, and therefore client satisfaction. It is likely that having this as a CSF will help LAA achieve its objective to 'delight clients with the quality of work', as creative design is an important part of the service which LAA provides.

It is not clear, however, whether this CSF will help achieve the second of LAA's objectives to provide excellent value for money. It may be that other agencies produce a similar quality of work, but charge a lower price. Alternatively, the quality of LAA's design work may exceed that required by the client, who will be unlikely, therefore, to perceive it as good value for money.

Identifying this CSF will not directly help achieve the stated objective of providing clients with access to local and specialist knowledge. External suppliers may have more specialist knowledge than LAA can realistically replicate in its own design department.

The relationship between the quality of the creative design and the clients' perception of its value for money will determine whether the fourth objective, to have returning clients, will be achieved or not. All other things being equal, high quality design work will probably make clients more likely to return. Other aspects of LAA's service though, such as designing effective advertising campaigns and negotiating competitive rates for media buying, may be at least as important to the client.

(ii) **KPI to buy 90% internally**

Setting a KPI should lead managers to try and achieve this target, as they are appraised (and presumably rewarded) according to their performance against the target.

Having this target will only help achieve the objective of delighting clients if the quality of the design done internally exceeds that done by third party external designers. Though LAA has set up the 'centre for design excellence', this does not automatically mean the quality of work is any better than external agencies.

Encouraging managers to buy creative services internally does not necessarily help achieve the objective of giving value for money for clients. Managers at both B and C have indicated that the prices charged by the in-house design department are significantly higher than other agencies in the market. The use of the internal design department may not be best value for the client.

Encouraging the use of internal services may not help achieve LAA's third objective to offer specialist and local knowledge to clients. The design department is based entirely in Geeland and may not meet the needs of clients in other countries. The manager of B has already commented that the department did not understand the requirements of consumers in Veeland. This is also inconsistent with the objectives to delight clients and to have them return to LAA.

Similarly, managers in A have also commented that the internal department did not have specialist knowledge to meet the needs of a new client. Again, encouraging managers to use the internal department seems contrary to the objectives of providing clients with specialist knowledge in order to delight them and to have them as return customers.

(b) Transfer pricing policy

Autonomy of the subsidiaries

The purposes of a transfer pricing policy are to encourage subsidiaries' autonomy, facilitate performance evaluation and to promote overall goal congruence with the aim of LAA to maximise shareholder wealth.

As the three subsidiaries are profit centres, they will tend to make decisions which maximise their own profit. This may be at the expense of the other subsidiaries. By charging a higher transfer price to B and C for design services, A will increase its own revenue and also the costs for B and C. This may also be at the expense of LAA as a whole, for example, as C's client was unhappy by the high charges levied by A.

A transfer pricing policy helps to prevent subsidiaries from acting in an entirely self-interested way where this may not be in the best interests of LAA as a whole. Though a transfer pricing policy should promote autonomy of the subsidiaries, LAA's head office should have the power to impose a transfer price to maintain goal congruence across the organisation. This is not currently happening, and the high transfer prices charged for design services are causing dissatisfaction.

Both B and C have commented that they have spent large amounts of time trying to negotiate transfer prices with A. This is a waste of managers' time. The ability of head office to impose a transfer price, or the existence of a clear transfer pricing policy, would allow managers more time to deal with other key aspects of the business, such as ensuring client satisfaction.

Performance measurement in the three subsidiaries

A transfer pricing policy will enable the performance of the individual subsidiaries to be fairly measured. If the policy is unfair, for example, the gross margin at subsidiary C was reduced by the seemingly excessive transfer prices charged by A, managers' motivation will be reduced, especially if this reduces the subsidiaries' managers' rewards.

Setting clear, transparent and understandable transfer prices

Managers at B have complained that the basis for setting the transfer price from A is unclear. A transfer pricing policy should ensure that the basis for setting the prices is transparent, straightforward and well understood by managers so that they do not see prices as being set unfairly and thus become demotivated.

The basis for the prices set between subsidiaries in different countries should also be clear about how exchange rate movements are reflected in the transfer price, so that managers' performance is not appraised on factors which are outside their control.

Also, the transfer pricing policy for transfers between different countries should ensure that the prices are likely to be acceptable to the local tax authorities. The tax authorities in Veeland, where B is located, are already investigating the transfer prices charged by A. This is presumably because the authorities suspect that the transfer price may be set at an artificially high level in order to reduce tax paid on profits earned in Veeland. Having a clear transfer pricing policy may help to demonstrate that B is operating within relevant taxation laws and is acting ethically in setting a fair transfer price. As the internal design department has no external customers, then it may be preferable to operate it as a separate cost centre and make all transfers at marginal cost.

Tutorial note

An approach which addressed the question based on the aims of a transfer pricing system, i.e. encourage autonomy, facilitate performance evaluation and promote goal congruence, would have been acceptable.

(c) Advantages of setting transfer prices on the basis of market value

Transfer prices on the basis of market value reflect the prices of purchasing creative design services on the open market. Both buying and selling subsidiaries will know what the market price is and be able to compare this to the price they are paying or charging internally.

Where subsidiaries have autonomy to negotiate their own transfer prices, in order to maximise the performance of the individual subsidiaries, the transfer price agreed is likely to reflect market price. The buyer will be unwilling to pay more than the price it can pay on the open market. The seller will be unwilling to charge less to sell internally than can be obtained on the open market. This encourages efficiency in A, which has to compete with external suppliers of creative design services.

Where a market value transfer price is used, it will usually be beneficial for buyer and seller, as well as for LAA as a whole, to transfer internally. This is because selling and administration costs overall for both parties are reduced, and the buyer should get better customer service and reliability of supply by buying internally.

The transfer price charged by A currently includes an allowance for marketing costs and bad debts. These are unlikely to be incurred where internal transfers are made. The costs savings may be shared by both parties and the transfer price reduced to a level below the market value. This lower transfer price is known as the adjusted market price.

If the transfer price charged by A is calculated on a different basis from market value, which appears to be the case as A's prices are higher than the market rates, the subsidiaries will waste time arguing over the transfer price. This current approach may improve the subsidiaries' own performance, but this is not in the best interests of LAA overall.

Disadvantages of using market price

The use of external market price will only be the optimal transfer price when a perfectly competitive external market exists. For example, though creative services can be purchased on the open market, those services may not be identical with those provided internally. Subsidiary A had to use a third party design agency for its new client as it did not have the industry knowledge to do the work itself. In this case, there may not be an equivalent service available internally to those available externally, and vice versa. There may therefore be no realistic option to buy on the open market in this situation and the use of an external market price as a transfer price would be inappropriate.

The market price may be temporary, changing according to capacity of the service providers, changes in economic circumstances, or in the case of LAA, short-term variations in the exchange rate. In which case, the transfer price would need to be frequently changed if it were to continue to reflect market conditions. This would be time consuming and probably confusing to the subsidiaries' managers.

Where allowance is made in the transfer price for the reduced costs, for example, of marketing and bad debts, it may be difficult to agree an adjusted market price which is acceptable to both A and the subsidiary purchasing design services from A.

Examiner's comments

Part a) was done quite badly with many candidates focusing on the areas they felt the entity should specialise in or on actions that the company would need to undertake in order to be successful. This is an analysis of business performance, not on whether the CSFs and KPIs are appropriate measures that help the entity in their overall management of performance.

Part b) tended to see candidates scoring better: the scenario was rich with data as to how the transfer of goods between different divisions was causing many problems in terms of performance management, autonomy and the achievement of overall entity objectives and most candidates were adept at highlighting where those areas specifically were and relating it to the theory of transfer pricing.

Part c) asked for a specific focus on one area of transfer pricing and in this area it was clear that candidates were lacking in technical knowledge. Many could explain the basic technique but did not advise as to whether it should be used or not: such a suggestion involves an in-depth analysis of the advantages and disadvantages of this technique relative to the scenario and very few candidates engaged in this level of analysis. Also common was an explanation/definition of all types of transfer pricing. This is irrelevant to the question in two ways: a) what was presented were mere definitions that contained neither discussion nor recommendation and b) it did not address what the question was looking for, which was a specific analysis of the relevance of one technique to the scenario depicted. Future candidates are advised again to focus on the specific requirement of the question.

ACCA marking scheme			
			Marks
(a)	Discussion of CSF with objectives – up to 6 marks Discussion of KPI with objectives – up to 6 marks		
		Maximum	**8**
(b)	Each relevant point – 1 mark	**Maximum**	**9**
(c)	Benefits of a market value approach – up to 6 marks Problems with a market value approach – up to 6 marks		
		Maximum	**8**
Total			**25**

57 LOL CO (DEC 10)

Key answer tips

This was a reasonably straightforward question provided you understood the main ideas surrounding VBM and EVA. Unfortunately many students were uncertain on these key concepts.

(a) The value-based approach takes the primary objective of the business to be maximising shareholder wealth and seeks to align performance with this objective. The principle measure used at the strategic level will be economic value added (EVA™). EVA™ is equivalent in the long term to discounted cash flow which is widely used as the valuation method for shares by equity analysts. (Other relevant value measures might be market value added and shareholder value added.)

By using this as the sole measure of performance, management is focused and they will be able to avoid conflicts which occur when there are multiple objectives and measures. The measure can be applied to decisions at all levels within the organisation (strategic, tactical and operational) so that the company is unified in its goal. As only a single measure is used, the variables which drive performance are clear within the calculation of EVA™. These value drivers can be used by managers to achieve their value-based targets which are set from the strategic value-based goal.

(b) The performance of LOL has declined with earnings per share falling by 23% (W2) from last year. Normally, this would imply that the company would be heavily out of favour with investors.

However, the share price seems to have held up with a decline of only 12% compared to a fall in the sector of 26% and the market as a whole of 35% (W3). The sector comparison is more relevant to the performance of LOL's management as the main market index will contain data from manufacturing, financial and other industries. Shareholders will be encouraged by the implication that the market views LOL as one of the better prospects within an outperforming sector.

This view is consistent with the calculated positive EVA™ for 2010 ($22·6m, (W1)) which LOL generated. EVA™ has fallen from 2009 but it has remained positive and so the company continues to create value for its shareholders even in the poor economic environment. It therefore remains a worthwhile investment even in a falling market.

Workings:

(W1) EVA calculations for the periods given are

	2009	**2010**
	$m	$m
Profit after interest and tax	35.0	26.8
Interest (net of tax at 25%)	3.0	5.9
Net operating profit after tax (NOPAT)	38.0	32.6
Capital employed (at year start)	99.2	104.1

Assumptions:

Economic and accounting depreciation are equivalent.

There are no non-cash expenses to adjust in the profit figure.

There are no operating leases to be capitalised.

There are no additional adjustments to make regarding goodwill.

Cost of capital

WACC = (%e × Ke) + (%d × Kd)

2009 (50% × 12.7%) + (50% × 4.2%) = 8.45%

2010 (50% × 15.3%) + (50% × 3.9%) = 9.60%

EVA = NOPAT – (Capital employed × WACC)

2009 38.0 – (99.2 × 8.45%) = 29.6

2010 32.6 – (104.1 × 9.6%) = 22.6

(W2)

	2009	**2010**	**Change**
EPS (profit after interest and tax/ av no of shares) cents	21.88	16.75	–23.4%

(W3)

Stock market information	**2009**	**2010**	**Change**
Main market index	2,225.4	1,448.9	–34.9%
Retailing sector index	1,225.6	907.1	–26.0%
LOL share price ($'s)	12.2	10.7	–12.3%

(c) VBM provides focus on shareholder wealth but it can be argued that a single profit measure can do the same. Value measures are considered to be superior to profit measures because they take into consideration the capital employed and cost of capital. These variables are less clear in a profit measure. Also, although value measures are calculated from profit figures they are adjusted in order to bring them closer to a cash flow measure of performance which is less affected by the various accounting adjustments such as depreciation. (Here we have assumed in calculating EVA™ that accounting and economic depreciation are the same but with greater information on the company we may be able to make a better estimate to the cash performance of the company.)

A disadvantage of value-based measures like EVA™ compared to profit is the unfamiliarity and complexity of the calculation. The calculation of the cost of capital is encumbered by the assumptions of CAPM and it is based on historic data which may not be repeated in the future (share values are based on expected dividend flows). These difficulties can be overcome by a process of education and training for the staff and shareholders. Additionally, the use of EVA™ as the sole value-measure as suggested by Stern Stewart may be too simple and overlook other value drivers.

As a tool for decision-making, EVA™ can be subject to manipulation by choosing projects with low initial costs to provide a short-term boost to the value measure in the same way as profit measures. It may not address the weaknesses in project appraisal that drive many companies to use net present value, which recognises the increase in shareholder wealth over the life of the whole project in question.

(d) The principal objective of financial management is to maximise shareholder wealth. This raises two key questions – how can we measure whether shareholder value is being created or destroyed, and which performance appraisal targets ensure that managers act in such a way as to generate shareholder value?

We therefore require a wealth metric for measuring shareholder value, and a performance metric to use for target setting.

NPV is mainly used as a wealth or investment metric for project appraisal. The main advantage of this approach is the high correlation between NPV and shareholder value, so the technique should result in projects being selected that will increase shareholder wealth.

What is lacking, however, is an operating performance measure for managers that will help them to maximise NPV. Some firms attempt to use cash flow targets but with mixed success. Many more firms set targets based on traditional measures, such as profit and ROI, without resolving the inconsistency of using NPV for project appraisal and then ignoring it when appraising managers.

The EVA™ approach is primarily a performance metric rather than a wealth metric and has the advantage that it is consistent with the use of NPV.

Examiner's comments

Requirement (a). There were often lengthy and irrelevant discussions about non-financial factors which suggest incomplete knowledge of VBM.

Requirement (b) was also typically passed but few candidates scored 9 or more out of 12. The assessment of the numerical work was often lacking. Candidates infrequently compared the change in share price of LOL to the market and sector performance – which demonstrated that the company was doing well in a falling market. Some candidates could not perform the EVA computation which was surprising as this is a key performance measure and the scenario offered few of the possible technical adjustments. Having performed the calculation of EVA, a significant minority then failed to note that it was positive choosing to focus on the fact that it had fallen from the previous year.

Requirement (c) was the most difficult part of the question and was generally poorly done, probably as a result of the failure to explain VBM which was illustrated in part (a).

ACCA marking scheme

			Marks
(a)	Up to 2 marks on the explanation of VBM and then up to 2 marks on how it aids focus in the management process		
		Maximum	**4**
(b)	Workings:		
	NOPAT		1
	Capital employed		1
	Cost of capital		1
	EVA™		1
	Assumptions 0.5 each up to a maximum of		1.5
	EPS		1
	Share price 3 × 0.5		1.5
	Comments: 1 mark per reasonable point up to 2 on EPS and share price and 2 on EVATM.		
		Maximum	**12**
(c)	1 mark for each point made	up to a maximum of	**4**
(d)	1 mark for each point made	up to a maximum of	**5**
Total			**25**

58 PATTACK (SEPT/DEC 21) (AMENDED)

(a)

Key answer tips

APM scenarios typically start with a paragraph or so of organisation information, commonly including some discussion of the mission and strategic objectives or strategic focus. Therefore, in part (a) it is important to consider how the BPR proposal could improve performance in regards to the four different areas of strategic focus and the main aim. It would be a good idea to use these five areas as sub-headings and to consider each area in turn, using the scenario information to support the discussion in each area.

Business process re-engineering (BPR) involves rethinking how a process is undertaken at a fundamental level and is based on the radical redesign of business processes to achieve dramatic improvements. It starts by asking questions such as: "why do we do things this way?" and "would we do things exactly the same way if we were starting again?"

Pattack has an overall aim supported by several strategies. The main aim is to maximise shareholder value and this will be achieved through having a strategic focus on costs, by being the best delivery company in Geeland, by being innovative in its approach and by having an engaged and committed workforce. It is likely that all these goals can be better achieved by the BPR proposal.

Strategic focus on costs

There are several areas in the new proposal where costs will be saved over the long term. Upon collection by Pattack drivers, the parcels will not now require to be taken to Pattack's premises to enable the delivery schedules to be planned by delivery administration. Instead, the deliveries will be planned through the electronic transfer of data from the retailers. This will save costs in two main areas. Firstly, the drivers are not required to return to Pattack's premises which will save the costs of the drivers' time, vehicle fuel and associated vehicles costs. Secondly, the same drivers who collect the parcels from the distributors will deliver the parcels to the end users. This will save cost as there is no need to employ two different types of driver for two different purposes. The process has merged the collection and delivery functions and therefore there is only a requirement for only one type of driver.

There will also be a cost saving as the date and time of delivery to the end user is now undertaken automatically and accurately. The current process is not accurate and has been a source of complaints from the retailers. The current process is likely to damage Pattack's relationship with the retailers and Pattack is likely to lose business in an increasingly competitive environment. Introducing a system whereby the end user has to sign for receipt of the parcel, along with the date and time of the confirmed receipt, will save Pattack the costs associated with recording the data when the drivers return to Pattack's premises. It will also save the cost of the damage to Pattack's relationship with the retailer and may help ensure future business.

The fundamental idea of a strategic focus on costs is that cost savings are considered over the long-term. The bar coding technology and the hand held devices used by the drivers would certainly represent an expense in the short term. However, it is clear that the benefits in terms of process improvement represent a permanent change to Pattack's processes. From the evidence in the scenario, it is very likely that such process improvement will result in significant cost savings in the long term.

Being best delivery company

The redesign of the process to tag the parcel at source will also help Pattack achieve its aim of being the best delivery company in Geeland as it will enable route planning to be undertaken on a more pro-active basis. Routes can now be planned as orders are communicated from retailers instead of waiting until all parcels have been brought back to Pattack's premises. This is likely to enhance retailer satisfaction with the service Pattack is offering.

Electronic vehicle tagging will enable the delivery manager to respond to any requests from the retailers concerning delivery. Pattack can thereby demonstrate that it is reacting to retailer demands for real time information regarding delivery and can show that it is putting the overall retailer experience at the centre of its process redesign.

The receipt by the end user, combined with the original bar coding of the order, would enable a digital audit of every order Pattack received to be undertaken in the event of any subsequent problem the retailer may have with the end user. This would enhance retailers' trust in Pattack and their overall satisfaction with the service Pattack is providing.

Innovation

Pattack makes clear in its strategic goals that it will be innovative in its approach. The current process appears outdated, time consuming and ineffective as it appears to be hindering Pattack in the achievement of its overall aim.

Adopting the BPR proposal would certainly evidence Pattack's aim of being innovative in its approach. More importantly, however, the innovation would lead to tangible, and perhaps financially measurable, process improvement. For innovation to be meaningful, it has to be of measurable benefit to Pattack.

Engaged and committed workforce

Much of the work currently undertaken by the computer operators will now be addressed by the bar-coding operation. It is not clear, however, if there is a new position for these staff members within the new process. Likewise, there is no need now for both collection and delivery drivers and it has to be assumed that Pattack will require fewer drivers overall. The main purpose of the BPR proposal is to make Pattack's operations more efficient and it is clear that long term cost reduction is part of that. It is inevitable that this will include employees as some of the tasks they perform are replaced by enhanced technology. There would clearly be an effect on staff morale if some workers were made redundant and this may lead to the workforce feeling under threat rather than committed or engaged.

Tutorial note

Although the focus of the answer is on the positives, it is also important to point out any relevant reasons as to why performance may suffer, rather than improve, in relation to the overall aim.

There are some elements of the BPR proposal, however, that are likely to enhance employee engagement and commitment. The remaining drivers, for example, should have schedules that are better planned and more efficient than the current ones which should enhance their trust and faith both in the organisation generally and in the redesigned processes that has been initiated specifically. The delivery manager should also feel that he or she has more control over the entire process if he or she is able to see where delivery vehicles are at any given moment.

Maximisation of shareholder value

It is not clear from the scenario if Pattack has undertaken or will undertake a net present value calculation for the BPR proposal. This would allow us to make a more objective judgement as to whether the proposal is adding to shareholder value.

Tutorial note

It is useful in your answer to point out any additional information needed.

However, Pattack's aim is to maximise shareholder value by undertaking the strategies outlined above. It is very unlikely that the BPR proposal will enhance strategic performance in all those areas and not contribute to the maximisation of shareholder value. Overall, therefore, it is extremely likely that the BPR proposal will help with Pattack's aim of maximising shareholder value.

(b)

Key answer tips

It is useful to spend some time reading the suggested answer below since it gives you one useful idea of how to structure the answer to maximise marks. There is a short introduction to begin with (clearly stating that the customer is the retailer and not the delivery recipient) and then the scheme is evaluated in terms of clarity, controllability and motivation (these three areas are included in the third block of the building block model). The building block model is not specifically asked for but it does lend itself nicely to this answer and its use will help give a logical structure.

Drivers' Bonus

The retailers are Pattack's customers as it is the retailers who employ Pattack to deliver the parcels on their behalf. The end user is the retailer's customer, not Pattack's, so it is appropriate to measure satisfaction of the retailer.

Clarity

The measurement of satisfaction has to be clearly defined. Pattack may choose to measure this by a survey of the retailers but would need to be clear with regard to the questions asked and, in particular, the options offered in terms of potential responses. Surveys are well-known, for example, for respondents choosing middle values on a scale of one to five. There may also be a lack of shared understanding around the word satisfaction and perhaps measuring customer delight, happiness or something more tangible such as the possibility of the retailer using Pattack for its next delivery may be more meaningful.

It should also be clear as to when a bonus will be awarded and whether there is a scale to it. For example, it should be made clear to the drivers that a basic bonus will be awarded when overall customer satisfaction reaches the specific detailed figure of 85% and if the bonus will increase if this satisfaction level reaches 90% or 100%. As it currently stands, the bonus scheme does not identify these levels.

Controllability

There are some factors which are in control of the drivers in their interaction with the retailers and, in that sense, the measure can be seen as a fair one. For example, they are in control of how they personally interact with the retailers when they collect the parcels and as such are in control of how Pattack is represented in this part of the relationship. They are also in control of the physical condition of the parcels and should be able to assure the retailers that the parcels will be delivered in the same condition that they were collected.

The other area of most concern to the retailer will be whether the goods are delivered on time and this is only partly in the drivers' control. They cannot control the conditions on the roads and there may be accidents, traffic jams, adverse weather conditions and problems with access to end user premises for certain types of vehicle that could affect delivery. If deliveries are late, the end users are likely to complain to the retailers and, as a result, the retailers' satisfaction with Pattack could potentially be affected adversely. Such an eventuality may mean that the drivers are not awarded their bonus on the basis of factors beyond their control.

The drivers are also not in control of the entire relationship with the retailer. The retailer's view of satisfaction will be influenced by all their dealings with Pattack, which will also cover such things as the ordering process, invoicing and customer relations with Pattack's office staff. These factors may adversely affect the retailers' view of their satisfaction with Pattack and are out of the drivers' control.

It seems unfair, therefore, to award the drivers a bonus based on these significant factors that are out of their control.

Motivation

Motivation to achieve a bonus is usually related to how clear it is and how achievable it is deemed to be. As neither the potential scale of the bonus nor the monetary reward attached to it is clear, and it appears to contain several aspects which are beyond the control of the drivers, it is unlikely that they will be motivated to achieve it as it currently presented.

There is a danger with this bonus system that the drivers focus on this measure to the exclusion of other factors. For example, the need to deliver parcels on-time as part of ensuring the retailers' satisfaction may cause the drivers to break speeding laws or to take more chances than they would normally when driving.

Conclusion

As a starting point, the idea of basing drivers' bonus based on retailer satisfaction does sound appropriate, but the proposed bonus could be further clarified and should also be better defined to relate to the specific elements that are in the drivers' control. As it stands, the scheme is too general and should not be adopted.

Examiner's comments

Part (a) of the question tended to be quite poorly done, with candidates generally not relating their responses to Pattack's aims or spending too long on repeating information from the scenario. The best responses to this part were structured around the aim and set out exactly what was involved in the aim at the start of the response. The better responses were then set out in distinct subheadings (e.g. Strategic focus on costs). Setting responses out in this manner makes it clear to the examiner that candidates understand what they are being asked to do and appreciate that their responses should demonstrate how the new proposal will help Pattack to improve in the areas of importance to it. Poorer responses here were unstructured and made little or no attempt to relate comments made to Pattack's aims. Other inadequate responses were often generic in nature. Candidates often respond to questions with short bullet points in the style and structure of the above quote, or with comments such as "reduction in movement of materials". The examining team really need to see these points developed by candidates relating them to the aim. Another area where candidates could have performed better by focusing on the question requirement was by ensuring that their responses addressed the area of improvement specifically.

Part (b) was also, generally, poorly done. Responses in this area were underdeveloped and short and many responses were also very generic and discussed the advantages and disadvantages of having bonus schemes and the potential overall effect of these schemes on behaviour. Another area where candidates did not score as highly as they might was by not offering an overall conclusion. There were also several examples of candidates offering a conclusion which was not based on any evidence which had been presented in their previous discussion. It was also clear that many candidates were not aware of who Pattack's customer actually was. As with part (a), candidates often offered comments which had to be further developed and explained to be worthy of merit.

ACCA marking scheme	
	Marks
(a) Definition of BPR – 1 mark 1 mark per relevant point: Strategic focus on costs Being best delivery company Innovation Engaged and committed workforce Maximisation of shareholder value	
Maximum	**12**
(b) Identifying Pattack's customer – 1 mark Bonus scheme – 1 mark per relevant point, up to 7 marks Conclusion – up to 2 marks	
Maximum	**8**
Professional marks **Analysis and Evaluation** • Comprehensive evaluation of how the BPR proposal could help improve performance in relation to the main aim and also each of the four areas of strategic focus • Problems of the suggested bonus scheme clearly explained and appropriate advice and recommendations given **Scepticism** • Recognition of the failings of the suggested bonus scheme and that the BPR proposal should improve performance but is not without its challenges **Commercial Acumen** • Effectiveness of examples drawn from across the scenario information and other practical considerations related to the context to illustrate the points being made throughout	
Maximum	**5**
Total	**25**

D – PERFORMANCE EVALUATION

59 HARRAY (MAR/JUN 21) (AMENDED)

(a)

Key answer tips

The examining team is not interested in testing your detailed book knowledge on this area and is unlikely to ask you to list all of the key headings. Instead, you need to be able to apply and evaluate the pyramid as a way to link strategy, operations and performance. In this specific requirement, this involves completing the work on the performance pyramid, with a focus on the operational level and related indicators.

There are four operational headings in the pyramid which shall be considered in turn.

Waste is about optimal use of resources and minimisation of non-value adding activity. There are 1.05 million keyboards produced but this only represents 86% utilisation of the capacity of the factory (2,695,680 minutes of production line time are available at 2.2 minutes per keyboard meaning that the factory can produce 1,225,309 at full capacity). Therefore, capital invested in the factory is underutilised, although an 80+% utilisation would be considered efficient for many manufacturing operations.

Quality can be measured through four cost types: inspection and prevention costs (which represent the costs of preventing faults in the production process and inspecting to avoid faulty goods leaving the factory) and internal and external failure costs (which are costs resulting from faulty goods being identified before and after delivery to the customer). There are no data given for 20X5 on the costs of inspection and prevention. However, the effectiveness of inspection can be measured in that only 0.4% of orders were returned while inspection stopped the delivery of 1.5% of faulty goods. There was a loss of $50,400 at standard cost from the scrapping of faulty keyboards although 60% of faulty boards identified were able to be repaired. The effectiveness of prevention can be measured in that there is a roughly 1.9% failure rate in total, which must reflect the good production practice at the factory. There are data on measures of the costs of internal failure from reworking goods ($18,900). But there are no data on the costs of external failures from 0.4% of customer returns which may incur further repair or warranty claim costs.

Delivery has been outsourced to Achall and Harray is reliant on Achall to provide the data on the quality of Achall's own service. This represents a risk which Harray can control by monitoring its own customer feedback to identify if Achall is under-reporting the late deliveries. Based on Achall's data, 92% of orders are delivered on time at an average time of 3.4 days.

Cycle time for working capital is being measured but this should be done for all the significant processes in Harray. The processes which have been identified so far are setting up production lines, running the production on an order and delivering the order. Measurement of production cycle times is likely to be particularly important in assessing the efficiency of such a cost-conscious business. There are data on delivery time (3.4 days on average) and on production time (2.22 minutes per production line). These should appear in the pyramid of indicators if they are deemed sufficiently important.

(b) In order to understand the issues surrounding measurement of non-financial indicators, it is necessary first to consider the more commonly used financial ones. Financial indicators will be produced by Harray's financial systems. These systems will generate much of the cost information used, for example, in measuring the costs of quality. They are internally controlled and additionally monitored by the external auditors of the organisation. Such systems are by definition working with easily quantified data (invoice values). For these reasons, they are likely to be the most reliable data available.

However, for the measurement of headings such as cycle time, the data are often going to be nonfinancial. Cycle time requires measuring how long processes take, for example, the length of time it takes a production line to produce a keyboard. These data are within the control of Harray and the data will be obtained by production records and interviewing the key personnel. However, they will not be subject to the checking and controls over financial data and therefore, may be more prone to error.

Other non-financial data used may come from external sources. For example, at Harray, they are using the delivery data of Achall. This data must be treated carefully as there is an incentive for Achall to under-report late deliveries as there may be penalties for such non-performance in their contract with Harray (there is also the threat of losing the contract). Harray will want to ensure that Achall's data is reliable by checking it against its own customer complaint records. Also, the definition of non-financial data is more subjective, for example, what constitutes a late delivery (though this should be consistent with the service level agreed in the contract).

Tutorial note

There is a wide variety of possible answers to this question which will be given credit, provided they are consistent with part (a).

Examiner's comments

This question was about a family-owned keyboard manufacturing company, Harray Keyboards (Harray), which was seeking to use the Performance Pyramid (PP) to analyse its performance indicators.

Part (a) which asked for an analysis of performance indicators for the PP to be completed and then an evaluation of the operational indicators was generally badly done.

Of most concern to the marking team was the very significant number of candidates who did not comprehend which indicators that the operational level related to even though the appendix of information listed out the headings of the pyramid in order.

As a result of not appreciating which were operational level indicators, many candidates attempted to evaluate the performance indicators for every single heading of the PP. As there are only four operational headings, and ten headings overall, this led to candidates spending much of their time writing on areas that were irrelevant to the question asked. Such responses were only worthy of merit when their answers addressed the operational indicators.

The other consequence of this was that candidates wasted time which they probably did not have, given that this was the last question attempted in many cases. It was undoubtedly one of the reasons for the very brief responses in part (b).

The part of the question that asked for the analysis to be completed was asking for indicators to be calculated, based on the information given in the question's appendix. Many candidates did undertake relevant calculations and the vast majority of those calculations were undertaken correctly. The three areas where calculations were most relevant were the areas of waste, quality, and delivery.

Candidates were less competent, however, at offering an evaluation of the indicator. Many candidates simply undertook the calculations and did not add anything additional by way of discussion or evaluation. Often candidates simply gave an indication as to what a measure might be, for example, % of late deliveries for the Delivery heading, without saying why that would be useful for Harray. A response which had indicated – "% of late deliveries would be an appropriate indicator to use for the Delivery heading, as a high proportion of late deliveries is likely to have an adverse effect on customer satisfaction. Whereas customers who receive their goods on time cannot always be assumed to be satisfied, it can be logically inferred that a high proportion of late deliveries would lead to unhappy customers" – would have demonstrated an evaluation of the suitability of the indicator.

Some candidates offered a very brief discussion or a discussion which showed little by way of commercial acumen. For example, Harray was working to approximately 86% utilisation and many candidates felt that this represented an unacceptable level of wasted resource. In a similar manner, many candidates felt that Harray's on-time deliveries at 92% represented terrible performance. In truth, whereas the indicators used show there is a potential for improvement even if they do not pinpoint exactly where that potential may lie, they nevertheless indicate that the company is performing, generally, quite well.

A good approach to this requirement would be:

- Use headings for each of the operational indicators
- Under each heading perform the calculations where there was clear information in the appendix to do so.

Discuss what those indicators signify. For example, 'waste would be a good thing for Harray to measure as it would focus the entire production department on continually improving performance to attempt to get to as close as 100% as possible. By so doing, Harray would also be able to enhance its productivity'.

(b) This part of the question was the poorest part undertaken overall.

The main reason for this is that many candidates either did not attempt this part or wrote so little that it would have been impossible for them to score beyond one or two marks at the very most. It is certainly not the case that a great deal of narrative will automatically lead to many marks but, likewise, it is very difficult to award any credit to any candidate response when so little has been written.

For those responses that did try to address the question, many (if not most) did not fully appreciate that what they were being asked about was the reliability of non-financial performance indicators (NFPIs) and not about the usefulness of NFPIs to Harray. This latter area tended to be the focus of many responses and the advantages of data such as on-time deliveries, customer satisfaction and time from placing of order to delivery of it were given. It was, however, almost impossible for the marking team to award any credit to such responses as they did not respond to the question asked.

Some responses also gave an indication of the potential effects of some of the NFPIs. For example, an on-time delivery rate of 82% would surely mean that 8% of Harray's customers would go elsewhere. Such responses offered almost nothing on the actual reliability of the NFPIs themselves.

A further area of concern with this part of the question was that, again, many candidates did not recognise that they were only being asked about the reliability of operational NFPIs, not NFPIs at every level in the PP.

Some candidates addressed this question as though it were asking for ways in which Harray could improve their performance in the NFPIs that had been given in the scenario and, in some cases, calculated in part b). Many responses therefore indicated what Harray might do to enhance customer satisfaction, which often took the question into areas such as changing strategic direction. Sadly, such responses again failed to address the question asked.

Some responses did address the question demands and those responses tended to focus on the information given in the scenario that was relevant to the question asked.

For example, a very good response would highlight: "Harray is relying on information from Achall to detail the percentage of on time deliveries. As this information is supplied to Harray by Achall from Achall's systems, Harray seems to have little or no way of verifying that it is correct. We do not know what the service level agreement (SLA) between the two companies indicates but it can be safely assumed that Achall would not want to pass on to Harray information which indicates that it has broken the SLA and may be liable for a payment penalty. The information is not only unreliable, therefore, but Achall also would appear to have a motive to manipulate it should it be unfavourable for them."

A good response to this question would to take each operational NFPI in turn and discuss how reliable it might be. Quality, for example, relies upon the quality inspector's count of the rejected keyboards. The quality inspector may not have counted accurately and/or, possibly, may have missed some keyboards which perhaps should have been rejected. The indicator in its current format is therefore unreliable and there should either be an automated way of ascertaining which keyboards should be rejected or someone else should work with the production manager to ensure that there is some verification of both the inspector's work and the number of rejected keyboards.

ACCA marking scheme

		Marks
(a)	Complete the analysis and evaluate the operational performance indicators at Harray, using the headings and data in Appendix 1. Waste – up to 4 marks Quality – up to 6 marks Delivery – up to 4 marks Cycle time – up to 4 marks 1 mark for correct calculation of each suitable indicator and 1 mark for each point in commentary	
	Maximum	**13**
(b)	Evaluate the reliability of non-financial indicators as requested by the CEO, using the operational performance indicators – 1 mark per relevant point	
	Maximum	**7**

Professional marks	
Analysis and Evaluation	
• Appropriate use of data to perform suitable calculations to complete the work started by the junior accountant	
• Comprehensive evaluation is made of the four operational indicators	
Scepticism	
• Recognition that more than just working capital should be assessed under cycle time	
Commercial Acumen	
• Addresses in the three areas of focus in requested advice on the reliability of the NFPIs	
Maximum	5
Total	**25**

60 ROAN UNIVERSITY AND SAUGH UNIVERSITY (SEPT/DEC 20) (AMENDED)

(a) Managing performance

Establishing common objectives

The initial problem with regard to managing performance in any joint venture is establishing its objectives and goals and the aims of each university for the joint venture of RSU are different.

Roan's main purpose for undertaking the joint venture is to find a new revenue stream. The word profit is not explicitly stated in their view of the joint venture but nevertheless it has to be assumed that Roan is seeking to make a financial return from this and that its focus will be on maximising that return rather than maximising revenue to the disregard of cost. In terms of performance management, therefore, the focus of Roan is likely to be on ensuring that these main goals are met and therefore areas of finance and resource utilisation and consumption are likely to form the core of the management system.

Saugh's main purpose for undertaking the joint venture is to enhance its status within its own country, and perhaps globally, as a renowned institution of learning. The focus for Saugh in terms of how performance of RSU is managed is likely to be on the reputation of Saugh, staff development and the destinations of its graduates.

Developing a joint venture in terms of its financial return and in terms of the contribution that it makes to society may be possible within a performance management framework but it is clear that these aims are contradictory. At a simple level, focusing on the financial aspects can lead to a lack of investment which may damage the quality of the joint venture's provision and, ultimately, the contribution that the graduates of RSU can make to society.

Lack of stable leadership

It is clear from the scenario that the rotational nature of the chairman of the management board (MB) will almost ensure that there is a lack of stable leadership. Unless the universities can agree on a common and mutually acceptable aim, the chairman is likely to be acting more in the interests of their own university than in the interests of the joint venture.

The inclusion of at least one government official from Deeland on the MB may also present problems from the perspective of Roan with regard to performance management. As the current balance of the MB membership is 50:50, the inclusion of representatives from Deeland would clearly tip the balance in favour of Saugh. This is likely to lead to a loss of control for Roan which would clearly have an effect on the manner in which the joint venture is managed in terms of its performance.

Measuring performance

Given the challenging funding environment in Teeland, reflected in the overall view of Roan with regards to what the aim of the joint venture should be, Roan will be focused on the financial return of RSU. This means that Roan would seek to measure traditional financial measures such as return on investment and operating surplus. Roan's focus is likely to be specifically on the fees charged, student numbers, costs incurred and on return on investment overall. The measures that Roan would like to see would therefore relate to fee growth, student numbers and cost reduction. It is not clear how quickly Roan is seeking to achieve a return on the investment but from the scenario it can be assumed, given the cuts to governmental funding, that it would prefer a return to be achieved in the short term as well as over the long term. Roan may therefore be keen to spend a significant amount on advertising, to boost student numbers in the short term, rather than wait for the reputation of RSU to grow by word of mouth.

Saugh appears to be free from any financial constraints, at least in the short term. Its funding is secure and this means that Saugh is unlikely to be interested in assessing the performance of RSU with any traditional financial metrics. As a result, this may place Saugh in direct conflict with Roan with regard to many decisions. For example, Saugh may feel that enhancing classroom technology in RSU is necessary and should be undertaken immediately without understanding that this would represent a significant further investment for Roan.

Saugh will be more focused on the quality of the students that are admitted to RSU, their performance whilst at university and their occupation and perhaps salary level on leaving the university. There is likely to be conflict with Roan with regard to students that are admitted to RSU as Roan will be more focused on recruiting as many students as possible whereas Saugh will be more focused on the grades that these students have achieved either at school or in previous study.

Both universities will be interested in how the students perform at RSU. Roan's reputation would suffer significantly, for example, if it were to accept students who failed its programmes in large numbers. However, Roan will be less focused on the level of excellence achieved by students of RSU than Saugh. Again, this is likely to lead to conflict as Saugh will be motivated to undertake additional investment, be it in terms of staff time in the form of extra classes or through extra resources that are likely to help students achieve higher grades.

Roan is also likely to be interested in how graduates of RSU perform after graduation but it is not as important to them as it is to Saugh. Saugh may therefore be keen to devote significant resource to developing strong links with local industry to ensure that RSU graduates are equipped with the correct skills. Saugh will also want to devote significant resource to monitoring and measuring how the graduates perform after graduation. Saugh may, for example, initiate surveys at various points following graduation at intervals of perhaps one, five and ten years. Given the focus of Roan, it is unlikely to want to devote much by way of resources to such measurement.

As a measure of commitment to the joint venture, Saugh will definitely be motivated to measure how many of Roan's staff will teach at RSU. Saugh may try to impose specific measures here, such as percentage of Roan staff from Teeland teaching on each programme, as it is clear that the involvement of Roan is a critical success factor for Saugh in achieving its aims.

Tutorial note

Do break the answer down into two parts; problems managing performance and problems measuring performance. In addition, there are 14 marks available here and so it is essential that you plan your answer to ensure that you have enough points, have prioritised your points, related your points to Saugh and Roan and not repeated your points.

(b)

Key answer tips

This is a nice example of how stakeholders may be examined in APM. There are two marks available here for each stakeholder. To gain a good mark you should begin by explaining the interest/objectives of each stakeholder group and then once this is established, you can go on to consider a relevant performance measure for this interest.

Government of Teeland

The government of Teeland is only likely to be interested in the performance of RSU if there is a significant failing. The most obvious examples relate to a financial default through overspend or, potentially, a scandal involving staff of Roan in Deeland whilst working at RSU. It would be impossible to either plan for or meaningfully measure this latter scenario and hence the most likely aspect to be of interest to the government of Teeland is the liquidity of Roan.

A simple measure of this, even something as straightforward as the cash surplus of Roan, would confirm to the government of Teeland that Roan is unlikely to go into liquidation. This measure should be considered alongside the long-term liquidity of Roan and the government would be interested in knowing if Roan had taken on any long-term debt to fund the joint venture and, if so, its overall proportion in Roan's capital structure.

Teachers' trade union

The teachers' trade union would be interested in the number of programmes or courses that are being offered in RSU. The more programmes that are offered, the more likely it is that Roan staff will be required by their employer to teach in Deeland. Fewer courses would increase the possibility that local provision for teaching could be found. However, the more courses that are offered, the less likely it is that the necessary specialism could be found through local provision in a developing country.

Public pressure group

The public pressure group would be interested in how much time is being spent by staff of Roan, perhaps teaching staff in particular rather than those of a higher level of management, in Deeland. The pressure group would like to see this figure probably presented in absolute terms and measured month by month to allow for comparison and trend analysis. The higher this figure becomes the more active the pressure group is likely to become and the more the membership of the pressure group is likely to grow.

Examiner's comments

Part (a) was generally well answered by candidates. Those candidates who structured their answers to specifically cover problems managing performance **and** problems measuring performance went on to score well. Candidates should be aware that there is a difference between managing performance and measuring performance. The former is trying to generally improve performance, whereas the latter is using metrics to gauge the relative success or failure of the former.

Poor performance here was usually based around one of two problems. The first was a misunderstanding of the organisation that was being considered in the requirement – namely the joint venture university, and not the individual universities who have set up the joint venture. The second problem was the brevity of some points made, mainly candidates simply repeating the features of the organisations listed in the scenario, as opposed to specifically identifying the problem.

Part (b) was on average very poorly attempted by the majority of candidates. As noted previously, candidates who structured their answers along the lines of the requirement scored well, i.e. use a heading for each stakeholder and then under that heading recommend a performance measure and justify the measure recommended. The majority of candidates failed to do this, with poor answers ranging from very brief comments suggesting generic performance measures such as 'gross profit' or 'student satisfaction scores' with no justification as to why they might be appropriate, to those who entered into lengthy discussions of how the organisation can manage each stakeholder to keep them happy, which wasn't what was asked for.

Several candidates also focused on the Mendelow assessment which was provided in the scenario and discussed the accuracy and appropriateness of this assessment, despite this not being asked for either. This did not score any marks and wasted precious time.

ACCA marking scheme

		Marks
(a)	1 mark per point Discussion of issues in relation to performance management – up to 8 marks Discussion of issues in relation to performance measurement – up to 8 marks	
	Maximum	**14**
(b)	For each stakeholder group: justification of the measure – up to 2 marks	
	Maximum	**6**

Professional marks **Analysis and Evaluation** • Comprehensive evaluation of the problems of managing and measuring performance in a joint venture **Commercial Acumen** • Demonstrate an understanding of the incompatibility of the objectives of the two organisations • Performance measures recommended for the three stakeholder groups are practical and plausible in the context of the organisation situation	
Maximum	**5**
Total	**25**

61 VEYATIE (SEPT/DEC 19) (AMENDED)

(a) Subjectivity

Customers' own assessments of satisfaction are subjective. Different customers could buy the same goods in the same store and at the same time, but still score their satisfaction differently. Different customers may have different expectations of their visit to the store and will attach different levels of importance to different aspects of their visit. Some may place a high importance on being able to move around the store and access goods easily, whereas to others this may be unimportant and would not affect their satisfaction.

Another reason why the data may be misleading is that, when rating their satisfaction, customers may tend to use the middle scores and be reluctant to use the highest and lowest scores. This appears to be the case in the data given where in most quarters customers do not give the scores of 1 or 5.

Aggregated and mean data

The collection of data of a single measure of customer satisfaction does not indicate what aspect of their visit to the store customers are satisfied, or dissatisfied, with. Customers may consider the price, design and quality of the goods, the comfort and layout of the store or the friendliness and product knowledge of the staff when scoring their satisfaction. Without knowing which aspects of their visit customers are satisfied with, it will be hard to know what to do to improve customer satisfaction.

Using the mean score may also make the data hard to interpret. For example, in Quarter 1 20X4, 50% of the customers are completely satisfied (a score of 5) and 50% of the customer are completely dissatisfied (a score of 1). This may be due to an error in collecting or compiling the data, but the mean score of 3 indicates that, overall, customers are satisfied, whereas 50% of them are completely dissatisfied. The calculation of the median or modal score may be preferable because this reduces the distortion to mean scores caused by very high or low scores.

Incomplete data

The data may not represent the views of a wide range of customers. The scores are collected when customers are buying goods at the till. This does not reflect the views of the customers who were so dissatisfied that they did not buy anything.

The prizes offered in the draw to encourage customers to leave the satisfaction score may appeal differently to male and female customers and to customers of different ages. For example, tickets to amusement parks may appeal more to younger customers than to older ones. Using this data as if it represents a wide range of customers' views may be misleading and lead to incorrect decisions being taken.

Identifying trends

Identifying trends is one way of overcoming some of the problems of interpreting the customer data, but it may be difficult to identify trends. In a fashion retailer such as Veyatie, there may be seasonal and short-term or cyclical trends, which make it hard to interpret what the long-term trend is.

In the limited data given, there appears to be a seasonal trend where customer satisfaction is worse in Quarter 4 than in any other quarter in each year. Overall there seems to be a downward trend, with every quarter being worse than the same quarter in the previous year.

(b) Problems of implementing and using the balanced scorecard

Selecting measures

Veyatie's strategic objectives are to maximise shareholder wealth by increasing the number of retail stores, making customers completely satisfied, ensuring its stores are attractive and offering the widest range of fashion clothing in the market. Measures must be selected which are congruent with Veyatie's critical success factors (CSFs) and strategic objectives. Though it is unclear what the CSFs are, at least one of the strategic objectives, to increase the number of stores, is not reflected at all in the measures selected. The lack of a suitable measure for this objective could be the reason why Veyatie is unlikely to open new stores in the near future.

Measures must not be selected just because they are easy to measure. The human resources department already records the total number of employee training days, so this measure could have been selected just because the data is readily available.

The number of days spent on the different types of training is unclear. Though clearly important, staff health and safety training does not directly help Veyatie achieve its strategic objectives. It may simply reflect Veyatie's legal obligations and so would not help gain competitive advantage. It would be better to measure the days spent training staff to understand the range of products available and how to display them attractively in the store, as this directly relates to Veyatie's strategic objectives.

One of the benefits of the balanced scorecard approach is that it presents a holistic view of a business, covering financial and non-financial and internal and external factors. The measures selected do cover all four perspectives of the balanced scorecard, but do not seem to be well balanced as there are more measures in the financial perspective than in each of the other perspectives. Also, most of the measures are internally focused.

The bias towards financial measures may reflect the fact that the board has so far seen little need for non-financial indicators. Financial measures, however, are backwards looking and measure the results of actions taken in the past. It is non-financial factors, such as customer satisfaction, which drive future performance and which will enable Veyatie to achieve its strategic objectives.

Conflicting measures

When selecting measures to use in the balanced scorecard, care must be taken to select measures which do not conflict with each other. Otherwise, without further guidance, managers will not know which measure to focus on, or may simply ignore one measure and focus on another.

Several of the measures selected by the consultant may potentially conflict with one another. For example, in order to achieve a low stock out percentage, Veyatie may have to hold higher levels of inventory which may worsen inventory turnover. This could apply at the overall company level or at individual stores.

The financial measure of operating profit margins conflicts with some of the measures in the other perspectives. The total number of employee training days has been selected to measure the learning and innovation perspective. The cost of this training, at least in the short term, will reduce operating profit margins. Similarly, having a high market share may imply that Veyatie will have to be competitive on price, which will also lower operating profit margins.

Board commitment

If the introduction of the balanced scorecard approach is to be successful, the commitment of the board is essential. Without this, other managers in the business are unlikely to work hard to implement and use the approach.

The board is already sceptical about the benefits of the balanced scorecard. There is the danger that it may simply be abandoned if it is found difficult to use, as was proposed for the collection of customer satisfaction data which was found to be difficult to interpret. The board's apparent disregard of non-financial performance measures is also clearly inconsistent with a successful introduction of the balanced scorecard approach.

Collecting and interpreting data

Interpreting the measures used in the balanced scorecard may be difficult, for example, for qualitative data such as customer satisfaction, which Veyatie has already had difficulties in interpreting. A lack of expertise in interpreting this data, may lead to wrong decisions being made.

The collection and interpretation of the data for the balanced scorecard will take time and resources. There may be staff resistance to the change, though this may be overcome by training in the benefits and use of the balanced scorecard.

Veyatie's information systems are basic for a business of its size and focus just on the use of financial information. They will need to be replaced or upgraded in order to collect and process non-financial and external data required for the balanced scorecard. The cost of implementing and using the balanced scorecard should be compared to the benefits of doing so.

Tutorial note

This question focuses on qualitative information and the balanced scorecard. The areas covered are not difficult but obtaining a good mark may be more challenging if you do not have enough relevant points or do not relate the points made to the scenario. A good answer plan should help here.

Examiner's comments

Part (a) was fairly well done with candidates identifying numerous issues from the description of how the survey was conducted. The better candidates made good use of the table of data given in the scenario to generate further ideas about the problems of interpreting such data.

Part (b) was surprisingly poorly answered given that the BSC has been a common topic at APM and often well answered. The issue with this question was the failure to answer the specific question asked. Often candidates seemed to be trying to answer the question 'advise the board on whether the given set of indicators is suitable for a BSC at the company'. These answers frequently ignored the further guidance in the scenario that 'the board does not want you to give a detailed evaluation of the advantages and disadvantages of each performance measure or to suggest completely new measures.' and did not focus on the actual requirement to address the 'problems of implementing and using the balanced scorecard (BSC) approach'.

ACCA marking scheme

		Marks
(a)	1 mark per relevant point covering: – subjectivity and customer perception – mean and aggregated data – incomplete data – trends and seasonal factors	
	Maximum	**8**
(b)	1 mark per relevant point covering: – problems of selecting measures – problems of measurement – the need for balance – problems of conflicting measures – need for board and management commitment – collecting and interpreting data – information system requirements – use of illustrative examples from the measures in Appendix 2	
	Maximum	**12**

Professional marks	
Analysis and Evaluation	
• Appropriate and logical use of the scenario information to correctly identify and explain the problems of the external information used, with discussion of how a unified corporate database could help to overcome each problem identified	
• Advice given on problems of measuring but also managing performance in the joint venture and problems discussed are clearly supported with examples from the scenario	
Scepticism	
• Recognition that there are factors which might limit the usefulness of the external information and there are potential problems with the joint venture but communicating these in a constructive, courteous and professional manner	
Commercial Acumen	
• Effective use of examples drawn from scenario information and other practical considerations related to the context to illustrate points being made throughout the answer	
Maximum	**5**
Total	**25**

62 VUNDERG (MAR/JUN 19)

(a) Activity based management

Activity based management (ABM) applies activity based costing (ABC) principles in order to satisfy customer needs using the least amount of resources. Activity based costing groups overheads into cost pools for an activity and identifies the cost driver for each activity. This gives a more accurate calculation of product costs.

ABM makes it possible to better control costs by controlling the activities which drive the costs. ABM would also help Vunderg to identify value added activities and non-value added activities. Activities which do not add value should be reduced, which would allow cost reduction without affecting the quality of service or product for Vunderg's customers.

Choosing which products to manufacture

ABM can help to improve Vunderg's performance in terms of deciding which products to manufacture. This is particularly important where a large proportion of a company's costs are overheads. This is the case in Vunderg, where overheads relating primarily to procurement, customer administration and product design **are high**. By understanding the cost of a product, and therefore its profitability, Vunderg can decide whether to discontinue an unprofitable product or whether to produce a new one. This will be relevant for the proposed large windows for commercial buildings. These are bespoke items and the cost will include a large amount of overheads, such as design.

Loss making products identified using ABM are often those which are highly customised and produced in low volumes, such as the conservatories. By using ABC principles, Vunderg could identify the high overhead costs of the sourcing of special materials and finishes for these by the procurement department. Using ABM, Vunderg could take action to reduce these costs, for example, by standardising the range of materials and finishes used, so that the procurement department spends less time sourcing them. The conservatories earn 8% of Vunderg's total contribution in 20% of the factory space. This implies that conservatories account for a disproportionate level of factory overheads.

Review of costs, prices and designs

By understanding what drives the costs of a product, Vunderg can take actions to make an unprofitable product profitable, for example, in response to the initial quality problems when the glasshouses were first manufactured, but which now command premium prices. The use of ABM may have led to a faster resolution of these initial quality problems by identifying the causes, or drivers, of the product cost and taking action to manage these.

ABM will also help identify products which may need to be re-priced. For example, customers may be prepared to pay more for the use of special materials and finishes in the conservatories. Vunderg could charge customers more for the use of special materials and finishes to cover the high overhead cost associated with procuring them.

ABM may identify possible improvements to the design of a product by focusing on activities which add value for the customer and eliminating those which do not. Selling leaking conservatories does not add value to the customer and incurs rectification costs. The improvement in design to prevent the leaks occurring in the first place is an example of how ABM can be used to make the conservatories business more profitable.

Customer profitability analysis

Customer profitability analysis (CPA) involves apportioning overhead costs to different types of customers, or categories of customers, using ABM principles. This enables a better understanding of the profitability of selling to different customers and can help Vunderg to decide whether to stop selling to certain customers or take other actions to improve their profitability.

At Vunderg, CPA would be most useful for the glasshouses which are sold through 40 different retailers. Some of the costs of selling to these customers, such as trade discounts, should be relatively easy to identify. Other overhead costs, such as those driven by the number of customer orders processed, may only be identified using ABM principles and may differ considerably between customers as the size of orders they place varies greatly.

The profitability of selling to the 40 retailers will therefore also vary considerably. Vunderg could act to improve the profitability of the least profitable ones. This could include insisting on minimum order sizes to reduce the costs driven by the number of orders processed. They could also offer more product training or contribution towards advertising costs to increase sales volumes.

(b) Limitations of using the ABM method

Identifying key activities and drivers

It may be difficult to separately identify all of the key activities and what drives them, which makes the application of ABC principles difficult. It may also be hard to assign responsibilities for individual cost pools which may cut across departmental boundaries.

Limited use

ABM is most useful where products are customised and contain high overhead costs such as design, procurement and customer administration. While the use of ABM may be worthwhile for the conservatories business, which is highly customised, and for the bespoke windows for commercial buildings, 84% (9,800/11,679) of Vunderg's contribution is from windows used in residential housing. These are highly standardised and are likely to include few overhead costs, for example, relating to design and after sales service. The manufacturing process after many years will already be efficient. The costs may already be well understood and controlled, in which case the implementation of ABM may not be worthwhile. Vunderg does, however, need a good understanding of the overhead costs, as the residential windows market is competitive.

As windows are highly standardised, Vunderg may be unable to pick and choose which items to produce. Design, specification and size will be dictated by the large construction companies who buy them and who will expect Vunderg to supply a complete range of windows. These companies would just buy from a competitor if Vunderg stopped producing the items they needed. As this market is very competitive, there may be little Vunderg could do to improve profitability, for example, by increasing prices, so the use of ABM to choose which products to sell could therefore be of little use. Similarly, as there are only a few large construction companies, the use of ABM may also not be worthwhile as Vunderg could not realistically stop trading with any one of them, nor could it raise prices because of the competitive market.

Incorrect decisions

Despite the difficulties in using ABC, for example, in identifying cost drivers, the use of cost drivers to charge overhead costs to conservatories should give a clearer indication of their profitability than under the current system. Vunderg can then take action to increase the profitability of these products, for example, by increasing the prices or reducing the costs.

The decision on whether these products should be discontinued should, however, take into account the effect on glasshouse sales as customers like to buy glasshouses which match the materials used in the conservatories. Discontinuing conservatories could reduce contribution from glasshouses by up to 17.1% (650/3,800), a total loss of contribution of approximately $166,000 (17.1% of $969,000), which is significant. As conservatories are at the start of their life cycle, expecting them to be profitable immediately could be unrealistic.

Just because a large proportion of factory space is dedicated to manufacturing conservatories does not mean that these costs will be saved in the short term if the products are discontinued. The depreciation or lease costs of the factory are fixed. Vunderg's main business is saturated and there is no prospect that the factory space could be better used in making other products. The factory may already not be fully utilised.

Problems of implementing ABM

Resource and cost impact

As Vunderg does not have an ABM system, considerable resources and management time will be needed to set this up. There may be resistance from staff, for example, because they do not want to change from the current costing system, which has been in use for a long time. Staff may not understand the benefits of ABM, or how it works. They would need training, which is expensive and it may take a considerable time before ABM is working effectively.

As Vunderg has only basic information systems, it may need to invest in these in order to collect large volumes of data on costs. Vunderg will have to consider whether the benefits of implementing ABM are greater than the costs of doing so.

Tutorial note:

In APM you need to build on your knowledge from PM and apply it to ABB and ABM. So, for example, for ABM you need to be able to discuss and evaluate its application.

Examiner's comments

Part (a) – Some candidates took the productive path of discussing the general benefits of the method and then illustrating each of these for the relevant products. Many candidates though took the approach of treating each product type individually which lead to answers which repeated the same general point several times (wasting time) and not discussing the impact of their advice on the business overall.

Part (b) – Candidates provided fair answers on the general problems of identifying cost drivers and issues in resourcing the implementation of ABM. However, their lack of knowledge of ABM lead to generally weak answers, lacking in detail relevant to the company.

ACCA marking scheme

			Marks
(a)	1 mark per point: Defining ABM – up to 2 marks Choosing which products to manufacture – up to 4 marks Review of costs, prices and designs – up to 4 marks Customer profitability analysis – up to 4 marks		
		Maximum	**13**
(b)	1 mark per point: Limitations of the ABM method – up to 9 marks Implementation – up to 5 marks		
		Maximum	**12**
Total			**25**

63 ZONES (DEC 18)

Key answer tips

A great revision question on the performance pyramid and Six Sigma – do complete this before the exam. If you find the question difficult then take the time to review the answer in detail; there is a lot to learn from.

In (a) do make sure you advise on how the performance pyramid can help to achieve corporate vision rather than simply explaining what the performance pyramid is.

In (b) it's also important to address the specifics of the requirement with a focus on operational performance required.

Requirement (c) is more difficult, particularly because there are 9 marks available. Answer planning should be a normal part of your approach to questions and should help here in generating enough relevant ideas.

(a) The performance pyramid covers not only financial performance but also performance relating to a wide range of underlying processes which drive financial performance. As such, it helps to set financial and non-financial performance measures, such as on-time stops. Non-financial measures are leading indicators which can help to achieve long-term future financial performance. This would be useful to Zones, which has had excessive focus on financial objectives and inadequate systems to measure and manage performance of the underlying processes driving financial performance. It is unclear exactly what the current financial objectives are.

The elements of the pyramid are interrelated, and each level in the pyramid supports the one above it. For example, on-time stops will increase customer satisfaction, which will eventually lead to greater market share, one element of the corporate vision.

Objectives cascade down the pyramid from the strategic to the operational level. The vision to increase shareholder wealth can be supported by financial objectives such as EVA™ at the level below. Measures flow up the pyramid, so that measurement of on-time stops can help determine whether Zones is achieving customer satisfaction.

The pyramid ensures that all aspects, both internal and external, of performance are measured. The right hand side of the pyramid covers internal efficiency, such as flexibility and productivity, while the left hand side covers external effectiveness, such as customer satisfaction. Using on-time stops again as an example, which relates to the quality (external effectiveness) element of the pyramid, will lead to improved performance up the left hand side of the pyramid.

(b) Operational performance is represented by the four elements at the bottom level of the performance pyramid, which are quality, delivery, cycle time and waste. It is unclear what quality means in the context of the corporate vision, though the measure of on-time stops could be interpreted as a measure of quality, which is valued by customers. There is no direct measure of cycle time, for example, the time taken between collecting a parcel and delivering it. Also, there is no direct measure for delivery, which in this context would be the amount of time needed to arrange a collection or delivery.

Vehicle utilisation

This is a good way to measure waste. The greater the utilisation of vehicle capacity, the lower the waste, for example, of vehicle running costs. In the long run, higher vehicle utilisation would mean the number of vehicles operated could be reduced for the same level of activity. This would lead to increased productivity and financial performance, so helping to achieve the corporate vision.

Vehicle utilisation will vary, according to location, time of year and type of vehicle used, and is also measured inconsistently, according to the type of vehicle. Vehicle utilisation may be too broad a measure, making it difficult to manage performance. Areas of poor performance may mask other areas of good performance. Similarly, measuring utilisation as an average between that at the beginning and end of each day may not actually represent the average utilisation during the day.

Fuel consumption

Reducing fuel consumption would lead to a significant increase in financial performance at Zones. Measuring average fuel consumption per kilometre travelled does not, however, relate directly to activity, for example, to the number of parcels delivered.

Average fuel consumption will vary between type of vehicle and between rural and urban areas. A large vehicle may have high fuel consumption per kilometre travelled, but will also carry a large number of parcels. Average fuel consumption per kilometre is not a good measure of waste, or any other aspect of operational performance. To be useful in managing operational performance, this measure should be changed to average fuel consumed per parcel delivered. In this case, this would be a suitable measure for waste.

On-time stops

Customers are likely to value on-time stops very highly, and along with value for money, this will be one of the main reasons they will choose to use Zones. This is reflected in the corporate vision. The proportion of on-time stops is a measure of operational performance which relates to the quality element of the performance pyramid and is a key driver of customer satisfaction.

Tutorial note

Answers structured on the basis of the four operational elements of the pyramid would be acceptable.

(c) The DMAIC acronym stands for define, measure, analyse, improve and control. These are the five phases by which the six sigma methodology is implemented. To be suitable for use in the DMAIC method, measures defined must have certain characteristics.

Percentage of stops made within 10 minutes of the booked time

According to the six sigma method, only those measures which are valued by the customer should be measured. On-time stops will be valued by customers, and contribute to customer satisfaction.

Currently, however, of all complaints which Zones receives from customers relating to stops not made on time, less than around 1 per million of these relate to those made within 30 minutes of the booked time. This level of complaints is so low that this would already achieve the very low number, 3.4 per million, of failures targeted by implementation of the six sigma methodology.

It seems that customers will not value stops made within 10 minutes of the booked time, any more than they would value those within 30 minutes. Another principle of six sigma methodology is not to measure what customers are already satisfied with. They are already satisfied with stops made within 30 minutes of the booked time.

The percentage of stops made within 10 minutes of the booked time is not a suitable measure. The time and costs of making the measurements will exceed the benefits of doing so.

Failed deliveries

Failed deliveries will represent a considerable cost to Zones in terms of wasted fuel and driver time. It may also reduce flexibility by using up vehicle capacity which could be used to carry more parcels. Even though deliveries may fail due to traffic congestion, they will still reduce customer satisfaction.

The percentage of failed deliveries is currently 5%, well above the target rate for failures under the six sigma methodology (which is better than 3.4 per million accuracy), and in this respect would be a suitable measure.

According to the six sigma method, only those measures which can be improved should be measured. Failed deliveries arising from customers being unavailable to take the delivery is completely out of Zones' control. Deliveries failing due to incorrectly addressed parcels could be reduced to some extent, for example, by the use of information technology to check the correct address, but most failures due to this are outside Zones' control. As failed deliveries cannot be significantly improved, this is not a suitable measure.

Examiner's comments

Part (a). Responses to this part were fairly good as many answers collected a reasonable number of marks by going through the individual headings in the model and explaining how they link to the achievement of the vision. However, many candidates did not capitalise on the marks available as they failed to address how the application of the model as a whole helps.

Part (b). Performance on this part was fairly good. Many candidates identified strengths or weaknesses of each measure using the data in the scenario. Answers could often have been improved by candidates realising that there were possibly both strengths and weaknesses for each measure rather than tending to think in simplistic terms that each measure was either all good or all bad.

Part (c). This part was usually poorly done. If the requirement had asked the candidates to apply the DMAIC approach to the two areas covered by the measures then the answers would have been more relevant and consequently scored more marks. Candidates gain credit for making points which are both technically correct and relevant to the question asked.

Future candidates should note that APM is likely to continue to focus in detail on measurement problems within its various methods as this is the area where candidates are expected to have particular expertise.

ACCA marking scheme		
		Marks
(a)	1 mark per point: How performance pyramid helps to achieve Zones corporate vision	
	Maximum	**7**
(b)	1 mark per point: Each performance measure, up to 3 marks each	
	Maximum	**9**
(c)	Evaluating suitability of the two measures, 1 mark per point, up to 4 marks each Conclusion on the suitability of the two measures, up to 2 marks	
	Maximum	**9**
Total		**25**

64 BAZEELE (MAR/JUN 18)

Key answer tips

In requirements (a) and (b) you should have the relevant knowledge in place and be able to apply it to the relatively simple specifics of the scenario. VBM should not be viewed as an unimportant area. This question serves as an important reminder that any syllabus area can or may be examined and that this subject area must be fully understood.

Requirement (c) is on EVA. This calculation has been tested a number of times and it's really important that you feel comfortable with the calculation before sitting the exam. The examining team are not interested in testing a large number of adjustments. Rather the focus will be on your ability to demonstrate that you understand the concept of EVA and that you are able to do a small number of adjustments correctly.

(a) In the context of VBM, value of a business is measured by discounting cash flows at the business's cost of capital. When investment returns exceed the cost of capital, value will be created for shareholders. When returns are lower than the cost of capital, value will be destroyed.

The VBM approach is to ensure that all activities and decisions in a business are undertaken so as to create value for shareholders. Currently, Bazeele's overall objective is to maintain ROCE at historic levels, but this does not necessarily create value for shareholders.

This is particularly so now that Bazeele has diversified into hiring large items of plant for use in major infrastructure projects. These projects last up to 10 years, so the time value of money is likely to be significant, as is the initial capital expenditure for the plant. Long-term hire agreements may give an acceptable ROCE, but may have a negative net present value, and hence destroy value for shareholders. The prediction of large increases in bank interest rates will increase Bazeele's cost of capital, and further reduce the net present value of long-term agreements.

Similarly, business unit and branch managers are given the objective of maintaining net profit margins. Thus, managers may avoid activities which reduce profits in the short term, but which have future long-term benefits and create value for shareholders, such as investment in staff training.

With VBM, decisions are taken to create value for shareholders by considering value drivers, which are any factors which affect the value of the business. Value drivers may be non-financial, such as the customer satisfaction which may have been improved by the postponed staff training. A VBM approach is, therefore, suitable for Bazeele as it will encourage creation of value for shareholders.

(b) To adopt a VBM approach, Bazeele would need to use a different set of performance indicators, as ROCE and net profit margin do not necessarily create value for shareholders. Economic value added (EVA™) is a performance measure for shareholder value. Though more complex to calculate and more difficult to understand than the existing measures, EVA™ does encourage managers to make decisions, such as undertaking staff training, which have future long-term benefits. By encouraging managers to make investments which give a positive EVA™, value will be created for shareholders.

With VBM, managers would be given targets according to their areas of responsibility. For example, the board may have objectives to maximise value by making acquisitions which create value. Branch managers' objectives may be focused on non-financial value drivers such as customer satisfaction.

To identify value drivers, Bazeele will need good information which is accurate, reliable and timely, for example. It is unclear whether the current management information system is able to provide good information, but the CEO has said that information on customer satisfaction is not available. Resources, such as financial investment, time and training, may be needed to improve Bazeele's management information. Managers may resist the change in culture which would be required to adopt VBM; not least the CEO would need to set the 'tone at top' for what would be a disruptive and major change to Bazeele. However, the benefits of adopting VBM seem to outweigh the costs of doing so.

(c) As the economic value added (EVA™) is \$(13.1m), Bazeele has destroyed value for shareholders.

Calculation of net operating profit after tax (NOPAT)

	\$m	\$m
Net profit after tax		10.0
Add: depreciation on non-current assets	6.0	
Deduct: economic depreciation	(14.0)	
	———	(8.0)
Add: interest (accounted for in the WACC)	15.0	
Less: tax on interest (\$15.0m × 20%)	(3.0)	
	———	12.0
Deduct: reduction in bad debt provision		(4.8)
Add: advertising for long-term benefit		0.6
		———
NO PAT		9.8
		———

	$m
Capital employed at the start of the year	250.0
Deduct: difference in accumulated depreciation	(16.0)
Add back: increase in bad debt provision	4.8
Economic value of assets	238.8

Calculation of EVA™

	$m
NO PAT	9.8
Deduct: capital charge ($238.8 × 9.6%) (W1)	(22.9)
EVA™	(13.1)

W1 – Weighted average cost of capital (WACC)

Cost of equity:	12.0%	
After tax cost of debt:	8.0%	(10% × (1 – 20%))
WACC:	9.6%	((40% × 12%) + (60% × 8.0%))

Examiner's comments

Part (a). Many candidates provided much irrelevant information in an attempt to cover this lack of knowledge.

Part (b). As for part (a), this part was poorly answered reflecting a poor understanding of the VBM method.

Part (c). Candidates' performance in this part was often good. However, a significant minority committed simple errors where they had identified a suitable adjustment to make to profit or capital employed but then added/subtracted it when it should have been subtracted/added.

ACCA marking scheme

			Marks
(a)	1 mark per point: General explanation/evaluation of VBM – up to 2 marks Application to Bazeele – up to 4 marks Recommendation – 1 mark		
		Maximum	**7**
(b)	1 mark per point: Changes required on adoption of VBM – up to 7 marks		
		Maximum	**7**

(c)	Calculation of EVA^{TM} WACC – 1 mark NOPAT adjustments: Depreciation – 1 mark Economic depreciation – 1 mark Interest – 1 mark Tax on interest – 1 mark Reduction in bad debt provision – 1 mark Advertising – 1 mark Capital adjustments: Difference in accumulated depreciation – 1 mark Add back: increase in bad debt provision – 1 mark Calculation of EVA^{TM} – 1 mark Conclusion on the creation or destruction of value – 1 mark	
	Maximum	**11**
Total		**25**

65 DIBBLE (MAR/JUN 16)

Key answer tips

A great revision question covering the core elements of ABC and ABM. Ensure that you are very comfortable with this before the exam.

(a) (i) Implementation of ABC

ABC is an alternative to absorption costing, which is the method currently used by Dibble. ABC is a detailed fact gathering and data analysis technique.

In order to implement ABC production, overheads need to be grouped into cost pools as in the analysis of production overheads for Dibble in the management accounts extracts.

Then cost drivers for each cost pool must be identified. Cost drivers are the activities which bring about the costs, for example, the setup of the CAM machinery in Steel Division will be driven by the number of batches of production.

Once the cost pools and their associated cost drivers have been established, the cost per unit of cost driver can be calculated for each individual activity. The overhead costs are absorbed into each unit based on how much of the activity the unit uses, therefore, for example, units which require more inspection and testing will be allocated more of those costs. The overhead costs are then added to the prime costs in order to calculate the full cost of production.

(ii) Appropriateness of ABC

ABC is especially useful where there is a wide range of complex products and where production overheads form a larger proportion of total production costs. In Steel Division, there is a large range of products, many of them bespoke or one-off designs. Production overheads form 28% (4,472/(20,605 – 4,533)) of total production costs, and the use of ABC will be appropriate in this division.

ABC enables a more accurate cost of production to be calculated, which is very useful in setting product prices. This could be especially useful in Steel Division which has a wide range of products subject to a number of manufacturing processes. It will help to ensure that each product is priced high enough in order to produce an acceptable margin, but not so high so as to become uncompetitive. This is especially important as Steel Division's strategy is to produce bespoke products at prices comparable to competitors who produce simpler, more conventional products.

ABC enables managers to determine what activities drive the costs, and so focus on reducing those activities to control costs. Not all production overheads, for example, inspection costs of the coatings in Steel Division, are related to production volumes. It is equally possible to apply ABC techniques to overheads other than production overheads.

Problems with ABC

ABC is less useful in businesses such as Timber Division where there is a small range of relatively simple products and where production overheads only comprise around 1% of total production costs. Of the production overheads in Timber Division, storage is by far the biggest and is likely to be driven by production volumes.

It may be difficult to determine what the drivers of production costs are. Storage costs could also be related to the insolvency of a customer. It may be impossible to allocate all overheads to the specific activities which drive them and so management will have to apply judgement.

Calculation of ABC may be time consuming, complex and poorly understood by managers. As such, the time and expense of doing so may not be justified. This appears to be the case in Timber Division where there are only a few, relatively simple products and few production overheads. Whereas in Steel Division, where there is a wide range of more complex products and a high proportion of production overheads, ABC is more appropriate than the traditional absorption costing method currently used at Dibble.

(b) ABM is the use of ABC methods in order to improve organisational performance by meeting the needs of customers using the lowest possible amount of resources or costs. ABM can be applied at the operational level or to help develop strategy.

Product pricing

By accurately determining the cost of each product using ABC, Dibble would be able to ensure that prices are set so as to achieve an acceptable margin and also remain competitive with the prices currently charged in the rest of the market.

Steel Division charges customers a standard mark up of 10% on top of the $650k subcontractor's costs for the coating and painting of the steel. This means that customers are only being charged $65k whereas the costs of storage of goods awaiting subcontract work and of transporting the goods to the subcontractor total $695k.

By identifying the cost pools relating to the subcontract work, Steel Division can determine that it is making a loss on the subcontract work as a whole. It could therefore adjust the price of painted and coated products to ensure that an acceptable contribution margin is achieved. This is an example of operational ABM. At the strategic level, this type of information could help Dibble decide which product types to develop or discontinue.

The same principle may also apply where ABC can be used to identify which types of customers are the most profitable. In that way, resources can be focused on retaining and managing these customer groups. Action can be taken by additional advertising or product development in order to focus on these particular markets. By analysing customer profitability, it may be possible to reduce costs or increase revenue to make certain customer groups or product lines more profitable, both in the short and long term.

By identifying lines of business with poor profitability, Dibble could discontinue selling to particular customers, or selling particular products, if appropriate action could not be taken to improve profitability.

Analysis of activities

By analysing the activities which drive the costs, Steel Division could determine which activities may not be required or could be done in a more efficient way. It may be possible to introduce improvements in the short term, for example, changes in the production process which may improve efficiency. In the longer term, strategic changes could be made to the way in which activities are undertaken, such as by outsourcing other activities in addition to the painting and coating which is currently outsourced.

Identifying the costs of transporting painted finished goods back from the subcontractors to Steel Division could lead them to evaluate ways to reduce this cost, for example, by despatching goods to customers directly from the subcontractors' premises. This is a non-value added activity, i.e. one which consumes resources, such as time and cost to transport goods to and from the subcontractors, but which is of no additional value to the customer. In contrast, ABM may help identify value adding activities, such as the coating and painting, which customers are prepared to pay for.

Of the five categories of production overheads, only machining time is a value adding activity, sometimes categorised as a primary activity. Setting up the CAM machinery is a secondary activity, which does not itself add value, but is required in order to perform a value adding activity (machining).

The other overheads, storage, transfer and inspection, are all non-value adding activities which should be eliminated or reduced. By identifying the activities which drive these costs managers can attempt to do this.

However, given the nature of Dibble's products, it is likely that some inspection will still be required for safety or commercial reasons, as shown by the litigation case relating to the faulty product. The production manager's proposal to increase the costs of inspection is inappropriate, as having identified inspection as a non-value adding activity, it would be better to focus attention on getting the product right first time.

Design improvements

Steel Division has a wide range of relatively complex or even bespoke products. ABM can help managers take decisions at the product design stage, where many of the product's costs are already committed. These can include using fewer or more standardised components, such as a more limited range of paints and coatings.

Where strategic decisions are being taken, for example, about new product lines or lines of business, such as with Steel Division's strategy to develop novel innovative products, ABM can help assess whether such developments are likely to be profitable at an early stage. This would help avoid development costs for products which could turn out to be unprofitable. This could also help allocate resources, such as capital investment, to the most profitable lines of business.

Performance measurement

For ABM to be successful, it will require the commitment of senior management and effective communication and training of employees at all levels in the organisation as to the benefits and methods of ABM. This will incur management time and cost, and divert attention from existing management activities.

New performance measurement systems will need to be developed. Employee rewards will need to be aligned to key performance measures, such as the reduction of non-value adding processes like inspection. This will ensure that employees work towards the objectives of the organisation. Additional information gathering systems, or adaptations to existing information systems, will also be required, which will again incur additional cost and may disrupt existing activities.

Examiner's comments

Part (a) (i). It was a simple question which surprisingly was not answered very well by those who chose the question. The jargon of ABC was generally known but was often not correctly used. A lack of understanding of the basics of ABC meant that it was difficult to score well in the next part of the question.

Part (a) (ii) was reasonably done although weakness in basic understanding of ABC shown in part (i) led to vague answers. In particular, it was surprising to see candidates often apparently unaware that ABC is specifically an overhead allocation system.

Part (b) was not well done with many candidates providing lists of benefits that were not specifically related to the use of an activity based approach and reflected again the lack of a grounding in what an analysis of activities, cost drivers and cost pooling could do.

ACCA marking scheme

			Marks
(a)	Implementation of ABC – 1 mark per point	**Maximum**	**4**
(b)	Appropriateness of ABC – up to 6 marks Problems with ABC – up to 6 marks		
		Maximum	**8**
(c)	Improving performance using ABM – 1 mark per point	**Maximum**	**13**
Total			**25**

66 FORION ELECTRONICS (JUN 15)

Key answer tips

Make sure you answer the question set. In part (a) you were asked to assess the impact of the ERPS on performance management issues at Forion. This should have given you three clear points to structure your answer around. In part (c) make sure you evaluate reliability of information sources and don't simply list them.

(a) Enterprise Resource Planning Systems (ERPS) are software systems designed to support and automate the business processes of large enterprises. ERPS help in identifying and planning the use of resources across the organisation in all activities. As a unified database of corporate information, ERPS will aid the flow of information between all functions both within Forion and also with key outside stakeholders (e.g. suppliers such as BAS).

ERPS handle many aspects of operations including manufacturing, inventory, distribution, invoicing and accounting. They also cover support functions such as human resource management and marketing. These all seem appropriate for Forion.

ERPS can also contain SCM (supply chain management) and CRM (customer relationship management) software. Automated systems would seem appropriate at Forion given the number of customer and supplier relationships which Forion has to manage.

An ERPS also addresses the common issue of poor communication between departments. It will help across the three problems mentioned.

The inefficiencies arising from ordering the wrong volume of subcomponents would occur because purchasing and manufacturing are not using a common database so that purchasing may be using erroneous or out-of-date information. This will lead to extra costs in inventory handling and storing.

The stock-outs will result in poor customer service as goods are not available for immediate shipment. The obsolescence problems will result in direct financial losses as inventory is written off. Both of these problems will be the result of poor integration of the manufacturing schedule with the expected level of orders. ERPS will be welcomed as it will make use of the expertise of the marketing department in forecasting and making this available to manufacturing managers when setting their production plans.

The lack of vehicles available to meet delivery deadlines could be aided by the manufacturing schedule linking in to the delivery schedule so that optimal use can be made of the delivery fleet. This would also allow the delivery managers to plan for use of subcontractors to do delivery if there is not internal transport available and so avoid customer disappointment.

(b) Considering the points raised overall, it is surprising that they seem to be addressing the strengths of BAS. BAS will have been chosen as an ally because it is a good company. However, it may be worth considering if there are weaknesses and if measures should be put in place in the agreement to guard against these.

The points seem reasonable given the critical nature of the screen in the production process of a smartphone and the setting of penalties is wise. Taking each point in turn:

Manufacturing quality would be expected to be high given BAS' reputation; however, it will be a critical part of the assembly process and faults will lead to either delayed delivery (if spotted in internal inspection) or else lead to customer dissatisfaction and rework costs to repair faulty items.

The time of delivery will dictate the volume of screen inventory which Forion has to hold and so impact on any attempt to run a just-in-time system of manufacturing. It may be necessary to give BAS access to Forion's production scheduling system (via the new ERPS possibly) in order to achieve such a close working relationship.

Unlike the other two issues, the point on the provision of technical upgrades does not provide a metric for measuring this. It will be difficult to set a minimum performance level as such upgrades will be difficult to predict and it would be reasonable for BAS to reject (or ignore) a vaguely worded clause which would not be enforceable.

The size of the penalties would need to be commensurate with damage to the reputation of the product from BAS' failure. Mobile phone customers are notable for having rapidly dropped previous market leaders when their products fail to deliver (e.g. Nokia, Blackberry). Therefore, it would be reasonable for potentially large penalties to be payable. Forion should note that these will only be claimable if they hold to their side of the agreement and so must carefully attend to the information and resources which need to be provided to BAS.

(c) **Financial and non-financial data**

Financial data has the advantage of being heavily checked and policed as part of the annual audit regime operating in most organisations. Financial data also has the advantages of being quantitative and so objective, whereas it can be difficult to judge the relative value of, for example, two customer complaints.

For the accountant, the collection and interpretation of financial data is thus straightforward and an everyday activity. Qualitative, non-financial data will often require to be transformed into quantitative data by applying 1–5 scales but it will never escape from the problem of being judgemental and subjective. Not all non-financial data is qualitative; however, the planning and scheduling data will be quantitative.

Internal and external sources

Forion will have greater control over the accuracy of internal data within its own ERPS than the external data, such as might be supplied by suppliers for their deliveries. External sources of data such as for the SLA will obviously be highly contentious if there is the possibility of penalty payments resulting from breaches of the agreement. Therefore, Forion may want to put in place its own inspection regime in order to confirm such data. Unreconciled differences between information systems are often a source of dispute in alliances such as the one with BAS.

Examiner's comments

Part (a) was often fairly well done with many good answers relating to the three specific problem areas in information management at Forion.

Part (b) was generally fairly well done with candidates showing a good appreciation of how BAS's performance links to Forion's. The most common fault in answers was a failure to focus on the performance measurement aspects of the areas.

Part (c). This has been a common topic in past examinations and performance in this question was unexpectedly poor. Many candidates seem unaware of what constitutes internal and external sources and surprisingly many consider audited, financial data to be amongst the least reliable sources. Possibly as a result of these weaknesses, the markers saw numerous answers that discussed only the type of information that both parties to the alliance would need without discussing its reliability.

ACCA marking scheme

		Marks
(a)	1 mark per point up to 5 marks for description of ERPS and how it integrates information up to 6 marks for ERPS impact on problems at Forion	
	Maximum	**10**
(b)	1 mark per point; to score highly, all three issues must be addressed	
	Maximum	**8**
(c)	1 mark per point; to score highly, both issues financial/non-financial and internal/external must be addressed	
	Maximum	**7**
Total		**25**

67 THE SPARE FOR SHIPS COMPANY (SFS) (JUN 10)

Key answer tips

This is a fairly tough question that looks at ABC and ABM. Ensure that you have learnt the key knowledge aspects of both of these and appreciate the difference.

In particular, make sure you are comfortable considering how different models and methodologies can work together.

(a) **(i)** The differences in the reported cost estimates calculated under each of the two costing systems are significant. This is especially the case with regard to Job order 973. The management accountant's calculations for the cost estimates produce the following increase/(decrease) in reported costs:

	Job order 973	Job order 974
	$	$
Unit cost per job under existing system	1,172.00	620.00
Unit cost per job under activity based costing	1,612.00	588.89
Increase/(decrease) in reported cost	37.54%	(5.02)%

Job order 973 shows an increase in reported cost of 37.54% [(1,612 – 1,172)/1,172] whereas Job order 974 shows a decrease in reported cost of 5.02% [(88.89 – 620)/620].

A common occurrence when activity-based costing is implemented is that low-volume products show an increase in their reported costs while high-volume products show decreases in their reported costs. This is very much the case with regard to the products which are the subjects of Job orders 973 and 974.

The reported costs also differ due to the following:

- Job orders 973 and 974 differ in the way they consume activities in each of the five activity areas within SFS's premises
- The activity areas differ in their indirect cost allocation bases. In particular no activity area uses direct labour hours as the basis of allocating indirect costs.

Two areas where the differences in reported product costs might be important to SFS are as follows:

Product design – since it is more probable that those involved in the design of products will find the results produced by the activity-based approach to be much more credible. This is especially the case in a machine oriented environment where direct labour hours are unlikely to be the major cost-driver. Activity-based costing can be of more assistance to product designers and may signal areas where cost reductions can be achieved, for example using fewer cuts on the lathe and/or reducing the number of machine hours required in the milling area.

Product pricing – The application of activity-based costing shows that the cost of Job order 973 is being understated while the cost of Job order 974 is being overstated. The management of SFS should be aware of the danger of failing to recover the costs incurred on Job order 973. Conversely, they may well be overpricing Job order 974 which might well entail losing business to its competitors.

(ii) Two problems SFS would have had to deal with in the successful implementation of an activity-based costing system are as follows:

(i) initially it would be very time consuming to collect a large amount of data concerning the activities relating to each job undertaken by SFS. Hence the cost of buying, implementing and maintaining a system of activity-based costing is likely to be significant

(ii) it would be vital to identify the real 'cost-drivers' within the activity-based costing system of SFS otherwise results given by the ABC system would be inaccurate leading to incorrect decisions by management.

Tutorial note

Additional credit was available for staff/culture issues which would be resolved by adequate training and motivation to change.

(b) Operational ABM is about 'doing things right'. Those activities which add value to products can be identified and improved. Activities that do not add value should be reduced in order to cut costs without reducing product value. Where for example a product or service has been estimated to require a longer activity time than other products or services then every effort should be made to find ways of reducing the number of hours required.

Strategic ABM is about 'doing the right things' using the ABC information to decide which products to develop and which activities to use. It can focus on profitability analysis, identifying which products/customers are the most profitable and for which sales volume should be developed.

An activity may have implicit value not necessarily reflected in the financial value added to any service or product. SFS might decide to cut back on the level of expenditure involved in servicing customers. This may lead to a poorer perceived value by customers of the service provided by SFS with a consequent fall in demand.

There are risks attaching to the use of ABM insofar as ABM can give the wrong signals. For example a particularly pleasant work environment can help attract and retain the best staff, but may not be identified as adding value in operational ABM. By the same token, a customer that represents a loss based on committed activities, but that opens up leads in a new market, may be identified as a low value customer by a strategic ABM process.

Tutorial note

Other risks or potential problems were also accepted such as pricing errors arising or the cost/benefit of such an expensive system.

(c) ABM can be used alongside performance management improvement strategies, such as Total Quality Management, Six Sigma and Business Process Reengineering, where the information provided can support the projects.

TQM

In TQM, costs are analysed into costs of conformance (appraisal and prevention costs) and costs of non-conformance (internal and external failure costs). The aim of TQM is to reduce the costs of non-conformance.

ABM enables organisations to more accurately calculate these quality related costs by identifying the appropriate cost drivers and then monitoring improvements.

Six Sigma and Business Process Reengineering

Six Sigma and BPR typically involve projects to achieve large one-off improvements in particular business processes relating to efficiency and better customer satisfaction.

ABM can support these approaches in several ways:

- Identifying processes that need improvement and establishing priorities
- Providing cost justification for proceeding with the project, for example by enabling more useful cost-benefit analysis
- Monitoring the benefits of the projects.

Examiner's comments

Overall, answers to this question were mixed. The comparison of different methods of costing and performance measurement is a basic element of this exam and surprisingly, many candidates seem unprepared for part (a)(i). Better answers to this part focussed on how the two methods can produce different answers by comparing their underlying approaches. Again, candidates scored more heavily if their answer used the information in the scenario as illustrative example of the general points made about the different costing methods. Most candidates realised that there were price implications arising from the two costs but few realised the internal process implications for example in designing products.

Requirement (a)(ii). Candidates who focussed on the implementation stage and considered how it might be affected by such an IT system scored well. A few candidates cleverly took two subheadings and then discussed issues within these in order to ensure that they scored the two marks available for each problem.

Requirement (b). There were effectively four parts to this question the three topics itemised plus the risks of using ABM. There was a wide spread of marks to this part with a few knowledgeable candidates scoring close to full marks but a number of weaker answers which failed to relate the general definitions of operational and strategic ABM to SFS. Many candidates did not realise that implicit value was the value which does not immediately appear in traditional performance measurement systems but nevertheless, is important in a long-term management of a successful business.

ACCA marking scheme

				Marks
(a)	(i)	Comments (on merit):		
		Cost per unit comparisons		2
		Reasons for differences		2
		Potential consequences	Up to 2 each	4
			Maximum	**8**
	(ii)	Problems	Up to 2 each	**4**
(b)	Comments (on merit):			
	Operational ABM			2
	Strategic ABM			2
	The implicit value of an activity			2
	Risks			2
			Maximum	**8**
(c)	1 mark per relevant point			**5**
Total				**25**

68 APX ACCOUNTANCY (JUN 11)

Key answer tips

Make sure you learn the details of different models fully – for example, the building block model is more than simply a list of 6 dimensions – there is the distinction between results and determinants as well as dimensions v standards v rewards.

This is also a good example of a question where it is essential that you answer the question set! In the exam requirement (b) asked 'Evaluate the existing performance management system at APX by applying the building block model' but was often wrongly interpreted to mean 'Evaluate the existing performance of APX' – responses to this imagined question were often quite good but sadly, irrelevant and so scored poorly.

(a) Fitzgerald and Moon's building block approach

The building block model is an analysis that aims to improve the performance measurement systems of service businesses such as APX. It suggests that the performance system should be based on three concepts of dimensions, standards and rewards.

Dimensions fall into two categories: downstream results (competitive and financial performance) and upstream determinants (quality of service, flexibility, resource utilisation and innovation) of those results. These are the areas that yield specific performance metrics for a company.

Standards are the targets set for the metrics chosen from the dimensions measured. These must be such that those being measured take ownership of them, possibly by participating in the process of setting the standard. The standard must be achievable in order to motivate the employee or partner. The standards must be fairly set, based on the environment for each business unit so that those in the lower growth areas of, say, audit do not feel prejudiced when compared to the growing work in business advisory.

Rewards are the motivators for the employees to work towards the standards set. The reward system should be clearly understood by the staff and ensure their motivation. The rewards should be related to areas of responsibility that the staff member controls in order to achieve that motivation.

(b) The current system

APX's performance management system does not cover all the areas that the building block model would suggest are necessary. The downstream dimensions appear to be covered as the competitive performance (market share) and financial performance (revenue growth and profit margin) can be measured. However, the determinants of this performance appear less well covered with only the quality of service aspect handled by the customer satisfaction rating.

The standards are unclear from the information provided. It appears that the industry averages can be used to compare competitive performance but there are no figures for the industry on profitability. The measure must therefore be internal, comparing practice areas to each other. This may breach the fairness criterion as it is likely that business advisory can negotiate better fees than audit or tax due to market conditions being favourable from that area. No standard is mentioned on the document for quality of service.

The non-partner reward system at APX is related to performance as assessed by the line manager but this will be compromised by the limited measurement of the dimensions of performance. The partner reward system appears to be based on the level of responsibility of the partner and the performance of the whole firm rather than that individual's contribution to performance. Therefore, there is a strong probability that the reward level is not controllable by the partner and this may affect their motivation.

For example, a tax partner may view the growth in recovery work as sufficient to merit reward to all partners and so not optimise the performance of their own area of the practice.

(c) Main building block improvements

The first improvement obtained by using this model will be to ensure that all the key determinants of success in performance are being measured. The next benefit will be that the targets set for each measure are set in such a way as to engage the staff. Finally, the reward system will operate in a way to optimally motivate the individual staff members.

Improvements to existing performance measurement system

The existing performance measurement system requires measures for flexibility which address the speed of delivery of the service (e.g. a punctuality measure of percentage of jobs delivered on time), the customer's attitude (e.g. the existing customer service survey could be broken down to include the customer's perception of whether objectives were achieved) and the degree to which the practice handles busy periods (e.g. amount of overtime worked).

It is surprising that APX does not seem to measure resource utilisation, for example, by considering the percentage of billable hours worked to the total working hours of the firm. This is a commonly used measure of the productivity of staff in accounting practices. Finally, the dimension of innovation is not measured. Innovation is an important source of competitive advantage. The efficiency of the innovation process can be measured by the time it takes to launch a new service once the initial customer need is identified. The outputs of innovation process within APX could be measured by the number of new customer initiatives launched or by the revenue that they generate.

Examiner's comments

Requirement (a). Within each of the building blocks, weak knowledge of the aspects emphasised by the model were demonstrated. For example, very few candidates appreciated the distinction between the upstream determinants and the downstream results.

Requirement (b). Many candidates offered an irrelevant assessment of APX's performance. To illustrate why this is irrelevant consider the analogous question 'evaluate the accounting system at company X' and then consider the response, 'Company X is performing well with profit increasing by 10% to $100m in the last year.' The response does not address the question which is about the system and not the performance. Many candidates only evaluated the performance measures with little comment given to the standards applied to these or the reward system at APX.

Requirement (c). Better candidates had read the full requirement and so held back from offering improvements to the faults recognised in part (b) until the answer to this part. Again, answers were limited due to the poor quality of responses to the earlier parts although some candidates offered valuable practical ideas to the management at APX.

ACCA marking scheme

		Marks
(a)	Taking each building block, up to 1.5 marks for a description. Maximum 4 marks.	
	Maximum	**4**
(b)	Taking each building block, up to 3 marks for evaluating the existing system at APX. Maximum 8 marks.	
	Maximum	**9**
(c)	Main improvements from use of model 1 mark per point up to 4 marks. Specific suggestions for APX 1 mark per point which must relate to the scenario by way of examples up to 8 marks.	
	Maximum	**12**
Total		**25**

69 COD ELECTRICAL MOTORS (DEC 11)

Key answer tips

Try to ensure you understand the rationale behind performance management models such as the performance pyramid. A key element here is the hierarchy where measures near the bottom of the pyramid are more relevant to people doing day-to-day operational tasks, whereas those at the top are more strategic and intended for Board use. Many students failed to develop this split in their answers. The answer below includes the diagram of the performance pyramid. This is included to assist with learning. You will not be expected to reproduce diagrams in the CBE.

(a) The key features of performance measures are that:

- they should measure the effectiveness of the business and its processes in meeting the organisation's objectives in order to link to the overall strategy
- they should measure the efficiency of resource utilisation within the organisation
- they should contain internal and external measures of performance
- they should comprise a mix of financial and non-financial (quantitative and qualitative) methods
- they will require to make clear the different dimensions of performance so that judgements on trade-offs between them are explicit (e.g. quality and cost)
- they will link to the targets set for employee motivation
- they should cover both the short-term and long-term performance of the organisation; and
- they should be flexible in order to respond to changes in the business environment.

The key performance indicators (KPIs) at Cod fail to have many of these key features. The KPIs at present are purely focused on financial performance and do not address issues of quality, customer service and product innovation which are all mentioned in the mission statement. The KPIs have no strong external features such as customer satisfaction or share price performance. It is unclear how they will link to employee motivation and indeed, the board recognise this fact and intend to use the performance pyramid in order to address it. The overall picture of the performance measurement system is a traditional one which will lack the flexibility to address the concerns of the key stakeholders of Cod.

(b)

The pyramid diagram is:

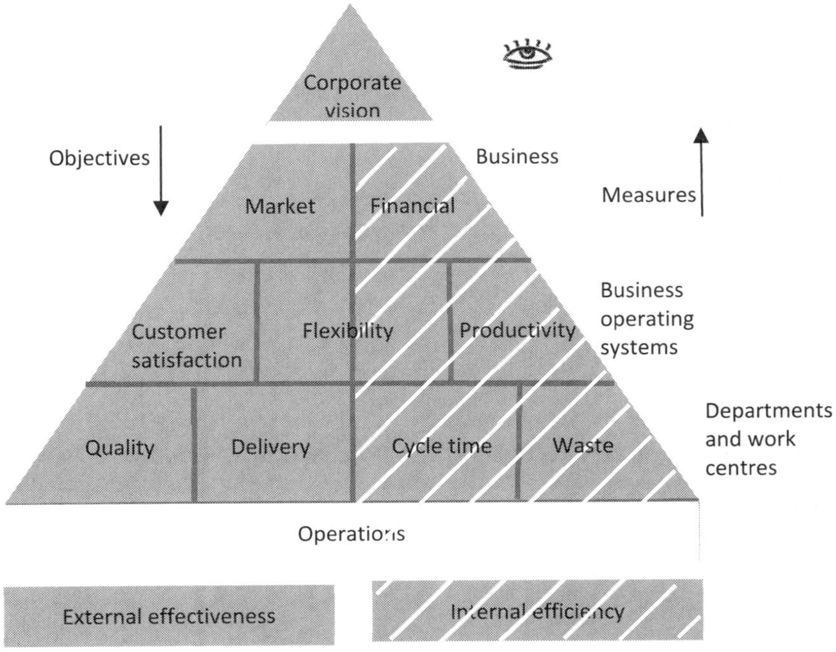

The pyramid firstly focuses on the development of a coherent set of objectives from the overall corporate vision. The pyramid views a range of objectives from the strategic to the operational, linking these through the themes of external effectiveness and internal efficiency.

The strategic level concerns relate to market and financial factors and these are fed by the tactical level drivers of customer satisfaction, flexibility and productivity. These objectives will reflect that business systems at this level will cross functional boundaries and so cannot be drawn into the specifics of the operational details. The operational objectives are then derived from the tactical drivers.

The performance measurement system is then built up to reflect the objectives and so ensure that each of the performance measures at the operational level feed the tactical level requirements and measures at this level drive the strategic objectives of the organisation. For example, cycle time reductions will improve productivity which will enhance the profitability of Cod.

This will help Cod to achieve the coherence that the board desires in the performance measurement systems.

(c) The driving forces, according to Lynch and Cross that are appropriate to meeting an organisation's objectives are customer satisfaction, flexibility and productivity. At present Cod's KPIs do not address these as they lack any mention of areas of customer satisfaction (quality and service standards), flexibility (innovation and the ability to adapt to change in the external business environment) and productivity (efficiency and waste). It could be argued that some of these are more appropriate at the tactical and operational levels of the management hierarchy but the existing measures have only a tenuous link to them and hence the board is right to be concerned by the current KPI system.

The additional performance information provided would allow the calculation of various indicators appropriate to these driving forces. For example:

Customer satisfaction

- Percentage of orders generating a complaint (5.4% in 2011 compared to 5.0% in 2010) measures customer satisfaction.
- Preferred supplier status (58% of market in 2011 and 50% in 2010 [if we assume that there are only 24 possible customers that offer this status]).

Flexibility

- New products launched in the year (one each of 2011 and 2010) measures innovation.

Productivity

- Quality costs ($4.35m in 2011 and $3.46m in 2010) measures inefficient production.

These should be added to the current KPIs used by the board.

The operational performance measures suggested by the pyramid will involve the four areas of quality, delivery, cycle time and waste.

Quality

The existing measures of failure costs supply a measure of quality, although variances to budget may be a more helpful presentation. The customer complaint numbers also address this issue, although they are a weak measure as no indication of the strength or ease of resolution of the complaint is given. It should be noted that the complaint category of 'other' is unacceptably large compared to the other categories and it should be broken down into further subcategories. The level of training days and long-term unfilled posts indicates the employee environment that will also impact on quality and delivery. It would be helpful to have industry benchmarks for these figures in order to understand them better.

Delivery

The preferred customer status indicates customer satisfaction and is fed by the complaint numbers on delivery and service. As before, it is worth noting that the severity of the complaint is not being measured, for example, by discounts offered or orders lost as a result.

Cycle time

There is no useful information currently collected to allow measurement of the cycle times of processes.

Possibly the indicative numbers on products being developed may give an idea of time to market, however, an average measure of this in months would be more useful.

Waste

No figures are collected that indicate waste in production. Variance analysis of idle time for employees and materials usage would be helpful in measuring this area.

Examiner's comments

Requirement (a) was generally well done although answers could have been improved by using illustrations of points from the scenario. For example, a modern system would expect to have both qualitative and quantitative indicators and Cod fails this as it focuses only on quantitative, financial indicators. Thus, Cod has no qualitative customer experience satisfaction measure which would help to address one of its mission statement objectives.

Requirement (b) was generally well done as most candidates knew the make-up of the pyramid and understood how its structure helps to ensure coherence of vision between the strategic and operational levels of a company such as Cod.

Requirement (c) was generally poorly done as most candidates did not apply the pyramid. The candidates who did well in this part realised that the scenario provided the split of performance indicators into key (strategic) ones and others (operational) in the current system. Their answers then addressed these levels separately making clear what was considered to be a key indicator and what was just an operational indicator. Those who performed poorly on this part took the pyramid as a tick list of indicator headings (rather that appreciating that it supplied a hierarchy of measures). Thus, far too many candidates simply provided wish lists of every indicator they thought appropriate to Cod and this would have the board drowning in a wave of data.

ACCA marking scheme

			Marks
(a)	Describe key features – 0.5 mark per point		4
	Assess key features– 1 mark per point		6
		Maximum	**7**
(b)	General explanation of the pyramid		1
	Explanation of how it can help with goal – 1 mark per point	up to	5
		Maximum	**6**
(c)	Strategic level		
	Describe drivers – 0.5 mark per point		1.5
	Assess current system – 1 mark per point	up to	2
	Suggest new KPIs – 1 mark per point	up to	3
	Operational level – 1 mark per point made (address all 4 areas)	up to	8
		Maximum	**12**
Total			**25**

70 CALLISTO (JUN 12)

Key answer tips

This question, concerning an e-tailer with a complex business structure, is tricky as it does not lend itself some pre-ordained template or method. However, provided you use the information in the scenario to good effect, you should be able to gather the marks to pass.

(a) Performance measurement problems at Callisto

In a virtual organisation such as Callisto, performance measurement can be difficult due to the fact that key players in the business processes and in the supply chain are not 'on site'. Callisto has the problem of collecting and monitoring data about its employees working from home and the outsourcing partners.

At Callisto, there is a reliance placed on information technology for handling these remote contacts. Collecting and monitoring performance should therefore be done automatically as far as possible. A large database would be required that can be automatically updated from the activities of the remote staff and suppliers. This will require the staff and supplier systems to be compatible.

The employees can be required to use software supplied by Callisto and in fact, at Callisto, they use the internet to log in remotely to Callisto's common systems. Although this solution requires expenditure on hardware and software, it is within the control of Callisto's management. Even with reviews of system logs to identify the hours that staff spend logged in to the systems, there are still the difficulty of measuring staff outputs in order to ensure their productivity. These outputs must be clearly defined by Callisto's managers, otherwise there will be disputes between staff and management.

One further outstanding issue is the need to ensure that such communication is over properly secured communication channels, especially if it contains customer or financial data.

The strategic partners, such as RLR, will have their own systems. A problem for Callisto is that there is disagreement over the measurement of the key SLAs. In order to resolve such disputes, lengthy reconciliations between Callisto's and RLR's systems will have to be undertaken otherwise there are no grounds for enforcement of the SLAs and the SLAs represent Callisto's key control over the relationship. The solution would be for the partners to agree a standard reporting format for all data that relates to the SLAs which would remove the need for such reconciliations.

Finally, there is the problem that Callisto and the partner organisation may have differing objectives – the obvious conflict over price between supplier and customer being one. However, at Callisto, this is being addressed by the use of detailed SLAs which both organisations can use to develop performance measures such as inventory levels and delivery times.

Performance management problems at Callisto

The performance management of employees is complicated due to the inability of management to 'look over their shoulder' since they are not present in the same building. However, employees will enjoy the advantages of homeworking, such as lower commuting times, more family contact and greater flexibility in working hours.

The disadvantages are the difficulties in measuring outputs mentioned above and ensuring motivation and commitment. The motivation and commitment can be addressed through suitable reward schemes which would have to be tied to agreed outputs and targets for each employee. Work could be divided into projects where the outputs are more easily identified and pay and bonuses related to these.

The performance management issues of handling the strategic partners include:

- confidentiality where the partners will have access to commercially sensitive information about customers' locations and suppliers' names and lead times
- reliability where the partner is supplying a business critical role (as for RLR with Callisto) such that it would take considerable time to replace such a relationship and affect customer service while this happened
- relationship management where the interface between the organisations can create wasteful activity if there is not an atmosphere of trust. At Callisto, this is illustrated by the problem of reconciliation of performance data
- profit sharing where given the collaborative nature of the relationship and the difficulty of breaking it combine to imply that it will be in the interest of both parties to negotiate a contract that is motivating and profitable for both sides. For Callisto, the business aim is to increase volume and this will require customer loyalty so the quality of service is important.

(b) Performance measures

It is important that performance measures used for Callisto are in line with the overall business objectives.

Employees

There are likely to be a wide range of roles performed by employees across the functions of production, finance and supplier relationship management and the chosen measures need to reflect these differences.

Volume based measures could be used to assess those working in video clip production, for example the number of minutes of video produced. However the videos produced are not part of the physical product being sold by Callisto and so an increase in volume will not have any positive impact on the level of complaints which are received, a key concern for the company. Measures applied to these employees should concentrate more on the quality of the video produced and its ability to attract customers to the site. Web based measures relating to the number of 'hits' each video has and the number of purchases that then result would be more appropriate. This information should be readily available through the company's website.

Finance employees should be measured according to the quality and timeliness of the information they provide such as the number of deadlines met within a period of time. This should prove relatively easy to monitor through a review of the reports produced each period.

In order to accurately measure the performance of those employees involved in supplier relationship management, Callisto should consider the quality of communication between employees and strategic partners. From the employees perspective this can be measured by looking at the number of breaches in an SLA although this may be difficult due to the way the information is currently gathered. Regular reviews of the SLAs should allow this information to be collated.

Strategic partners

Performance of the strategic partners working with Callisto should be measured through delivery of the SLAs. Each of these agreements will have different terms depending on the nature of the supplier. So for example, a suitable measure for RLR may be that 90% of orders are despatched within 3 working days of receipt. Customer receipt documentation will ensure this can be tracked and regular reviews of the SLA should identify any areas of concern.

Examiner's comments

Requirement (a) focused on the difficulties of performance management and measurement in such a complex business as Callisto. Candidates were correct to split this into areas such as the general impact of such a complex structure on the business as a whole and then the impact on employee management and strategic partner management. The key to scoring well was making relevant points for Callisto – the difficulties of measuring and managing home-working employees and strategic outsourcing partners.

ACCA marking scheme			
			Marks
(a)	Performance measurement, up to 2 marks per point made to a maximum of 9, e.g. on geographical distance, reliance on IT, difference between employees and strategic partners, technology solutions, use of SLAs Performance management, 1 mark per point to a maximum of 8 marks Employees up to 4 marks Strategic partners up to 6 marks		
		Maximum	**17**
(b)	Performance measures: Employees – up to 4 marks Strategic partners – up to 2 marks Methods of data collection – 1 mark per point		
		Maximum	**8**
Total			**25**

71 GRAVITON CLOTHING (DEC 13)

Key answer tips

As with many APM questions you need not only to know the content – here the performance pyramid – but also to be able to apply the model to the specific circumstances given. The examining team are interested in application of knowledge and so simply providing book-learned definitions of terms scored only a few marks. The answer below includes the diagram of the performance pyramid. This is included to assist with learning. You will not be expected to reproduce diagrams in the CBE.

(a) The performance pyramid is based on the belief that each level of an organisation has different concerns but they must support each other in order to achieve the overall objective of the organisation. The aim is to produce a set of performance measures which cover the outputs and drivers of the outputs of the organisation. The pyramid shape is to emphasise that the measures from the operational up to the strategic levels should support the corporate vision.

A general criticism of the system at Graviton could be that it is suffering from tunnel vision which is over-focusing on those areas which are actually measured. This can be managed by ensuring that the set of performance measures are comprehensive in examining the results and the determinants of those results for the organisation. The performance pyramid is a systematic method which tries to achieve this goal. Tunnel vision may explain why, although revenue is rising rapidly, the operating profit is fairly static. There is a danger that the company is focusing on making more sales to the exclusion of making higher profits. This may result from the measuring of revenue growth but not of cost related metrics or profit margins. It is notable that there are no variances from budget given in the performance report.

The pyramid diagram is:

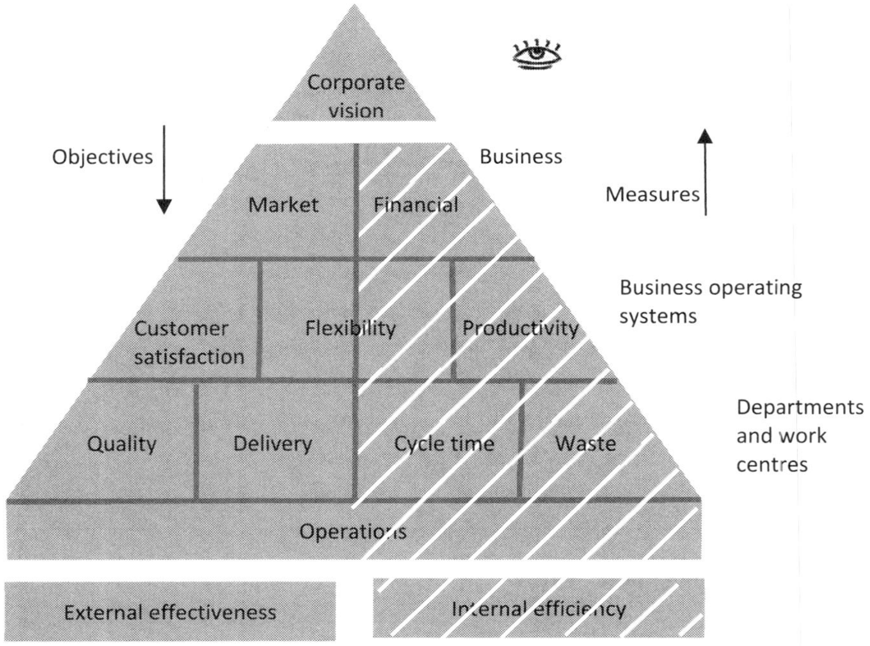

The pyramid begins with the corporate vision. At Graviton, the company objective is to maximise shareholder wealth by being flexible in response to market demand and controlling the production chain closely. The current performance measures as illustrated in the example report do measure all of these factors in some way but may not be comprehensive.

- Return on capital employed (ROCE) is reported but this is not directly measuring shareholder wealth and it is surprising that there is no mention of measures such as total shareholder return which will cover dividends and share price growth. The failure to provide a dividend measure may be a reason why the dividend growth has been allowed to slip.

- Flexibility in manufacturing is measured through the time to market for new designs. The design awards won indicate the innovative abilities of the employees at Graviton. The ability of the manufacturing chain to replenish successful lines and so take advantage of a fast-selling product is not measured.

- Close control of production is not evident as the problems with quality of clothes (durability complaints by customers) demonstrate. There may be a lack of cost control which explains the disconnection between growing revenue and the operating profits performance.

The next level of the pyramid is the driving of the vision by satisfying the market and performing well financially. As noted above, the financial measures are lacking a focus on costs through profit margins (such as gross margin) or key cost headings such as labour costs which would highlight the higher costs of designers. Therefore, the danger exists at Graviton that profitability is being sacrificed for revenue growth. Productivity measures of waste are likely to be important as designs become obsolete in this market quickly and the manufacturing process for clothes can lead to waste of materials in production. The problem of obsolescence can be significant in a fashion-driven industry since it is important to get the right garments in the right place at the right time. Inventory write-offs would measure such waste.

Market satisfaction is driven by customer satisfaction and flexibility. Graviton measures flexibility through time to market and delivery and these are obviously given a high priority in order to meet this objective in the corporate vision. Customer satisfaction can be considered to be measured through the revenue growth and indirectly through the winning of design awards but the failure to address quality may detract from this in the long term. (There is also evidence of short-term thinking at factory site 2 where the reason for the excess equipment repairs could be the failure to invest in new equipment which may be driven by the desire to keep the capital employed figure low to enhance ROCE.) An exercise should be undertaken to identify how strongly customers value the durability of Graviton's products and if this is significant, then measures of quality such as level of complaints should be made. It is possible that in a fast-changing, trend-driven industry such as Graviton's, there is little interest from customers in the durability of their garments, as they will be purchasing new ones on a regular basis to keep up with fashion.

(b) Myopia is prioritising short-term issues over long-term ones and is evident here in factory site 2. The variance in repairs expenditure could be due to a failure to invest in new machinery and so having excess repair work to do on old machinery. This could be exacerbated by using ROCE as a performance measure, since continuing to use old machinery (possibly written off) will require little or no capital employed. The use of longer term measures rather than those over just one accounting period might help to capture the effect of such behaviour.

Gaming is dysfunctional behaviour (from the organisation's perspective) where an individual manager is trying to meet their individual targets while ignoring the good of the whole organisation. There is evidence at factory site 1 of this behaviour where a manager is manipulating revenue and profit across the accounting cut-off. This behaviour can be dealt with by emphasising a culture of honesty in the organisation and by ensuring that the manager is rewarded for average gains over long periods rather than block payments for hitting simple profit-triggers in a single period.

Ossification is the unwillingness to change from an existing performance system, especially when it shows adequate or good results are being achieved. The board is clearly exhibiting this problem in resisting change at Graviton. The CEO will need to persuade them that there are issues in the omissions from the current set of performance measures which will lead to long-term difficulties in achieving their overall goal of enhancing shareholder wealth. The targets and remuneration of the board should be set so that the board is rewarded if current good performance is sustainable in the future.

Examiner's comments

Although many candidates showed a clear understanding of the terms of the pyramid in part (a), many were unable to apply these to the dashboard at Graviton. Too many candidates simply listed new indicators without justification to the circumstances at Graviton. Those that scored well took each heading within the pyramid and discussed a) how it linked to the aim of the business (maximising shareholder wealth by focussing production on changing trends through maintained flexibility and close control of the supply chain) and; b) evaluated how the existing dashboard addressed these issues. For example, a valuable (but often ignored) connection could be made between flexibility in a fashion business and the time to market indicator.

With part (b) many candidates could not describe the terms (especially ossification) which indicates a lack of knowledge of the subject. However, most candidates did score some marks for suggesting suitable, justified solutions to the problems discussed even if they had not been able to state clearly which of the buzzwords was being addressed. (One detailed point of note on the suggested solutions is that these need to be justified, for example, a minority of candidates simply threw in a suggestion to use EVA™ with no explanation at this point.) A successful structure for an answer to this part was to define the buzzword then show how it related to a particular issue at Graviton and finally, suggest a solution to the issue.

Future candidates should note that explanation and appropriate application of jargon (rather than merely bandying those terms) will often feature in APM as the valuable accountant is one who can demystify the subject.

ACCA marking scheme

		Marks
(a)	General description of model – up to 3 marks Remaining marks must have relevance to Graviton – Tunnel vision – up to 5 marks Up to 4 on the link of the metrics to the vision Then 1 mark per point up to 6 marks on Market satisfaction Financial performance including: Customer satisfaction Flexibility Productivity Quality Delivery Cycle time Waste 1 mark per point for other relevant points	
	Maximum	**15**
(b)	1 mark for clear definition of the term then 1 mark per point made of relevance to Graviton and possible management solutions up to 3 on any one topic. Myopia Gaming Ossification	
	Maximum	**10**
Total		**25**

72 VICTORIA-YEELAND LOGISTICS (JUN 15)

Key answer tips

As with many APM questions you need not only to know the content – here the balanced scorecard – but also to be able to apply the model to the specific circumstances given and give commercially valuable advice. The examining team are interested in application of knowledge and so simply providing book-learned definitions of terms scored only a few marks.

(a) The success factors in the customer perspective will drive improved customer satisfaction. This should improve the customer perception of our service and so drive revenue growth. The increase in revenue could come through two routes:

1. winning customers from the competition and thus increasing volume or
2. increased selling prices as we may be perceived to offer a premium service.

Increased selling prices will immediately improve the profit margin of the service.

Increased volumes may indirectly improve our margins as we can spread the increased activity over our existing fixed cost base, for example, by increasing capacity utilisation (having more packages on each lorry).

As these improvements to operating profit occur without additional capital expenditure, they may feed through to an increased return on capital employed.

(b) **Ability to meet customers' transport needs**

This is a measure of the flexibility of the business and would be measured by the percentage of customer requests which Victoria can actually undertake:

$$\frac{\text{Total number of packages transported}}{\text{Total number of customer transport requests}} = \frac{548{,}000}{610{,}000} = 89.8\%$$

Ability to deliver packages quickly

The difficulty of this measure is that different packages may travel different distances and so take longer. Therefore, a measure based on time taken per kilometre which a package travels is appropriate:

$$\frac{\text{Total minutes spent in transit by each package}}{\text{Total package kilometres travelled}} = \frac{131{,}520{,}000}{65{,}760{,}000} = 2.0$$

Ability to deliver packages on time

This is measured by the number of packages delivered within the time window given to the customer:

$$\frac{\text{Deliveries within window}}{\text{Total number of packages transported}} = \frac{(548{,}000 - 21{,}920}{548{,}000} = 96\%$$

Ability to deliver packages safely

This is measured by the number of undamaged packages delivered within the time window given to the customer:

$$\frac{\text{Deliveries of undamaged packages}}{\text{Total number of packages transported}} = \frac{(549{,}000 - 8{,}220)}{548{,}000} = 98.5\%$$

Problems with measurement using customer complaints

There are two dangers with measuring performance through customer complaints. The first is under-reporting where the customer does not bother to report a problem although it negatively impacts on their perception of Victoria. The customer simply walks away from Victoria's service. This could be alleviated by automatically discounting the invoice of any late delivery as Victoria should be recording its own delivery performance and not only relying on customers to provide data nor delay the process by waiting for their complaint.

The second is reporting of unjustified complaints to obtain compensation payments/credits. As the measures stand, they record all customer complaints whether reasonable or not. This could be addressed by using the number of customer credits issued for the fault rather than the number of complaints.

(c) The senior management rewards system appears open to manipulation as the board is effectively setting their own rewards. There is the danger that targets are set to be easily achieved and so the profits of the business are siphoned off to the managers rather than the shareholders. The introduction of the BSC should assist in creating coherence between the objectives of the senior management and those of the shareholders. However, it appears that the major, financial measures suggested in the BSC do not directly address shareholder wealth although return on capital will be related. Finally, in a market where competition is fierce, the ability of management to grow revenue will be heavily constrained and there appear to be important factors in profit which are outside of the control of senior managers (fuel costs).

The operational managers should have their measures of performance set through a cascade down from the strategic measures in the BSC. These measures will often come from the customer and process perspectives. In this way, the reward system should be consistent with the overall objectives of the business. The suggestion that operational managers should be involved in setting their own targets should be treated carefully as it may present problems. This suggestion often arises from a confusion of the idea of explaining the target setting process to the manager with the idea of actually setting the target. The setting of the target should be done by a higher level of management so that the target is achievable with above normal effort. The target should not be set to be unreachable as this can cause demotivation. The target set should then be explained to the employee involved so that they understand what they have to do in order to earn this additional reward. It would be advisable for operational management, where most improvements are incremental, that the target is one where the bonus increases as the performance improves rather than a simple one of obtaining a given level of performance.

Tutorial note

The building block model headings of fair, achievable, owned standards and clear, motivational and controllable rewards are relevant to this answer but the answer needs to distinguish between the standards used and the targets set.

Examiner's comments

Part (a). Those candidates that showed how success under each factor linked to changes in each of the three metrics scored all the marks. However, many candidates chose not to answer the question and instead discussed how the customer perspective factors aided achievement of the business strategy or else had a broadly positive effect on the financial position of the business. These were inadequate answers from APM candidates who are expected to be able to talk in detail about factors affecting ROCE, profit margin and revenue growth.

Worryingly, many candidates assume that revenue growth automatically means profit margin improvement and so improvement in ROCE, without any further consideration of cost or capital implications.

Part (b) was well done by most candidates with many scoring 10 or 11 out of 11.

Part (c) was surprisingly poorly answered. Many candidates used the building block model as a template for their answer but failed to go further than a generic response and did not address the specific issues for Victoria. Successful candidates briefly outlined the model and then showed how each aspect could be applied to the situation at hand.

Candidates seemed unwilling to say that the employees (senior management/operational managers) may be unhappy but that need not be an issue for Victoria as there will usually be a conflict of interest between the employees and the company/shareholders. Good answers identified and discussed how to address this issue fairly. Baldly stating that employees should set their own targets is not a practical solution.

Future candidates should address the specific issues in a scenario in order to give commercially valuable advice to those involved.

ACCA marking scheme

		Marks
(a)	1 mark per point To score 5, must discuss all three financial metrics	
	Maximum	**5**
(b)	For each success factor, 1 mark for justification and 1 mark for calculation of suitable metric Up to 4 marks for problems identified	
	Maximum	**11**
(c)	Up to 5 marks on senior management rewards Up to 5 marks on operational management	
	Maximum	**9**
Total		**25**

73 SOUP RAIL SERVICES (SEPT/DEC 15) (AMENDED)

Key answer tips

As with many APM questions you need not only to know the content – here the balanced scorecard – but also to be able to apply the model to the specific circumstances given and give commercially valuable advice. In part (a) you had to justify how the balanced scorecard would improve the performance management system. The examiner is interested in application of knowledge and so simply providing book-learned definitions of terms scored only a few marks.

(a) The balanced scorecard consists of four perspectives: customer, internal, innovation and learning and financial. It requires an organisation to have a number of goals supported by performance measures in each perspective. The customer perspective measures what it is that customers value from the business; internal looks at what processes does the organisation need to be successful; innovation and learning considers how future value can be created and financial measures whether performance is acceptable to investors.

It is useful because it uses both internal and external information to assess performance and measures financial and non-financial aspects of a business to ensure long-term future success, rather than just focusing on historic results. It can also be used as a mechanism to link KPIs into the CSFs which are vital to deliver strategy.

Soup currently uses return on capital employed (ROCE) as its key financial performance measure, but this does not correlate directly with the objective to maximise shareholder wealth and could encourage short-term decisions to be taken at the expense of long-term success. This is the case at Soup which purchased old trains and subsequently failed to reinvest, meaning that Soup's ROCE is probably higher than its rivals. However, the trains are becoming unreliable and their condition is deteriorating. In the long term this will reduce customer satisfaction and financial performance.

Using the scorecard, Soup should have a broader range of financial measures which encourage managers to take decisions, such as investment decisions, consistent with the objective to maximise shareholder wealth in the long term. EVA™ would be a suitable measure to help achieve this, and would be preferable to the current focus on ROCE.

Soup does measure growth in passenger numbers which could be a measure of customer satisfaction. However, it is a limited, quantitative measure. Though Soup does have rivals and is likely to be required to operate a specified level of service under the terms of the licence from the government, some passengers may be forced to travel on Soup trains, rather than those of another operator because of where they live or the times they need to travel. The number of operators (competitors) is limited by the capacity of the railway infrastructure as well as by passenger demand. This means that the level of repeat customers may not be appropriate for Soup.

Passenger numbers are also externally focused but again this fails to fully consider the environment in which Soup operates.

Within the customer perspective Soup could use a range of performance measures. This will be beneficial as where passengers are able, they are likely to choose to use Soup if they provide a good service. This can be easily measured by surveying or asking passengers' opinions. This will give Soup more qualitative information about their customers and their expectations, which will vary, for example, passengers will have different perceptions of overcrowding, or what is an acceptable delay. Certain groups may be more affected by overcrowding like frequent travellers and the elderly. Passengers who are unable to find a seat will probably be the most dissatisfied, though this will depend on how long their journey is. Other aspects of Soup's service may be less valued than reliability and occupancy, like wireless access and the on-board cafe, but will be important to certain groups.

Another key element of customer satisfaction will relate to the amount of fare paid. Fares are regulated in Deeland so the interaction between fares and other aspects of the service is unknown. Many customers while valuing a particular aspect of the service may be unwilling to pay more for it; some may accept a reduction in the level of service if fares were reduced.

This detailed information about customers will allow Soup to focus performance improvements on key areas using more external data to make decisions.

Measures of the internal processes are likely to be closely linked to customer satisfaction. Soup apparently neglects this area in its performance management system. The scorecard could be used to help to address reliability, overcrowding and environmental factors.

Reliability will be highly valued by customers especially those who travel frequently and who rely on rail travel to get to work. The number of trains arriving late would be a suitable measure of reliability, as would the number of train services cancelled, though the length of the delay is also critical and should be carefully defined. The scorecard would allow more detailed measures as some of the factors affecting reliability will be within Soup's direct control but others such as failures in the railway infrastructure are controlled by the government. This is useful information for Soup to effectively assess their controllable performance and feedback as necessary to external parties.

Seat occupancy, the number of passengers on a train compared to the number of available seats on different routes and at different times, is a suitable measure of train overcrowding and is important for passenger safety. To fully utilise its trains and achieve its objective of maximising shareholder wealth, Soup must try and maximise both the seat occupancy and the amount of time its trains are actually running. These internal measures would then help to support financial targets.

Soup's licence to operate rail services in Regions A and B expires in three years' time, and as with the operator from whom Soup purchased the trains, it may not be renewed. Soup must balance the needs of shareholders for short-term increases in dividends and share price with the long-term need to renew to its operator's licence.

The creation of long-term future value can be addressed by the innovation and learning perspective. The immediate scope to innovate the service experienced by the passenger is limited, but there are some quick wins available in the choice in the on-board cafe and improving the reliability of the internet access. Also time spent training staff may improve customer satisfaction and reduce maintenance time. Fundamental innovation like the use of faster or environmentally less harmful trains requires long-term planning and large capital investment. The scorecard will encourage Soup to be forward looking, unlike the present system which is limited to historic performance.

(b) To measure the extent of overcrowding, some measure of occupancy is needed. The number of passengers per available seat can be used as a measure of occupancy.

Seats available per train is 490 (7 coaches × 70 seats) in Region A and 420 (7 coaches × 60 seats) in Region B.

Seats available per day	**Region A**	**Region B**
Peak times	1,960 (490 × 4)	1,680
Other times	2,940	3,360

Seat occupancy	**Region A**	**Region B**
Peak times	128%	83%
Other times	83%	55%

Total seat occupancy = 82.5% (8,200/9,940)

Overall occupancy is below 100% which means on average there are more seats available than passengers, which is not consistent with the government's claims that the trains are overcrowded. However, these averages may be misleading as trains running on certain days or at certain times may be relatively overcrowded. This may generate customer dissatisfaction even on services which are on average not fully occupied. The total number of passengers without seats would be a better measure.

There are significant variations between regions and times travelled with only the trains in Region A travelling at peak times being over occupied. This affects only 18% (4/22) of all services.

Most affected by this will be the 28% of the passengers travelling at peak times in Region A who are unable to obtain a seat. This represents only 9% (28% × 2,500/8,200) of total passengers per day. There is some overcrowding but the claim that Soup's trains are overcrowded seems exaggerated given the data provided. However, certain routes or specific times or sections of the trains may be more affected and more analysis is needed.

The impact of overcrowding on passengers also depends on journey times, with passengers being less satisfied by not obtaining a seat on longer journeys rather than on short ones. Assuming trains are available for 14 hours per day and there are 22 services, each service is on average almost 1.5 hours which may be a significant length of time for passengers to stand on a train.

(c) When applying the balanced scorecard in Soup, the measures need to be chosen carefully. A balance needs to be struck and only measures which help Soup to achieve its objectives should be chosen. Currently Soup focuses on short-term financial measures such as return on capital employed, whereas the balanced scorecard considers more long-term measures.

Some measures are more important than others, so prioritising measures will be difficult. Customers may value some aspects of the service more than others, for example, the choice available in the on-board cafe is probably unimportant to most passengers provided they can obtain some food and drink. The punctuality of Soup's trains or whether they even run at all is fundamental to achieving customer satisfaction and needs careful measurement. Soup must have measures for regulatory or safety reasons too.

Some aspects of the business may be harder to measure than others. For example, it may be relatively easy to measure seat occupancy as a measure of overcrowding, but passengers' perceptions of overcrowding may differ. Non-financial aspects such as customer satisfaction may be subjective and any surveys done may not reflect the experience of the majority of passengers. Performing and analysing surveys would also be time consuming and resource intensive.

Measures chosen may conflict. Overcrowding may be unwelcome by passengers but making them less crowded conflicts with Soup's presumed objective of fully occupied trains. Time spent maintaining trains to reduce their impact on the environment or ensure reliability will mean they are not operational for periods of time, though safety will be a key factor here.

Care must be taken to avoid overloading with too many performance measures. The current objective to maximise shareholder wealth is very broad. Having a clearer strategy would enable Soup to determine suitable performance measures so it is not overloaded with KPIs which do not contribute towards achieving this strategy.

Examiner's comments

Part (a). The majority of candidates clearly knew the structure of the theory, although some merely listed the four perspectives as opposed to explaining what they were. Candidates should be aware that few marks are awarded at this level for providing superficial lists.

The emphasis of the question was how the balanced scorecard can improve the system. Therefore, it is essential that candidates recognise that they need to identify specific aspects of the model and how they would benefit the system. Simply listing potential metrics scored few marks unless the candidate could clearly demonstrate the benefit. For example, explaining that the company could use EVA as a measure under the financial perspective provides little evidence that a candidate understands how using the balance scorecard is beneficial. However, to score well, a candidate could explain that the approach aims to ensure the long-term success of the company and using EVA would be an improvement on using, say, ROCE.

Part (b). The calculations for this part of the question were generally performed well. Credit was given to various approaches to show whether or not overcrowding was evident given the data presented. It is therefore worthwhile mentioning that candidates do not have to follow prescribed methods to demonstrate a point as long as there is a logical approach and the answer is well explained.

However, few candidates attempted to discuss the claim of overcrowding in any detail other than to say whether or not capacity was exceeded. Candidates should be aware that the scenarios on APM are written to reflect real world examples and as such, in this scenario, discussing practical considerations would be beneficial.

Part (c). This part of the question was well attempted by many candidates. This is a clear example of where understanding the advantages and disadvantages of a model, and then demonstrating how they relate to the given scenario, will allow candidates to score well. One of the main shortcomings in many responses to this question was a failure to specifically answer the question, which focused on selecting and interpreting, for example, there can be conflicting metrics. Several candidates simply discussed the difficulties in adopting a balanced scorecard approach, such as commitment from management, and a general discussion of target setting, such as measure fixation. Again, re-iterating earlier comments, candidates should ensure that they specifically answer the question that has been set.

ACCA marking scheme

		Marks
(a)	1 mark per relevant point made. Also consider the below: No marks for a list of new measures without justifying why they would benefit Soup 1 mark only for a generic description of the balanced scorecard without clear references to the scenario	
	Maximum	**9**
(b)	Calculation, 4 marks in total with 1 mark each for: Seats available per train Seats available per day by region/time Seat occupancy by region/time Total seat occupancy Comment on whether consistent with governments claims about overcrowding, 1 mark per point up to 2 marks Up to 2 additional marks for identifying journey time is an important factor and for attempting to quantify journey times from the data given	
	Maximum	**6**
(c)	Maximum of 3 marks if general points not applied to Soup Selection of appropriate measures – up to 2 marks Prioritisation of measures – up to 2 marks Difficulties of making measurements – up to 2 marks Conflicting measures – up to 2 marks Overload of measures – up to 2 marks	
	Maximum	**5**
Professional marks		
Analysis and Evaluation		
•	Balanced and reasoned advice on how the balanced scorecard could help improve the performance management system; helping to balance the needs of passengers and shareholders	
•	Appropriate and use of data in appendix 1 to perform relevant calculations and support the discussion of overcrowding	
•	Reasoned assessment of problems in selecting and interpreting balanced scorecard measures, rather than a general discussion of balanced scorecard difficulties	
Commercial Acumen		
•	Effective use of examples drawn from the scenario information and other practical considerations related to the context to illustrate points being made throughout the answer in a practical and plausible way	
	Maximum	**5**
Total		**25**

Section 5

SPECIMEN EXAM QUESTIONS

Section A – This ONE question is compulsory and MUST be attempted

1 DEELAND POLICE

Organisation Information

You are a performance management consultant brought in by the chief executive officer (CEO) of the Department for Internal Affairs (DIA) for the country of Deeland. The department handles, among other areas, the policing of Deeland. The CEO is a government employee reporting to the Minister for Internal Affairs. The Minister for Internal Affairs is an elected politician appointed by the leader of the Deeland government.

The government of Deeland has recently changed and the new Minister for Internal Affairs has instructed the CEO of the DIA to improve the performance of the Deeland Police (DP) by implementing the Minister's new mission statement for DP: 'to protect the community and prevent crime while providing a value for money service.' As part of this implementation, the CEO has identified the following four key areas for action:

1 Protecting and supporting those at risk of harm

2 Ensuring criminals are caught and brought before the courts

3 Achieving long-term sustainable solutions to the causes of crime

4 Addressing new forms of crime arising in the virtual world

The new Minister wants general improvement in the first three of these areas, as her political campaign was based around criticism of the previous government's perceived failure on these points. It is widely agreed that in the second area, the major concern is the catching of criminals since, historically, there is a high probability that once caught they are brought before the courts. The third area is being addressed through increased involvement with local communities in order to identify and address the causes of crime. The fourth area of crime in the virtual world (the use of computers to facilitate crime) was hardly addressed under the previous government and the Minister wants to see the creation of a task force which will develop skills in detection and prosecution of virtual crime.

CSFs and KPIs

In a recent meeting with the CEO, the Minister indicated that she felt that the four key areas were too vague and in order to better focus actions, the Minister's adviser has suggested the following critical success factors (CSFs):

1 Greater protection and more support for those at risk of harm

2 Be better at catching criminals

3 Reducing the causes of crime by increased involvement with local communities

4 Create a task force to develop skills in detection and prosecution of virtual crime

Initially, the CEO did not see why the four key areas originally given could not be used as CSFs. He wants you to provide justifications in the light of the Minister's concerns for the changes which the adviser has made to each of these. Then, using the above CSFs, he wants you to provide justified recommendations of up to two key performance indicators (KPIs) per CSF in order to measure performance.

In order to help you with the KPIs, the CEO has provided you with a table of data (Appendix 1) which has been used in the past when considering DP's performance. However, you are allowed to suggest new data which would help in measuring performance. The CEO has made it clear that at this stage, no calculations are required.

Value for money

Since DP is funded wholly through Deeland's general taxation, the CEO wants to be able to report on whether DP is providing a value for money (VFM) service as required by the new mission statement. He has heard of the 3Es (economy, efficiency and effectiveness) but needs an explanation of these three headings and how this links to the work on CSFs and KPIs already requested. Then, he requires an evaluation, using the data given in Appendix 1, of whether DP provides such a service. He understands that the evaluation may be limited, as Appendix 1 may not give a data set to perform a full VFM exercise.

League tables

The Minister is interested in benchmarking as this was often done during her days in business. As a result, she joined an international initiative for creating a league table of fire service data by sharing information with other nearby countries. The CEO believes that the Minister will want to introduce this idea for DP and so wants an assessment of the use of an international police force performance league table and its link to targets for DP. The CEO is especially concerned about the police officers' reaction to this new idea as they have a powerful union, which has widespread public support. Therefore, he also needs you to explain how the use of league tables and targets might affect police officers' behaviour.

Required:

It is now 1 September 20X5.

Write a report to the CEO of the Department for Internal Affairs to respond to his instructions for work on the following areas:

(i) **the critical success factors and key performance indicators for Deeland Police** **(16 marks)**

(ii) **an evaluation of the value for money service provided and** **(14 marks)**

(iii) **the use of league tables in measuring the performance of Deeland Police.** **(10 marks)**

Professional marks will be awarded for the demonstration of skill in communication, analysis and evaluation, scepticism and commercial acumen in your answer. **(10 marks)**

(Total: 50 marks)

Appendix 1

Deeland Police data for each year ending 30 June

	20X5	**20X4**	**20X3**
Population (000s)	11,880	11,761	11,644
Number of police officers	37,930	38,005	38,400
Number of administrative staff	12,320	12,197	12,075
Number of crimes reported in the year	541,735	530,900	520,282
Number of violent crimes reported in the year	108,347	106,180	104,056
Number of crimes solved in the year	297,954	300,934	303,943
Number of complaints	7,624	7,512	7,483
Response to an incident within the allocated time limit	84%	86%	87%
Cost of police force for the year ($m)	2,248	2,226	2,203
Staff costs (all staff including police officers) ($m)	2,026	2,103	2,141

Section B – BOTH questions are compulsory and MUST be attempted

2 CORUISK

Company information

Coruisk is a clothing manufacturer in Teeland which produces a range of dresses which it sells to Ericht. The range of dresses are the only products which Coruisk produces and Ericht is its only customer.

Ericht is a well-known retailer in Teeland. Ericht has recently been affected by changes in consumer purchasing preferences to buying clothes online and, as a result, is keen to reduce its inventory holding as a way of reducing its costs. Ericht is also finding that it has an excess of goods which it has to discount as consumer tastes appear to change more quickly than in the past.

The chief executive officer (CEO) of Coruisk has given you some tasks.

Current purchasing policy

Coruisk currently obtains its raw material from four suppliers. Each of these suppliers operates differently in terms of the processes and procedures which they adopt in trading with Coruisk. Coruisk has been agreeable to this, as the quality of the raw material supplied has generally been acceptable.

More recently, however, Coruisk has found reason to question the accuracy and quality of the raw material delivered from one supplier. Additionally, another supplier now only despatches material to Coruisk in full-load quantities as it wishes to optimise the use of its delivery vehicles.

Current production methods

The performance metric at Coruisk for production efficiency is the number of dresses produced per period. Coruisk's method of production is to produce individual dresses in long production runs which has helped in maximising output. Staff working in the production department have their bonus based on this metric.

Coruisk has a practice of testing goods at the final stage of production and before they leave the factory. Goods which have not been produced to the required standard have traditionally been rejected at the end of the production process. Coruisk's production control manager has indicated to you that the current production methods have been successful, as the company only has 5% of its goods returned from Ericht due to poor quality.

Just-in-time (JIT)

Ericht would like to move to a just-in-time (JIT) system of purchasing its goods from Coruisk and as a result Coruisk is contemplating major changes to its working practices.

Coruisk's CEO has asked you, as a management consultant, to assess the changes which Coruisk will have to make in the areas of purchasing and production in order to supply goods to Ericht on a JIT basis.

Costs of quality

Coruisk's CEO has also made available to you a cost of quality report which she believes addresses all relevant costs of quality. This report is in Appendix 1.

She would like you to discuss the potential quality cost changes in light of the proposed move to JIT. She indicated that some of these costs have never been measured before and have been given financial values to help you in your discussion. She also told you that Coruisk's current revenue is $4.5 million.

Required:

It is now 1 September 20X5.

Respond to the CEO's request for work on the following areas:

(a) the introduction of a just-in-time (JIT) systems and **(13 marks)**

(b) costs of quality changes. **(7 marks)**

Professional marks will be awarded for the demonstration of skill in analysis and evaluation, scepticism and commercial acumen in your answer. **(5 marks)**

(Total: 25 marks)

Appendix 1

Cost of quality report

	$000	$000	**% of revenue ($4.5m)**
Costs of conformance:			
Prevention costs:			
Preventative maintenance	8		
Total		8	0.18%
Appraisal costs:			
Quality control supervisor	35		
Quality audit	2		
Total		37	0.82%
Costs of non-conformance:			
Internal failure costs:			
Rework cost	72		
Machine downtime	38		
Scrap	58		
Total		168	3.73%
External failure costs:			
Cost of complaints from Ericht	135		
Foregone contribution from lost sales*	85		
Product recalls and cost of goods returned	180		
Total		400	8.89%
Overall total	613		13.62%

* The foregone contribution from lost sales is an estimate of potential sales lost to Ericht due to problems related to production and delivery experienced by Coruisk.

3 TOTAIG

Company information

Totaig manufactures high quality and innovative small electrical appliances such as hairdryers and vacuum cleaners. All of the board of directors, who are the strategic decision makers, have always worked in the business and are members of the Totaig family. Most of the operational managers joined as factory workers when the business started and have taken on more responsibilities as the business has grown.

Totaig has basic and outdated IT systems for a business of its complexity and has always used traditional financial performance measures such as return on investment (ROI) and operating profit margin.

Totaig has historically had few competitors and the directors have focused on improving financial results from one year to the next, with little long-term planning. A number of overseas competitors have, however, recently entered Totaig's market. It is estimated that, within one year, these competitors will be able to produce at a similar unit cost to Totaig and that within three to five years, the quality of the competitors' products will be comparable to the current quality of Totaig's products. Totaig may have to invest heavily in product development and make acquisitions in the future in order to compete effectively.

Value based management (VBM)

A consultant has recently told the directors that implementing VBM may help Totaig to respond to the increase in competition over the next one to five years. The consultant has defined VBM as 'the alignment of the business strategy, management processes and culture on maximising shareholder wealth by focusing on key drivers of value'. The directors have accepted this as a reasonable definition of VBM and most of them now agree that VBM would be useful, though others are not yet convinced.

The directors have, however, asked you for further advice on one aspect of the implementation of VBM at Totaig. At her recent presentation, the consultant presented a slide (Appendix 1) showing the four steps in implementing VBM. The directors want your advice on how to implement Step 2, which is defining performance targets. Your advice should focus on the following four areas:

1 Selection of appropriate measures and targets.

2 Timescales to which the targets should relate.

3 Management levels (strategic and operational) in the business to which the targets should relate.

4 Difficulties in measuring and managing performance using VBM.

Measuring value

The directors are unsure of a suitable financial performance indicator for them to use to measure whether Totaig is creating value. As an illustration, they have asked you to evaluate, by calculating economic value added (EVA^{TM}), whether Totaig has generated value for the year to 30 June 20X5. You should use the financial information given in Appendix 2.

Required:

It is now 1 September 20X5.

Respond to the directors' request for work on the following areas:

(a) the implementation of Step 2 of VBM and **(15 marks)**

(b) measurement of value. **(5 marks)**

Professional marks will be awarded for the demonstration of skill in analysis and evaluation and commercial acumen in your answer.

(Total: 25 marks)

Appendix 1

Four steps in implementing VBM

Step 1 – Produce a strategy for maximising value

↓

Step 2 – Define performance targets

↓

Step 3 – Create a plan to achieve the targets

↓

Step 4 – Set up measurement and reward systems

Appendix 2

Income statement for the year to 30 June 20X5

	$000
Operating profit	10,000
Interest expense	(1,500)
Profit before tax	**8,500**
Tax at 22%	(1,870)
Profit after tax	**6,630**

Notes:

1 During the year, $450,000 of advertising cost which will generate sales in future periods was expensed to the income statement.

2 The allowance for doubtful debts at the end of the period was $300,000, a reduction of $200,000 from the beginning of the period.

3 The capital employed at the beginning of the period was $88,944,000.

4 Totaig's after-tax weighted average cost of capital (WACC) is currently 9%. The company is financed by a mixture of equity and fixed and floating rate loans.

Section 6

SPECIMEN EXAM ANSWERS

1 DEELAND POLICE

To: The CEO, Department of Internal Affairs (DIA)

From: An Accountant

Date: 1 September 20X5

Subject: Performance measurement and management at Deeland Police (DP)

This report recommends and justifies critical success factors (CSFs) and key performance indicators (KPIs) for DP based on the four critical areas of performance. DP is then evaluated on the value for money (VFM) provision of its service. The usefulness of non-financial performance indicators (NFPIs) in the public sector is explained. Finally, the use of a league table of police performance and the setting of targets for DP is assessed, with comment on the employee reaction to such a management approach.

(i) Critical success factors (CSFs) and key performance indicators (KPIs)

The CSFs must follow from the four areas which are addressing the overall mission. The four key areas to consider are:

1 Protecting and supporting those at risk of harm

2 Ensuring criminals are caught and brought before the courts

3 Achieving long-term sustainable solutions to the causes of crime

4 Addressing new forms of crime arising in the virtual world

The first three areas are ongoing in the activities of DP and the Minister wants improvement in each. The adviser's suggested CSFs all appear to be reasonable improvements to manage the Minister's concerns about the vagueness of the key areas as follows:

1 Greater protection and more support for those at harm (this is a straight-forward improvement to the existing position in this area).

2 Be better at catching criminals (bringing them before the courts does not appear to be critical as it seems to automatically follow).

3 Reducing the causes of crime by increased involvement with local communities (improvement using the mechanism suggested).

The fourth area is relatively new, so it will be more in the nature of a separate project to:

4 Create a task force to develop skills in detection and prosecution of virtual crime (as desired by the Minister).

Key answer tips

The suggested answer is straightforward and succinct but fully addresses what is required. Do not worry that you need to say more here or that your points should be more complex.

The KPIs for the four CSF areas

Area 1

The CSF breaks into two parts – protecting and supporting. There should be a KPI measuring the change in each of these areas:

- Percentage change year on year of the number of victims of violent crimes, once they are identified as at risk (a register of 'at risk' people would need to be created).
- Percentage change of staff hours spent with each victim on average in support activities.

Neither of these KPIs can currently be measured as the data is not collected. The first point could be indirectly addressed by measuring the number of victims of violent crimes, which should see a fall if those at risk are better protected.

Area 2

This CSF is looking at what is often referred to as the clear-up rate, which is the percentage of crimes where the criminal is caught. The data given allows this to be measured through

- the percentage change in the percentage of crimes solved (although care must be taken that 'solved' is not the same as 'criminal caught' as there may be cases where the police know the criminal, but they escape capture).

The second part of bringing the criminal before the courts once caught does not appear to be a critical area needing measurement since this appears to be a low risk possibility. The critical area might be better stated as 'Ensuring crimes are solved and criminals are brought before the courts' since the second part would then be an appropriate area to measure.

Area 3

From the data in Appendix 1, the KPI could be:

- the percentage change in the total number of crimes in Deeland in the year.

The effect of reducing the causes of crime would be to create a long-term trend downwards in this measure. It may be better to use a three-year moving average of the change as a result. However, there may be many factors which cause such changes including the number of police officers and so the underlying causes of crime may not be accurately measured. The suggested KPI does not capture whether the changes are sustainable in the long term, which will be difficult to do.

Area 4

The KPIs for the fourth area require examination of the number and qualifications of those working on the task force on virtual crime. The data in Appendix 1 is not sufficient to measure this.

KPIs could include:

- percentage of roles in the task force filled (this requires that there is a plan for the organisation of a suitable task force, which may be complicated as this is a new area where knowledge of how many staff and what qualifications they should have may not be present).
- percentage of virtual crimes reported which are solved (shows the effectiveness of the task force).

(ii) Value for money (VFM)

The standard criteria for analysis of the value for money of a service are:

- Economy – the optimisation of the resources which the organisation has; ensuring the appropriate quality of input resources are obtained at the lowest cost
- Efficiency – the optimisation of the process by which inputs are turned into outputs
- Effectiveness – how the outputs of the organisation meet its goals.

The 3Es above link to the CSFs and KPIs in the area of effectiveness. The KPIs measure the achievement of the goals of DP and all relate to outcomes rather than processes or inputs in this case.

In order to judge VFM, comparison can be made internally to the historic performance of DP, but it should also be benchmarked against external organisations. The need for external data is also reflected in the desire to benchmark in league tables although no data is given for this here and so the VFM can only be judged against previous years' data.

Considering the situation at DP specifically

Economy could be measured by looking at the cost of buying inputs; the principal input is staff (90.1% of total costs) and so the cost per employee ($40,318) is relevant. This represents a 3.8% reduction on the previous year although it should be noted that the mix of staff is changing with more administrative staff replacing police officers who may be more expensive as they are more qualified. It would be useful to obtain the data on the average police officer salary as they make up 75.5% of the total staff and they are critical to the achievement of outcomes.

As noted above, in order to judge whether this is good or bad, the Department should also compare this to external figures such as the national average wage and, also, the average salary of staff in other police forces in similar countries.

Efficiency can be measured in a number of different ways.

	20X5	**20X4**	**20X3**
Solved crimes per police officer	7.855	7.918	7.915
Solved crimes per employee (police officers and admin staff)	5.929	5.994	6.022
Police officers per 1,000 population	3.19	3.23	3.30

The trend in the number of police officers is downward which would suggest improvement. However, the more important outcome is not the resources poured in but the crime results and these show that by decreasing the number of police officers, the number of crimes which each is solving is falling (down 0.8% from 20X3). Performance in this area is therefore poor.

Effectiveness must be measured against DP's goals in its four areas:

1 Protection and support of those at risk – the percentage of violent crime remains flat over the three years of data at 20% of the total number of crimes reported. This suggests that protection remains broadly unchanged. As noted above, there is no measure of support provided.

2 Solving crimes – the clear-up rate has fallen from 56.7% to 55.0%. This probably reflects the change in staff mix as police officer numbers have fallen.

3 Causes of crime – the trend is clearly upwards with an increase of 2% each year over the last two years which may again reflect the falling numbers of police officers in DP.

4 Virtual crime – as noted above, it is not possible to measure the achievement of the creation of the task force from the data provided.

Tutorial note

Some students do find an evaluation of a value for money (VFM) service difficult. Do make sure that you adequately cover this syllabus area; learning what is required and attempting other past exam questions on VFM. ***Note****: the numbers and calculations included below would be included in the spreadsheet response option in the CBE.*

(iii) League tables

The use of league tables effectively benchmarks performance and can have a positive effect on behaviour. The sharing of data on performance can indicate areas of best practice and so offers the possibility of improving performance by copying that best practice. Additionally, the use of league tables gives, by the rank in the table, a clear, immediate answer to questions of relative performance.

However, the use of league tables only measures relative performance. The best force in the table could still be producing an unacceptable performance in absolute terms. The different forces in different countries will face different external environments. Each force will have to react to the economic situation in that country and may allocate resources differently according to the priorities of the government of that country. So, it will be difficult to get a single measure, such as the rank in the league table, to balance these competing factors.

This leads on to another area which will prove difficult, which is how to rank the different forces. Usually, there is a scoring system giving points across different areas for each force's performance. The selection of the areas and the weighting given to them within the rank score will affect the position of the different forces. In an example of 'what gets measured, gets done', it may be that the DP management will change their priorities from those given by the DIA to those measured in the rank score and so undermine the alignment of their behaviour with the given mission of DP.

Therefore, to be of value to the Minister, the calculation of the rank must encompass the key variables which will drive DP's desired performance.

Therefore, there is a link between league tables and employee behaviour which comes from the setting of targets based on the league table rank.

The impact on the employees includes whether they feel a sense of accountability for the score. If the police officers do not feel that they can affect the rank, then they may ignore it or actively undermine it in public through their union's public statements. This will present the government with difficulty as the police are considered the experts in this area of public policy and their criticism will carry weight with the electorate.

Specifically, the police officers may be demotivated by the league tables if they feel:

(a) that the league table rank does not reflect the valuable work which they do (for example, in creating the new virtual crime task force); or

(b) that the rank is driven by factors outside of their control. (For example, the budget for the force may be cut, as appears to be happening with DP, or there may be a link between the number of crimes reported and the economic conditions in Deeland which they do not have power to affect.)

Deeland Police data for each year ending 30 June

	20X5	**20X4**	**20X3**
Population (000s)	11,880	11,761	11,644
Number of police officers	37,930	38,005	38,400
Number of administrative staff	12,320	12,197	12,075
Number of crimes reported in the year	541,735	530,900	520,282
Number of violent crimes reported in the year	108,347	106,180	104,056
Number of crimes solved in the year	297,954	300,934	303,943
Number of complaints	7,624	7,512	7,483
Response to an incident within the allocated time limit	84%	86%	87%
Cost of police force for the year ($m)	2,248	2,226	2,203
Staff costs (all staff including police officers) ($m)	2,026	2,103	2,141

Workings

Economy			
Staff costs/total cost (%)	90.1	94.5	97.2
Costs per employee ($)	40,318	41, 891	42,417
Efficiency			
Solved crimes per police officer	7.855	7.918	7.915
Solved crimes per employee	5.929	5.994	6.022
Police officers per 1000 of population	3.19	3.23	3.30
Economy			
Clear up rate (%)	55.0	56.7	58.4
Violent crime (%)	20.0	20.0	20.0
Increase in crime reported year on year (%)	2.0	2.0	

ACCA marking scheme	
	Marks
(i) **CSFs and KPIs**	
4 marks for the justification of the changes to the four CSFs	
Up to 4 marks for discussion of KPIs for each area	
Maximum	**16**
(ii) **VFM**	
3 marks for defining each of the 3Es	
Up to 3 marks for comments on the link to the CSFs/KPIs	
Up to 3 marks each for discussing each heading at DP	
Up to 3 marks for supporting calculations	
Maximum	**14**
(iii) **League tables**	
Up to 7 marks for general evaluation of league tables	
Up to 7 marks for the link of tables to targets and police officer reaction	
Maximum	**10**
Professional marks	
Communication:	
• Report format and structure – use of headings/sub-headings and introduction	
• Style, language and clarity – appropriate tone of report response, presentation of calculations, appropriate use of CBE tools, easy to follow and understand	
• Effectiveness of communication – content of the report is relevant and tailored to the question scenario	
• Adherence to the CEO's specific request to not provide more than two KPIs	
Analysis and Evaluation	
• Appropriate use of the data to support discussion and draw conclusions on performance in relation to VFM, including recognition of further analysis which could be carried out to enable a full evaluation of VFM to take place	
• Balanced appraisal to make a recommendation on the introduction of league tables, demonstrating reasoned judgement when considering key organisational matters and impacts	
Scepticism	
• Demonstration of the ability to probe into why the CSFs were refined	
• Recognition that data provided does not allow some of the CSFs/KPIs to be adequately measured	
Commercial Acumen	
• Effective use of examples drawn from the scenario information and other practical considerations related to the context to illustrate points being made throughout the report	
Maximum	**10**
Total	**50**

2 CORUISK

(a) Just-in-time (JIT) is defined as a system which has the objective of producing or procuring products as they are required and not for inventory purposes. Coruisk is being asked to produce to JIT principles, the basis of which is where production is driven by demand for the finished product. Each part of the production process is therefore determined only by what is required for the next stage of production.

> ***Tutorial note***
>
> *A short introduction is useful here. Explain what JIT purchasing/production is and outline that changes will need to be made at Coruisk. Then look at 'purchasing' and 'production' in turn.*

Purchasing

Coruisk has too many suppliers at present. Adhering to JIT production principles involves reducing suppliers to a minimum and establishing strong relationships with them, based on flexibility and understanding of each other's needs. Coruisk's four main suppliers are too many to develop this type of close relationship with, especially since these suppliers operate to different working practices. The effect of this, from a JIT production perspective, would be that Coruisk would require to undertake discussions with each supplier about the fundamental changes which would be required for the supply of goods in a JIT production environment. Coruisk would not have the time to do this with all four suppliers nor would the supply of goods from four companies be desirable. Coruisk should choose two of the companies it feels it has the strongest relationship with and initiate discussions with them around its needs when producing to JIT principles.

When producing to JIT principles, suppliers will effectively be an extension of Coruisk's own business. As such, Coruisk must be aware of and must understand how changes in suppliers' operations will affect Coruisk's own operations. It is clear that Coruisk does not currently have this level of relationship. The supplier who is seeking to optimise the cost of its delivery vehicles, for example, is undertaking practices which are very much opposed to the type of practices which Coruisk will need when it is producing to JIT principles. JIT only produces goods when needed by the next stage in the process (the 'kanban' principle) and Coruisk would need its supplier to understand this and be willing to supply it with goods accordingly. This would clearly be impossible for a supplying company which is insistent on supplying full-load quantities only.

Coruisk must also ensure that the raw material it receives is defect free, unlike the goods which are received currently from one supplier. Having the wrong quantity of material or material which is sub-standard, is unacceptable if Coruisk is producing to JIT principles as such problems will mean an inevitable delay in supplying goods to Ericht. Coruisk will therefore need to spend time in defining and agreeing requirements with suppliers to clarify requirements in terms of both quality and quantity and may need to also develop improvement teams with their suppliers to ensure that the raw material it receives is reliable.

Coruisk will most likely need to undertake official supplier assessments as part of this as such assessments and on-going reviews are a vital part of ensuring the quality of the raw material in a JIT production system.

Production

The manner in which Coruisk produces its goods will need to change significantly. Efficiency can no longer be measured by volume of output. Ericht will seek supply of goods as and when required in order to avoid obsolete inventory and Coruisk must adapt to this. The concept of producing as much as possible is one which Coruisk may struggle to abolish. It is clearly embedded in the culture of the organisation with its importance confirmed by the awarding of a bonus based on the quantity of goods produced. Presumably this bonus has been awarded without taking account of any goods which have been rejected and it is possible that the current system is encouraging production to be undertaken quickly with rejected goods seen as an acceptable part of the production process.

Producing to JIT principles would demand a fundamental rethink at Coruisk in terms of the way production runs are determined. Of most significance, initially, is that such runs would be shorter as all parts of the production process should match the rate at which Ericht is demanding the final product. For example, Coruisk can no longer focus on producing large runs of one dress. Necessary changes here may involve the development of machine cells. Such cells are composed of groups of team members to facilitate operations by eliminating setup and unneeded costs between operations. Cells might be designed for a specific process or part of a product. In Coruisk's case, this may mean workers being grouped together by the dress they are producing at that time rather than as part of a long production run. Enhancing worker flexibility, and developing their skillset in several areas of the operation, may be the best way to react to this new environment where demand is much more unpredictable. This may also involve changing the layout of the factory to try to ensure production is as flexible as possible.

Coruisk cannot supply faulty goods to Ericht and the previous belief that a 5% rejection rate was acceptable practice must be replaced by an understanding of the zero defects philosophy. This will require more fundamental change as quality of the finished good will need to be assured throughout the production process and not simply inspected at the end. This will most likely involve an initial discussion with Ericht as to the quality level it is seeking and, potentially, a redesign of the current processes and systems to which Coruisk is operating. For example, prevention and appraisal costs would be expected to increase as Coruisk would have to establish both goods inwards testing procedures and testing procedures for work in progress. There would also be a need for Coruisk to develop a culture where workers are flexible in terms of their capabilities and trained much more in identifying defective products (and ensuring they do not progress further on the production line) than in ensuring the maximum quantity of output is produced.

Key answer tips

The number of marks here may feel overwhelming but there are lots of ideas that can be drawn on from the scenario; use it to help you in your answers rather than feeling overwhelmed by the information given.

(b) The results of the cost of quality report are representative of a company which undertakes quality control as opposed to quality assurance in that the majority of the costs relate to failure, either of an internal or external nature. Additionally, since the costs have been amassed for the first time for this task, it is possible that they are inaccurate and probably understated as some costs are likely to have been omitted.

Costs of conformance

Coruisk will need to invest more in quality audits and, possibly, in testing equipment to ensure that the product is being produced to the right standard as it progresses through the production process. Whereas there may still be a requirement for final inspection, it should not be someone's full-time occupation and the supervisor may be more meaningfully deployed elsewhere for at least part of his/her role. These practices should reduce both the internal and external failure costs, particularly those of scrap and rework, which both appear very high currently. Machine downtime is perhaps due to the very little amount currently spent on preventative maintenance and the cost of internal failure should also fall with enhanced maintenance.

Costs of non-conformance

The significant external failure cost is of most concern. To operate to the JIT principles which Ericht is seeking, Coruisk has to ensure that these costs are as close to zero as possible. It is concerning, for example, that 3% ($135,000) of the revenue figure is taken up by dealing with complaints from Ericht. Some of this may be due to misunderstandings between the companies which could be rectified by the closer working relationship that JIT production principles demand. Nevertheless, it is clear that Coruisk must ensure that it addresses these costs as it is completely reliant upon Ericht for its business.

The amount of money attributed to product recalls and cost of goods returned (4% of the revenue figure) is concerning as this suggests that defective products have not been detected in Coruisk's current quality control system. This may be due to the bonus system currently in place and the desire to produce quantity, quickly, and not quality. A change to the production process should address this but it could be met with hostility if the workers' bonus is under threat and Coruisk may need to introduce an alternative bonus scheme based on a quality-related metric which specifies, for example, the percentage of defects detected.

The forgone contribution from lost sales is also concerning as it indicates that Ericht has alternative supplier(s). It is possible, given the cost detailed of dealing with complaints from Ericht, that this figure is considerably higher than Coruisk is estimating.

The balance of the costs must change so that the majority of Coruisk's costs are prevention and appraisal (costs of conformance) and not costs of internal/external failure (costs of non-conformance). Coruisk must ensure that it is producing to the standard which Ericht requests at the first time of asking and therefore Coruisk must ensure that it provides more training for staff, more preventative machine maintenance, more supplier appraisal and vetting as mentioned previously and moves to encourage a culture of zero defects with no faulty goods moving forward in the production process.

Key answer tips

The final paragraph is key to this requirement but to score well you must expand on each of the cost categories and how they would be expected to change.

ACCA marking scheme		
		Marks
(a)	Description of JIT – 1 mark Changes in purchasing and production – 1 mark per point up to 13 marks	
	Maximum	**13**
(b)	Quality cost changes – 1 mark per point, up to 7 marks **Maximum**	**7**
Professional marks		
Analysis and Evaluation		
•	Balanced and reasoned assessment of the changes which will be required to both purchasing and production as a result of introducing JIT	
•	Appropriate use of data to support discussion on quality cost changes and draw relevant conclusions	
Scepticism		
•	Demonstration of effective challenge of assumptions of both the production manager and the CEO	
Commercial Acumen		
•	Effective use of examples drawn from the scenario information and other practical considerations related to the context to illustrate points being made	
	Maximum	**5**
Total		**25**

3 TOTAIG

(a) Selection of appropriate measures and targets

Value drivers create long-term value. Totaig is facing competition from overseas businesses, which will soon be able to produce at a similar unit cost to Totaig and produce items of comparable quality. The unit cost of production and product quality would be value drivers for Totaig and targets should be set for these two measures.

Targets should be both financial and non-financial. This will ensure that there is not too much emphasis on financial targets, which tend to be backwards looking, rather than relating to the present value of future cash flows, which is the focus of value-based management (VBM).

The existing targets of return on investment (ROI) and operating margin are backwards looking. They will also discourage managers to make investments, for example, in product development, which might be detrimental to Totaig's long-term performance. This is because investments in new products will reduce both of these measures in the short-term.

Having targets related to product quality would ensure that the business does not focus too much on cutting the unit cost of production, for example, by using cheaper, lower quality materials. It appears that to create long-term value, Totaig must be competitive on both unit cost of production and product quality.

Timescales to which the targets should relate

Totaig must set short-term and long-term targets, which should be linked together, for key value drivers. Competitors will be able to produce at a similar unit cost to Totaig within a year. A suitable short-term target would therefore be to reduce unit production costs within that timescale. As VBM is concerned with long-term value, Totaig should set longer term targets relating to quality in anticipation of the new competitors' ability to improve on this aspect within three to five years.

The possible need to invest heavily in product development and make acquisitions will probably require longer term targets to be set.

Levels in the business to which the targets should relate

Value can be created at all levels in the company and targets should be set according to the different layers of management. Targets relating to unit cost of production and product quality are under the control of operational managers and these would be suitable for this level of management.

Targets relating to possible future acquisitions are under the control of the directors, who are the strategic decision makers.

Difficulties in measuring and managing performance using VBM

Totaig will require good information to implement VBM. It may be difficult to identify value drivers and reporting systems need to be able to provide the information which is required. Currently, IT systems are basic and outdated for a business of its complexity. This may mean that it is difficult to identify value drivers for the setting of targets. The implementation of VBM may require significant investment in IT systems to measure performance against targets and take up management time. The costs of implementing VBM may exceed the benefits.

The operational managers are unlikely to have any experience of VBM since most of them joined Totaig, which itself has never used VBM, when the business first started. They will require training on VBM if they are to understand the targets set. For example, new value-based performance measures, such as EVA™, will be needed, which will be unfamiliar to directors and managers in the business.

Using VBM to manage performance at Totaig will require a culture change amongst all employees, who will need to work towards creating shareholder value. The directors will need to demonstrate commitment to the use of VBM in order to motivate operational managers to accept the change. Currently, some directors at Totaig seem not to be convinced of the usefulness of the approach.

It may be difficult to measure economic depreciation, for example, or to determine whether and for when the anticipated heavy investment in product development will create value. These difficulties will affect the reliability of performance measures for value, such as EVA™, in managing performance.

Key answer tips

There are 15 marks available here but by breaking your answer down under the four headings requested, the requirement is much more manageable. It is vital to have your knowledge in place here; VBM could be examined for a significant number of marks.

(b) Calculation of EVA™

	$000
Profit after tax	6,630
Advertising costs expenses	450
Decrease in allowance for doubtful debts	(200)
Interest net of tax (1,500 × 78%)	1,170
NOPAT	8,050

	$000
Opening capital employed	88,944
Opening allowance for doubtful debt	500
Adjusted opening capital employed	89,444

	$000
NOPAT	8,050
After-tax WACC × adjusted capital employed (9% × 89,444)	(8,050)
EVA™	0

As EVA™ is zero, Totaig has neither created nor destroyed value.

Tutorial note

In this context, 'evaluation' requires a calculation of the EVA™ and a brief comment on whether or not value has been created. In the CBE, the spreadsheet response option should be used for the answer to requirement (b).

ACCA marking scheme	
	Marks
(a) 1 mark per point (under the four headings): • Selection of measures and targets • Timescales • Management levels • Difficulties	
Maximum	**15**
(b) Calculation of NOPAT: Advertising cost – 1 mark Decrease in allowance – 1 mark Interest – 1 mark Calculation of adjusted capital employed – 1 mark Calculation of EVA™ – 1 mark Conclusion – 1 mark	
Maximum	**5**
Professional marks **Analysis and Evaluation** • Demonstration of reasoned and balanced judgement to support arguments and communicate advice on the introduction of VBM. • Use of information provided to perform and evaluation on EVA™ **Commercial Acumen** • Effective use of examples drawn from the scenario information and other practical considerations related to the context to illustrate points being made on the implementation of Step 2 of VBM	
Maximum	**5**
Total	**25**